2V 17.00

P9-BTX-912

TECHNIQUE OF ORGANIC CHEMISTRY

PHYSICAL METHODS
of Organic Chemistry

Editor:
ARNOLD WEISSBERGER

Contributors:

W. F. BALE
N. BAUER
J. F. BONNER, JR.
L. O. BROCKWAY
J. D. H. DONNAY
K. FAJANS
I. FANKUCHEN
A. L. GEDDES
W. D. HARKINS

W. HELLER
E. E. JELLEY
H. MARK
L. MICHAELIS
O. H. MÜLLER
M. A. PEACOCK
T. SHEDLOVSKY
E. L. SKAU
C. P. SMYTH

D. W. STEWART
J. M. STURTEVANT
W. SWIETOSLAWSKI
G. W. THOMSON
M. J. VOLD
R. D. VOLD
R. H. WAGNER
H. WAKEHAM
W. WEST

VOLUME I

1945
INTERSCIENCE PUBLISHERS, INC., NEW YORK

Copyright, 1945, by
INTERSCIENCE PUBLISHERS, INC.
215 Fourth Avenue, New York 3, N. Y.

A WARTIME BOOK

THIS COMPLETE EDITION IS PRODUCED
IN FULL COMPLIANCE WITH THE GOVERN-
MENT'S REGULATIONS FOR CONSERVING
PAPER AND OTHER ESSENTIAL MATERIALS

Printed in the United States of America
by the
MACK PRINTING COMPANY, EASTON, PA.

PREFACE

In recent years, the science of physics has become increasingly important to the organic chemist. Physics has given much greater precision to the concepts of atoms, bonds, and structural formulas, and it has made possible the development of new and the improvement of older methods for the examination of chemical systems. With the increasing number and complexity of physical methods for the treatment of organic chemical problems there has resulted a specialization of research workers in the methods which they employ, and the selection of a research problem is frequently governed more by the physical method to be used than by the chemical nature of the problem. Some workers have made themselves familiar with several methods in order to deal with their individual problems. In other cases, however, physical methods have been used without adequate preparation.

The chemist, in order to acquaint himself with a certain physical method, has in the past been compelled to search through periodicals and specialized books. The present work has been compiled with the hope of relieving him of much of this burden. It has been the object of the authors to provide a description of tested methods, the theoretical background for understanding and handling them, and the information necessary for a critical evaluation of the experimental results.

Because of the diversity of the methods discussed, no attempt has been made to secure a uniformity of presentation which might have been desirable for formal reasons. In some chapters a discussion of theory was unnecessary, in some a relatively brief theoretical treatment sufficed, and in other chapters a rather complete exposition of the theory appeared necessary. Some methods have been treated in monographs, while for others no comprehensive modern presentation is available. Therefore, a rather severe selection and delimitation of material was exercised in some chapters and a more complete treatment given in others.

The book is also calculated to appeal to the student who seeks to increase his understanding of the methods described, although he may not practice them himself. For him, chapters like those on x-ray and electron diffraction should be adequate, but the practical application of these techniques will require the use of the supplemental literature to which reference is made.

The authors and editor will welcome any suggestions for improvements. The editor wishes to express his sincere thanks to the authors whose labor, often under difficult circumstances due to the war, made possible this treatise. He also acknowledges gratefully the assistance of his colleagues in reading the manuscripts, particularly of Drs. L. G. S. Brooker, I. Fankuchen, M. L. Huggins, E. E. Jelley, C. J. Kibler, E. Loewenstein, J. E. LuValle, J. Spence, J. Russell, C. V. Wilson and Messrs. R. H. Wagner and K. F. Weaver, and the help of the Misses G. Das and A. M. Hyman in the clerical work.

The publishers and their staff deserve special recognition and thanks for their eager and understanding cooperation.

A. W.

Research Laboratories
Eastman Kodak Company
Rochester, New York

CONTENTS

VOLUME I

CHAPTER I

Determination of
MELTING AND FREEZING TEMPERATURES

EVALD L. SKAU AND HELMUT WAKEHAM

Southern Research Laboratory, New Orleans, La.

I. INTRODUCTION

The freezing point or melting point of a pure compound is the temperature at which solid crystals of the substance are in equilibrium with the liquid phase under its own vapor pressure. If this equilibrium condition is approached by cooling the liquid, the temperature is commonly called the freezing point, and if approached by heating the solid, it is designated as the melting point. Since, for most practical purposes, the effect of atmospheric pressure upon the equilibrium temperature is negligible, the

1

melting point is usually taken with the equilibrium mixture in contact with air. The melting temperature is thus not a true triple point, but differs from it by a very small temperature interval (0.008° C. in the case of water),[1] too small to be measured by the ordinary types of melting-point apparatus. According to thermodynamic definition the terms "freezing point" and "melting point," frequently used interchangeably, designate the same temperature.

For solid substances which melt without decomposition, the melting point has become the most important physical property in practical organic chemistry. It is usually the first property determined on a newly synthesized compound, being a basis for characterization, identification, and estimation of purity.

Numerous reasons can be cited why the organic chemist has chosen the melting point rather than another property for this purpose. As generally determined, only small amounts of material are needed for the melting-point determination, and the procedure and equipment required are very simple. The melting point is practically independent of pressure and can, therefore, be taken without making extra physical measurements or corrections, as is necessary, for example, with the boiling-point determination. The change from solid to liquid usually occurs without such troublesome effects as superheating and its accompanying sources of error. Relatively few substances, furthermore, decompose when heated to the melting point. The "mixed melting-point" method of identification is especially effective since the melting point is not, as a rule, an additive property.

One of the most important applications of the melting point is its use as a criterion of purity. If a substance is pure, the melting point will usually be sharp. With mixtures, melting usually occurs over a range of temperatures; and, conversely, melting over a range practically always indicates that the material is a mixture.

In the case of some isomeric substances, a mere comparison of the melting points can be used in the identification of the isomers. For example, it is possible to distinguish the para from the ortho or the meta isomers by the fact that the para has the highest melting point of the three.

In spite of the advantages enumerated above, the determination of melting point presents to the observer many occasions for misinterpretation of data. The most useful applications can be made only if the organic chemist has a thorough knowledge of the possibilities involved. This chapter is concerned with the uses to which the melting-point method may be applied with a description of methods of measurement and with a discussion of sources of error which may arise in the interpretation of melting

---

[1] A. Findlay, *The Phase Rule and Its Applications.* 8th ed., Longmans, Green, New York, 1938, p. 28.

points observed by various experimental methods. For additional details on the subjects discussed in this chapter consult the general references on page 45.

The precision with which the melting point should be determined varies with the information desired. For ordinary purposes of characterization or identification, the capillary-tube method gives results of adequate accuracy—in fact, if the compound is known to be one of several possibilities, an approximate melting point may be sufficient to establish its identity. If the compound is a new one, greater precision is required because the melting point reported should be sufficiently accurate to distinguish the material from others which melt at approximately the same temperature. For very high precision, the cooling-curve method may be resorted to for obtaining true equilibrium between solid and liquid.

When the melting point is used as an indication of purity, some knowledge of the behavior of binary mixtures is valuable for proper interpretation of the data obtained. Some of the factors affecting the melting point of such mixtures as shown by the freezing-point equation will be considered first.

II. THEORETICAL CONSIDERATIONS

1. Ideal Systems

THE FREEZING-POINT EQUATION

In the case of a mixture containing a large amount of component A and a small amount of a second component, B, as for example a nearly pure organic compound, the melting point of the mixture will usually be lower than that of pure A. The extent of the lowering depends upon a number of variables and may be estimated by calculation on the basis of certain assumptions. If the two components form an "ideal solution," the additive properties of the solution are linear functions of its composition. Thus, the partial vapor pressure, or the activity, of each component is, as defined by Raoult's law, proportional to its mole fraction. Using this relation with the familiar Clausius-Clapeyron equation as applied to a liquid mixture in equilibrium with crystals of pure A, it is possible to derive the freezing-point law. The approximate form of the Clausius-Clapeyron equation, which follows from the second law of thermodynamics on the basis of certain assumptions, is as follows:

$$d \ln p = \frac{\Delta H_2}{RT^2} \cdot dT$$

where p is the partial pressure of component A, ΔH is its molar heat of fusion, R is the constant of the ideal gas law, and T is the equilibrium temperature in degrees absolute. The lowering of the melting point or freezing point of component A can be determined by integrating this equation between the limits T_0 to T and p_0 to p, respectively, T_0 and p_0 being the freezing point and partial pressure of pure A. Thus, if ΔH is constant, we obtain:

$$\ln \frac{p}{p_0} = \frac{\Delta H}{RT_0} - \frac{\Delta H}{RT} = -\frac{\Delta H(T_0 - T)}{RTT_0}$$

Raoult's law may be written:

$$p = N_A p_0$$

where N_A = mole fraction of A = $\dfrac{\text{moles of A}}{\text{total number of moles in mixture}}$.

Then we may write:

$$\ln N_A = -\frac{\Delta H_0(T_0 - T)}{RTT_0}$$

and, if $\Delta T = T_0 - T$, we obtain an expression for the freezing-point lowering, ΔT:

$$\Delta T = -\frac{RTT_0}{\Delta H} \ln N_A = -\frac{2.303RTT_0}{\Delta H} \log_{10} N_A \qquad (1)$$

The derivation of this simplified equation describing the extent of freezing-point lowering caused by impurities in A involves the following assumptions: (1) that the components in question are mutually ideal; (2) that the vapor over the liquid and solid at equilibrium behaves as an ideal gas within the temperature and pressure ranges involved; (3) that the volume of the liquid and solid phases are negligible in comparison with the corresponding volume of vapor; and (4) that ΔH is a constant over the temperature range considered. From this equation it is possible to calculate ΔT with fair accuracy even in concentrated solutions for systems of two components which behave in an ideal manner. In some instances, where the necessary data are available, it is possible to obtain more accurate values by taking into account the slight differences due to the assumptions mentioned.[2]

From equation (1) it is apparent that the freezing-point (melting-point) lowering observed for substance A is a direct function of the mole fraction of A in the mixture, that it is inversely proportional to the molar heat of fusion of A, and that it is directly proportional to the product of the freezing points of the mixture and of pure A in degrees absolute. The

---

[2] J. H. Hildebrand, *Solubility of Non-Electrolytes.* 2nd ed., Reinhold, New York, 1936.

depression is thus independent of the kind of impurity present provided ideal solutions are formed. Thus, 1 mole per cent of any substance or mixtures of substances forming an ideal solution will lower the freezing point of benzene by 0.65° C. Naphthalene, biphenyl, and benzene form mutually ideal solutions of this nature, and the complete binary freezing-point lowering curves show, as expected, that this relation holds even in concentrated solutions. In extremely dilute solutions all substances

TABLE I

CALORIMETRIC HEATS OF FUSION

	M. p., ° C.	Mol. wt.	cal./g.	ΔH	ΔT for 0.1 mole fraction of impurity (calcd.)
Acetic acid	16.55[a]	60.05	46.7[c]	2800	6.14
Aniline	−6.15[a]	93.12	27.1[e]	2520	5.79
Anthracene	216.5[e]	178.22	38.7[f]	6890	7.18
Benzene	5.45[a]	78.11	30.40[b]	2370	6.69
Benzoic acid	122.45[a]	122.12	33.9[g]	4140	7.76
Benzophenone	47.85[a]	182.21	23.5[g]	4280	4.96
Biphenyl	68.6[f]	154.20	28.8[f]	4440	5.42
Butyl alcohol (tert)	25.4[b]	74.12	21.43[b]	1590	11.29
Camphor	178.4[b]	152.23	10.74[b]	1650	24.27
Capric acid (n)	31.3[e]	172.26	38.8[g]	6680	2.88
Cetyl alcohol	49.10[a]	242.44	33.8[g]	8190	2.63
Cyclohexanol	25.46[a]	100.16	4.27[d]	428	38.03
Dibenzyl	51.2[a]	182.25	30.7[f]	5600	3.88
Dichlorobenzene(p)	53.2[a]	147.10	29.7[g]	4370	5.02
Ethylene dibromide	9.97[a]	187.88	13.5[g]	2540	6.45
Methyl cinnamate	34.5[g]	162.18	26.5[g]	4300	4.54
Naphthalene	80.22[a]	128.16	35.8[e]	4590	5.60
Nitrobenzene	5.65[a]	123.11	23.53[e]	2900	5.50
Stearic acid	68.8[g]	284.47	47.5[g]	13510	1.80
Trichloroacetic acid	59.1[g]	163.4	8.6[g]	1405	15.67
Triphenylmethane	92.1[f]	244.32	21.1[f]	5160	5.33
Water	0.0	18.00	79.67[f]	1434	10.45

[a] Landolt-Börnstein, *Physikalisch-Chemische Tabellen*, Erg. **III a,** Table 84. [b] *Ibid.*, Erg. **III c,** Table 305. [c] *Ibid.*, Erg. **II b,** Table 305. [d] *Ibid.*, Erg. **I,** Table 305. [e] *Ibid.*, Erg. **III c,** Table 313. [f] G. S. Parks and H. M. Huffman, *Ind. Eng. Chem., Ind. Ed.*, **23,** 1138 (1931). [g] *International Critical Tables.* Vol. V, McGraw-Hill, New York, 1929, pp. 132–134.

are said to exhibit ideal behavior. However, this generalization does not hold without qualification. For instance, in the classical case of electrolytes in ionizing solvents, the deviation from the behavior predicted by the ideal freezing-point equation increases with the dilution.

The magnitude of the molar heat of fusion of component A is an important factor when the melting point is used as a criterion of purity. Substances such as camphor or cyclohexanol, which have very low molar heats of fusion, will exhibit a large lowering of the melting point with only very small mole fractions of impurity. On the other hand, a solvent with a relatively high molar heat of fusion such as stearic acid will show very little change in melting point with even a high concentration of solute. Table I shows a comparison of the molar heats of fusion for a number of substances and the freezing-point lowering (ΔT) for one-tenth mole fraction of impurity calculated from equation (1) by the method of successive approximations.

The extent of melting-point lowering of a given substance is a function also of its melting point in degrees absolute. A compound with a high melting point will show a greater ΔT for a given mole fraction of impurity than a solvent with a low melting point, other things being equal. Thus, anthracene ($\Delta H = 6890$ cal.) and capric acid ($\Delta H = 6680$ cal.) (see Table I) have nearly identical molar heats of fusion, but since their melting points are 489° and 305° K., respectively, anthracene will in the ideal case show a lowering about 2.5 times as great as that of capric acid for 1 mole per cent of an impurity.

In establishing purity or identity, it is therefore evident that the mere comparison of melting points will afford more valid conclusions if the heat of fusion of the substance is also available for the interpretation. A freezing point which is "within a few degrees of the true value" does not in all cases indicate the same degree of purity. Consider, for instance, samples of camphor and trichloroacetic acid, each melting 2.0° C. below its true melting point. Calculations from equation (1) and table I indicate that this lowering corresponds to only 0.8 mole per cent of impurity in the camphor but to 13 mole per cent in the trichloroacetic acid.

In this connection, it is interesting to note that the use of melting points has been suggested as a method of analyzing binary fatty acid mixtures. The accuracy required by this application is shown by the fact that 1.0 gram of palmitic acid in the presence of 9.0 grams of stearic acid would lower the melting point of the stearic acid from 69.4° to 67.1° C., a difference of only 2.3 degrees.[3] The depression is small because stearic acid has a relatively low melting point and a high molar heat of fusion. These factors conspire to cause a large amount of impurity to have relatively little effect on the melting point of the stearic acid.

2. Systems Which Deviate from Ideality

In contrast to the binary systems considered above, most of the mixtures encountered by the organic chemist are not ideal in that they do not follow Raoult's law. The lowering of the freezing point is a colligative property calculable from the freezing-point equation for ideal cases; it is possible in some instances, therefore, to explain the observed deviations

---

[3] J. C. Smith, *J. Chem. Soc.*, **1936,** 625.

from ideality in terms of known characteristics of the substances involved. A few of the more common causes for such deviations are mentioned in the paragraphs below.   The term "solvent" is used here with reference to the substance which will freeze out of a dilute solution.

(1) If the solute is known to associate to form dimers or trimers, the number of effective molecules in the system will be reduced accordingly, and the observed lowering of the freezing point will be less than that predicted for the ideal case.   Acetic acid is such a substance, and its lowering of the melting point of naphthalene, indicated graphically in figure 1, is less than that of benzene or biphenyl, both of which show essentially ideal behavior in naphthalene.

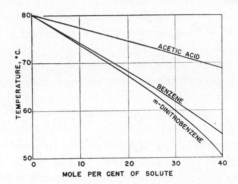

Fig. 1.—Lowering of the freezing point of naphthalene (data from Ward[8] and Skau[50]).

(2) Another very common form of deviation occurs when the solvent and solute, A and B, combine partially in the liquid phase to form a third substance, AB.   In such cases, the deviation from ideality is often said to be due to solvation, or molecular compound formation.   The formation of AB does not increase the number of solute molecules in the solvent but actually decreases the number of molecules of free solvent remaining.   The mole fraction of solvent is, therefore, smaller, and the mole fraction of solute greater than expected, so that the depression of the freezing point is more than that predicted by the freezing-point equation.   m-Dinitrobenzene forms such a molecular compound with naphthalene; the resulting melting-point curve of mixtures of these two substances is shown in figure 1. Picric acid in naphthalene would be expected to show a similar deviation, since the compound, naphthalene picrate, is readily formed, having a melting point of 149° C.[4]

---

[4] *International Critical Tables*, Vol. IV, McGraw-Hill, New York, 1928, p. 120, System 612.

(3) In some cases, the solute molecules dissociate to form two or more molecules, thus increasing the effective mole fraction of the solute and giving rise to freezing-point depressions greater than those calculated for the ideal case. Hexaphenylethane dissolved in naphthalene dissociates partially to form the triphenylmethyl radical, and the observed melting points for the mixture are lower than those for benzene in naphthalene.[5] This behavior for the analogous case of tetraphenyl-di-β-naphthylethane in benzene will be discussed in connection with figure 15. Similarly, naphthalene picrate has been shown to dissociate into naphthalene and picric acid when dissolved in alcohol, acetic acid, or benzene.[6] This phenomenon corresponds to the well-known abnormal depression of the freezing point of water by the addition of electrolytes.

The above deviations represent typical cases which may be explained in a simple manner. Often, however, an explanation is not possible because the system is too complicated or because the behavior of the system is not sufficiently known. In determining the molecular weight of a substance by melting-point or freezing-point depression, the experimenter must always keep in mind possible causes of deviation and their effect on the results obtained. A solute which dissociates does not always cause an abnormally high freezing-point depression. In naphthalene, for example, naphthalene picrate dissociates to some extent to form naphthalene and picric acid.[7] The solvent, naphthalene, will therefore be increased in mole fraction by an amount depending upon the extent of dissociation, so that the observed depression of the melting point of naphthalene will not be greater, but less, than that predicted from ideality.

Other possible causes for deviations from the freezing-point solubility law have been the subject of investigations by Hildebrand[2] and others.[8]

3. Cooling and Heating Curves

Extending the original definition of the freezing or melting point of a pure compound to include impure compounds or mixtures, one may define the melting point as the temperature at which a liquid of given composition is in equilibrium with the type of crystals which form on initial crystallization. When heat is added to such an equilibrium mixture, more crystals will melt (or dissolve in the liquid phase); and when heat is removed more crystals will form. The equilibrium temperature, *i.e.*, the freezing point, will depend only upon the composition of the liquid phase at any moment, and not on the relative proportions of liquid and

[5] M. Gomberg and C. S. Schoepfle, *J. Am. Chem. Soc.*, **39**, 1664 (1917).

[6] W. P. Jorissen and J. Rutten, *Chem. Weekblad*, **6**, 261 (1909).

[7] R. Kremann, *Monatsh*, **25**, 1252 (1904).

[8] H. L. Ward, *J. Phys. Chem.*, **30**, 1316 (1926).

solid.   In general, whenever the crystals have the same composition as the liquid phase, no change in the liquid composition takes place during freezing, and, consequently, the equilibrium temperature remains constant; the loss of heat to the surroundings will be exactly counterbalanced by the heat of fusion of the crystals formed.   If, on the other hand, the composition of the crystals differs from that of the liquid, the freezing temperature will change as more and more of the solid forms.   This change is the fundamental principle behind cooling-curve and heating-curve behavior, a knowledge of which is essential to a full understanding of melting- and freezing-point phenomena, abnormalities in behavior, and their significance.

In the phase diagram for mixtures of phthalic anhydride and naphthalene shown in figure 2, the temperature of the freezing point is plotted against the mole per cent of naphthalene in the mix.   The curve AC therefore indicates the freezing

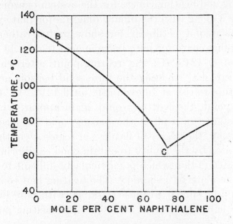

Fig. 2.—Freezing points of mixtures of naphthalene and phthalic anhydride.[8a]

point observed for various concentrations of naphthalene.   Point A represents the melting point of pure phthalic anhydride, namely 130.8° C.   When pure liquid anhydride is cooled to this temperature, solid anhydride forms and, according to the phase rule, the temperature must remain constant as long as the two phases exist.   Adding or subtracting heat changes only the amounts of solid and liquid present but does not change the equilibrium temperature.

Consider the behavior of a mixture of phthalic anhydride and naphthalene having the composition represented by point B.   If liquid of this composition is cooled, the initial freezing point will be 124° C., at which temperature crystals of pure

---

[8a] Data for figures 2, 3, 4, 5, 6, are from *International Critical Tables*, Vol. IV, pp. 180 179, 136, 119, and 108, respectively.

phthalic anhydride will begin to form.   This removal of solvent from the solution
will result in an increase in the concentration of the naphthalene and a further lowering of the freezing point as predicted by the freezing-point equation.   Thus, as
the concentration of naphthalene increases, the equilibrium temperature gets
lower and lower (that is, ΔT of Eq. 1 becomes larger and larger) following curve BC.
According to the phase rule, the presence of the additional component (naphthalene)
permits an additional degree of freedom; hence the temperature changes.

Cooling (or heating) curves are obtained by permitting the system under
investigation to lose heat to (or gain heat from) the surroundings at a
uniform rate.   The temperature of the sample is then measured at convenient time intervals during the phase change of the system.   The
temperature is plotted against the time to obtain either the heating or
cooling curve depending upon whether heat was added to or withdrawn
from the sample.

Schematic cooling and heating curves for the system benzoic acid–cinnamic acid
are shown in figure 3 along with the binary diagram for that system.   (The actual
experimental curves are not rectilinear, but show gradual rather than sharp changes
in slope.)   The cooling curve for pure benzoic acid (curve A) would exhibit a flat
region or "halt," ab, at 121.5° C., the freezing point, after which the temperature
would drop quite rapidly.   Heating the pure solid benzoic acid (curve D) would
cause the temperature to rise at an even rate until 121.5° C., the melting point, is
reached.   At this point, the halt ab would again appear, while the temperature
would remain constant, until all of the benzoic acid has been changed into the
liquid state.   Actually, the degree of flatness of region ab in the heating or cooling
curve would be limited by the ability to obtain good equilibrium between the solid
and liquid states, a condition which is particularly difficult to attain when only a
small fraction of the material is liquid.   The heating and cooling curves for pure
cinnamic acid would be similar to those obtained with pure benzoic acid with the
exception that the halt would occur at 136.8°, the melting point of the pure cinnamic acid.

Cooling a liquid solution of benzoic acid containing 20 mole per cent of cinnamic
acid, one would obtain schematically a curve similar to curve B in figure 3.   In this
case, the temperature would drop at a uniform rate to 105° C.   At this point, c, the
slope of the cooling curve would change, as shown, since here pure benzoic acid
would start to crystallize from the solution.   As mentioned in the case of naphthalene in phthalic anhydride, the temperature would continue to change because
the concentration of solute in the solution would increase with the separation of
solid benzoic acid.   Thus the cooling curve would indicate that the temperature
is still dropping, but at a different rate, as shown by the slope of the section cd.
Finally, at 82° both the cinnamic acid and benzoic acid would crystallize from the
solution, each in its own crystalline form, and in a ratio equal to that of the solution composition.   The composition of the liquid would, therefore, not change
during this part of the freezing process, and the temperature would remain constant.   The cooling curve would exhibit a brief halt, de, at this temperature until

all the liquid is converted into solid. This temperature is known as the eutectic temperature of the mixture. The eutectic composition for the system shown in figure 3 is 57 mole per cent benzoic acid and 43 mole per cent cinnamic acid.

On heating a solid with the over-all composition of 20 mole per cent cinnamic acid in benzoic acid, the curve obtained would be the reverse of the cooling curve (curve E, Fig. 3). The first liquid formed at the eutectic temperature of 82° C.

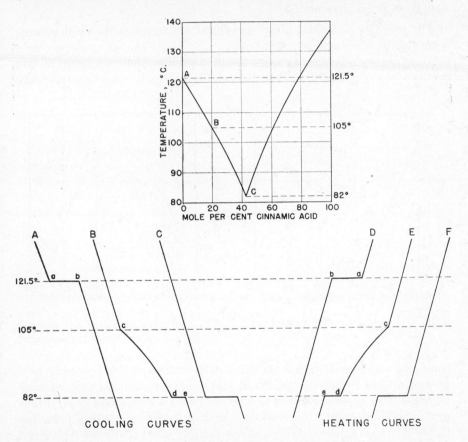

Fig. 3.—Freezing points and heating and cooling curves for mixtures of benzoic and cinnamic acids.[8a]

would have the eutectic composition indicated above. The heating curve would exhibit a brief halt, ed, during which interval the eutectic liquid would continue to form until all the cinnamic acid is in the liquid solution and only pure benzoic acid remains in solid form. The temperature would then gradually rise, following curve dc as the benzoic acid dissolves in the liquid mixture until the sample is all liquid. The temperature would then have reached 105°, at which point the heating curve would exhibit an increase in slope as shown.

If the over-all composition of the benzoic acid–cinnamic acid mixture were the same as the eutectic composition, the cooling and heating curves would be like those shown in curves C and F of figure 3. The halt obtained would be similar in shape to those observed for the pure substances, but would occur at the eutectic temperature of 82° C. The composition of the liquid would not change during the crystallization process and the temperature, therefore, would remain constant until no more liquid remains.

The behavior described above is typical for any system, ideal or not, which exhibits a simple eutectic point.

Many binary mixtures are more complicated than those discussed above, in that components A and B are in equilibrium with one or more loosely

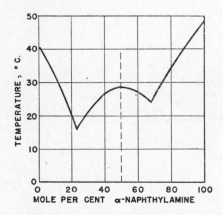

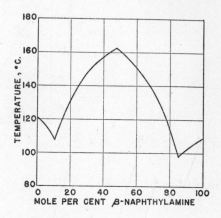

Fig. 4.—Freezing points of mixtures of phenol and α-naphthylamine.[8a]

Fig. 5.—Freezing points of mixtures of trinitrobenzene and β-naphthylamine.[8a]

combined compounds (e. g., AB, AB_2, A_2B) which usually dissociate to a greater or less extent in the liquid state. The compound formed may be one of two types according to whether it has a congruous or an incongruous melting point. A compound with a congruous melting point behaves as a pure substance since, at the melting point, both the liquid and the solid phases have exactly the same composition as the compound. If the compound has an incongruous melting point, it decomposes upon melting to form another solid and a liquid, each having a composition different from that of the original compound.

Phenol and α-naphthylamine combine to form a molecular compound which has a congruous melting point, that is, one in which the liquid form has the same composition as the solid. See figure 4. This diagram can be divided by a vertical line at 50% composition to give two ordinary eutectic systems of the type discussed above. In one case, we would have α-naphthylamine and the α-naphthylamine–phenol compound, and in the second system, phenol and the compound. The system *sym*-trinitrobenzene and β-naphthylamine is one in which the 1:1 compound formed has a congruous melting point 40° C. higher than either of the pure components. See figure 5.

In the case of incongruously melting compounds, the melting point of the compound represents a condition of unstable equilibrium. The solid compound, upon melting, decomposes reversibly into a new solid phase and a liquid. This liquid is saturated both with respect to the compound and the new solid.

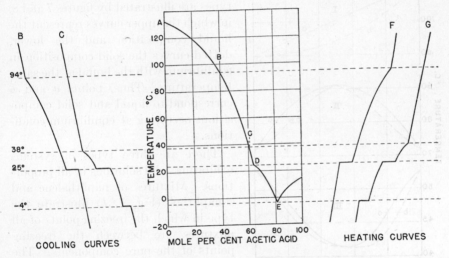

Fig. 6.—Freezing points and heating and cooling curves of mixtures of acetic acid and dimethylpyrone.[8a]

Such a system is illustrated by acetic acid and dimethylpyrone, which form a 1:1 compound with an incongruous melting point. See figure 6. Upon cooling a system of composition B, pure dimethylpyrone would be deposited between 94° and 25° C.; and, at 25°, a liquid of composition D would dissolve the dimethylpyrone, producing crystals of the compound represented by a 1:1 mixture, the composition of the liquid phase remaining constant meanwhile until all of the liquid is exhausted. From the over-all composition of the system, it is evident that excess dimethylpyrone would remain. The same three phases would be in equilibrium at 25° in a system having the original composition C; but since more acetic acid would be present than is required to form the compound, some would remain as liquid after all the solid dimethylpyrone has dissolved. Crystals of the 1:1 compound would then separate until the eutectic composition E is reached, when both the compound and acetic acid would crystallize out together as in a simple eutectic system. The heating curves are the reverse of the cooling curves just described, as can be seen from a study of curves F and G in figure 6.

The above systems have been mixtures from which a crystalline substance in definite proportions separates on freezing. Frequently this is not the case, and the organic chemist may often prepare an homogeneous crystal phase containing both components but in indefinite proportions.

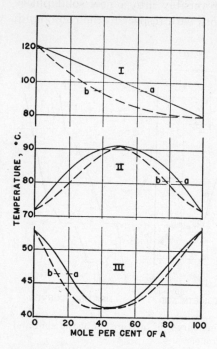

Fig. 7.—Freezing points of solid solutions.[8b] Curve I: Component A, naphthalene; B, β-naphthol. Curve II: A, d-carvoxime; B, l-carvoxime. Curve III: A, p-chloroiodobenzene; B, p-dichlorobenzene.

These solid solutions, or mixed crystals as they are sometimes called, may form either in all proportions or with limited solubility. Examples of these two types are illustrated by figures 7 and 8, in which the upper curves represent the liquid composition and the lower, dotted curves the solid composition in equilibrium with the liquid at the same temperature. Thus, points a and b correspond to liquid and solid compositions occurring at equilibrium conditions.

There are three types of systems exhibiting solid solutions in all proportions. Mixtures of naphthalene and β-naphthol (Fig. 7, I) illustrate the type in which the freezing points of all mixtures are between the freezing points of the pure components. The second type (Fig. 7, II) is one in which the freezing-point curve passes through a maximum. Very few systems of this type are known, the system d-carvoxime and l-carvoxime being probably the best example. In the third type (Fig. 7, III) the freezing point passes through a minimum, as illustrated by the system p-chloroiodobenzene–p-dichlorobenzene. It should be noted that, in the first two types, the freezing and melting points exhibit a rise due to the presence of the second component, contrary to expectations based upon the freezing-point equation.

[8b] Data from *International Critical Tables*, Vol. IV, p. 155 for *I*, p. 154 for *II*, and p. 123 for *III*.

Monochloroacetic acid and naphthalene form a system (Fig. 8) in which a discontinuous series of solid solutions are formed upon cooling. The first liquid formed upon melting any mixture containing between 2 and 53 mole per cent of naphthalene would have the eutectic composition of 30 mole per cent naphthalene. Outside this range, the initial melting point as determined by a refined method of measurement would not be the eutectic temperature, but some higher temperature as indicated by the dotted curve, and the first liquid would have a composition indicated by the corresponding point on the liquid curve.

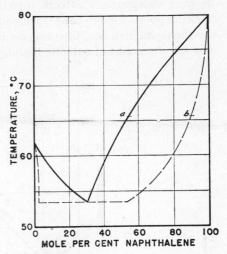

Fig. 8.—Freezing points of mixtures of naphthalene and monochloroacetic acid.[8c]

Mixtures also exist which form a series of solid solutions with the same melting point. In such a case, since the cooling curves for all compositions would be identical, it is impossible to distinguish between the two pure constituents and their mixtures by means of the melting point. An example of this type of system is that of d-camphor–l-camphor, mixtures of which have melting points as shown in table II. Systems of this type are also found with the d- and l- forms of camphoroxime, borneol, camphoric anhydride, and camphene.[9]

TABLE II

MELTING POINTS OF MIXTURES OF d- AND l-CAMPHOR[a]

d-Camphor, %	M. p., ° C.
100	178.6
86.2	178.8
81.0	178.6
70.8	179.1
57.9	178.7
48.7	178.6
30.1	178.3
19.1	177.8
11.3	178.5
0.0	177.7

[a] J. D. M. Ross and I. C. Somerville, J. Chem. Soc., 1926, 2770.

[8c] Data from H. P. Cady, J. Phys. Chem., 3, 127 (1899).

[9] J. D. M. Ross and I. C. Somerville, J. Chem. Soc., 1926, 2770.

It is evident from this discussion of cooling and heating curves that, with some exceptions, the observation of sharp melting points is limited to pure substances or eutectic mixtures. In actual practice, however, the melting points for substances which are nearly pure appear sharp because, by the usual methods, the observer is unable to see the initial formation of the small amount of eutectic liquid.

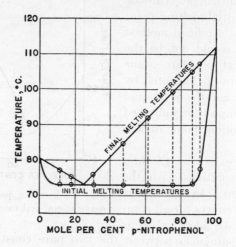

Fig. 9.—Observed melting ranges for mixtures
of naphthalene and *p*-nitrophenol.[9a]

Consider, for example, a mixture of 1% naphthalene and 99% phthalic anhydride. By means of the ordinary melting-point determination in a capillary tube, the mixture would be found to melt very close to the melting point of pure phthalic anhydride (130.8° C.). An accurate heating curve would show a slight halt during the melting of the eutectic mixture at the eutectic temperature (64.9° C.), at which all the naphthalene would liquefy. The remaining solid phthalic anhydride would then dissolve in the mixture (if true equilibrium were preserved) until the entire system has liquefied at a temperature just below the melting point of pure phthalic anhydride. Thus the sample would actually melt over the range of 64.9° to almost 130.8°, even though the melting would not be perceptible by ordinary techniques until the higher temperature is almost attained.

Figure 9 shows the observed initial and final melting temperatures observed in capillaries for mixtures of naphthalene and *p*-nitrophenol with different compositions. The initial melting temperatures were obtained by a special technique for observing the "softening point."[10] The melting ranges are indicated by the dotted lines. It will be noted that, for mixtures near the middle of the diagram,

[9a] Data from H. Rheinboldt, *J. prakt. Chem.*, **219**, 242 (1925).

[10] H. Rheinboldt, *Ber.*, **74**, 756 (1941).

the initial melting temperature is the same as that of the eutectic mixture; but, whenever nearly pure naphthalene or nearly pure p-nitrophenol is melted, the apparent melting range as observed in a capillary tube is small, although the range actually starts at the eutectic temperature. The very nature of the phenomenon is such that the appearance of the liquid is gradual and the choice of the lower point of the range is empirical.

Strictly speaking, no really pure substance has ever been prepared; if the melting point could be determined with sufficient accuracy, any substance would exhibit a certain amount of premelting. In connection with the determination of heats of fusion, the purest water prepared by Dickinson and Osborne of the National Bureau of Standards exhibited premelting to the extent of 0.0005° C., probably because of the presence of slight impurities.[11] It is thus evident that sharp melting points are reported for substances of ordinary purity only because the observer with the usual apparatus is unable to see the small amount of liquid formed during the premelting stage.

III. TECHNIQUES AND APPARATUS

1. Melting Temperatures from Cooling Curves

The essential parts of an apparatus for the determination of a cooling curve are: a bath to permit cooling at a slow, steady rate; an inner sample tube which can be heated to melt the sample; a stirrer to maintain equilibrium throughout the sample; and a thermometer or thermocouple of low heat capacity to measure the temperature of the sample. Lynn[12] has described an apparatus of this sort which is simple to construct and easy to operate, requiring only 0.5 gram of sample for the determination of a suitable cooling curve. See figure 10. The bath consists of a small unsilvered Dewar tube inside of which is a Pyrex tube wound externally with fine nichrome wire. A thin-walled test tube holding the sample is placed inside the heater tube. Heating and cooling rates may be controlled by a rheostat or variac in series with the heater. The thermometer or thermoelement placed in the sample or a separate ring stirrer may be used for stirring. A more elaborate setup permitting application of the method to samples only 200 to 300 milligrams in size was devised by Smit.[13]

In making the observations for the cooling curve, the sample is first melted by means of the heater and then allowed to cool slowly by read-

[11] H. C. Dickinson and N. S. Osborne, *J. Wash. Acad. Sci.*, **5**, 338 (1915).

[12] G. Lynn, *J. Phys. Chem.*, **31**, 1381 (1927).

[13] W. M. Smit, *Chem. Weekblad*, **36**, 750 (1939).

justing the current through the heater. Some supercooling of the liquid should take place so that, when crystallization starts crystals are formed quickly throughout the sample; equilibrium between the liquid and solid phases is then retained by slow, steady stirring. Care should be taken, however, that supercooling not be too great, especially if the sample is small; otherwise the heat evolved by the formation of crystals (heat of fusion) may be too small to raise the temperature of the sample and the thermometer back to the freezing point before the entire mass solidifies. Time–temperature observations should be taken throughout the cooling process and plotted to show the shape of the curve. Often, crystallization of the supercooled liquid may have to be induced by seeding or by tapping the thermometer or tube, or by stirring vigorously momentarily.

The time–temperature diagrams obtained by this method afford a good basis for determination of the freezing point of a substance. If the substance is pure, the observed temperature will remain constant at the freezing point for about one-half the time required for complete freezing. In any case, the maximum temperature attained after crystallization starts is taken as the freezing (or melting) point of the sample.

If considerable impurity is present, the flat portion of the experimental curve will be much shorter, and may never be horizontal at all, in which case the freezing point obtained will be considerably lower than the true value. See pages 30 and 31. This apparatus is therefore not applicable to the determination of binary freezing-point diagrams.

In determining cooling curves as outlined above, it is essential that the temperature gradient between the sample and the surroundings be not too high. If heat is being removed from the sample by the bath at too great a rate or if the rate of crystallization is too slow, the observed freezing point may be lower than the true temperature of solidification, because the heat loss from the sample to the surroundings is greater than the heat of fusion supplied by the formation of crystals. This difficulty can sometimes be overcome by increasing the initial degree of supercooling, since it has been found that the rate of crystallization increases, within certain limits, with the extent of supercooling. The fact that the temperature is constant during the halt does not necessarily mean that errors due to the above sources have been eliminated. Hence, it is

F i g. 1 0. —
Cooling curve
apparatus.[12]

always desirable to repeat the determination using different degrees of supercooling; the highest value observed will be the most nearly correct.

Although heating curves may be obtained with the apparatus described, they cannot be used for accurate melting-point determinations or as a criterion of purity.   In the case of heating curves, no need exists for starting crystallization, a troublesome feature of the cooling-curve determination; but equilibrium between the solid and the liquid phases is more difficult to attain because it is impossible to stir the mixture from the beginning.

It is possible to obtain more accurate information concerning the purity and the melting and freezing points of substances by obtaining the cooling or heating curves in more refined apparatus than that described in this section.   For details concerning these methods, the reader is referred to the chapter on calorimetry.

2.   Melting Temperatures by the Capillary Method

The melting point most commonly reported by the organic chemist, and probably the most conveniently determined, is that obtained by packing the finely divided sample in a glass capillary, immersing the tube in a bath whose temperature is gradually raised, and noting the temperature of the bath adjacent to the capillary when the substance is seen to melt. This method has two advantages: only a small amount of material is required;   and a fair accuracy may be obtained with very simple equipment.   The bath should be well stirred, heated at an even rate—about 1° C. per minute in the vicinity of the melting point for ordinary purposes—and should permit unrestricted visibility of the melting-point tube and the thermometer.

The temperature at which the last crystal dissolves is usually taken as the melting point.   As was pointed out in the section on heating and cooling curves, if the substance appears to melt over a range, the initial melting is not observable, and the initial melting point reported varies greatly with different experimenters.   Many substances when heated in a capillary tube exhibit a "sintering" effect at some temperatures a little below the melting temperature.   This sintering, or settling of the substance in the capillary tube, which may be due to partial melting of the solid at or above the eutectic temperature, gives notice that the sample is approaching the melting temperature.

Certain precautions should be observed in constructing and filling the capillary tubes.   They should be drawn down from thin-walled soft glass tubing to a diameter of about 1 millimeter.   Smaller tubes are difficult to fill; and, in fact, with waxy or similar materials it may be necessary to use tubes of slightly larger diameters.   Thermal equilibrium throughout the sample is more easily obtained with smaller tubes.

If large tubes are used for impure substances or binary mixtures, the substance next to the walls may liquefy first and allow the solid to float or sink. The resultant segregation between the solid and liquid may cause the observed melting point of the mixture to be too high. Resolidification and remelting would tend to increase this segregation and magnify the error involved.

The tubing from which the capillaries are made should be washed and dried before drawing. Alkali and products of devitrification on the walls of the tube are known to lower the melting point, especially in the case of substances such as those having free aldehydic or ketonic groups.[14] Likewise, Dieckmann[15] has shown that slightly different melting points are obtained with capillaries of different glasses. After the capillaries are drawn, they should be sealed at both ends to keep them clean until they are to be used.

In filling the tube, a small amount of the material to be tested is scooped into the open end. It is then worked into the bottom of the tube. This can be accomplished by a number of methods, for example, by rasping the bottom of the tube with a file, or by dropping the capillary a foot or more inside a larger tube so that the bottom of the capillary strikes the desk or table top. In any case, it is important that the substance under examination be well packed into the bottom of the tube to insure the maximum contact between the sample and the walls of the tube. It is advisable to seal the tube when the sample is subject to change or decomposition through continued exposure to air, or when it is desired to retain the sample for some time before using. Such samples should be introduced through a long thin "funnel" so that no organic material will be in the neck of the tube to decompose during the sealing. Upon decomposition additional components would form which would tend to lower the melting point.

The ideal type of bath for melting-point determinations is one in which the temperature of the liquid surrounding the thermometer and capillary tube can be closely controlled at all times. This can be accomplished only with efficient stirring and a readily controlled heat source, preferably one with a minimum lag. It should be possible to maintain the temperature fairly constant for some time since, in accurate determinations, it is frequently desirable to set the temperature at some point just below or above the melting point. The rate of response of different thermometers to a change in temperature of the bath will differ depending upon their heat capacities. In order to compensate for this factor, the rate of heating must be slow if the melting-point determinations are to be accurate.

The capillary and the thermometer bulb should be contiguous so the

[14] A. Georg, *Helv. Chim. Acta*, **15**, 924 (1932).

[15] W. Dieckmann, *Ber.*, **49**, 2204, 2213 (1916).

temperature registered by the thermometer will be as nearly as possible the actual temperature of the sample. Common practice is to fasten the capillary to the thermometer by means of a rubber band or similar device above the surface of the bath liquid. If the capillaries are long and straight, they will adhere to the thermometer by capillary action of the liquid. The use of thermometers which can be completely immersed in the bath is preferred because it eliminates the necessity of troublesome stem corrections. Thermometers and their calibrations and stem corrections will be discussed in a later section.

The bath liquid should be relatively nonvolatile and inert. The liquids chosen may vary for the range of melting points most likely to be encountered. Liquid paraffins, such as commercial clear mineral oil, are excellent for moderate temperatures provided their viscosities are not too high. At higher temperatures, they tend to fume and discolor. For high temperatures (above 200° C.), concentrated sulfuric acid, phosphoric acid, or a mixture of six parts of sulfuric acid and four of potassium sulfate have been recommended.[16, 17] A common satisfactory bath liquid for temperatures above 150° C. is dibutyl phthalate. Its viscosity at the lower ranges, however, is somewhat high to permit good control of the bath temperature.

Thiele Apparatus.—The principle of the Thiele tube is the basis of a variety of types of capillary melting-point baths. In this apparatus, the bath is in the shape of a vertical loop in which the liquid is heated on one side and the capillary and thermometer suspended on the other. The liquid in the heated side rises, causing the liquid in the capillary side to descend, thus setting up a circulation of the fluid by convection. Of the many modifications of this principle, probably the best is the apparatus described by Hershberg,[18] a diagram of which appears in figure 11. Here, the liquid is kept moving around the loop at a rapid rate by means of a stirrer mounted on a ball-bearing assembly. The sample capillary and a total-immersion thermometer are placed in an adiabatic zone inside the tube in which the deviation in temperature is said not to exceed 0.025° C. The heater can be regulated so that the rate of temperature rise can be reduced to about one-tenth of a degree per minute. The top of the thermometer side of the tube is so constructed that capillaries can be inserted and withdrawn with little difficulty.

Another refinement of the capillary method employs an optical system

---

[16] F. D. Snell, *Ind. Eng. Chem., Anal. Ed.*, **2**, 287 (1930).

[17] A. A. Morton, *Laboratory Technique in Organic Chemistry*. McGraw-Hill, New York, 1938.

[18] E. B. Hershberg, *Ind. Eng. Chem., Anal. Ed.*, **8**, 312 (1936). See also K. S. Markley, *ibid.*, **6**, 475 (1934).

whereby the sample and the thermometer may be viewed simultaneously through a telescopic eyepiece.[19]   This apparatus is claimed to give melting points reproducible by different observers to within 0.03° C.

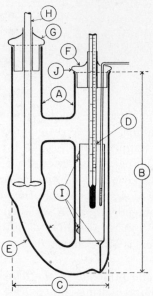

Fig. 11.—The Thiele apparatus as modified by Hershberg.[18]   *A*, 28-mm. outside diameter and 25-mm. inside diameter.   *B*, 17 cm.   *C*, 8.5 cm.   *D*, sleeve, 19-mm. outside diameter, 17-mm. inside diameter, 9 cm. long; loops, No. 26 B. and S. gage platinum wire.   *E*, 18-mm. outside diameter.   *F*, thermometer cap; thermometer tube, 7-mm. inside diameter.   *G*, stirrer cap.   *H*, stirrer, 5-mm. outside diameter glass tubing; ball bearings with 0.61-cm. (0.25-in.) hole and 2.2-cm. (0.875-in.) outside diameter, unground.   *I*, knobs to center sleeve.   *J*, lip and wedge to prevent rotation of cap.

Copper Block.—The Thiele tube method has disadvantages, especially at high temperatures: the bath liquid discolors and produces fumes; and there may be unequal heat distribution due to streamline currents and high heat losses to the surroundings.   These difficulties are overcome to some extent by replacing the heating liquid with a metal block made of a good heat conductor such as copper.   This scheme was originally devised by Thiele[20] and has been modified by Berl and Kullmann.[21] The apparatus consists of a copper block or cylinder in which holes are bored for two thermometers and for two capillary tubes.   The holes are of such sizes that the thermometers and capillary tubes fit snugly and make

[19] F. Francis and F. J. E. Collins, *J. Chem. Soc.*, **1936**, 137.

[20] H. Thiele, *Z. angew. Chem.*, **15**, 780 (1902).

[21] E. Berl and A. Kullmann, *Ber.*, **60**, 811 (1927).

good thermal contact with the block.   A hole perpendicular to the capillary wells, and intersecting them, is cut through the block for observing the bottoms of the capillaries.   This opening may be closed with a strip of mica to prevent access of air currents through the slit or hole and yet retain visibility.   The block is then covered with asbestos and resistance wire so that it may be heated electrically.   In using the apparatus the block is heated and the melting point observed with the aid of a light on the far side of the block.   Various optical arrangements have been proposed to aid in observation of the capillaries when melting takes place. A good account of these and further details of the copper block method can be found in the original papers[22] or in Morton.[17]

3. Hot Stages

Melting temperatures are frequently determined by one of several hot-stage methods.   In such a method, the sample is placed on a plate or bar which is heated, and the temperature at which melting occurs is noted by means of a thermometer or thermocouple arrangement.   Hot stages present the advantages of rapid heating, elimination of a liquid bath, and an ease of operation not usually obtained by other methods of melting-point measurement, and are particularly adaptable to substances which melt with decomposition.   They lack, however, the accuracy and precision attainable with a refined capillary apparatus.

An interesting application of the hot-stage method is the melting-point apparatus described by Dennis and Shelton.[23]   In this apparatus, the powdered sample is sprinkled in a thin line on a copper bar heated at one end.   A temperature gradient exists on the surface of the bar from the hot to the cold end, and the substance melts instantaneously where the temperature of the bar exceeds the melting point.   A line of demarcation between the solid and liquid indicates the point at which melting first takes place.   The temperature is usually determined by touching the bar at this point with a constantan wire to form a thermocouple with a definite electromotive force corresponding to the melting temperature.

In the Fisher-Johns melting-point apparatus, the sample is placed between cover glasses on an aluminum stage which is electrically heated. A magnifier is placed above the sample to facilitate ready observation of the crystals at the melting temperature.   A thermometer with its bulb imbedded in the stage immediately below the sample records the temperature of the stage at the melting point.

[22] W. L. Walsh, *Ind. Eng. Chem., Anal. Ed.*, **6**, 468 (1934).   W. Friedel, *Biochem. Z.*, **209**, 65 (1929).   C. F. Lindström, *Chem. Fabrik*, **7**, 270 (1934).

[23] L. M. Dennis and R. S. Shelton, *J. Am. Chem. Soc.*, **52**, 3128 (1930).

Several hot stages for microscopes have been designed for the determination of melting points with very small quantities of material. In most of these, the temperature is measured with a sensitive thermocouple, although modifications permitting the use of a mercury thermometer have also been described. For all compounds except those which are isotropic or become so on heating, the melting point can best be observed by means of a polarizing microscope, since the temperature at which the color disappears and the space lattice is ruptured is the true melting point. With an instrument of this sort Zscheile and White[24] claimed a precision of ±0.04° C. For further details of this method of determining melting point, the reader is referred to chapter XI, "Microscopy," page 435.

4. Mixed Melting Points

The method of mixed melting points may be used in the identification of organic substances. Approximately equal amounts of the unknown and a substance thought to be the same compound are pulverized and intimately mixed in a mortar or on a watch glass. Capillary melting points are then taken of the known, the unknown, and the mixture. If all three melting points are essentially the same, or if the melting point of the mixture lies between that of the two components, the identity of the unknown with that of the known is fairly certain. If the substances are not identical, the melting point of the mixture is usually 10° to 30° or more below that of the components and the mixture melts over a range.[25] These melting points should all be taken in the same bath simultaneously, since factors which affect the melting point, such as decomposition and rate of heating, will then be the same in all three cases.

It is not necessary to have a very pure substance in order to identify it by the method of mixed melting points. If the melting point is a few degrees too low, addition of the known will give a melting point which is between the known and the unknown when the substances are identical.

The method of identification by mixed melting points is based on the assumption that a mixture of any two substances will have a melting point which is appreciably lower than that of either alone. That this assumption does not hold in all cases is apparent by a study of typical binary system diagrams already mentioned. As illustrated by the systems in figures 7, *I* and 7, *II* and by table II it is quite possible for two different substances to have mixed melting points which are either higher than or equal to those of the two components. For example, if tricosanoic acid is mixed with an equimolecular proportion of tetracosanoic acid its melting

---

[24] F. P. Zscheile and J. W. White, Jr., *Ind. Eng. Chem., Anal. Ed.*, **12**, 436 (1940).
[25] E. Kordes, *Z. anorg. allgem. Chem.*, **154**, 93 (1926); **167**, 97 (1927); **168**, 177 (1927).

point is raised by 0.2° C. and is very sharp.   This and a number of similar cases of fatty acid mixtures have been described.[26]   When *d*-dimethyl tartrate and *l*-dimethyl tartrate (m.p., 43.3° C.) are mixed in equal proportions, a melting point of 89.4° C. is obtained.[27]   Gibby and Waters[28] reported that, for pure 3-bromo-5-iodo-4-aminobenzophenone (m.p., 145.9° C.) and pure 3,5-dibromo-4-aminobenzophenone (m.p., 146° C.), the mixed melting point is only about 0.5° lower, whereas in a previous paper it had been concluded that these two compounds were identical.   Lock and Nottes[29] have cited many other cases where mixed melting-point behavior is abnormal.   Failure to observe a lowered melting point for the mixture would thus not be absolute proof of the identity of the known and unknown.   Additional means of identification, *e. g.*, crystal structure, optical rotation, and chemical analysis, should be applied in cases in which the identity of the unknown is still in question.

When mixed melting-point determinations are made on substances which decompose on melting, the information gained may not be conclusive.   If the decomposition point of the mixture is not lower, the two constituents may or may not be identical; if the decomposition point is lower, however, the two constituents are shown to be different compounds.

As long as the possibility of the anomalous cases mentioned above is kept in mind, the mixed melting-point technique is useful, especially when one is employing very small quantities of the unknown.   The fact that this method of identification does not require a highly purified sample eliminates the necessity for the final purification and the resultant loss of material.   The method may even be used for substances which are liquid under ordinary conditions by measuring the temperature of the melting point of the frozen mixture.[30]   Successful application of the method requires some knowledge of the melting-point behavior of binary mixtures, including a familiarity with the various possible types of binary freezing-point diagrams.

5.   Melting Points of Substances Which Decompose

If a substance melts with decomposition, the melting temperature observed will be lower than the melting point of the pure substance because of the presence of decomposition products.   This is especially true if de-

[26] F. Francis, S. H. Piper, and T. Malkin, *Proc. Roy. Soc. London,* **A128,** 214 (1930). A. C. Chibnall, S. H. Piper, and E. F. Williams, *Biochem. J.,* **30,** 100 (1936).

[27] J. H. Adriani, *Z. physik. Chem.,* **33,** 453 (1900).

[28] C. W. Gibby and W. A. Waters, *J. Chem. Soc.,* **1931,** 2151.

[29] G. Lock and G. Nottes, *Ber.,* **68,** 1200 (1935).

[30] R. Hollmann, *Z. physik. Chem.,* **43,** 129 (1903).

composition occurs in the solid state before the substance actually melts; and, since premelting is invariably present to some extent, the melting point of a substance which decomposes is usually considerably lower than the true melting point. The amount of decomposition products formed depends upon the length of time the sample has been heated near the decomposition temperature before the melting point is reached. It is apparent, then, that the melting point of a substance which decomposes will depend upon the rate of heating of the melting-point bath. Thus, pure tyrosine melts at 280° C. when heated slowly[31] and at 314-318° C. when heated rapidly.[32]

Therefore, if the substance shows any indication of decomposing, the melting-point sample should be heated rapidly. This can be accomplished by constructing the bath so that the temperature rise is as rapid as one degree for every two seconds. Another method of heating the sample rapidly is immersion of the capillary in the preheated bath so that the bath temperature has to be raised only a few degrees before the melting point is reached.[33] When melting points with decomposition are reported in the literature, it is essential that complete details of the method and rate of heating be given in order that the melting point can be reproduced by another experimenter.

Organic substances which decompose when heated near their melting points may exhibit any one of a number of types of decomposition. These may frequently be distinguished simply by watching the sample closely with a magnifying glass during melting. The substance may merely darken, as in the case of 1,4-anthraquinone.[34] It may undergo the loss of certain products. Thus, dibromomalonic acid gives off carbon dioxide[35]; nitroguanidine evolves ammonia[36]; diiodomalonic acid decomposes to give off iodine[35]; and aniline sulfate loses water and sulfur dioxide. Some substances, such as iodoxybenzene, explode at the melting temperature.[37] In some cases, the compound may melt and form a new compound which is solid at the high temperature so that the observer may note two melting points. This is usually true of substances which form anhydrides easily.[38] In general, although melting points with decomposition are in many cases uncertain, in some cases they are fairly reliable and reproducible.

---

[31] E. Fischer, *Ber.*, **32**, 3641 (1899).

[32] R. Kempf, *J. prakt. Chem.*, **78**, 242 (1908).

[33] A. Michael, *Ber.*, **28**, 1629 (1895).

[34] I. J. Pisovschi, *Ber.*, **41**, 1436 (1908).

[35] R. Willstätter, *Ber.*, **35**, 1375 (1902).

[36] J. Thiele, *Ann.*, **270**, 18 (1892).

[37] C. Willgerodt, *Ber.*, **26**, 358 (1893).

[38] E. Noelting and K. Philipp, *Ber.*, **41**, 584 (1908).

6.   Anomalous Melting Points

Pure substances may exist in more than one crystalline or polymorphic form and may, therefore, exhibit two or more melting points, and possibly one or more transition points.   A substance is termed enantiotropic when the transition temperature is below the melting temperature of either form, as when one crystalline form is transformed to another without melting. If it is necessary to melt one form to obtain the other polymorph, the substance is monotropic.

An enantiotropic substance existing in two forms exhibits a transition point below which one form (alpha) and above which the other form (beta) is stable.   When the alpha form is heated slowly, it transforms to the beta form at the transition temperature.   This transition is reversible so that, if the beta form is cooled below the transition point, the alpha form is again formed.   If the beta form is heated, it exhibits a normal melting point.   When the temperature of the alpha form, is raised through the transition temperature so rapidly that transition fails to occur, the melting point of the alpha form is observed.   The liquid obtained by melting is metastable with respect to the solid beta form, however; and if the temperature is not allowed to rise above the melting temperature of the latter, the liquid may solidify.   The solid so formed will on further heating exhibit the melting point of the beta form.

Carbon tetrabromide is an example of a substance which exhibits enantiotropism. At ordinary temperatures, the stable form (solid II) is monoclinic.[39]   When heated to 46.9° C. (the transition point), a cubic form with tetrahedral symmetry (solid I) is formed which melts at 90.1°.   The velocity of transformation of the metastable to the stable form above 46.9° is probably very rapid, so that the melting point of the pure solid II has probably never been observed.   In the well-known case of sulfur, however, the transformation from the rhombic to the monoclinic form above the transition point (95.5°) is so slow that the melting point of the rhombic form can easily be observed to be 112.8°.   At this temperature, both rhombic sulfur and the liquid are metastable. The melting point of the monoclinic form is 119.25°.[40]

A monotropic substance is characterized by the fact that the transformation from the unstable to the stable crystalline modification is irreversible.   Thus, if the unstable form, which always has the lower melting point, is melted, transition to the solid stable form may occur.   This solid would melt at some higher temperature.   Resolidifying the liquid would give either the unstable form which melts as described above or the stable form which would melt at the higher temperature.   The unstable form may transform to the stable form on standing.

[39] K. J. Frederick and J. H. Hildebrand, *J. Am. Chem. Soc.*, **61**, 1555 (1939).
[40] A. Findlay, *The Phase Rule and Its Applications*.   8th ed., Longmans, Green, New York, 1938. pp. 54–58.

Menthol[41] crystallizes in at least four different forms, α, β, γ, and δ, only one of which (α) is stable between zero and its melting temperature, 42.5° C. The other three forms are monotropic and have lower melting points as follows: $\beta = 35.5°$, $\gamma = 33.5°$, and $\delta = 31.5°$. All these unstable forms finally revert to the stable alpha form on standing. The melted menthol may be undercooled to 32° or lower before it crystallizes in any reasonable length of time. The unstable forms are obtained by rapid cooling of the melt to different extents. If a mixture of the unstable and stable forms is heated to, say, 36° C. the unstable forms liquefy. This liquid then begins to crystallize in the stable alpha form which will melt when the temperature of 42.5° C. is reached.

Another interesting case of anomalous melting points is caused by "dynamic isomerism." On melting either of two geometric isomers, for example, a more or less rapid transformation sometimes takes place into a definite equilibrium mixture of the two forms. On resolidification, this mixture persists and exhibits its individual melting point different from that of either of the isomers.

The two isomeric benzaldoximes are an interesting example of this type of "pseudobinary system."[42] This *cis* modification has a melting point of 34–35° C., whereas the *trans* modification melts at 130°. The system exhibits a eutectic point at about 25° at a composition corresponding to 92% of the *cis* form. The "natural" equilibrium mixture freezes at 27.7°, however, and will be found to melt at the same temperature immediately after solidifying. No matter what the composition of the original mixture of *cis* and *trans* forms, if it is once melted, resolidified, and then melted again, the melting point of 27.7° will be observed.

The *cis*- and *trans*-anisaldoximes show the same type of behavior; but in this case the rate of transformation to the equilibrium mixture is relatively slow, so that the third melting point determined would be lower than the second, the fourth lower than the third, and so on until a minimum is reached.[43] For a more detailed discussion of systems of this sort, the reader is referred to Findlay.[44]

Many substances form liquid crystals upon heating,[45] and may appear to have melting ranges instead of sharp melting points. The observer will usually notice the formation of a turbid liquid at some temperature below that at which the liquid becomes clear. Upon cooling, this phenomenon will be found to be reversible. Actually, no solid remains in the turbid liquid but the substance is in an anisotropic liquid–crystalline state. *p*-Azoxyanisole, one of the most common examples of such a substance,

---

[41] F. E. Wright, *J. Am. Chem. Soc.*, **39**, 1515 (1917).

[42] F. K. Cameron, *J. Phys. Chem.*, **2**, 409 (1898).

[43] E. L. Skau and B. Saxton, *J. Phys. Chem.*, **37**, 197 (1933).

[44] A. Findlay, *The Phase Rule and Its Applications*. 8th ed., Longmans, Green, New York, 1938, Chapter X.

[45] *International Critical Tables*, Vol. I, McGraw-Hill, New York, 1926, pp. 314–320.

has been found to transform into the liquid crystal state at 118.3° C. and melt into a clear liquid at 135.9° C.[46]

The effect of a second component on the melting point of a substance forming liquid crystals is of interest. De Kock[47] investigated the addition of p-methoxycinnamic acid to p-azoxyanisole. Each of these substances forms liquid crystals, but the addition of the second component results in a lowering of both the solid crystal and the liquid crystal melting points by about the same amount. The melting point of the liquid crystal form is, apparently, lowered by the presence of an impurity to just the same extent as is the melting point of the solid crystal.

7. Melting Points Requiring Special Techniques

The ordinary methods of melting-point determination must be modified for many substances because of their special nature. In most of these cases simple changes in technique, some of which will be discussed below, may be employed to accomplish the desired measurement. For greater detail concerning these methods, the reader is referred to Houben.[48]

If the substance is highly colored and melting is not visible Piccard[49] has suggested forming a plug of the material in a capillary by melting and resolidification and noting the temperature at which the plug moves along due to air pressure on one end of the tube.

For substances likely to explode, a very small amount of the material is laid on a liquid metal surface or on a cover glass floated thereon. Mercury is used for moderate temperatures, and soft solder in a nickel crucible for temperatures between 170° and 450° C. The sample is covered with a watch glass or funnel, and the temperature of the thermometer immersed in the bath is observed when melting occurs. Serious accidents might occur if explosive substances are handled in the usual way, so any questionable compound should be tested first by heating a small amount on a spatula in order to determine whether precautions are necessary.

Hygroscopic substances, such as benzensulfonic acid, tend to take up water, which changes the melting point. Such materials are probably best treated by placing them in a capillary, drying, and sealing the tube to prevent further absorption of moisture. Drying may be accomplished by heating or passing warm dry air over the sample before sealing.

Some substances, such as chloranil and hexamethylethane, tend to sub-

[46] G. A. Hulett, Z. physik. Chem., 28, 629 (1899).

[47] A. C. de Kock, Z. physik. Chem., 48, 129 (1904).

[48] J. Houben, Die Methoden der organischen Chemie. 3rd ed., Vol. I, Thieme, Leipzig, 1925, pp. 812–820.

[49] J. Piccard, Ber., 8, 687 (1875). See also H. Landolt, Z. physik. Chem., 4, 349 (1889).

lime below their melting temperatures.   This type of material is handled
by testing in a short, sealed capillary totally immersed in the bath.   Heating the entire capillary prevents sublimation and keeps the solid confined
to the bottom of the tube.

If the material is sensitive to the presence of air at high temperatures
the capillary should be evacuated before sealing or the air should be replaced by an inert gas.   Strychnine derivatives do not generally melt
sharply when air is present.   In all cases in which the capillary is sealed,
as pointed out above, the sample should be introduced through a long
funnel to avoid decomposition of the substance which might otherwise
stick to the neck of the tube.

Fats, waxes, and paraffin-like materials usually do not melt sharply and
therefore exhibit melting ranges which may not be too reliable.   One
difficulty in handling these materials is the problem of filling the capillary
tube.   This may be done in most cases by melting the substance and
sucking it up into the bottom of a long, thin-walled U tube which is then
cooled well below the melting point and allowed to stand for several hours.
The melting point is taken by immersing the bottom of the U in the bath
alongside the thermometer bulb.

8.   Freezing Temperatures of Binary Mixtures

The capillary method of determining melting points cannot be relied
upon to give data of suitable accuracy for binary diagrams because it does
not readily permit the attainment of a true melting-point equilibrium
between solid and liquid phases.   A large number of binary systems
have been constructed using data obtained with apparatus similar to the
Beckmann freezing-point depression apparatus but with an ordinary thermometer in place of the Beckmann thermometer.   It has been shown, however, that the errors involved in this method are sometimes so large that
false conclusions may be drawn even as to the type of freezing-point diagram involved.[50]

Andrews, Kohman, and Johnston[51] have developed a method which
eliminates most of these errors, but its applicability is limited to systems
with favorable crystallization characteristics.   In the apparatus they
employed, a small, thin, glass tube containing the sample is suspended
in a copper cylinder within a Dewar tube.   The temperature of the cylinder
is carefully controlled to fall at a uniform rate, as represented by the
lower curve in figure 12.   The temperature of the sample is measured by

[50] E. L. Skau and B. Saxton, *J. Phys. Chem.*, **37**, 183 (1933).   E. L. Skau, *J. Am.
Chem. Soc.*, **52**, 945 (1930).

[51] D. H. Andrews, G. T. Kohman, and J. Johnston, *J. Phys. Chem.*, **29**, 914 (1925)

means of a thermocouple made of very fine wire, so that there is very little loss of heat by conduction and very little lag. The temperature of the cylinder is started high enough so that, when the freezing point is reached, the temperature fall of sample ABC is almost parallel to that of the surroundings, LJ. The maximum temperature, D, reached after crystallization sets in is the temperature at which solid and liquid are in equilibrium. This will differ under given conditions with the degree of supercooling, *i. e.*, with the amount of crystals formed when equilibrium has

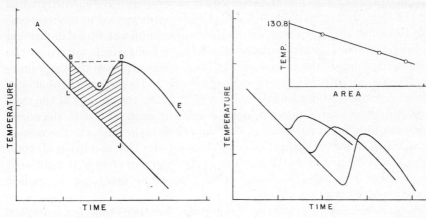

Fig. 12.—Typical controlled cooling curve for a binary mixture.[51]

Fig. 13.—Cooling curves for different degrees of supercooling and corresponding area—maximum graph.[51]

been attained. Point D is therefore not the true freezing point because the composition of the liquid in equilibrium with crystals at D differs from that of the original solution, due to the separation of the crystals of pure solvent.

It can be shown from Newton's law of cooling that the amount of crystals formed is proportional to the area $BCDJL$. The true freezing point of the original solution can be obtained by plotting the area against corresponding values of D for a number of such curves, and extrapolating to find the value of D for zero area or for no crystal formation. Figure 13 shows three actual curves for the same sample, with different degrees of supercooling, superimposed on each other. The change of the maximum can be seen to be such that direct extrapolation of the maxima back to the curve is uncertain. Plotting the area against the temperature of the maximum, however, permits a correct extrapolation to the true freezing point of the solution, in this case 130.8° C.

A simpler and equally reliable method of obtaining data for binary freezing-point diagrams is that of Collett and Johnston.[52] This is a static method in which the samples are made up in sealed tubes about 15 mm. in diameter, and the tubes are vigorously shaken in a constant-temperature bath. Two temperatures about 0.1° C. apart are found, one at which crystals will just disappear and the other at which a few crystals will remain undissolved on prolonged shaking. The correct melting or freezing point must lie between these two temperatures.

9. Thermometers

Some thermometers are graduated to read temperatures correctly when the bulb and the entire liquid index in the stem are exposed to the temperature to be measured. These thermometers are known as "total immersion thermometers" and, when calibrated, have corrections which will reduce the observed reading of the thermometer to true temperatures if the thermometer is used as a total immersion thermometer. If such a thermometer is used as a "partial immersion thermometer," i. e., with a part of the mercury column emergent into the space above the bath, and with the emergent stem therefore either colder (or warmer) than the bulb, the thermometer will read lower (or higher) than it would under the condition of total immersion. Hence, since the mercury in the emergent stem is at a different temperature from the bulb, a so-called stem correction must be applied to the observed reading.

The general formula used in computing the correction for emergent stem is:

$$\text{Stem correction} = Kn(T - t)$$

where K = the differential expansion coefficient of mercury (or thermometer liquid) in the particular kind of glass of which the thermometer is made, n = the number of degrees emergent from the bath, T = the temperature of the bath, and t = the mean temperature of the emergent stem. The average temperature of the exposed stem is read on an auxiliary thermometer placed alongside with its bulb at the middle of the exposed mercury thread. The values of K differ for different kinds of glass and for different temperatures. For centigrade mercury-in-glass thermometers, 0.00016 is a sufficiently accurate value of K for the calculation of emergent stem corrections in most melting-point determinations. Additional details concerning the correction for emergent stem are given in the explanation attached to National Bureau of Standards reports on thermometers which are tested by them. This sheet is known as *NBS 187-b*.

"Partial immersion thermometers" are so graduated that they will read correct temperatures when only the bulb and a short length of the stem of the thermometer are immersed in the bath whose temperature is to be

[52] A. R. Collett and J. Johnston, *J. Phys. Chem.*, **30**, 70 (1926).

measured.   The depth of immersion for which the thermometer is graduated is usually marked on the thermometer.   When properly calibrated and used immersed to this depth, the stem correction is theoretically unnecessary.   Actually, the partial immersion thermometers are subject to variations in readings if the exposed-stem temperatures differ from those at which the calibrations were made.   It is, therefore, probably more accurate to make measurements with total immersion thermometers and to apply the stem correction when they are used partially immersed.

For the greatest accuracy, however, even the use of stem corrections should be avoided because of the difficulties involved in measuring precisely the average temperature of the portion of the stem outside the bath.   A special thermometer with a long capillary bulb should be used in measuring the stem temperature, but these are not common to the organic laboratory.   Total immersion thermometers are, therefore, preferred and are used in such apparatus as the Hershberg apparatus described on page 21.

Thermometers may be calibrated in two ways: by measurement of the freezing points or boiling points of reference substances, or by comparison with a standard thermometer which has been previously calibrated over its range.   In the former method, the most common reference point is the ice-point temperature obtained by means of a slush of pure ice and water. For a higher temperature, the melting point of pure benzoic acid has been advocated as a secondary thermometric standard (m.p., 122.36° C.).[53] The boiling points of liquids may also be used as reference points in thermometer calibrations, but have several disadvantages—superheating interferes and pressure corrections must be applied to the boiling temperature if the calibration is to be at all accurate.   Timmermans and Martin[54] have given a list of liquids which may be used for the calibration of thermometers.   For temperatures higher than the boiling point of naphthalene, 218° C., the freezing points of tin (231.85°) and lead (327.4°) may be used as reliable fixed points for thermometry since these materials may be obtained in pure form from the National Bureau of Standards.   Numerous other reference temperatures used in thermometer calibration are to be found in the International Critical Tables.[55]   In all thermometer calibrations in which the stem is not exposed to the temperature of the calibrating bath, appropriate stem corrections must be made.

The melting-point thermometer may conveniently be calibrated by direct comparison with a standard or calibrated thermometer.   This may be done by immersing the two thermometers in a liquid bath and then allowing the temperature of the bath to change slowly with good

[53] F. W. Schwab and E. Wichers, J. Research Natl. Bur. Standards, 25, 747 (1940).
[54] J. Timmermans and F. Martin, J. chim. phys., 23, 747 (1926).
[55] International Critical Tables.   Vol. I, McGraw-Hill, New York, 1926, p. 53.

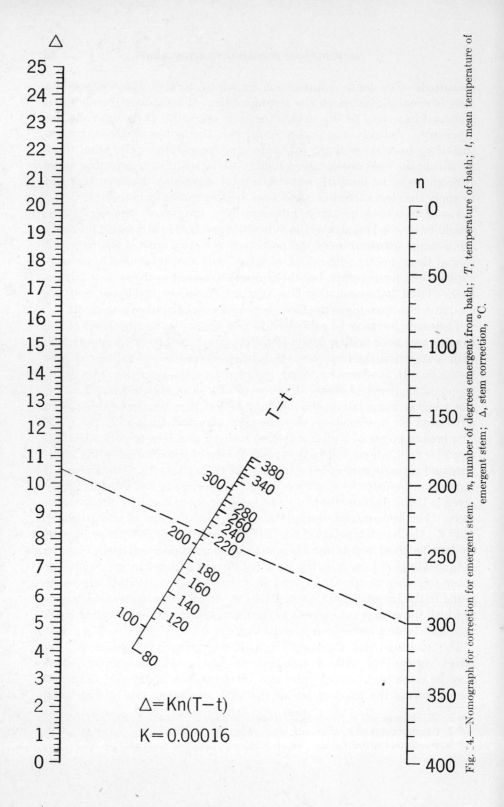

Fig. 4.—Nomograph for correction for emergent stem. n, number of degrees emergent from bath; T, temperature of bath; t, mean temperature of emergent stem; Δ, stem correction, °C.

mixing over the range desired. Simultaneous readings are then taken on both thermometers and the corrections determined for the thermometer being calibrated. This method has the advantage of dispensing with the problems of purity encountered in the method using reference materials, and can usually be carried through much more rapidly.

It has not been uncommon in the past to report melting points in the literature as "uncorrected" when melting temperatures were obtained with a thermometer to which the stem correction was not applied. This practice should be discouraged; a melting point to which an unknown correction must be applied before it can properly be compared with other literature values is almost worthless.

To aid in the calculation of stem corrections, Berl and Kullmann[56] prepared a nomograph from which the correction may be determined by the simple use of a straightedge. A similar nomograph is reproduced in figure 14. The dotted line in this figure represents the position in which the straightedge must be placed in order to obtain the stem correction for a case in which $n = 300$ centigrade degrees and $T - t = 220$ degrees. The corresponding correction, 10.5 degrees, is read on the left-hand scale.

IV. FREEZING-POINT MOLECULAR-WEIGHT DETERMINATIONS

1. Theory

Since the lowering of the freezing point of a solvent by a solute is proportional to the logarithm of the mole fraction of the solvent, it is possible to determine the molecular weight of the solute in a binary mixture from the freezing-point equation.

By definition, $N_A = 1 - N_B$, where N_A is the mole fraction of the solvent and N_B is the mole fraction of the solute present in the mixture. By substitution, it follows from equation (1) on page 4 that:

$$\Delta T = - \frac{RTT_0}{\Delta H} \ln (1 - N_B)$$

For dilute solutions in which N_B and ΔT are small, we can make the mathematical assumptions that $-\ln (1 - N_B) = N_B$ and $TT_0 = T_0^2$, because in

$$-\ln (1 - x) = x + \frac{x^2}{2} + \frac{x^3}{3} \cdots$$

$x^2/2$, $x^3/3 \ldots$ may be neglected if x is small enough. Then:

$$\Delta T = \frac{RT_0^2}{\Delta H} N_B$$

---

[56] E. Berl and A. Kullmann, *Ber.*, **60**, 815 (1927).

This equation may also be expressed in terms of molality, m, that is, in terms of the number of moles of solute per 1000 grams of solvent. By definition:

$$N_B = m + \frac{m}{\frac{1000}{M_A}}$$

where M_A is the molecular weight of the solvent. Hence:

$$\Delta T = \frac{RT_0^2}{\Delta H}\left(\frac{m}{m + \frac{1000}{M_A}}\right)$$

For very dilute solutions, where m may be neglected in comparison with $1000/M_A$, we may write:

$$\Delta T = \frac{RT_0^2}{\Delta H}\left(\frac{mM_A}{1000}\right) = \frac{M_A RT_0^2 m}{1000\Delta H} = Fm$$

where F is a constant characteristic of the solvent and is defined as:

$$F = \frac{M_A RT_0^2}{1000\Delta H}$$

Now, if W_B is the number of grams of solute per 1000 grams of solvent, $m = W_B/M_B$ in which M_B is the molecular weight of the solute. Substituting this expression for m, we have $\Delta T = FW_B/M_B$, and solving for the molecular weight, $M_B = FW_B/\Delta T$. This is the equation used in the determination of molecular weight by means of freezing-point depression.

The use of this equation requires knowledge of the molal freezing-point depression constant, F, the concentration involved, and the measured depression of the freezing point. Although it is possible to calculate F by substitution of the factors in the defining equation shown above, values of this constant determined experimentally using a substance of known molecular weight are much to be preferred.

Although F is considered constant, it may vary considerably depending upon the substances used to determine it. Factors which contribute to lack of ideality, as mentioned on page 7, would also tend to cause variation in experimentally determined values of the constant. These factors would result in an incorrect molecular weight, as will be discussed on page 39 in connection with figure 16. The accuracy which one may anticipate from a freezing-point molecular-weight determination is limited by the accuracy with which the constant, F, is known.

Table III presents a comparison of theoretical and experimental constants. The theoretical values were calculated from measured heats of fusion, whereas the experimental values were obtained using known substances in actual determinations.   For constants of additional solvents the reader is referred to the *International Critical Tables* or to Landolt-Börnstein.

TABLE III
FREEZING-POINT MOLECULAR-WEIGHT CONSTANTS

Compound	M. p., ° C.	F (calculated)	F (observed)
Acetic acid[a]	16.55	3.57	3.9
Benzene[b]	5.45	5.069	5.7
Borneol[b]	204.	..	35.8
Camphor[b]	178.4	37.7	40.0
Dioxane[b]	11.7	4.71	4.63
Ethylacetanilide[b]	52.0	8.7	8.58
Indene[b]	−1.76	7.35	7.28
Naphthalene[a]	80.1	6.98	6.899
Nitrobenzene[c]	5.82	6.9	8.1
Trimethylcarbinol[d]	25.1	8.15	8.37
Water[a]	0.0	1.859	1.853

[a] Landolt–Börnstein, *Physikalisch-Chemische Tabellen*, Erg. **II b**, p. 1468.
[b] *Ibid.*, Erg. **III c**, pp. 2667–2669.
[c] *Ibid.*, Hw. **II**, pp. 1427–1430.
[d] F. H. Getman, *J. Am. Chem. Soc.*, **62**, 2179 (1940).

2.   Apparatus and Technique

The procedure for the experimental determination of molecular weights by freezing-point depression, sometimes known as the Beckmann method, is described in detail in many elementary physical chemistry manuals.[57] The apparatus consists essentially of a cooling bath, *B*, covered with a metal lid, *L* (see Fig. 15).   Through a hole in the center of the lid passes a large glass test tube, *T*, held in place by a tightly fitting cork.   Held inside the test tube is another smaller tube containing the freezing mixture, a Beckmann differential thermometer, and a small stirrer.   The freezing-point tube is therefore surrounded by an air layer through which heat must be transferred, thus insuring a slow and uniform rate of cooling of the solution.

After the apparatus is assembled, a weighed amount of pure solvent is placed in the sample tube and the system allowed to come to thermal equilibrium with the sample cooling at a steady rate.   Temperature measurements to the nearest 0.001° C. are made as the liquid is supercooled and caused to crystallize with stirring.   The final equilibrium temperature between the liquid and a small proportion of crystals is taken as the freezing point.   If the temperature were to be plotted against the elapsed time, a

[57] A. Findlay, *Practical Physical Chemistry*, 7th ed., Longmans, Green, New York, 1941, Chapter VIII.   F. Daniels, J. H. Mathews, and J. W. Williams, *Experimental Physical Chemistry*, 2nd ed., McGraw-Hill, New York, 1934, pp. 58–64.

curve similar to the cooling curves for a pure substance as described on page 10 would be obtained. The solvent is then remelted by brief removal of the inner test tube, and the process repeated using different degrees of supercooling. A weighed amount of the unknown is then added to the solvent, and the freezing temperature is again determined as before.

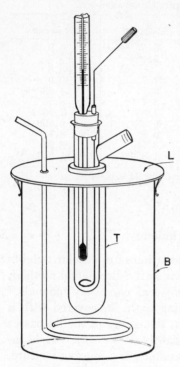

Fig. 15.—Beckmann freezing-point depression apparatus.[57]

From the calculated concentration of solute and the observed difference in freezing point of the pure solvent and the solution, the molecular weight of the solute is computed.

In the freezing-point molecular-weight determination, the precautions to be observed are similar to those outlined in the section on cooling curves (pages 17 *et seq.*). The temperature of the cooling bath should not be more than about 3 degrees below the normal freezing point of the solvent, otherwise the rate of heat loss will exceed the rate at which heat is furnished the solution by the heat of fusion of the freezing solvent, and the observed temperature will be too low. The amount of supercooling should not be greater than about one-half a degree, so that the amount of solvent freezing out will not appreciably alter the concentration of the solute. Stirring should be just rapid enough to maintain the contents of the tube at a uniform temperature, and the thermometer should be tapped throughout the determination to prevent the mercury from sticking in the fine capillary of the Beckmann thermometer. For greater detail concerning the procedure and apparatus for determination of the molecular weight by freezing-point depression, the reader is referred to the concise and complete description by Findlay.[58]

Freezing-point lowering offers one of the most convenient means of molecular-weight determination. The depressions are easy to measure experimentally because the molal freezing-point depression is relatively large and the freezing point is not affected by such external factors as changes in the atmospheric pressure. The measurement can be made at low temperatures at which volatility of the solvent or the solute is not

[58] A. Findlay, *The Phase Rule and Its Applications.* 8th ed., Longmans, Green, New York, 1938, pp. 125–136.

likely to cause a change in the composition of the mixture.   The extreme accuracy attainable by this method employing special refinements of technique is illustrated by the data of Batson and Kraus,[59] as shown in table IV.   Data such as these indicate that inaccuracies may in many cases be due to experimental error.

TABLE IV

FREEZING POINTS OF TRIPHENYLMETHANE IN BENZENE[a]

Molal concentration	Freezing-point depression, ° C.	Molecular weight
0.000313	0.00158	244.5
0.000634	0.00322	243.5
0.000986	0.00497	245.4
0.004096	0.02082	243.5
0.0248	0.1263	243.1
0.04375	0.2214	244.6
	THEORETICAL:	244.32

[a] F. M. Batson and C. A. Kraus, J. Am. Chem. Soc., **56,** 2017 (1934).

The accuracy of the freezing-point depression method may be even less than that expected from the experimental accuracy of the measurements. It should be recalled that the derivation of equation (1) involved a number of assumptions, one of which was the mutually ideal behavior of solvent and solute.   It was also pointed out on page 6 that truly ideal behavior between organic substances is the exception rather than the rule. Although the behavior of most solutes approaches ideality in extremely dilute solutions, the concentrations involved in freezing-point experiments is such that, in most cases, abnormalities due to nonideality are not eliminated.   Any factors causing deviation from the freezing-point law would cause corresponding errors in molecular weights by freezing-point depression.   Thus, using benzene as a solvent (see Fig. 16) the molecular weight determinations would be expected to give: the correct value in the case of naphthalene or tetrachloroethane, which behave ideally with benzene; too high a value for propionic acid, phenol, or aniline, which in the concentration involved tend to associate in benzene; and too low a value for hexaphenylethane or tetraphenyl-di-β-naphthylethane, which dissociate in benzene into triphenylmethyl or diphenyl-β-naphthylmethyl, respectively.

Recent improvements in semimicro- and microtechniques have made it possible to determine freezing-point molecular weights on extremely small samples of organic substances.

[59] F. M. Batson and C. A. Kraus, J. Am. Chem. Soc., **56,** 2017 (1934).

The method of Rast[60] employs camphor as a solvent because of its unusually high molal freezing-point constant (see Table III). The melting point of the pure camphor is compared with that of the camphor–unknown mixture, and the molecular weight of the unknown is calculated in the usual

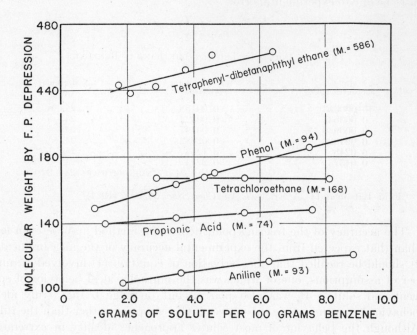

Fig. 16.—Freezing-point molecular weights in benzene solutions as affected by concentration.[61] M, true molecular weight.

manner. The melting points are determined by means of a capillary method essentially the same as that described above. The procedure has been modified[62] so that one can determine the molecular weight with a sample weighing a fraction of a milligram.

Details of this micromethod may be found in any microchemical labora-

[60] K. Rast, *Ber.*, **55**, 1051, 3727 (1922).

[61] Data from M. Gomberg and F. W. Sullivan, *J. Am. Chem. Soc.*, **44**, 1810 (1922), for tetraphenyl-di-β-naphthylethane; W. E. S. Turner and S. English, *J. Chem. Soc.*, **105**, 1786 (1914), for phenol; E. R. Jones and C. R. Bury, *ibid.*, **127**, 1949 (1925), for tetrachloroethane; C. J. Peddle and W. E. S. Turner, *ibid.*, **99**, 685 (1911), for propionic acid and aniline.

[62] F. Pregl, *Quantitative Organic Microanalysis*. 3rd ed., Blakiston, Philadelphia, 1937, pp. 237–244.

tory manual.[63]   In its application it is essential that the sample and the camphor be thoroughly mixed in order to insure good equilibrium.   This is probably best accomplished by grinding the substances together and pre-melting before determining the melting point.   The mixture should be well packed to a depth of about 2 mm. in the bottom of the capillary in which the melting point is to be measured.   The correct melting tempera-ture is the temperature at which the last of the crystalline camphor skele-ton dissolves in the liquid.   When proper technique is employed, it is possible to obtain by this micromethod molecular weights within 5% of the theoretical value.

V. PREPARATION OF SAMPLES BY CRYSTALLIZATION

Reliable melting points for characterization or identification can be determined only on pure crystalline material.   It is therefore essential that the experimenter use good crystallization techniques and procedures in preparing his substance for the melting-point determination.

If other methods for purification are available, crystallization of the material should not be attempted until the substance is reasonably pure. When a binary mixture, *e. g.*, such as represented in figures 2 and 3, is dis-solved in a solvent and cooled, its crystallization behavior can be rep-resented by a ternary diagram.[64]   From such diagrams it can be shown that the presence of large amounts of impurity reduces greatly the amount of pure crystals which can be obtained before the impurity also crystallizes out.   Impurities, furthermore, frequently act as crystallization inhibitors, slowing down or even preventing crystallization in the temperature range where the material can be conveniently handled.

Unless the experimenter has previous knowledge of the best solvent to be used in a particular crystallization, the solvent must be determined by a trial-and-error process.   The best solvent is usually one with a good temperature coefficient of solubility and one in which the impurities, if their nature is known, are very soluble.   The solute should not be too soluble in the cold or the excessive losses encountered will require the use of special techniques.   The usual procedure for selecting a solvent is to dissolve small amounts of the substance in small portions of different sol-vents by heating.   These solutions, which are nearly saturated, are then allowed to cool slowly, note being made of the nature and amount of

---

[63] F. Emich, *Microchemical Laboratory Manual.*   Wiley, New York, 1932, pp. 138–140. W. W. Scott, *Standard Methods of Chemical Analysis*, 5th ed., Van Nostrand, New York, 1939, p. 2533.

[64] H. W. B. Roozeboom, *Die heterogenen Gleichgewichte vom Standpunkte der Phasen-lehre.*   Vol. III, Part I, Vieweg, Braunschweig, 1901–1913, p. 46.

crystals which form. Several solvents with the desired characteristics may be found, in which case it is generally best to use the one which has a moderately high boiling point, since this reduces evaporation and allows the use of a larger temperature change during crystallization. High-boiling solvents have the disadvantage of being more difficult to remove completely from the final crystalline product.

The two most important steps in a good crystallization procedure are: first, the preparation of pure crystals (or as nearly pure crystals as it is possible to obtain); and second, complete separation of the liquid from the solid. In general, the procedure for crystallization is to heat the mixture of solvent and solute until the latter dissolves, filter hot, reheat to dissolve any solid which may have formed, add a seed crystal, allow the mixture to cool slowly until crystals form in sufficient quantity, and finally separate the crystals from the mother liquor. The amount of solvent employed should usually be sufficient just to dissolve the material at a temperature fairly close to the boiling point of the solvent so that the maximum cooling effect can be obtained. To follow the progress of the purification, the melting point of these crystals should be taken. If it is higher than that of the original substance, the crystallization process should be repeated until no further rise is observed. Before determining the melting point, care should be taken to remove the last traces of solvent. This can best be done by heating *in vacuo* below the melting point in an Abderhalden drier.

An additional crop of crystals may be obtained from various mother liquors, either by cooling to a lower temperature or by partial evaporation, heating to dissolve any solid formed, and then cooling. The second crop of crystals is usually considerably less pure because the proportion of impurities is higher in the second mother liquor than in the first mother liquor.

Impurities may be carried down by occlusion in the crystals formed, especially if the rate of crystallization is too high. When crystals are formed rapidly, the concentration of impurity in the vicinity of the crystals is relatively great, due to the removal of the main solute from solution. Further growth on these crystals will therefore be less pure. Slow cooling, *i. e.*, slow crystal formation, permits the main solute to diffuse in the direction of the crystals and thus maintain a more uniform concentration throughout the solution. A low degree of supercooling, seeding, a slow rate of cooling, and gentle stirring—all aid greatly in obtaining pure crystals.[65]

Evaporation of the solvent during crystallization should be avoided

---

[65] F. W. Schwab and E. Wichers, *J. Research Natl. Bur. Standards*, **32**, 253 (1944).

because evaporation from the surface of the liquid tends to leave a crust of solute and impurities on the edges or sides of the container, thus adding to the amount of impurity present in the final product. It is therefore advisable to carry out the crystallization in stoppered Erlenmeyer flasks or similar closed containers. Crystallization by evaporation of the solvent is usually considerably less efficient as a means of purification than is crystallization effected by temperature change.

Separation of the mother liquors from the crystals is the second important step in obtaining a pure product. The common method of decantation or filtration on a funnel leaves mother liquor upon the crystals even if the crystals are washed with pure solvent. When this liquid is evaporated off in drying the crystals, all the impurities present therein are deposited on the crystals. Experiments by Richards[66] demonstrated the superiority of centrifugation as a means of separating the liquid from the solid phase. Two crystallizations of sodium nitrate with nitric acid as an impurity removed only 90% of the impurity when the decantation method was used and 99.995% when centrifugation was used for separating the solid. If, however, the substance is almost pure, little may be gained for practical purposes by the use of the centrifugation method. The impurities remaining on the solid after decantation or filtration may often be removed to some extent by washing the wet crystals with more of the pure solvent, thus diluting the concentration of the impurities in the mother liquors remaining. This procedure has the disadvantage, however, of washing away part of the product and thus lowering the yield.

It is often difficult to find a solvent which has the correct solubility characteristics for a desired crystallization. In such cases, the method of mixed solvents may sometimes be successfully used. The material is first dissolved in solvent A, in which it is very soluble. The solution is then brought to an elevated temperature and solvent B, in which the substance has a limited solubility, is added until turbidity is observed. The solution in the mixed solvents is then warmed a little until clear and allowed to cool slowly, permitting crystallization to take place. A less pure second crop of crystals may be obtained from the mother liquor by repeating with the addition of more solvent B or merely by cooling the mother liquor to a lower temperature.

To crystallize small quantities successfully, mechanical loss must be avoided. This can be accomplished in many cases by means of a hot-extraction apparatus as described by Blount[67] or by means of a combination filter and crystallization vessel described by Craig.[68] In the Blount

[66] T. W. Richards, *J. Am. Chem. Soc.*, **27**, 104 (1905).

[67] B. K. Blount, *Mikrochemie*, **19**, 162 (1936).

[68] L. C. Craig, *Ind. Eng. Chem., Anal. Ed.*, **12**, 773 (1940).

apparatus, the material is placed in a sintered-glass filter funnel or a small Soxhlet thimble suspended from a condenser and is dissolved by refluxing the hot solvent from a vessel directly below.   When extraction is complete, the solution is allowed to cool and the substance crystallizes.   The substance has thus been dissolved, filtered hot, and crystallized without handling, exposure, or removal from the apparatus.

An efficient method of crystallization in which separation is made by centrifugation instead of filtration, and which is applicable to crystallizations below room temperature is afforded by the centrifugal filtration tube[69] and its modifications.[68]

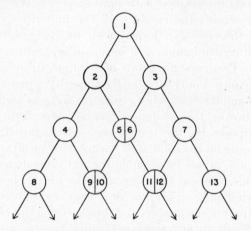

Fig. 17.—Scheme for systematic fractional crystallization.[70]

When it is desired to separate two or more substances or to purify a substance with the maximum yield by crystallization, a process of systematic fractional crystallization is employed.   This involves separating the substance into a number of fractions of varying composition or purity and recombining crystals and mother liquors of like composition or purity according to a specified plan, thus avoiding unnecessary accumulation of small crops and mother liquors.   This method has been used in the isolation of rare earth salts[70] and is described in many textbooks and manuals. It is concisely outlined by Cumming, Hopper, and Wheeler[71] as follows in connection with figure 17.

[69] E. L. Skau and W. Bergmann, *J. Org. Chem.*, **3**, 166 (1938).   E. L. Skau, *J. Phys. Chem.*, **33**, 951 (1929).

[70] J. N. Friend, *Textbook of Inorganic Chemistry.*   Vol. IV, Griffin, London, 1928.

[71] W. M. Cumming, I. V. Hopper, and T. S. Wheeler, *Systematic Organic Chemistry.* 3rd ed. rev., Van Nostrand, New York, 1937, p. 15.

"The mixture is dissolved with the aid of heat in a solvent to give solution (1). From this solution on cooling, crystals separate which are filtered off, and solution (1) is thereby divided into crop (2) and mother liquor (3). Crop (2) is dissolved in the minimum quantity of hot solvent, and from the resulting solution, after cooling, crop (4) and mother liquor (5) are obtained. Mother liquor (3) is concentrated, and from the concentrated solution after cooling, crop (6) and mother liquor (7) are obtained. Crop (6) and mother liquor (5) are united to form a single fraction, and after being heated to dissolve, are subsequently cooled to give rise to crop (10) and mother liquor (11). Crop (4) is dissolved in a small portion of pure solvent by heating and after cooling is divided into crop (8) and mother liquor (9). Mother liquor (7) after concentration and cooling yields crop (12) and mother liquor (13). (9) and (10), likewise (11) and (12), are united to give single fractions. Proceeding in this way, the least soluble compound goes to the left in the diagram, while the most soluble goes to the right, and compounds of intermediate solubility lie between these extremes."

The crystalline crops obtained by this method should be tested for purity by observation under a lens or microscope or by melting-point determination. If the crop is found to be pure, it should be set aside. If the crystalline material consists of two different crystal fractions, the solution from which it was obtained was evidently saturated with respect to both. The solvent should be evaporated off, in this case, and another solvent tried, one in which the substances have different solubilities.

General References

American Institute of Physics, *Temperature, Its Measurement and Control in Science and Industry*. Reinhold, New York, 1941.

Bowden, S. T., *The Phase Rule and Phase Reactions*. Macmillan, London, 1938.

Findlay, A., *The Phase Rule and Its Applications*. 8th ed., Longmans, Green, New York, 1938.

Findlay, A., *Practical Physical Chemistry*. 7th ed., Longmans, Green, New York, 1941.

Hildebrand, J. H., *Solubility of Non-Electrolytes*. 2nd ed., Reinhold, New York, 1936.

Houben, J., *Die Methoden der organischen Chemie*. 3rd ed., Vol. I, Thieme, Leipzig, 1935.

Kempf, R., and Kutter, F., *Schmelzpunktstabellen zur organischen Molekular-Analyse*. Vieweg, Braunschweig, 1928.

Mair, B. J., Glasgow, A. R., Jr., and Rossini, F. D., "Determination of Freezing Points and Amounts of Impurity in Hydrocarbons from Freezing and Melting Curves," *J. Research Natl. Bur. Standards*, **26**, 591 (1941).

Morton, A. A., *Laboratory Technique in Organic Chemistry*. McGraw-Hill, New York, 1938.

Reilly, J., and Rae, W. M., *Physico-Chemical Methods*. 3rd ed., Van Nostrand, New York, 1939.

Roozeboom, H. W. B., *Die heterogenen Gleichgewichte vom Standpunkte der Phasenlehre*. Vieweg, Braunschweig, 1901-1913.

Smits, A., *Die Theorie der Komplexität und der Allotropie*. Verlag Chemie, Berlin, 1938.

Smits, A., *Theory of Allotropy*, translated by Thomas, J. S., Longmans, Green, London, 1923.

Tammann, G., *Kristallisieren und Schmelzen*. Barth, Leipzig, 1903.

Tammann, G., *Lehrbuch der heterogenen Gleichgewichte*. Vieweg, Braunschweig, 1924.

Tammann, G., *The States of Aggregation*, translated by Mehl, R. F., Van Nostrand, New York, 1925.

Volmer, M., *Kinetik der Phasenbildung*. Steinkopff, Leipzig, 1939.

CHAPTER II

Determination of
BOILING AND CONDENSATION TEMPERATURES

W. Swietoslawski

Mellon Institute

I. INTRODUCTION

It is a common practice to identify as the boiling temperature of a liquid the temperature which is established on the bulb of a thermometer, or on any other surface on which a thin layer of the condensed liquid co-exists with the vapor. This temperature should be called the condensation temperature of the vapor and not the boiling temperature of the liquid.[1] Any boiling liquid is superheated; and, since it boils under the pressure at the surface plus the hydraulic pressure at the level in the liquid at which the temperature is measured, the latter is not the true boiling point of the liquid. Special apparatus, ebulliometers, exist which make possible a direct measurement with high accuracy of the boiling temperature of a liquid or of a solution.[2] With differential ebulliometers,[3] the boiling and

[1] F. G. Cottrell, *J. Am. Chem. Soc.*, **41**, 721 (1919). W. Swietoslawski, *Ebulliometry*, Chemical Pub. Co., New York, 1937, pp. 1, 7, 10.

[2] F. G. Cottrell, *loc. cit.* E. W. Washburn, *J. Am. Chem. Soc.*, **41**, 729 (1919). W. Swietoslawski, *Ebulliometry*, Chemical Pub. Co., New York, 1937, p. 10.

[3] W. Swietoslawski, *Z. physik. Chem.*, **130**, 287 (1927); *Ebulliometry*, Chemical Pub. Co., New York, 1937, pp. 6, 16, 20.

the condensation temperatures can be measured simultaneously. Since both the boiling and the condensation temperatures can be measured, these terms should be used in the proper way to avoid confusion.

The conditions under which the boiling temperature of a liquid or a solution can be measured were investigated by several authors.[2] These conditions are fulfilled if a slightly superheated liquid is thrown onto the stem of a thermometer, or if it flows down the stem and the bulb of a thermometer. Instead of having the vapor and the liquid in direct contact with the thermometer, a thermometer well may provide the surface along which the liquid flows. When a superheated liquid is thrown onto a solid and flows down along its surface, a thermodynamic equilibrium is established very rapidly between the thin layer of the liquid and the vapor. If the liquid is superheated, a certain amount of it evaporates, and a temperature is established which corresponds to the equilibrium under the pressure in the apparatus. The author of this chapter and his collaborators examined the conditions existing in an ebulliometer and determined the range of superheating within which it is possible to establish an equilibrium very rapidly.[4] If a solution, instead of an individual liquid, is brought to a boil, the same phenomena take place. There is, however, a small increase in concentration of the solution, because of the evaporation of the solvent, which requires the introduction of a small correction.

II. CLASSIFICATION OF LIQUID MIXTURES

In many cases, *e. g.*, for purification and dehydration purposes, it is of great importance to know what phenomena take place when mixtures of two or more liquids are boiling. For reasons of simplicity, only binary mixtures are discussed. The following classification seems to be accepted.[5] The mixtures formed by two liquids may be: (*1*) homozeotropic, (*2*) heterozeotropic, (*3*) homoazeotropic, and (*4*) heteroazeotropic. In cases (*1*) and (*3*), the boiling mixture consists of one liquid phase only; in cases (*2*) and (*4*), the system is composed of two boiling liquid phases.

The term *zeotropic* refers to a liquid the components of which may be separated by distillation. The isotherm representing the dependence of vapor pressure, *P*, on concentration, *C*, of zeotropic mixtures, does not possess a maximum or minimum. If the mixture obeys Raoult's law, the isotherm is a straight line; if it does not, two kinds of curves may result. The isotherms may lie above the straight line expressing Raoult's law (positive

---

[4] W. Swietoslawski, *Ebulliometry.* Chemical Pub. Co., New York, 1937, pp. 7–11.

[5] W. Swietoslawski, *Bull. intern. acad. polon. sci.*, A, 472 (1933). See also M. Lecat, chapter on distillation in V. Grignard, editor, *Traité de chimie organique*, Vol. I, Masson, Paris, 1934, p. 127.

deviations) or below (negative deviations).   See figure 1a.   The corresponding isobars in which the boiling temperatures are plotted against the composition of the mixture are shown in figure 1b.

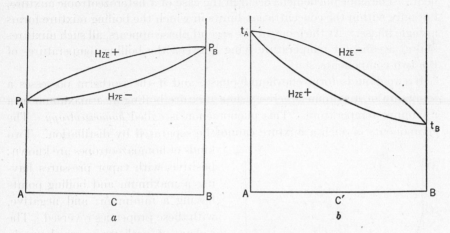

Fig. 1.—Positive and negative homozeotropic mixtures.

The isotherms and isobars of *heterozeotropic* mixtures are composed of three portions—two curves, and a straight line parallel to the axis of concentrations (Fig. 2).   Since boiling temperature and vapor pressure are in-

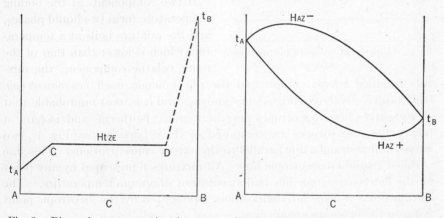

Fig. 2.—Binary heterozeotropic mixtures.   Fig. 3.—Positive and negative homoazeotropes.

verse functions (see Fig. 1), only the isobars are given in figures 2 to 5. Heterozeotropy is rarely encountered.   Any homo- or heterozeotropic mixture boils at a temperature which is higher than the boiling temperature of the more volatile component, and lower than that of the less volatile component. The boiling temperature of a homozeotropic mixture increases gradually with the increase in concentration of the higher-boiling component. The same phenomena occur in the case of a heterozeotropic mixture, but only within the concentration limits in which the boiling mixture forms a single phase. At the moment the second phase appears, all such mixtures boil at a constant temperature lying between the boiling temperatures of the two components.

If two liquids form one liquid phase, and if the isotherm possesses a minimum or maximum, there exists a mixture boiling at a maximum or a minimum temperature. This phenomenon is called *homoazeotropy*. The components of such a mixture cannot be separated by distillation. Two kinds of homoazeotropes are known: positive, with vapor pressures having a maximum and boiling points having a minimum; and negative, with these properties reversed. The isobars of both types are shown in figure 3. For instance, benzene and ethyl alcohol form a positive homoazeotrope, aniline and acetic acid a negative azeotrope.

If two components at the boiling temperature form two liquid phases, and the mixture boils at a temperature which is lower than that of the more volatile component, the mixture is called *heteroazeotropic* and the phenomenon itself *heteroazeotropy*. Only positive heteroazeotropes are known; and it is most improbable that any negative heteroazeotropes may be found. Isotherms and isobars of binary heteroazeotropes are composed of three portions (see Fig. 4), two curves and a straight line parallel to the axis of concentrations. This line is called the heteroazeotropic line. All mixtures represented by any point on the heteroazeotropic line boil at constant minimum temperature. The distillate has a constant composition, represented by the azeotropic point lying on the heteroazeotropic line.

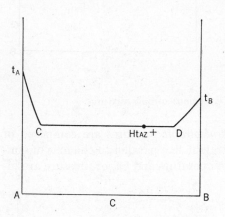

Fig. 4.—Binary heteroazeotropic mixtures.

If the pressure under which the distillation is carried out undergoes changes, the azeotropic point displaces toward one end of the azeotropic line (Fig. 5). It can reach the point of intersection of the azeotropic line with the curve representing the isotherm of a liquid phase system. If the pressure still increases, the heteroazeotropic point is now somewhere out-

side the straight heteroazeotropic line.   That means that the heteroazeotrope is transformed into a homoazeotrope.   This phenomenon demonstrates the close relation between
homo- and heteroazeotropy.

Large numbers of ternary homo-
and heteroazeotropes are known.
In many cases, water is the third
component of such azeotropes.   It
is of great importance to know
what impurities contaminate a
substance which is to be purified
by distillation, and to examine the
influence of the impurities on the
boiling temperature of the substance.   For instance, the phenomenon of azeotropy may be used
for drying purposes.   This "azeotropic method" is often   more
effective and convenient than
chemical methods because it is
free from complicating side reactions.   Not infrequently a substance dehydrated by chemical
agents is more contaminated after
the dehydration than before.

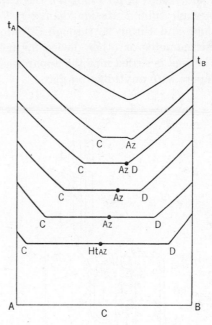

Fig. 5.—Transformation of heteroazeotrope
into homoazeotrope by increase of pressure.

III.   MEASUREMENT OF TEMPERATURES

The following determinations are carried out most frequently in organic
chemistry: determination of the condensation temperature of pure liquids;
determination of the degree of purity of liquids; measurement of the variation of the boiling temperature with the pressure; and measurement of the
effect of solutes on the boiling temperature of solvents.   In addition, the
boiling and condensation temperatures of mixtures of volatile substances
are very often measured in order to determine what kind of mixtures they
are forming.

1.   Apparatus

A.   TYPES OF EBULLIOMETERS

In figures 6, 7, and 8, different types of ebulliometers are shown which
may be used for examining any of the problems mentioned.

The simple ebulliometer in figure 6 is ordinarily used for measuring the boiling temperature of a liquid or solution.[6] The liquid is brought to a boil in an egg-shaped vessel A. Since the vessel is entirely filled with the liquid, there is no room for the vapors formed. They leave the vessel through tube I (inside diameter, 7 mm.) and carry the boiling liquid along and throw it, through C, onto the surface of well B, in which the thermometer or other device for measuring the temperature is located. The well is sealed into the apparatus to prevent contact of the liquid and vapors with anything but glass.

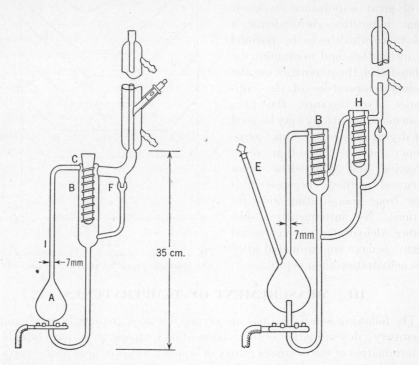

Fig. 6.—Simple ebulliometer.   Fig. 7.—Differential ebulliometer.

Experiments have shown that the liquid is always superheated, even after passing through I. This superheating ordinarily does not exceed 0,030–0.050° C. If Δt represents the superheating, c the heat capacity of the liquid and l the heat of vaporization of one gram of the liquid, the amount of the liquid to be evaporated, in order to reach an equilibrium with the vapors, may be expressed by: $m = c \cdot \Delta t / l$ per gram of the liquid.

For the majority of liquids, m is very small,[4] and for this reason the

[6] W. Swietoslawski and W. Romer, *Bull. intern. acad. polon. sci.*, A, 59 (1924); W. Swietoslawski, *Ebulliometry*, Chemical Pub. Co., New York, 1937, pp. 4, 7, 14.

equilibrium can be established very rapidly.   In fact, the temperature was found to be constant and equal to the boiling temperature of the liquid along the whole thermometer well except $1/4$ inch from the top, where the temperature is lower than the boiling temperature because of a heat loss in that part of the ebulliometer.

The intensity of heating of the egg-shaped vessel is regulated by using the drop counter F as a control device.   The number of drops, n, is practically proportional to the intensity of heating.   For a proper functioning of the apparatus, the number of drops must be neither too small nor too large.   There is, however, a range in which the temperature in B does not depend upon the change in the number of drops.   The intensity of heating should be maintained within these limits.   For instance, it was found that, for water, the number of drops may vary from 8 to 25 per minute.   If the number is smaller than 8, the heat supply is not sufficient; if the number is too large, the pressure inside the ebulliometer rises and the temperature obtained is too high.   Moreover, with the increased intensity of the heating, the superheating of the liquid may be too high to establish rapidly enough the equilibrium between the liquid and gaseous phases.   It should be remembered that water possesses a very high heat of condensation, so that a relatively small number of drops indicates that the apparatus is being heated at a sufficient rate.   With other liquids, the number of drops flowing down through the drop counter should be increased.

The differential ebulliometer is represented in figure 7.   Its lower portion does not differ from that of the simple ebulliometer.   The upper part contains a second thermometer well which makes it possible to determine the condensation temperature of the vapor.   The difference between the boiling temperature, measured in B, and the condensation temperature, measured in H, is significant in various respects, see page 64.   The side tube, E, serves for introducing the solute.

In figure 8, the differential ebulliometer with standardized dimensions is shown.   It differs from the apparatus in figure 7 by a short distilling column located between thermometer wells, t_1 and t_2, and drop counters f_1 and f_2.   This column contains no packing, thereby avoiding the creation of pressure in the lower portion of the apparatus.   Because of the lack of resistance and the short distance between the two levels at which the temperatures are measured (about 12 inches), the error caused by the difference in atmospheric pressure on these levels does not exceed $0.001°$ and can be neglected.   This ebulliometer is used for the determination of the degree of purity of liquid substances and for many other purposes.[7]

By the combination of more than two units, a multiple-stage differential

[7] W. Swietoslawski, *J. Phys. Chem.*, **38**, 1169 (1934); *Ebulliometry*, Chemical Pub. Co., New York, 1937, pp. 75–88.

ebulliometer is obtained. This is used for microanalytical determinations and for examining the purity of substances containing less than 0.05% of impurities.[7]

If less than 50–70 ml. of the liquid is available, microebulliometers are used. One of these[8] is similar to the ebulliometer with standardized di-

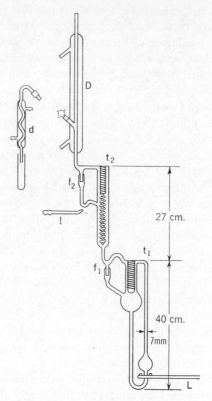

Fig. 8.—Differential ebulliometer
with standardized dimensions.

mensions (Fig. 8), the only difference being in the size of the egg-shaped vessel, which contains only 5–7 ml. of the liquid.

Another microebulliometer, shown in figure 9, permits the determination of the difference between two condensation temperatures measured at the levels T_1 and T_2. It is convenient for high boiling liquids. The samples are heated in A. The apparatus is provided with two drop counters, F_1 and F_2, and a large joining tube, P, which serve as a distilling

[8] W. Swietoslawski, *Ebulliometry*. Chemical Pub. Co., New York, 1937, p. 17.

column without packing.   The vapors are condensed in D, and flow down through drop counter F_2.   The precision obtainable is smaller than with the ebulliometer shown in figure 8, but often sufficient for determinations of purity (see page 60).

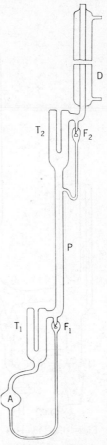

Fig. 9.—Differential apparatus for measuring the condensation temperatures on two levels.

The manipulation of all types of ebulliometer is practically the same.   The heating of the egg-shaped vessel is regulated in accordance with the indication of the drop counter.   In the differential and multiple-stage ebulliometers, the tube connecting the upper drop counter with the lower part of the ebulliometer is heated so that the same number of drops flows through each of the drop counters.   Heat may be applied with an electric heater or a micro gas burner. If the same number of drops flows through each of the drop counters, it can be assumed that the amount of vapor passing through any section of the apparatus per unit of time is the same.

If the boiling temperature of the liquid does not exceed 100–110° C., the thermometer wells may be filled with mercury.   If higher boiling liquids are examined, high-boiling mineral oil may be used.   In this case, more time must be allowed for the heat exchange between the inside surface of the ebulliometer and the bulb of the thermometer.

Electrical resistance thermometers, thermocouples, and mercury thermometers may be used for any kind of ebulliometric measurements.   If high precision is required and Beckmann thermometers are used, special care must be taken with the thermometers which have a relatively wide connection between the bulb and the very fine capillary in front of the scale.   Due to the width of this connection, a relatively small change in temperature of the emergent part of the stem may produce a large change in the position of the mercury meniscus.   To reduce this cause of error, the thermometer stem emerging above the test tube should be surrounded by a constant-temperature water jacket.

B.   HEAD OF DISTILLING COLUMN

Many devices have been recommended for measuring the condensation temperature of vapors during the purification of a liquid by fractional distillation. The head of the column presented in figure 10 is convenient, and permits measurements with an accuracy of several thousandths of a degree. This head is provided with two labyrinth passageways for the vapors, *a* and *b*, a condenser, *D*, and a drop counter, *F*. By manipulating stopcock *K*, it is possible to measure the temperature at any reflux ratio as well as at total reflux. The functioning of this head resembles that of the upper part of any ebulliometer, and therefore does not require further explanation. Ordinarily the head is attached to the distilling column by a ground joint. It can be protected against loss of heat with asbestos tape.[9]

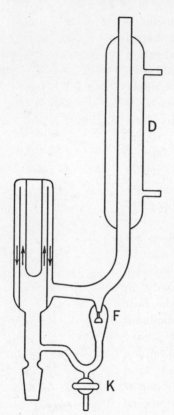

Fig. 10.—Head of a distilling column.

2. Comparative Ebulliometric and Tonometric Measurements

In 1938, the International Union of Chemistry accepted the proposal of the Committee on Physicochemical Data to use water as the primary standard substance in ebulliometry and tonometry[10]—in all cases, therefore, in which the boiling and the condensation temperature or the coefficients dt/dp or dp/dt are measured, water must be used as the reference substance.

This recommendation is based on the broader principle of comparative measurements recommended by the International Union of Chemistry.[11] According to this principle, all physicochemical measurements are divided into two groups: absolute, and comparative. When making absolute measurements, all values are expressed in absolute units and all corrections introduced. Such measurements which determine the physicochemical properties of standards should be carried out by specialists. In all other cases, the International Union of Chemistry recommends comparative measurements. The latter consist in the direct comparison of the sub-

[9] Another head of the column combined with an ebulliometer is described by M. R. Fenske in *Science of Petroleum*. Oxford Univ. Press, New York, 1938.

[10] W. Swietolawski, *Compt. rend. XIII Conf. union intern. chim. Rome*, **1938**. See also W. Swietoslawski, *J. chim. phys.*, **27**, 496 (1930).

[11] W. Swietoslawski, *Compt. rend. XII Conf. union intern. chim. Lucerne*, **1936**.

stance under examination with a standard.   Comparative measurements are made in such a manner that all or most of the corrections become unnecessary.   By means of comparative measurements, the accuracy of the results can be increased many times as compared with absolute measurements under similar conditions.   For instance, if water is used as primary standard or other liquids as auxiliary reference substances, the boiling temperature of a particular liquid may be determined with an accuracy of 0.005° C. and the coefficient dt/dp or dp/dt with an accuracy of 0.1% or better.   Such precision has never been reached when ordinary laboratory apparatus and instruments have been used for making absolute measurements.

The method of comparative measurements should be used also in the distillation of relatively pure liquids.   For this purpose, water or an auxiliary reference substance is boiled in a simple ebulliometer (Fig. 6), and the condensation temperature of the vapors passing or circulating (total reflux) in the head of the distilling column (Fig. 10) is compared with the boiling temperature of the standard.

3.   Water as Primary Ebulliometric Standard

Extensive and precise measurements have been made recently to establish the pressure–temperature relationships of water.[12]   The range of pressure from 660 to 860 mm. Hg has been examined so carefully that its boiling temperature under a given pressure can be calculated with an accuracy of 0.001° C.   Table I contains the best data.

TABLE I

BOILING TEMPERATURES OF WATER UNDER DIFFERENT PRESSURES[a]

Pressure, mm. Hg	Temp., ° C.
660	96.096
680	96.914
700	97.712
720	98.492
740	99.255
760	100.000
780	100.729
800	101.443
820	102.142
840	102.828
860	103.500

[a] In the original table, figures are given to ten-thousandths of a degree.

[12] A. Zmaczynski and A. Bonhoure, *Compt. rend.*, **189**, 1069 (1929); *J. phys. radium*, **1**, 285 (1930).   N. S. Osborne and C. H. Meyer, *J. Research Natl. Bur. Standards*, **13** (R.P. 691), 1 (1934).   L. B. Smith, F. G. Keys, and H. T. Gerry, *Proc. Am. Acad. Arts Sci.*, **69**, 137 (1934).   I. A. Beattie and B. E. Bleisdell, *ibid.*, **71**, 361 (1937).   A. Zmaczynski and H. Moser, *Physik. Z.*, **40**, 221 (1939).

For lower and higher pressures, in the range from 300 to 2000 mm. Hg, p and t are given by the following equation:[12]

$$t = 100 + 0.0368578 \, (p - 760) - 0.000020159 \, (p - 760)^2$$
$$+ \, 0.00000001621 \, (p - 760)^3$$
$$p = 760 + 27.1313 \, (t - 100) + 0.40083 \, (t - 100)^2 + 0.003192 \, (t - 100)^3$$

With individual pure substances as reference liquids, data may be used which were determined by Zmaczynski[13] in a series of comparative measurements for ethyl bromide, carbon disulfide, acetone, chloroform, carbon tetrachloride, benzene, toluene, chlorobenzene, and bromobenzene, against water as the standard.

4.　Condensation Temperatures of Liquids during Rectification

It is a common practice to determine the condensation temperature of a liquid when the purest (main) fraction is collected. In order to obtain accurate results, the following precautions should be observed: The head of the column should be provided with a device for measuring the condensation temperature in the space through which all the vapors pass— one portion refluxing and the other, leaving the head. No junctions other than ground joints should be used. One or several drop counters should be provided for determining the reflux ratio. A stopcock should be provided to make possible measuring the condensation temperature at total reflux. A simple ebulliometer with water or another reference substance should be placed side by side with the head of the column. The boiling temperature of the reference liquid should be measured at constant time intervals to allow interpolation of the condensation temperatures for changing pressure.

In the distillation of pure liquids, attention should be paid to changes in the condensation temperature at the beginning of the distillation in order to see whether or not an azeotrope containing water contaminates the foreruns. Often, when a few hundredths of a per cent of moisture contaminate the foreruns, a considerable decrease in condensation temperature is noticed.

Table II shows how relatively pure toluene, when submitted to fractional distillation, gave large fractions containing not more than 0.005% of impurities. Under column NN are listed the serial numbers of the fractions; under G, the number of grams of the fractions collected; under ΔT_w, the limits of temperature in thousandths of a degree within which the given fraction was collected; under T_w, the condensation temperatures calculated

[13] A. Zmaczynski, *J. chim. phys.*, **27**, 496 (1930); *Trabajos XI Congressod Intern. Quimica Pura Applicada, II Quimico-Fisica*, **2**, 225 (1934).

for 760 mm. Hg; and under Δt, the differences between the boiling and the condensation temperatures of the fraction, as determined with the differential ebulliometer (Fig. 8).   The last column gives the degree of purity according to the scale in table III.   Fraction No. 0 was not tested because of the large amount of moisture distilling as the heteroazeotrope, toluene-water.

TABLE II

DISTILLATION OF RELATIVELY PURE TOLUENE

NN	G	ΔT_w	T_w	Δt	Degree of purity
0	238	...	109.895	1.025	...
1	153	0.017	110.589	0.010	IV
2	179	0.018	110.598	0.005	V
3	199	0.008	110.599	0.004	V
4	156	0.005	110.603	0.005	V
5	182	0.005	110.611	0.004	V
6	203	0.004	110.613	0.004	V
7	193	0.004	110.614	0.004	V
8	202	0.005	110.614	0.003	V
9	176	0.014	110.615	0.007	IV
10	171	0.043	110.630	0.009	IV

TABLE III

SCALE OF PURITY

Degree of purity	Difference between boiling and condensation temperatures, ° C.
I..	1.00 –0.10
II..	0.10 –0.050
III..	0.050–0.020
IV..	0.020–0.005
V..	0.005–0.000

Such precision is not required in everyday laboratory technique, and is not obtainable with small amounts of material.   The corrections, however, for the change of pressure, as well as the direct comparison of the condensation temperature of the main fraction with the boiling temperature of water or a secondary standard, should always be made.   The difference found should be published with the other data characterizing the liquid. For instance, the results for the boiling temperatures of toluene should be presented by stating that the difference between the boiling temperature of toluene and water under one atmosphere is 10.61° C., from which it follows that the boiling temperature of toluene is 110.61°.   If the boiling temperature of the substance under examination is compared with the standard under a pressure other than normal, the difference between the boiling temperature of water at atmospheric pressure and that at the pressure of the measurement should be multiplied by the ratio:

$$(dt/dp)_{subst.}/(dt/dp)_{water}$$

The accuracy of the determination of the boiling temperature of liquids should be 0.05° C. or better.

It is very important that the numerical data be given characterizing the fractions which preceded and followed the main fraction. These data may be very useful in the future, especially when another raw material is employed for the synthesis of the substance or when another purification method is applied.

5. Degree of Purity of Liquid Substances

The simultaneous determination of the boiling and condensation temperatures of a liquid make it possible to determine the degree of purity of liquid substances. According to thermodynamic considerations, these temperatures should be identical if the substance is pure. In practice, except for water, this condition is hardly ever fulfilled. With organic liquids, very often the boiling temperature is higher than the condensation temperature because of the presence of small amounts of impurities, especially of moisture.

The determinations can be carried out in a differential ebulliometer (see page 52). The apparatus with standardized dimensions (Fig. 8) is suitable if more than 50–70 ml. of the liquid is available. For smaller amounts, the differential microebulliometers may be used.

As stated, table III gives a scale for the degree of purity of liquid substances.[7, 14] Experiments have shown that the difference between the boiling temperatures of several different samples of a liquid, each of them characterized by the degree of purity V, did not exceed 0.008° C. and were ordinarily within 0.001–0.003°. In most cases, a liquid with purity V does not contain more than 0.005% of impurities. However, this cannot be accepted as a general rule because the differences between the boiling and the condensation temperatures depend to a large extent upon the nature of the impurities. For instance, if the impurities are isomers of the substance under examination which boil at practically the same temperature as the latter, the differences between the boiling and condensation temperatures are small, regardless of large amounts of the contaminating substances. On the other hand, the purity of organic chemicals required in

---

[14] E. R. Smith and M. Wojciechowski, *J. Research Natl. Bur. Standards*, **17** (R.P. 947), 841 (1936). M. Wojciechowski, *ibid.*, **17**, 453, 721 (1936). J. Timmermans and L. Gillo, *Roczniki Chem.*, **18**, 812 (1938) (in French).

the course of preparative work is in many cases much lower than the ordinarily determined degree of purity of solvents and is often outside the scale.

The determination of the purity of a liquid may be combined with the determination of its boiling point. The sample may be prepared beforehand. It is easy, however, to collect the main fraction directly in the ebulliometer. First of all, the ebulliometer must be cleaned, dried, and washed with some of the liquid under examination. Then, after it is filled, the liquid is brought to a boil, and adequate heating is established. The number of drops flowing through the drop counter indicates the intensity of the heating. The limits of the smallest and the largest number of drops within which there is no change in boiling temperature of the liquid are determined. Some number within these limits should be accepted, and the same, or nearly the same, number of drops should be established in the upper drop counter. This is regulated with burner l (Fig. 8), which heats the bend of the tube below drop counter f_2. A simple ebulliometer containing the same liquid or some other fraction of it, and placed by the side of the differential apparatus, serves to determine the correction for the change in atmospheric pressure. An essential part of each determination of the purity of a liquid consists in the removal of moisture or other volatile impurities which often contaminate pure liquids. Some moisture may be present in the ebulliometer in spite of careful drying. Because of these impurities, the condensation temperature may be low, and it may be concluded that the liquid is of lower purity than that which would be indicated if the moisture or other low-boiling accidental impurities were removed. The following procedure is recommended: After the boiling and condensation temperatures have been determined, the cooling water is removed from the condenser, and, of the total amount of 50 ml. of liquid in the standard ebulliometer, 2 ml. is distilled off through the outlet in D provided with a ground joint and the small condenser, d (Fig. 8). If a microebulliometer is used, 2–3% of the total amount of the liquid is removed by each distillation. Then another determination of the difference in the boiling and condensation temperatures is made. These operations are repeated twice in order to have four determinations of the differences Δt_1, Δt_2, Δt_3, and Δt_4. The comparison of these values gives an idea of the kind of impurities present in the liquid. For instance, if $\Delta t_1 > \Delta t_2$ and the differences, Δt_3 and Δt_4, are equal or are slightly smaller than Δt_2, it can be considered as proof that moisture and other volatile impurities were removed with the first distillation. If, however, these differences are relatively large and decrease only slightly after each distillation, it is concluded that the impurities cannot be removed by this simple operation.

In table IV are shown the results obtained in the testing of isopropanol.

In following the suggestion[6] that the second difference between the boiling and the condensation temperatures be accepted for the classification of the purity of the liquid, the isopropanol examined was found to be of the degree of purity I.

TABLE IV[a]

DETERMINATION OF THE DEGREE OF PURITY OF ISOPROPANOL

Secondary Standard Substance: Benzene

Liquid examined	Δ Boiling and condensation temp., ° C.	Δ Boiling temp. of liquid and benzene, ° C.	Boiling temp. after each operation, ° C.
Isopropanol	$\Delta t_1 = 0.196$	$\Delta T_1 = 2.060$	$T_1 = 82.18$
After removal of 2 ml.	$\Delta t_2 = 0.195$	$\Delta T_2 = 2.098$	$T_2 = 82.22$
After second removal of 2 ml.	$\Delta t_3 = 0.144$	$\Delta T_3 = 2.108$	$T_3 = 82.23$
After third removal of 2 ml.	$\Delta t_4 = 0.083$	$\Delta T_4 = 2.124$	$T_4 = 82.25$

[a] W. Swietoslawski, *J. Phys. Chem.*, **38**, 1169 (1934).

After careful rectification of the same isopropanol the data in table V were found; the sample is now characterized by the degree of purity IV. The determination of the difference between the boiling temperature of isopropanol and benzene is made by transferring the same Beckmann thermometer from one ebulliometer into the other. The use of a multiple-stage ebulliometer is based on the same principle. This apparatus may be used in special cases in which liquids of high purity are examined.[15]

TABLE V[a]

DETERMINATION OF THE PURITY OF RECTIFIED ISOPROPANOL

Δ Boiling and condensation temp., ° C.	Δ Boiling temp. of liquid and benzene, ° C.	Boiling temp. after each operation, ° C.
$\Delta t_1 = 0.010$	$\Delta T_1 = 2.168$	$T_1 = 82.288$
$\Delta t_2 = 0.009$	$\Delta T_2 = 2.169$	$T_2 = 82.289$
$\Delta t_3 = 0.009$	$\Delta T_3 = 2.170$	$T_3 = 82.290$
$\Delta t_4 = 0.008$	$\Delta T_4 = 2.170$	$T_4 = 82.290$

[a] W. Swietoslawski, *J. Phys. Chem.*, **38**, 1169 (1934).

6. Determination of dt/dp

To calculate boiling temperatures at any given pressure, the function dt/dp must be known. It is rather easily determined by using the method of comparative measurements.

The apparatus consists of a simple ebulliometer filled with water, and a differential ebulliometer, both (A) connected with manostat W and the differential manometers M and M_1, as shown in figure 11. For relatively

---

[15] W. Swietoslawski, *Ebulliometry.* Chemical Pub. Co., New York, 1937, pp. 82–87; also pp. 134–146.

small pressure variations, one of the differential manometers may be filled with water or oil. In case of large changes in pressure, stopcock K_2 should be closed and mercury used in M for the approximate determination of the pressure.[12-14, 16] To avoid oxidation of the liquid and its vapors, air can be replaced by nitrogen, from L, by manipulating stopcocks K_3 and K_4.

The experiment consists in measuring the ratio of the change in the boiling temperatures of the liquid and of water, both produced by the same change in pressure:

$$(dt/dp)_{subst.}/(dt/dp)_{water} = \alpha$$

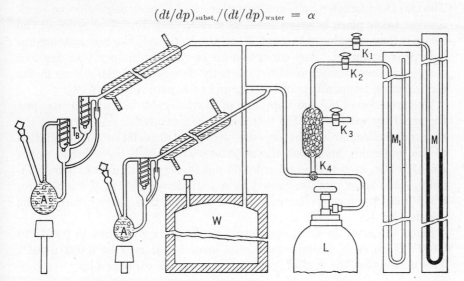

Fig. 11.—Simple and differential ebulliometers with manostat and differential manometer.

The absolute value of the coefficient $(dt/dp)_{subst.}$ is then determined by means of table I. With this method, no precise measurements of pressure are required. The values of the pressure can be calculated from the thermometer readings for the boiling temperature of water at the different pressures.

Beckmann thermometers are often used for these measurements. It should be remembered that the divisions of the scale do not represent exact degree centigrade values and that corrections must be introduced.

7. Molecular Weights by the Ebulliometric Method

The easiest way to determine molecular weights by the ebulliometric method is by using a differential ebulliometer (see Fig. 7). The author[16]

[16] W. Swietoslawski, *Ebulliometry.* Chemical Pub. Co., New York, 1937, pp. 147–152

considers the methods described in the following as sufficiently superior to
the Beckmann method to warrant the omission of the latter, particularly
since the Beckmann method is commonly described in textbooks.

The ebulliometer is filled with the solvent, and the difference between the
boiling and condensation temperatures is measured. If two Beckmann
thermometers are used they should be compared with each other by interchange between the two positions. If the solvent is relatively pure, the
difference between the boiling and condensation temperatures is small.
The two thermometer wells are located so close to each other that no rectification takes place between tubes B and H (Fig. 7). The pellet of the
solute is then introduced through E and the increase in the boiling temperature Δt is measured. Any correction for the boiling temperature due to a
change in atmospheric pressure is directly determined by a change in the
condensation temperature of the vapors of the pure solvent in H.

The precision of the determination of the molecular weight depends upon
the accuracy with which the increase Δt is measured. Furthermore, the
apparent molecular weight depends upon the dissociation or association
of the molecules, and upon the strictness with which the solution obeys
Raoult's law, even if the molecules do not undergo a change in size. Finally, some error may be caused by a partial volatility of the substance,
which may produce an increase in the condensation temperature of the
solvent.

Since the error in the temperature readings may amount to 0.001° to
0.002° C. in each determination, the error in Δt may be 0.002–0.004°.
This means that the possible percentage error, ϵ is expressed by·

$$\epsilon = 0.004 \cdot 100 / \Delta t$$

The molecular weight m is calculated according to:

$$m = a \cdot K \cdot 1000 / G \cdot t$$

where K represents the ebulliometric constant of the solvent and a and
G the weights of the solute and the solvent. The numerical constant K
may be found experimentally or calculated according to:

$$K = R \cdot T^2 / l$$

where R is the gas constant, T the absolute boiling temperature, and l
the heat of vaporization of one gram of the solvent. Several determinations should be made for each substance in order to ascertain whether or
not the molecular weight, as calculated by the above equation, undergoes
changes with the concentration of the solute.

It should be emphasized that deviations from Raoult's law are much
more frequent than was believed in the past. Therefore, it is rather an

exception if the Δt plotted against the increases of molar concentrations form a straight line.

If electric resistance thermometers are used, the accuracy of the temperature readings may be increased considerably. Experiments carried out with multithermocouples likewise increase the precision of ebulliometric measurements.[17] In the majority of cases, however, such high accuracy is not required in molecular weight determinations of organic compounds.

If the atmospheric pressure changes very rapidly, it is preferable to wait until more favorable conditions are established. It is possible that the correction for the change in atmospheric pressure may be greater than the increase in the boiling temperature produced by the dissolved substance. Under these conditions, the experimental error may be too great.

The use of a second ebulliometer, e. g., of the type shown in figure 6, is very desirable. It makes possible the elimination of errors which may be caused by the presence of a small amount of moisture in the solute, or the proof of whether or not the substance under examination is volatile. In both cases, the condensation temperature of the solvent vapors will undergo changes. It will increase if the solute is volatile, and decrease if the solid substance contains moisture and the solvent forms an azeotrope with water.

Precise ebulliometric measurements require a correction for the dead space in the ebulliometer. Inasmuch as some solvent is in the condenser, on the walls of the conducting tubes, and in the drop counter, the concentration of the boiling liquid is greater than that of the solution before boiling. The correction may be calculated by using empirical formulas established by direct measurements.[16] It is, however, much more convenient to make a comparative measurement, with a substance of known molecular weight. The latter should obey Raoult's law, or show only small deviations from it.

Comparative ebulliometric measurements may be made by introducing successively given amounts of the reference substance and of the substance under examination into the same ebulliometer; or the solutions of the two substances may be measured separately. In the first case, a very simple equation may be used to calculate the molecular weight:

$$m = a \cdot m_s \cdot \Delta t_s / a_s \cdot \Delta t$$

where a and a_s represent the weights of the substance under examination and of the reference substance, respectively, m and m_s, their molecular weights, and Δt and Δt_s, the increases of the boiling temperatures after a and a_s grams of both of these substances have been introduced.

[17] E. Plake, Z. physik. Chem., A172, 790 (1935).

When two solutions are examined separately, the "actual value" of K may be calculated from the equation:

$$K = m \cdot G \cdot \Delta t / a \cdot 1000$$

and used for the calculation of the molecular weight m of the substance examined.

In both cases, all corrections which must be taken into consideration with "absolute" measurements are eliminated, viz., the correction for the real concentration of the boiling solution, the correction for the real value of the thermometer division, and the correction for the real value of the ebulliometric constant of the solvent if this solvent is not entirely pure.

The following example illustrates the use of the first method in the determination of the molecular weight of thiourea with urea as a standard. The ebulliometer was filled with water, and, after introducing successively 0.9103 gram of urea and 0.8764 gram of thiourea, increases in boiling temperatures of 0.170° and 0.123° C. were noted. The molecular weight of urea is 60.06 and, therefore, the molecular weight of thiourea m is:

$$m = 0.8764 \cdot 60.06 \cdot 0.170 / 0.127 \cdot 0.09103 = 77.40$$

The theoretical value is 76.12. The error can be explained by the error in thermometric readings.

General References

Barbaudy, J., *Contribution à l'étude des mélanges liquides ternaires*. Hermann, Paris, 1925.

Biltz, H., *Practical Methods for Determining Molecular Weights*. Translated by H. C. Jones and S. C. King, T. Wiley, New York, 1899.

Daniels, F., Mathews, J. H., and Williams, J. W., *Experimental Physical Chemistry*. 3rd ed., McGraw-Hill, New York, 1941.

Fajans, K., and Wust, J., *A Textbook of Practical Chemistry*. Translated by B. Topley. Methuen, London, 1930.

Findlay, A., *Practical Physical Chemistry*. 7th ed., Longmans, Green, New York, 1941.

Grignard, V., *Traité de chimie organique, distillation*. Vol. 1, M. Lecat, Masson, Paris, 1934.

Hausbrand, E., *Principles and Practice of Industrial Distillation*. Translated by E. H. Tripp. Chapman & Hall, London, 1925.

Jones, H. C., *The Freezing-Point, Boiling-Point and Conductivity Methods*. Chemical Pub. Co., New York, 1912.

Lecat, M., *L'azéotropisme*. H. Lamertin, Bruxelles, 1918.

Ostwald, W., Luther, R., and Drucker, K., *Ostwald-Luther Hand- und Hilfsbuch zur Ausfürung physico-chemischer Messungen*. W. Engelmann, Leipzig, 1910.

Palmer, W. G., *Experimental Physical Chemistry*. Cambridge Univ. Press, London, 1941.

Swietoslawski, W., *Ebulliometry*.   2nd ed., Chemical Pub. Co., New York, 1937.

Taylor, H. S., *A Treatise on Physical Chemistry*.   3rd ed., Van Nostrand, New York, 1942.

Young, S., *Distillation Principles and Processes*.   Macmillan, New York, 1922.

CHAPTER III

Determination of
DENSITY

N. BAUER, *University of New Hampshire*

I. INTRODUCTION

Density measurements are a convenient aid in characterizing liquids. For this purpose an accuracy of a few units in the third decimal place is often adequate. Methods of greater precision, however, make possible the more exact characterization of substances. They are a valuable aid in differentiating between similar compounds and in detecting small amounts of impurities. They also allow one to detect small concentration changes in solutions and thus to follow the course of reactions. They permit the detection of small differences in the proportions of isotopes in solid, liquid, or gaseous compounds if the molecular weight is not too high, thereby affording convenient methods for the tracing of isotopes like D, C^{13}, N^{15}, and O^{18}. Moreover, the application of precision density methods furnishes information regarding the chemical forces operating within and between molecules when the data are studied in terms of the molar volume and apparent molar volume. The density is also required in the evaluation of molecular weights from x-ray diffraction measurements, of molar refractions, of dipole moments, and of other physical properties.

II. GENERAL CONSIDERATIONS

1. Definitions and Units

Density, d, is defined by the equation:

$$d = \text{mass/volume} = m/V \tag{1}$$

In accordance with the c.g.s. system of units, density measurements are expressed in grams of mass per cubic centimeter. However, this *absolute density*, d^t, if measured at $t°$ C., and defined by the equation:

$$d^t = \frac{m}{V_{cc.}} \text{ g./cc.} \tag{2a}$$

is seldom used. More commonly, density measurements are expressed in grams of weight per milliliter, which under most conditions is equivalent to grams of mass per milliliter. This, the *relative density* at $t°$ C., is defined by the equation:

$$d_4^t = \frac{m}{V_{ml.}} \text{ g./ml.} \tag{2b}$$

By definition, one milliliter = 0.001 liter = 0.001 part of the volume of one kilogram of pure, ordinary water at its temperature of maximum density (3.98° C.). Therefore, d_4^t gives the ratio of the (absolute) density at $t°$ C. to the (absolute) density of water at 3.98° and is frequently called "density relative to water at 4° C." or "specific gravity relative to water at 4° C."

In setting up the standards of mass and volume it was intended that 1 ml. should equal 1 cc. exactly, but subsequent measurements showed that 1 cc. = 0.999973 ml., that is:

$$V_{cc.} = 1.000027 \ V_{ml.} \tag{3}$$

The difference between g./cc., d^t, and g./ml., d_4^t, is evidently negligible for most purposes. Moreover, the weight, W, is connected with the mass, m, by the equation $W = mg$, where g, the acceleration due to gravity, is a constant for a given geographical location. Hence, $W_1/W_2 = m_1/m_2$, provided

TABLE I

DENSITIES $d_{(H_2O)}^t$ AND $d_{4\ (H_2O)}^t$ OF ORDINARY[b] AIR-FREE[c] WATER AT ONE ATMOSPHERE[a]

$t°$ C.	$d_{(H_2O)}^t$	$d_{4\ (H_2O)}^t$
0	0.999841	0.9998676
3.98	0.999973	1.0000000
10	0.999701	0.9997281
15	0.998102	0.9981286
20	0.998207	0.9982343
25	0.997048	0.9970751
30	0.995651	0.9956783

[a] Values of d_4^t from N. E. Dorsey, *Properties of Ordinary Water-Substance.* Reinhold, New York, 1940, p. 200.

[b] Isotopic ratio of $D_2O/H_2O = 1/4000$.

[c] The effect of dissolved air on the density of water at room temperature is noticeable only in the 7th decimal place. At 20° C. $d_{air-satd.}$ is less than $d_{air-free}$ by 4×10^{-7} units; at higher temperatures, the difference is still smaller.

that both weighings are carried out at the same place. Under this condition, *i. e.*, when both $V_{ml.}$ and m are determined by weighings in the same laboratory, no change in the numerical value of relative density is caused by using grams of weight (Eq. 2b) instead of grams of mass (Eq. 2a).

Instead of d^t, d_4^t is used because it can be accurately and conveniently measured by a direct comparison of the weights of equal volumes of the substance at $t°$ C. and of water at 3.98° C., while values of d^t are ultimately based on the less reliable measurements of the dimensions of some substance and on its absolute mass.

One also uses the *specific gravity*, d_t^t, which is defined as the mass, m, of a substance at $t°$ C. relative to the mass, m_0, of an equal volume of water at $t°$ C., *i. e.*, d_t^t is a dimensionless number:

$$d_t^t = (m/V)/(m_0/V) \tag{4}$$

2. Interconversion of Densities

By combining equations (2*b*) and (3) with (2*a*):

$$d^t = 0.999973 d_4^t \tag{5}$$

From equations (2*a*), (2*b*), and (4):

$$d_4^t = d_t^t \cdot d_{4\,(H_2O)}^t \tag{6}$$

and

$$d^t = d_t^t \cdot d_{(H_2O)}^t \tag{7}$$

The factor, $d_{(H_2O)}^t$ or $d_{4\,(H_2O)}^t$, used for converting specific gravities (d_t^t) into densities (d^t or d_4^t) will depend on the temperature. Dreisbach[1] has prepared tables which allow the rapid conversion of values for d_t^t at one temperature to values for d_4^t at any other temperature between 0° and 40° C., provided the coefficient of expansion β_t is known. Table I gives a list of the densities of water, $d_{(H_2O)}$, at several standard temperatures.

Sample calculation: If a sample of methanol at 25.00° shows a specific gravity of $d_{25}^{25} = 0.78664$, then, according to equation (6) and table I, $d_4^{25} = 0.99708 \cdot 0.78664 = 0.78434$ (g./ml.), and from equation (5) $d^{25} = 0.999973 \cdot 0.78434 = 0.78432$ (g./cc.).

3. Standard Liquids for Calibration

All instruments used in measuring density are calibrated directly or indirectly with pure water or with pure mercury. The following procedure is used for preparing pure standard water having a density corresponding to the values in table I:

(*1*) Ordinary tap water is distilled once. To avoid the possibility of too high a content of heavy water, D_2O ($d_{4\,(D_2O)}^{20} = 1.1059$ compared with $d_{4\,(H_2O)}^{20} = 0.9982$ for ordinary water), one should always start with fresh tap water. If a source of water is used which has been subject to many previous distillations, as might occur, for example, in a permanently installed laboratory still, the density will be appreciably greater than the values in table I. Thus, according to Lewis and Cornish,[2] a distillation in a still of 40 theoretical plates causes a change of 6×10^{-5} in the density.

(*2*) To each liter of the distillate is added 0.5 g. c.p. sodium hydroxide and 0.2 g. c.p. potassium permanganate. This alkaline solution is slowly distilled from an all-Pyrex, quartz, or tin-lined vessel with due precautions to prevent spraying, for instance by inserting a shield of tin foil in front of the condenser inlet. All connections must be glass-to-glass or metal-to-

---

[1] R. R. Dreisbach, *Ind. Eng. Chem., Anal. Ed.*, **12**, 160 (1940).

[2] G. N. Lewis and R. E. Cornish, *J. Am. Chem. Soc.*, **55**, 2616 (1933).

metal and the exposed parts covered with tin foil. The first and last third of this second distillate are rejected.

(*3*) For very careful work (6th place accuracy), a third distillation may be made in the same way except that a few drops of sulfuric acid per liter are added instead of alkaline permanganate.

For the purification of mercury, a number of good procedures are available in standard texts.[3] For other standard liquids see Chapter XVI.

4. Effect of Temperature on Density

The temperature coefficient of cubical expansion, β_t, is defined by $\beta_t = \partial V/\partial t \cdot 1/V$, where $V = $ volume. We can obtain an approximate relation between change in density per degree, Δd, and β_t by assuming β_t does not change with temperature. (For most liquids, β_t increases by only about 1% per degree C. rise in temperature.) In this case we have: $\beta_t = \Delta V/V$ per degree, where $\Delta V = $ change in volume V when the temperature is increased by $1°$ C. From equation (1) it then follows that $\Delta d/d$ per degree $= -\beta_t$, i. e., the per cent change in d per degree C. $= 100\,\beta$.

For water at room temperature, the density decreases by about 0.03% per degree C. rise in temperature ($\beta_t = 3 \times 10^{-4}$ deg.$^{-1}$). Most organic liquids have coefficients of expansion, β_t, which are two to five times greater than that of water. As a rough rule, nonpolar liquids of low molecular weight, e. g., aliphatic hydrocarbons, have the greatest coefficients of expansion. Also, abnormally high expansions are found for liquids near their boiling points, e. g., $\beta_t = 16 \times 10^{-4}$ for ethyl ether between $15°$ and $30°$. The density of organic solids usually changes somewhat less rapidly with temperature than that of liquids, e. g., $\beta_t = 0.9 \times 10^{-4}$ for benzoic acid, although $\beta_t = 6 \times 10^{-4}$ for paraffin.

The above facts lead to the conclusion that the temperature control required during density measurements should be within about $1°$ C. if an error of not more than ±0.001 in d can be tolerated, and correspondingly better for higher accuracy. The required temperature control will depend somewhat on the method as, for instance, when a pycnometer (see page 77) is used, the effect of temperature changes is lessened by the expansion of the glass container. In order to estimate more closely the influence of temperature fluctuations on the accuracy of measurement in each case, one can make use of the extensive compilations of data on coefficients of expansion, β_t, of liquids and of glass in standard tables, or else measure β_t directly.

---

[3] See, for example, F. Daniels, J. H. Mathews, and J. W. Williams, *Experimental Physical Chemistry*, 3rd ed., McGraw-Hill, New York, 1941, p. 444; also J. Reilly and W. N. Rae, *Physico-chemical Methods*, 3rd ed., Vol. I, Van Nostrand, New York, 1939, 283, 676.

5. Effect of Pressure on Density

The isothermal compressibility $\beta_P = (1/V)(\partial V/\partial P)_t$, which can be taken from standard tables, provides a measure of the influence of pressure on density. Similar to the case of the temperature coefficient of expansion, we have: $-\Delta d/d = \beta_P \cdot \Delta P$, assuming β_P is independent of pressure, i. e., the per cent change in d per atm. $= 100\beta_P$. The density of pure water at room temperature and pressure is *increased* by about 0.005% for a pressure increase of 1 atm., i. e., by about 5 units in the 6th decimal place ($\beta_P = 45.9 \times 10^{-6}$ atm.$^{-1}$ at 20°, 1 atm.). The compressibility of organic liquids at room temperature varies between about 20×10^{-6} atm.$^{-1}$ and 200×10^{-6} atm.$^{-1}$; most organic liquids are found in the range of $\beta_P = 60 \times 10^{-6}$ to $\beta_P = 100 \times 10^{-6}$. It is evident that the ordinary fluctuations in pressure encountered in the laboratory (about 20/760 atm.) cause only a very small, but not always negligible, change in density, e. g., for methyl alcohol ($\beta_P = 130 \times 10^{-6}$) d changes by 3 units in the 6th decimal place when p changes by 20 mm.

6. Effect of Impurities on Density

It is obvious that the method of measurement selected need be no more accurate than is justified by the purity of the substance.   In order to estimate roughly the influence which a given amount of impurity has on the density of a liquid one can use the *approximate* relation:

$$d = \frac{d_0 d_1}{0.01 p_1 (d_0 - d_1) + d_1} \tag{8}$$

where $p_1 =$ per cent impurity (g. per 100 g. solution), and d_0, d_1, and d refer to the densities of the pure substance, the impurity, and their mixture, respectively.   Equation (8) is based on the assumption that the specific volume of the mixture, v, is additively composed of the specific volumes of the solvent, v_0, and of the impurity, v_1, i. e., on the assumption that $v = 0.01\, p_1 v_1 + (1 - 0.01\, p_1)v_0$. Thus, equation (8) applies best to solutions for which no volume change occurs on mixing the components. This condition is approached closely by mixtures of similar nonpolar molecules.

As an example of the use of equation (8), we may consider a sample of benzene at 15° C. ($d_0 = 0.885$) which is suspected to contain as much as 0.1% thiophene ($d_1 = 1.070$). The possible difference between the density of pure benzene and the impure sample is given approximately by: $d - d_0 = [0.885 \times 1.070/ - 0.01 \times 0.1 \times 0.195 + 1.070] - 0.8850 = 0.0002$. Evidently there would be little use in measuring d to better than about $\pm 1 \times 10^{-4}$.

The density of organic liquids may be decreased appreciably by dissolved air; e. g., for toluene at 25° C. and 1 atm., $d_\text{air-satd.}$ is less than $d_\text{air-free}$ by about 0.01%.

7. Molar Volume

The molar volume of a compound is defined as M/d, when M denotes the molecular weight. It was calculated for liquids by Kopp[4, 5] from densities determined near the boiling point; additive atomic constants as well as increments for the effect of constitutive factors were evaluated by this author.

Biltz and coworkers[6] extrapolated temperature–density curves to absolute zero and treated the *nullpunkts volumina* in a similar way.

Density measurements of solutions of known concentration allow the calculation of the *apparent molar volume*, Φ, of a solute. The quantity $(\Phi - V)$, where V = actual molar volume of the pure substance, is a property which depends solely on the interaction between solute and solvent, and is therefore of considerable theoretical interest.[7] Φ is defined by the relation:

$$\Phi = V_{\text{soln.}} - V_{\text{solv.}} \tag{9}$$

where $V_{\text{soln.}}$ is the volume of solution containing one mole of solute and $V_{\text{solv.}}$ is the volume of the amount (N_0 moles) of pure solvent present in this solution, $N_0(M_0/d_0)$, i. e., the solvent is considered as unchanged. In terms of directly measurable quantities, Φ is given by:

$$\Phi = \frac{M_1}{d_0} - 1000 \, \frac{d - d_0}{C d_0} \tag{10}$$

where M_1 = molecular weight of the solute and C = concentration in moles per liter. Equation (10) shows that the accuracy of the determination of Φ depends largely on the difference, $\Delta d = d - d_0$. Therefore in the measurement of Φ, the solution and solvent should be compared under as nearly identical conditions as possible (differential measurement).

For the most accurate determinations of Φ, it is advisable to make up the solutions by mixing weighed quantities of a carefully analyzed stock solution and of the solvent, in order that the per cent error in concentration C be kept at least as small as that in the difference, $d - d_0$.

8. Expressions for Concentrations

When using density data as a measure of solute concentration or for the calculation of Φ, it may be necessary or convenient to express the concen-

[4] S. Smiles, *The Relation between Chemical Constitution and Physical Properties.* Longmans, Green, London, 1910.

[5] H. Gilman, *Organic Chemistry.* Wiley, New York, 1943, p. 1741.

[6] W. Biltz *et al., Ann.,* **453**, 259 (1927); *Z. physik. Chem.,* **A151**, 13 (1930); *Z. Elektrochem.,* **36**, 815 (1930).

[7] See, for example, K. Fajans and O. Johnson, *J. Am. Chem. Soc.,* **64**, 668 (1942).

tration in different units. For example, in applying equation (10), we must find the molarity, C, from the weight per cent, p. Other units often encountered are the mole fraction, X, the mole per cent, $100X$, and the molality (moles solute per 1000 grams solvent), C_g. If the molecular weight of solute and solvent are designated by M_1 and M_0, respectively, their mole fractions by X_1 and X_0, and their weights in the solution by W_1 and W_0, then:

$$X_1 = \frac{W_1/M_1}{W_1/M_1 + W_0/M_0} \tag{11}$$

and

$$p_1 = \frac{W_1}{W_1 + W_0} 100 = \frac{X_1M_1}{X_1M_1 + X_0M_0} 100 \tag{12}$$

$$C = \frac{10p_1d}{M_1} \tag{13}$$

$$C = 1000 \left(\frac{C_g d}{1000 + M_1 C_g} \right) \tag{14}$$

$$C = \frac{1000X_1d}{X_1M_1 + X_0M_0} \tag{15a}$$

and since, for a binary mixture, $X_1 + X_0 = 1$,

$$C = \frac{1000X_1d}{X_1M_1 + (1 - X_1)M_0} \tag{15b}$$

9.   Change of Density with Concentration

A plot of density *vs.* concentration generally gives a curved line.[8] When the concentration is expressed in terms of molarity, C, the density–composition curve is more likely to be nearly linear than with other concentration units. If the two components mix without a change in volume at all concentrations, *i. e.*, if the volumes are additive, the relation between d and C is exactly linear (Eqs. 8 and 13) over the whole range, whereas the corresponding relation between d and weight per cent, p (Eq. 8), approaches linearity only at low concentrations even if the volume is additive over the whole range. Volume additivity is fulfilled best for mixtures of similar nonpolar molecules. If the intermolecular forces in the mixture are strong and sufficiently different from those in the pure components, a maximum or minimum of density may occur. Thus, when density measurements are used to follow changes in concentration, a calibration curve of C *vs.* d

---

[8] R. Kremann, *Die Eigenschaften der binären Flüssigkeitsgemische. Sammlung chemischer und Chem.-Tech. Vorträge.* Enke, Stuttgart, 1917, p. 157.

containing many experimental points should be made instead of relying on theoretical equations.

III. MEASUREMENT OF DENSITY OF LIQUIDS

1. Measurement of Weight of a Known Volume

The most common method of density determination consists in finding the weight of liquid occupying a known volume defined by the shape of a given vessel. It is obviously impracticable to determine this volume from the geometry of the vessel. Instead, the vessel is calibrated in terms of the weight of pure water which it will hold.

A. PYCNOMETERS

A multitude of devices have been used for defining a volume so that the filling and weighing of the vessel are reproducible and convenient. Figure 1 shows various selected types of such "pycnometers," each having certain advantages. Even for the most accurate work (about $\pm 5 \times 10^{-6}$) it is hardly ever desirable to make the capacity of any of these pycnometers greater than about 30 milliliters, assuming that each necessary weighing is not in error by more than 0.1 milligram. An attempt to increase the accuracy beyond $\pm 5 \times 10^{-6}$ by using still larger quantities of liquid is accompanied by a compensating loss in balance sensitivity and by increasing uncertainties in such factors as the correction of weights to vacuum, the reproducibility of weight of objects having such large glass surfaces, and small accidental changes in volume of the pycnometer. The pycnometers are preferably made of some resistant glass, having a low coefficient of thermal expansion—such as Pyrex or Vycor, or fused quartz. Types A, B, C, and E in figure 1 are available commercially.

In the following section, the accuracy, advantages, and disadvantages of the six types of pycnometers shown in figure 1 are discussed. Detailed techniques for the use of types B, D, and E are described on page 82 *et seq.*

Type A is used for rapid measurements when an accuracy of only about ± 0.001 is required and when a regular thermostat is not available. Leakage around ground joints G and g is a drawback to the use of this pycnometer, especially when it is weighed at a temperature above that of filling.

Type B is a convenient, versatile model capable of an accuracy of about 5×10^{-5}. Without the expansion cup or cap, it is known as the "Weld specific gravity bottle." It can easily be used for solids as well as liquids because of the large neck opening. The volume depends somewhat on the amount of pressure exerted on the ground joint. Devices for putting in the

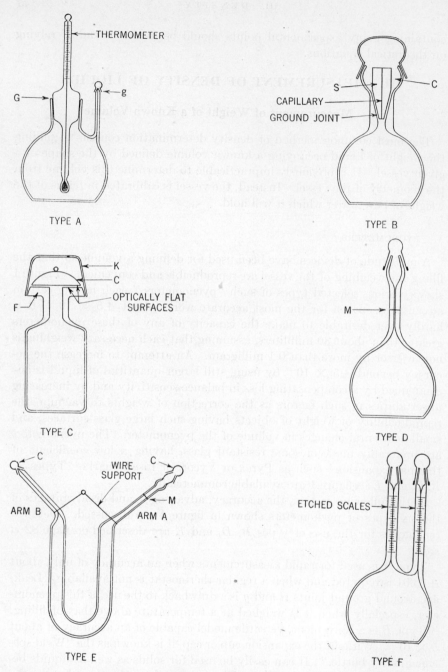

Fig. 1.—Selected types of pycnometers.

stopper, S, with the same pressure each time have been used.[9] Evaporation is minimized by the outside cap, while the cup, C, furnishes space for expansion of liquid in case the pycnometer warms up during weighing.

Type C, designed by Johnston and Adams,[10] permits a rapid adjustment of volume. It also is useful for solids as well as liquids because of the wide neck opening, and is capable of an accuracy of up to 5×10^{-6} in d_{liquid}. The flat cap, C, is slid over the surface of the flange, F, when the thermostated vessel is filled to overflowing, and the excess is then wiped off. If the two surfaces are optically flat, the amount of evaporation around their common edge is very small, and the layer of liquid between them will be so thin that the uncertainty in the volume is negligible even if the opening in the neck of the bulb is made conveniently large. If the whole weight of the filled pycnometer can be supported by the adhesion pressure of the liquid film, $i.$ $e.$, if it can be lifted by holding on to cap C, the surfaces can be considered satisfactorily polished and joined. The most serious disadvantage of this type is that a slight increase in temperature and the consequent expansion of the liquid cause the cap to be pushed off, resulting in a rapid loss by evaporation despite the protection of cover K. It is therefore advisable to keep the temperature of the room somewhat below that of the thermostat. Special care must be exercised when sliding on the cap to avoid trapping air bubbles in the neck.

Type D is in principle a volumetric flask having an etched mark, M, around the capillary which defines the volume. Space above the mark allows for expansion of the liquid during weighing. This simple "flask pycnometer" is recommended for measurements of *pure* (single-component) *liquids* for which an accuracy of anywhere up to 5×10^{-6} is required. Such a high accuracy is not practicable in using type D with *solutions* because of the difficulty of filling without losing, by evaporation, more of one component than of the other. The accuracy can evidently be increased by increasing the bulb size and decreasing the bore of the capillary. A capacity of about 30 ml. and a 1-mm. bore allow 5th place accuracy; but such a pycnometer is difficult to fill and clean. The convenience can be considerably enhanced by providing the capillary with a whole set of equally spaced reference marks. By using a cathetometer to interpolate between the marks, the tedious operation of bringing the meniscus to a given mark is avoided. The calibration of such a capillary is discussed under type F. Washburn and Smith[11] describe in detail a convenient dif-

---

[9] J. Reilly and W. N. Rae, *Physico-chemical Methods*. 3rd ed., Vol. I, Van Nostrand, New York, 1939, p. 477.

[10] J. Johnston and L. H. Adams, *J. Am. Chem. Soc.*, **34**, 563 (1912).

[11] E. W. Washburn and E. R. Smith, *J. Research Natl. Bur. Standards*, **12**, 305 (1934). See also E. R. Smith and M. Wojciechowski, *Bull. intern. acad. polon.*, **A1936**, 281; *Roczniki Chem.*, **16**, 104 (1936).

ferential method of using twin pycnometers of the flask type which allows
an accuracy of one part per million.

Type E is the standard Sprengel-Ostwald pycnometer. Having two
openings, this type is especially easy to fill and clean as compared with type
D, even when the side arms are made of small-bore capillaries. It can be
filled without danger of loss by evaporation, and is therefore suitable for
solutions. By making the capillary of arm A as narrow as 1 mm. in diameter and by grinding off irregularities from the end surface of the smaller
capillary (arm B, inner diameter 0.2 mm.), the accuracy can be increased
to $\pm 5 \times 10^{-6}$. If a standard ground joint is attached to arm B (see Fig.
2d), the end of the capillary should be ground down until a flat surface
intersects the bore at right angles. Space above the mark on arm A allows
for expansion of the liquid. For rapid, less exact measurements on smaller
samples, it is convenient to make the Sprengel pycnometer from an ordinary pipette by bending it to the appropriate shape and drawing out the
ends to make small openings. The caps, C, may be omitted. Hennion[12]
has described a self-filling (siphoning) Ostwald pycnometer, useful for volatile liquids.

Type F, a modification of type E, is more convenient than E and is
especially well adapted to precision measurements up to $\pm 5 \times 10^{-6}$ of
solutions containing a volatile component. The ends of the capillaries
are provided with ground joints so that an appropriate filling apparatus
may be tightly connected. For the highest precision, the two capillary
tubes can be made very narrow (<0.5 mm. in diameter). Both tubes
should be of the same uniform diameter. If a scale is etched along the
length of the capillaries, it is unnecessary to make the tedious adjustment
of volume by bringing the liquid meniscus exactly to some particular mark,
as with types A and E. Instead, the position of the meniscus is found
relative to some reference marks. Since it usually lies between two marks,
it is necessary, for the highest accuracy, to interpolate the position of the
meniscus by using a cathetometer or a telescope fitted with a micrometer
eyepiece. However, a rather laborious calibration is necessary. The volume corresponding to a unit length of the capillary can be most accurately
found by measuring the length and weight of various threads of pure mercury placed in the necks of the pycnometer. A calibration with water defines the bulb volume up to some selected pair of reference marks on the
necks. Subsequently, the sums of the heights of liquid above these marks
correspond to a definite volume which is found from a calibration curve.

Robertson[13] has described how to make a simple bicapillary pycnometer
from sections of graduated pipettes. Other forms of the bicapillary pycnom-

[12] G. F. Hennion, *Ind. Eng. Chem.*, *Anal. Ed.*, **9**, 479 (1937).

[13] G. R. Robertson, *Ind. Eng. Chem.*, *Anal. Ed.*, **11**, 464 (1939).

eter have been discussed by Wibaut[14] *et al.*, who have used this type for
careful measurements of a variety of organic liquids, by Smith[15] and by
Parker and Parker.[16]   Lipkin *et al.*[17] describe a convenient bicapillary
pycnometer which is available commercially.[18] They emphasize the importance of the narrow, unfilled capillary in minimizing evaporation for
obtaining 4th decimal accuracy on liquids as volatile as isopentane.

B. TECHNIQUE FOR PRECISION PYCNOMETRIC MEASUREMENTS

Weighing.—For 5th place accuracy, the individual weights should be
checked against one another to obtain their *relative* values, for example,
by the method of Richards,[19] which is especially convenient in the modification suggested by Blade.[20] It is not necessary to compare the set with a
certified standard mass. Since lacquered weights are most susceptible
to change with changing humidity, their use should be avoided. Un-
lacquered, metal-plated weights are much to be preferred.

An error of about 2×10^{-5} in density can be caused by changes in the
inequalities of the lengths of the two balance arms. This error can be
eliminated by making successive weighings with the object placed first
on one balance pan, then on the other, and taking the mean value. The
clean pycnometer is weighed before and after filling with water, as well
as before and after filling with the liquid in question. The second weighing of the empty pycnometer may be omitted in ordinary work if tested
precautions are taken in drying the vessel. The weighing of a vessel with
a considerable surface of glass and a large internal volume involves certain
difficulties:

(*1*) The weight of a glass object can change appreciably due to changes
in the amount of water adsorbed. For instance, a 30-ml. pycnometer
dried in a vacuum at room temperature for a couple of hours can gain
several milligrams of water by standing in a humid atmosphere. The effect
of adsorption is standardized by wiping the glass surface carefully with a
moist chamois or lintless cloth, then allowing the vessel to stand in the
balance case for 15 to 20 minutes before each weighing. A tare (dummy
pycnometer) having the same area as the pycnometer is treated in a simi-

[14] J. P. Wibaut *et. al.*, *Rec. trav. chim.*, **58**, 369 (1939).

[15] G. F. Smith, *J. Chem. Soc.*, **1931**, 3260.

[16] H. C. Parker and E. W. Parker, *J. Phys. Chem.*, **29**, 130 (1925).

[17] M. R. Lipkin, J. A. Davison, W. T. Harvey, and S. S. Kurtz, Jr., *Ind. Eng. Chem.*, *Anal. Ed.*, **16**, 55 (1944).

[18] *Ace Glass, Inc.*, Vineland, N. J.

[19] J. Reilly and W. N. Rae, *Physico-chemical Methods*. 3rd ed., Vol. I, Van Nostrand, New York, 1939, p. 61.

[20] E. Blade, *Ind. Eng. Chem.*, *Anal. Ed.*, **11**, 499 (1939).

lar manner. In the case of the empty pycnometer and its tare, the air inside is flushed out with air from the balance room; then they are wiped and allowed to stand with caps removed.

(2) The buoyancy effect of the air which is displaced by large vessels and their contents must be considered when an accuracy of 5×10^{-5} is required. The buoyancy correction of the vessel itself is eliminated by using a dummy pycnometer which has the same weight as the pycnometer, within 1 gram. The method of making the other buoyancy corrections is given on pages 86 *et seq*.

(3) If the air density in the tare or the pycnometer differs by a few per cent from that on the outside, large errors in the weight of both the full and the empty vessel can arise. To secure equality of air composition and pressure, the vessels should be flushed out with balance room air and the caps loosened just before weighing; temperature equilibrium is established in about 15 minutes. If a volatile liquid is present, it may not be possible to fill all the gas space with balance room air and a special correction becomes necessary (see page 86).

(4) Erratic behavior of the balance occurs if the vessels become electrostatically charged by friction; this can be eliminated by placing some radioactive material in the balance case.

Precautions in Handling the Pycnometers.—To avoid changes in the volume of the bulb, the pycnometer should not be excessively warmed above or cooled below the temperature of measurement or be subjected to pressure differences such as those caused by prolonged evacuation. Usually the bulb changes only very slowly back toward its original volume after the release of such stresses. A newly made pycnometer changes volume continuously for a period of weeks.

To clean the interior of the vessel, allow it to stand in contact with cleaning solution, a mixture of potassium dichromate and concentrated sulfuric acid, overnight, or until the last traces of grease have disappeared. After rinsing, it should be left in contact with distilled water for 24 hours to remove adsorbed acid, then rinsed thoroughly, drained, and dried. The drying is conveniently accomplished in about 20 minutes by inverting the pycnometer in a large vacuum desiccator and applying suction. The vacuum is broken from time to time if much water is initially present. The drying process is repeated until constant weight is obtained.

Filling and Adjusting the Pycnometers.—A detailed description of the best technique for handling pycnometers B, D, and E is given in the following section. To a considerable extent these techniques also apply to the other types (A, C, and F); for example, A is similar to B, and type F embodies features of both D and E. These similarities, in addition to the

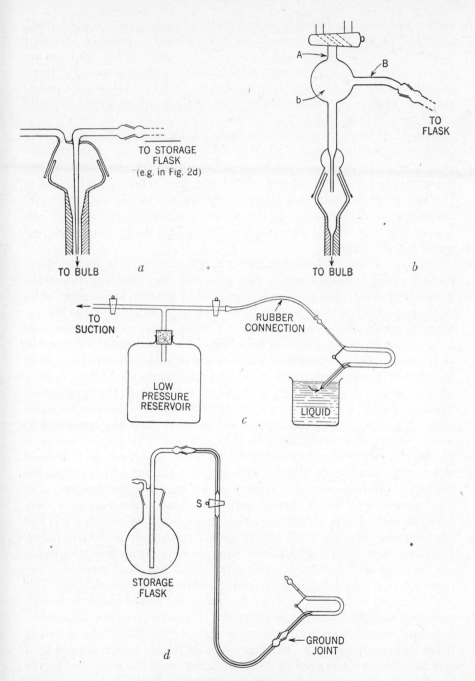

TO STORAGE
FLASK
(e.g. in Fig. 2d)

TO BULB   *a*

A

B

b

TO
FLASK

TO BULB   *b*

TO
SUCTION

RUBBER
CONNECTION

LOW
PRESSURE
RESERVOIR

LIQUID

c

S

STORAGE
FLASK

GROUND
JOINT

d

Fig. 2.—Pycnometer filling devices.

factors discussed on pages 77 *et seq.*, make the treatment of types A, C, and F self-evident. In all cases, the liquid should, if possible, be boiled shortly before filling to prevent the formation of air bubbles. Bubbles are the most frequent cause of large accidental errors in pycnometry. In all cases it is advisable to cool the liquid slightly ($\sim 1°$ C.) below the thermostat temperature just before filling in order to insure an excess of liquid when equilibrium is reached.

Type B. This pycnometer can be easily filled with a pipette, or, for more careful transfer, by means of the tube shown in figure 2a. After thermostating, part of the excess liquid is forced out through the capillary into cup C by inserting a ground stopper. (Check against trapping air bubbles in this operation.) After a few minutes more in the thermostat, the liquid remaining on the flat surface of the stopper is quickly wiped off with lens paper. The cup is dried with absorbent paper and the pycnometer is prepared for weighing.

Type D. When the bore diameter is 2 mm. or more, it is practicable to introduce the liquid through a fine glass capillary reaching below the pycnometer neck. The flow can be regulated by gravity, by pressure, or by siphoning. Hollow steel needles have been used as filling tubes for extremely narrow-necked pycnometers. A filling tube which can be used for *pure liquids only* is shown in figure 2b. The pycnometer is evacuated through arm A of this tube after a flask of the liquid is connected to arm B. By tilting the whole apparatus until liquid flows into the bulb at b, then allowing dry air to flow through A, the liquid is forced into the pycnometer. The liquid may be returned to the storage flask by distillation at low pressure. A modification of this method can be used when it is important to avoid the risk of a small change in bulb size caused by the evacuation—the pycnometer is placed in a close-fitting vessel which can be evacuated and is then completely covered with liquid. Making and breaking the vacuum a few times serves to remove all air from the pycnometer. The filled pycnometer, loosely capped, is immersed up to the mark in a thermostat; after about 15 minutes, the excess liquid is removed by just touching the meniscus with a fine glass capillary or a roll of paper. When the meniscus remains at the same position for several minutes, it can be concluded that temperature equilibrium has been reached. The pycnometer is removed, carefully rinsed, and prepared for weighing.

Type E can be filled by applying suction at the end of one arm through a one-liter air-filled flask, as in figure 2c. For a more careful transfer—necessary, for instance, for hygroscopic liquids—the filling tube shown in figure 2d is recommended. The flow of liquid in this tube is started by a slight suction, is maintained by a siphoning action, and is controlled by the stopcock S. No grease is used on this stopcock. If the leakage is excessive, its ground surfaces may be lapped together more smoothly by grinding with fine rouge. After thermostating, the meniscus is brought to mark M by touching the ground tip of the smaller capillary (end of arm B, figure $1E$) with absorbent paper, which removes the excess liquid.

C. CALCULATION OF DENSITY

Vapor Correction.—If, in measuring a volatile liquid, a pycnometer is used which encloses gas above the liquid level, the difference between the density of the enclosed gas (air + vapor) and the density of the outside air may cause a large error in the observed weight of the pycnometer contents. The correction, ΔW, to the weight of the filled pycnometer increases with: (1) an increasing partial pressure of vapor, which depends on how nearly saturated with vapor the air becomes, as well as on the vapor tension of the liquid; (2) an increasing difference between the molecular weights of the vapor (M_v) and of air; and (3) an increasing volume (V_g) of the enclosed gas space, as shown in the following equations:

$$\Delta W = V_g \left(d_{\text{air}} - d_{\text{air + vapor}} \right) \tag{16}$$

V_g is found experimentally and d_{air} is calculated by equation (24); $d_{\text{air + vapor}}$ can be estimated from the vapor tension of the liquid, P_v atm., the barometric pressure, P atm., and the room temperature, $t°$ C. ($T°$ K), according to equation (17), if the enclosed gas is saturated at atmospheric pressure and obeys the ideal gas laws with sufficient approximation:

$$d_{\text{air + vapor}} = \frac{P_v M_v}{RT} + \frac{(P - P_v)}{P} d_{\text{air}} \tag{17}$$

where R is the gas constant, 82.06 cc. $\times$ atm. Type B pycnometers (Fig. 1) always require a vapor correction. However, for types D, E, and F, the gas space can be kept free of vapor during weighing if the capillaries are sufficiently long and narrow.

Consider for example the determination at 20° C. of n-pentane ($M_v = 72$, $d = 0.61$) in a 25-ml. pycnometer of type B for which $V_g = 2.5$ ml. From tables we obtain $P_v = 425$ mm. $= 0.56$ atm. at $T = 293°$ K. Assuming $d_{\text{air}} = 0.0012$ g. per ml. and that the air is saturated at atmospheric pressure ($P = 760$ mm. $= 1.00$ atm.) we have:

$$d_{\text{air + vapor}} = 0.56 \times 72/82 \times 293 + 0.44 \times 0.0012 = 0.0022$$

Thus, $\Delta W = 2.5 \ (0.0012 - 0.0022) = -0.0025$ g. If the weight of the filled pycnometer was observed to be 15.2075 g. greater than that of the empty pycnometer, the corrected value for the weight of the liquid n-pentane would be 15.2050. Without the correction the value of d would have been in error by 1.7×10^{-4}.

Buoyancy Correction (Reduction of Weights to Vacuum).—A buoyancy correction must be applied to the apparent weight $(W' + W_{tare})$ of the *filled* pycnometer in order to obtain 5th place accuracy.   The magnitude of this correction depends on the weight of air displaced by each object on the balance pans, determined by the volume of each object and the density of the air.   The volume occupied by the glass of the pycnometer can be left out of the calculations of the buoyancy correction when a tare (dummy pycnometer) of weight $W_{tare} = W_{pyc.} \pm 1$ gram is used.   In this case, the difference between the buoyancy of the tare, $W_{tare}D_{air}/d_{glass}$, and that of the pycnometer, $W_{pyc.}D_{air}/d_{glass}$, is so small that it remains practically constant in all weighings;   thus, these two buoyancy effects practically cancel out.   It is more convenient if the tare weighs slightly *less* than the pycnometer itself than vice versa.   The volume of the weights and of the pycnometer contents can be calculated with sufficient accuracy if the density of each material is known to within about 2%.   In most cases the weights of large denomination are made of brass.   For 5th place accuracy, the error introduced by assuming $d_W = 8.5$ for all weights is negligible even when the small denomination weights $(<1$ gram) are made of some material of different density, such as aluminum or platinum.

The following derivation of the expression for the true weight difference (W) between the filled pycnometer and the tare should help eliminate trouble in applying the proper algebraic sign to the buoyancy correction: With the filled pycnometer on one balance pan and the tare on the other, the weights (W') are determined which must be added to the tare pan in order to bring about *apparent* equality between the masses on the right and left pans.   The buoyant effect of the air in the balance case contributes to the value of the apparent difference, W', since the downward force on each balance pan is *lessened* by an amount equal to the weight of the air displaced by the objects on it.   Thus, assuming that the buoyant force of tare and pycnometer balance each other, we have:

$$W' = W_{pyc.} + W_L - W_{tare} - V_p D_{air} + V_w D_{air} \qquad (18)$$

where $W_{pyc.}$, W_L, and W_{tare} refer to the *true* weights of the pycnometer, its liquid contents, and the tare, respectively. V_p and V_w refer to the volume of liquid contained by the full pycnometer and the volume of the weights, W', on the opposite pan, respectively. D_{air} is the density of the air.

But the true difference in masses (W) is given by:

$$W = W_{pyc.} + W_L - W_{tare} \qquad (19)$$

Thus, using a tare, we have by substitution in (18):

$$W = W' + V_p D_{air} - V_w D_{air} \qquad (20)$$

Usually W' is less than W because the weights used are almost always more dense than the liquid.

In using equation (20), it is evident that V_p can be found from:

$$V_p = W_{L0}/d_{L0} \tag{21}$$

where W_{L0} is the weight of liquid used in calibrating the pycnometer and d_{L0} its density. Similarly, for brass weights,

$$V_w = W'/d_w = W'/8.5 \tag{22}$$

i. e., equation (20) becomes:

$$W = W' + V_p \cdot D_{\text{air}} - \frac{W'}{8.5} \cdot D_{\text{air}} \tag{23}$$

where the unprimed symbol (W) refers to the true (vacuum-corrected) weight difference between filled pycnometer and tare.

It is obvious that a slightly modified form of equation (23) applies also to any instance in which the vessel is only partially filled, e. g., in the density determination of solids (page 101); in this case the factor V_p is replaced in equation (23) by W_S/d_S, where W_S refers to the weight of solid in the vessel and d_S to its density.

The magnitude of the buoyancy correction is about 0.1% of the weight W_L for a liquid of density $d \approx 1$. However, the correction need not be applied unless the required accuracy in d is about 0.005% because the error caused by neglecting the buoyancy of the liquid is partly cancelled by a similar error in the calibration with water.

Air Density.—It is often the practice always to use the same value of $D_{\text{air}} = 0.0012$ g. per ml. in making the correction of weights to vacuum. However, in pycnometry, the variation in D_{air} due to changes in room temperature ($t°$ C.), barometric pressure (P), and relative humidity (H) can be great enough (5% of D_{air}) to cause *changes* in the buoyancy correction between the time of calibration and measurement which affect the value of the density by several units in the 5th place. Thus, for an accuracy of $\pm 1 \times 10^{-5}$, it is advisable to record the value of t, P and H at the time of each weighing and calculate D_{air} from the formula:

$$D_{\text{air}} = \frac{0.001293}{1 + 0.00367t} \frac{(P - k)}{760} \tag{24}$$

where P is given in millimeters of mercury and k is a correction term which depends on the amount of moisture in the air. The value of k is calculated from the observed relative humidity, H, in per cent and the vapor pressure of water $P^t_{\text{H}_2\text{O}}$ in millimeters at $t°$ C. (given in standard tables) according to the relation:

$$k = 0.0038 H P^t_{\text{H}_2\text{O}} \tag{25}$$

It is convenient to prepare a set of linear graphs of D_{air} vs. $(P - k)$ from equation (24) for various values of t, from which the appropriate value of D_{air} can be quickly interpolated, as recommended by Weatherill and Brundage.[21]

Sample Calculation.—The following data were obtained for a sample of ethyl alcohol using a pycnometer of type D. A prime on the symbol W (e. g., W_2') indicates an *apparent* weight; the unprimed symbol (W_2) refers to the true, vacuum-corrected, weight.

Thermostat temperature, 25° C. $\pm$ 0.005°. W_{tare} is assumed constant.

Calibration

(1)   Apparent weight of empty pycnometer $(W_1' + W_{tare})$:

The empty pycnometer balances the tare and W_1' grams of brass weights; $W_1' = 1.1013_4$ g.

(2)   Apparent weight of pycnometer filled with V_p ml. of pure water at 25° C. $(W_2' + W_{tare})$:

Balance room $t = 30°$ C. $P = 740$ mm., $H = 75\%$.

The pycnometer filled with water balances the tare and W_2' grams of brass weights; $W_2' = 26.4251_4$ g.

Determination

(3)   Apparent weight of empty pycnometer $(W_3' + W_{tare})$:

The empty pycnometer balances the tare and W_3' grams of brass weights; $W_3' = 1.1012_8$ g.

(4) Apparent weight of pycnometer filled with V_p ml. of ethyl alcohol at 25° C. $(W_4' + W_{tare})$:

Balance room $t = 20°$ C. $P = 760$ mm., $H = 10\%$.   Vapor absent from cup.

The pycnometer filled with alcohol balances the tare and W_4' grams of brass weights; $W_4' = 21.0316_9$ g.

We now evaluate the *true* weight differences (W). Since the buoyancy corrections to W_1' and W_3' nearly cancel out in calculating d, we can use $W_1' = W_1$ and $W_3' = W_3$ for fifth place accuracy when $W_1 \leqslant 1$, $2 \geqslant d \geqslant 0.5$ and $V_p \geqslant 15$. Thus the value of W_{pyc} is $(1.1013_4 + W_{tare})$ for the calibration and $(1.1012_8 + W_{tare})$ for the determination. For the *filled* pycnometers W may be found from equation (23). In making the buoyancy corrections it is sufficiently accurate to calculate the value for the volume of liquid in the full pycnometer (V_p) with the uncorrected weights (W'). Accordingly (Eq. 21):

$$V_p \approx (W_2' - W_1')/d_4^{25}{}_{(H_2O)} \approx 25.325/0.997 = 25.40 \text{ ml.}$$

The air density during weighing (2) was (eq. 24):

$$D_{air} = \frac{0.001293}{1 + (0.00367)30} \cdot \frac{(740 - k)}{760}$$

[21] P. F. Weatherill and P. S. Brundage, *J. Am. Chem. Soc.*, 54, 3935 (1932).

where $k = (0.0038)(75)(31.8) = 9.1$, since $P_{H_2O} = 31.8$ mm. at $30°$ C.
Thus $D_{air} = 0.00112$ g./ml. Substituting in equation (23):

$$W_2 = 26.4251_4 + 0.00112 \left(25.40 - \frac{26.43}{8.5} \right)$$

$$W_2 = 26.4251_4 + 0.0249_7$$

$$W_2 = 26.4501_1$$

Thus the true weight of the pycnometer filled with water is $(26.4501_1 + W_{tare})$.

W_4 is obtained in a similar way. With P_{H_2O} $(20°$ C.) $= 17.5$ mm., for a humidity of 10%, using equations (24) and (25), $k = 0.7$ and $D_{air} = 0.00120$ g./ml.

$$W_4 = 21.0316_9 + 0.00120 \left(25.40 - \frac{21.06}{8.5} \right)$$

$$W_4 = 21.0316_9 + 0.0275_1$$

$$W_4 = 21.0592_0$$

Thus the true weight of the pycnometer filled with alcohol is $(21.0592_0 + W_{tare})$.

Volume of Pycnometer, V_p.—The true weight of water W_{H_2O} corresponding to V_p is given by $W_{H_2O} = W_2 - W_1 = 25.3487_7$. According to equation (2):

$$V_p = W_{H_2O}/d_4^{25}{}_{(H_2O)} = 25.3487_7/0.99707_5 = 25.4231_3 \text{ ml.}$$

Density of Sample.—The true weight of alcohol $W_{C_2H_5OH}$ corresponding to V_p is given by $W_{C_2H_5OH} = W_4 - W_3 = 19.9579_2$ g. According to equation (2):

$$d_4^{25}{}_{(C_2H_5OH)} = \frac{W_{C_2H_5OH}}{V_p} = \frac{19.9579_2}{25.4231_3} \text{ g./ml.}$$

$$d_4^{25} = 0.78503_0 \text{ g./ml.}$$

D. DILATOMETERS

The most convenient method of measuring densities of a given sample at many different temperatures with high precision ($d^{t_1} - d^{t_2}$ can be easily measured to $\pm 1 \times 10^{-5}$) depends on the principle of the dilatometer.

One form of weight dilatometer equivalent to that developed by Burlew,[22] is shown in figure 3. It is preferably made of vitreous silica so as to minimize the correction for thermal expansion of the vessel. The dilatometer is partly filled with mercury, and the remaining space with the liquid under investigation, L. The total volume is defined by the optically flat surfaces,

[22] R. E. Gibson and O. H. Loeffler, *J. Am. Chem. Soc.*, **61**, 2515 (1939).

S, and the tip, T, of the narrow mercury-filled capillary. This volume is determined at various temperatures by a calibration with mercury and water. When a certain amount of a liquid L is confined between S and the mercury surface and the temperature is raised, the expansion of L and of the mercury forces some of the latter out of the capillary into a previously weighed dish. By determining the weight of mercury in the dilatometer at both temperatures, the change in volume of L can be calculated if one also knows the change in volume of the dilatometer and the density of mercury at each temperature. The absolute value of the density at any temperature can be found by using the dilatometer as a pycnom-

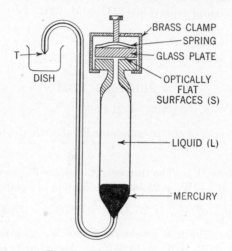

Fig. 3.—Weight dilatometer.

eter. In order to place into the dilatometer at any temperature a known amount of mercury so that the capillary is filled to tip T, the vessel is warmed while capillary tip T is immersed in a weighed dish of mercury. On cooling, some of the latter is sucked back into the dilatometer.

A detailed description of other convenient forms of the dilatometer is given by Gibson[23] and by Pesce and Hoelemann.[24] A more elaborate apparatus for especially precise work (1×10^{-6}) is described by Geffcken *et al.*[25] Tong and Olson[26] have described a dilatometer which is designed to allow measurements of reaction rate for cases involving an appreciable difference between the volumes of reactants and products. The effect of

[23] R. E. Gibson, *J. Phys. Chem.*, **31**, 498 (1927).

[24] B. Pesce and P. Hoelemann, *Z. Elektrochem.*, **40**, 1 (1934).

[25] W. Geffcken, A. Kruis, and L. Solana, *Z. physik. Chem.*, **B35**, 317 (1937).

[26] L. K. J. Tong and A. R. Olson, *J. Am. Chem. Soc.*, **65**, 1704 (1943).

the heat of reaction is taken into consideration. Observations of volume changes, instead of weight changes, are the basis of the method.

2. Buoyancy Methods

A number of methods for measuring density are based on Archimedes' principle, which states that the upward buoyant force exerted on a body immersed in a liquid is equal to the weight of the displaced liquid.

A. HYDROSTATIC WEIGHING METHOD OF KOHLRAUSCH (SUSPENDED SINKER)

An ordinary gravimetric balance can be adapted to high-precision density measurements by removing one of the pans and attaching to the balance arm a long, fine platinum wire at the end of which is fastened a cylinder of glass or metal ("sinker"). The wire passes through a hole in the platform of the balance so that the sinker may be conveniently immersed in a column of thermostated liquid placed below the balance case. The combined sinker and wire, whose effective volume, V, is known from a previous calibration with pure water, is weighed first in air (W_0'), then in the liquid (W_L'). The surface of the liquid is brought to the same mark on the platinum wire each time so that the wire always contributes the same (small) amount to the total volume, V, of immersed solid. The apparent loss in weight, $W_0 - W_L$, is equal to the mass of the displaced liquid, where W_0 and W_L refer to weights corrected for the buoyant effect of air (see Eq. 20, using $V_p = V$ for W_0; $V_p = 0$ for W_L). Thus, the density is:

$$d = (W_0 - W_L)/V \tag{26}$$

The Mohr-Westphal balance,[27] which is commercially available, is a direct-reading instrument based on the above principle, and can be used in certain cases (nonvolatile solutions, nonhygroscopic liquids) for the rapid measurement of d to a few units in the 3rd place.

The hydrostatic weighing method is rapid, lends itself readily to measurements of a given sample at a number of different temperatures, when the volume of the sinker is known as a function of temperature, and can give very precise results. Under optimum conditions,[28] the reproducibility of the measurements of d is as high as $\pm 2 \times 10^{-6}$; for the directly observed *difference*, $\Delta d = d - d_0$, between solution and solvent, the reproducibility has been increased to $\pm 3 \times 10^{-7}$ by Redlich and Bigeleisen.[29] However,

[27] J. Reilly and W. N. Rae, *Physico-chemical Methods.* 3rd ed., Vol. I, Van Nostrand, New York, 1939, p. 500.

[28] H. E. Wirth, *J. Am. Chem. Soc.*, **59**, 2549 (1937); W. Prang, *Ann. Physik*, **31**, 681 (1938)

[29] O. Redlich and J. Bigeleisen, *J. Am. Chem. Soc.*, **64**, 758 (1942).

the values obtained by this method are subject to an uncertainty arising from the surface tension effect between the liquid surface and the wire. This effect is strongly influenced by the presence of impurities. With a wire which is platinized in the region at which it contacts the liquid surface, the error caused by a change in surface tension is probably not greater than 1×10^{-5} in the absolute value of d, provided the wire is 0.1 mm. or less in diameter. Schulz[30] has described a vessel for immersing the sinker which is especially suited to the precision measurement of solutions of volatile or hydroscopic organic liquids. An accuracy of $\pm 1 \times 10^{-5}$ is obtained using about 50 ml. of sample.

B. ELASTIC HELIX (SUSPENDED FLOAT)

An ingenious device for precise, rapid measurements of the density of both liquids and vapors has been described by Wagner, Bailey, and Eversole.[31] A quartz float is attached to an elastic quartz helix and mounted in a long thermostated tube containing the fluid under investigation. The float end of the helix is free to move so that the helix is stretched by the buoyant force acting on the float. The density of the medium can be found from the change in length of the helix.

This method has two particular advantages: it responds rapidly to changes in density; and it is suited to investigations in which the fluid must be kept in a closed system. The accuracy of the method is limited only by the precision of the temperature and pressure control, assuming that a large amount of sample is available. The authors report that, with a float of 1.35 ml. attached to an unstretched helix 4 cm. long and 0.9 cm. in diameter, the density of water was obtained to within ± 0.00003 over the temperature range from $10°$ to $35°$. The method is evidently very well suited to following the course of a reaction. Unfortunately, there is a great amount of labor involved in the calibration of the helix.

C. FREE FLOATS

Hydrometers may be mentioned without much further discussion. These instruments are well known and suitable for rough determinations only. Even with large amounts of sample (25 to 50 ml.), the accuracy is not higher than ± 0.001, and each liquid requires a different calibration due to differences in surface tension. However, on the principle that a *totally* submerged solid object will neither rise nor fall when its effective density is exactly equal to that of the immersing liquid depend the most accurate methods for measuring small density differences (Δd) between two liquids.

---

[30] G. V. Schulz, *Z. physik. Chem.*, **B40**, 151 (1938).

[31] G. H. Wagner, G. C. Bailey, and W. G. Eversole, *Ind. Eng. Chem.*, *Anal. Ed.*, **14**, 129 (1942).

The exact condition of floating equilibrium is usually ascertained by direct observation of the float with a telescope. This method has been used for measuring small changes in isotope content.[32]

Various methods have been used for changing the effective density of the float relative to that of the liquid so as to accommodate a single apparatus to a variety of liquids. Most successful is the method of Lamb and Lee[33] who used a magnetically controlled float. A small bar of iron was sealed into the tail of the float. By passing a proper amount of current through an adjacent solenoid, a magnetic force could be applied which was just strong enough to balance the upward buoyant force. The greater the current required to obtain equilibrium, the greater is the density of the liquid. By placing various weights on top of the float, a wide range of densities could be covered with a single float. An accuracy of about $\pm 1 \times 10^{-7}$ in Δd was obtained. Subsequent refinements were made, especially by Geffcken *et al.*,[34] who used a differential method allowing the direct comparison of relatively small amounts (~ 60 ml.) of two solutions. The extremely high accuracy of $\pm 2 \times 10^{-8}$ in Δd was obtained, corresponding to concentration differences of about 0.1 mg. sodium chloride per liter of aqueous solution. The technique is laborious.

A simplified more practical version of the magnetically controlled float has been described in detail by Richards.[35] His "electromagnetic densitometer" was used to measure 200 small samples (5 ml. each) of petroleum oil every 8 hours. The values of d can be read directly from a graph of d *vs.* the solenoid current. A calibration was made with known liquids, and an accuracy of 1% in d was obtained. Measurements with this particular model were limited to the range $d = 0.62$ to $d = 0.82$ to avoid sacrifices in accuracy. However, the range of this type of densitometer can be shifted or widened, depending on the design; and, in principle, both the range and the accuracy can be increased at the same time by making the float so that its weight may be changed by the addition of some dense metal, as in the method of Lamb and Lee.[33]

There are other methods for controlling the free float:

(*1*) The temperature of the liquid is varied until the density of the liquid becomes equal to that of the float. This "temperature of flotation" is nearly a linear function of the concentration[36] for a given solute, and is

[32] See, for example, N. F. Hall and O. R. Alexander, *J. Am. Chem. Soc.*, **62**, 3455 (1940); H. J. Emeleus *et al.*, *J. Chem. Soc.*, **1934**, 1210.

[33] A. B. Lamb and R. E. Lee, *J. Am. Chem. Soc.*, **35**, 1668 (1913).

[34] W. Geffcken, C. Beckmann, and A. Kruis, *Z. physik. Chem.*, **B20**, 398 (1933). See also N. F. Hall and T. O. Jones, *J. Am. Chem. Soc.*, **58**, 1915 (1936).

[35] A. R. Richards, *Ind. Eng. Chem., Anal. Ed.*, **14**, 595 (1942).

[36] T. W. Richards and J. W. Shipley, *J. Am. Chem. Soc.*, **36**, 1 (1914).

used principally as a measure of small concentration changes. Randall and Longtin[37] have adapted the method to small amounts of solution (0.1 ml.).

(2)   The pressure on the liquid is changed until floating equilibrium is established.[38] The method is suitable for the routine detection of small differences ($\Delta d < 10^{-4}$). With special care in checking the constancy of the float calibration, it may be used to detect differences as small as 10^{-7}. The float can be made so that its volume changes considerably with pressure, thus making the rising or falling very sensitive to pressure changes (Cartesian diver).   Gilfillan and Polanyi[39] describe a "Cartesian diver" float which is attached to a capillary containing the sample. By immersing this float in a reference liquid, very small amounts (5×10^{-3} ml.) can be compared directly with the standard.

D.   FALLING DROP

The falling drop method of Barbour and Hamilton,[40] which is especially useful for the rapid precision measurement of small amounts of liquid, is based on the following principle: An insoluble spherical drop falling through a given liquid will acquire a constant velocity, v, characteristic of its size and density. This steady state is reached when the gravitational, frictional, and buoyancy forces are just balanced. All other things being constant, the rate of fall is proportional to the *difference* $(d_1 - d_0)$ between the density d_1 of the drop and d_0 of the medium (Stokes law), that is:

$$v_1 = k(d_1 - d_0) \tag{27}$$

By finding the time t required for the drop to fall through a fixed distance x ($x \approx 30$ cm.), it is possible to determine accurately the density of drops as small as 0.001 ml. provided that an appropriate calibration has been made with known liquids.   Thus, since $x = v_1 t_1$, it is apparent from equation (27) that for a given medium and a given drop size:

$$t_2/t_1 = (d_1 - d_0)/(d_2 - d_0) \tag{28}$$

where t_2 refers to the time of fall through the same distance x for a drop of known density d_2. Actually, equation (28) cannot always be applied. In general, an empirical calibration curve of d vs. t is used. According to

[37] M. Randall and B. Longtin, *Ind. Eng. Chem., Anal. Ed.*, **11**, 44 (1939).

[38] See, for example, E. S. Gilfillan, Jr., *J. Am. Chem. Soc.*, **56**, 406 (1934).

[39] E. S. Gilfillan, Jr., and M. Polanyi, *Z. physik. Chem.*, **A166**, 254 (1933).

[40] H. G. Barbour and W. F. Hamilton, *J. Biol. Chem.*, **69**, 625 (1926). See also R. H. Barbour, Jr., *Yale J. Biol. Med.*, **14**, 107 (1941).

Hochberg and LaMer,[41] there is a deviation from the simple linear relation between d and $(1/t)$ (Eq. 28) which becomes greater, the greater the velocity of the drop, *i. e.*, the greater the distortion of the drop from a perfect sphere. By making appropriate corrections, these authors were able to report values of Δd to $\pm 1 \times 10^{-5}$. The distortion effect is negligible for an accuracy of $\pm 1 \times 10^{-4}$, so equation (28) may be used in this case if the apparatus has been designed to eliminate other disturbing factors such as convection currents in the medium.

The apparatus required for the falling drop method is very simple. It consists chiefly of a tall, jacketed cylinder having two fine marks separated by the distance x, a stop watch, and a micropipette[42] for delivering droplets of uniform size. A convenient apparatus for rapid measurements good to ± 0.001 has been described in detail by Hoiberg,[43] who applied the method to petroleum oils using alcohol–water media. Falling drop gravitometers are available commercially.[44]

There are certain limitations to the applicability of the falling drop method:

(*1*) The range of densities which can be measured with a given medium is relatively small. In order to obtain an accuracy of ± 0.001, the difference between the densities of the liquid and the medium cannot be greater than about 0.05. Thus a large number of independently calibrated units would have to be set up and used by trial and error if the method were to be applied to a wide variety of unknown liquids.

(*2*) Difficulty may be encountered in finding a liquid medium which is not miscible with the sample and which has a density fairly close to that of the sample.

(*3*) Better temperature control is required for the falling drop than for any other differential method in order to minimize the effect of convection currents. Hoiberg[43] finds that a control to $\pm 0.2°$ is required for an accuracy of ± 0.001.

The falling drop method is well suited to the rapid routine detection of small changes in concentration. It was first developed as a rapid hospital technique for detecting changes in the composition of blood. A complete measurement of Δd can be made every minute or so if the samples are similar.

[41] S. Hochberg and V. K. LaMer, *Ind. Eng. Chem., Anal. Ed.*, **9**, 291 (1937).

[42] F. Rosebury and W. E. van Heyningen, *Ind. Eng. Chem., Anal. Ed.*, **14**, 363 (1942); K. Fenger-Erickson, A. Krogh, and H. Ussing, *Biochem. J.*, **30**, 1264 (1936).

[43] A. J. Hoiberg, *Ind. Eng. Chem., Anal. Ed.*, **14**, 323 (1942).

[44] LaMotte Falling Drop Densiometer, *LaMotte Chemical Products Co.*, Towson, Baltimore, Md. Eimer and Amend Falling Drop Apparatus, *Eimer and Amend*, New York, N. Y.

3. Balanced Column Method

Ciochina[45] has described a very simple device which is suited to the rapid measurement of liquids which must be kept in a closed system, e. g., volatile liquids. The relatively high accuracy of ±0.0005 is possible and only 1 or 2 ml. of the liquid is required. The method is based on the principle that the hydrostatic pressure of a given height of liquid is proportional to the density of the liquid. In Ciochina's apparatus, the liquid of unknown density d is contained in a U tube (diameter, 2 mm.) through one arm of which an arbitrary pressure is applied. The resulting difference Δh in the height of the liquid menisci in the two arms of the tube is measured on a millimeter scale and is compared with the difference Δh_0 obtained when the *same* pressure is simultaneously applied to a liquid of known density d_0 in a similar U tube. The density is then calculated from the relation:

$$d/d_0 = \Delta h_0/\Delta h \qquad (29)$$

Alternatively, the millimeter scale may be calibrated to read directly in terms of d by using a number of known liquids.

The range may be extended by using various reference liquids or by increasing the height of the U tube. The apparatus can be easily constructed in the laboratory from glass tubing and a few stopcocks. A compact, direct-reading instrument of this type, known as the Fisher-Davidson gravitometer, is available commercially.[46] This instrument covers the range from $d = 0.60$ to $d = 2.00$ with an accuracy of about ±0.005, and requires from 0.3 to 0.7 ml. of sample, depending on the substance. Frivold[47] has described a balanced column method for measuring small *differences* in density with an accuracy of about $\pm 2 \times 10^{-7}$.

4. Measurements with Small Quantities of Liquids

The requirements of micro density methods suitable for the characterization of organic substances have been reviewed by Alber.[48] Amounts of liquid less than about 0.020 ml. are considered to be microsamples.

Micromethods which are applicable in special cases are the falling drop method (page 94) and the "Schlieren" method[48, 49] which is based on the microscopic observation of the striations produced when the unknown liquid flows into a liquid of known density. The technique for the latter is

[45] J. Ciochina, Z. anal. Chem., **107**, 108 (1936); **98**, 416 (1934). See also E. Wiedbrauck, Z. anorg. Chem., **122**, 167 (1922).

[46] *Fisher Scientific Co.*, Pittsburgh, Pa.

[47] O. E. Frivold, Physik. Z., **21**, 529 (1920).

[48] H. K. Alber, Ind. Eng. Chem., Anal. Ed., **12**, 764 (1940).

[49] J. Gicklhorn, Mikrochemie, **22**, 1 (1937).

laborious, but accurate to ±0.0005 even on samples as small as 0.003 ml.

Micropycnometric methods are applicable to all liquids and involve no appreciable loss of sample. A simple pipette made from a piece of straight capillary tubing is a convenient micropycnometer. With liquids of low viscosity, the capillary ends may have an inner diameter as small as 0.005 mm., thus reducing loss by evaporation. The accuracy may be improved by placing ground glass caps over the ends. The ease of handling and the accuracy of defining the volume are both greatly enhanced by using several calibrated reference marks along the length of the capillary (compare type *F*, Fig. 1), so no tedious additions or removal of liquid are necessary. Using a microbalance, an accuracy of about 0.1% can be obtained with samples as small as 2 mg. For 4th place accuracy, 20-mg. samples are required. In these cases, no buoyancy correction for the weights is required if a tare is used.

Furter[50] has described a technique for using the graduated pipette micropycnometer at temperatures up to 300° C., thus providing for the relatively simple characterization of many substances which are solid at room temperature.

IV. MEASUREMENT OF DENSITY OF SOLIDS

1. General. Preparation of Samples

The methods for solids are considerably less exact than those for liquids, part of the uncertainty being due to the inhomogeneities (cracks, trapped air bubbles, occluded mother liquor) which all crystals have to some degree. The density of individual crystals taken at random from the same source may vary as much as 5%. The effect of inhomogeneities may be minimized by using crystal fragments obtained by cooling the molten substance. To eliminate cracks and strains, the fused solid should be crushed into a coarse powder. The technique of growing large homogeneous crystals from melts has so far been applied mainly to simple inorganic compounds.[51] Its more extended application to organic crystals would allow a considerable improvement in the accuracy of the density measurements.[52] No matter what method of preparation is used, more than one sample should be measured. Practically all methods of measurement depend on immersing the solid in some inert liquid of known density. The choice of the immersion liquid will depend on the solid and on the method. If no liquid is available in which the solid is completely insoluble, a satu-

[50] I. M. Furter, *Helv. Chim. Acta*, **21**, 1666 (1938).

[51] S. Kyropoulous, *Z. anorg. Chem.*, **154**, 308 (1926).

[52] S. B. Hendricks and M. E. Jefferson, *J. Optical Soc. Am.*, **23**, 299 (1933).

rated solution may be used, provided the temperature coefficient of solubility is not too large. If possible, liquids with a small compressibility and a small affinity for the solid should be used, especially when the sample is a fine powder. Culbertson and Weber[53] have presented evidence which indicates that, for samples with large surfaces, significant errors can arise in the density determination due to a compression of the immersion liquid at the interface.

2. Displacement Methods

A. VOLUMENOMETERS

Volumenometers allow one to evaluate the volume of a known weight of solid from the volume, V_{DL}, of a fluid which is displaced by the submerged solid. A bottle such as that of type D in figure 1, filled with liquid up to mark M on the neck, serves as a volumenometer. A known weight, W_S, of an insoluble solid is dropped into the liquid through the neck tube. If the density, d_S, of the solid is greater than that of the liquid, the level of liquid in the tube will be raised above M by an amount, Δh, which corresponds to the volume, V_S, of the W_S grams of solid added. We then have:

$$d_S = W_S/V_{DL} = W_S/(\Delta h)A \tag{30}$$

where V_{DL} is the volume of the displaced liquid and A is the uniform cross-sectional area of the tube.

The value of A can be found from the tube's inner diameter or by a calibration with known weights of some standard liquid. The change in level (Δh) can be found with a cathetometer or, more simply, from a calibrated scale placed on or in back of the tubular neck. An accuracy of about 1% is possible with this method. Another convenient form of volumenometer is described in Ostwald-Luther.[54] Blank and Willard[55] describe a mercury-filled volumenometer for measuring to within about 5% especially small samples (0.03 ml.) with densities less than 13.6. Some dilatometers (see page 86) can be used as volumenometers.

In cases where it is not desirable to immerse the solid in a liquid, some gas, $e. g.$, air, may be used as the medium which is displaced.[56] The method is seriously handicapped by the effect of gas adsorption, although an accuracy of from 0.1 to 1.0% is possible under favorable conditions.

[53] J. L. Culbertson and M. K. Weber, $J. Am. Chem. Soc.$, **60**, 2695 (1938).

[54] Ostwald-Luther, $Physiko-chemische Messungen.$ 5th ed., Akadem. Verlagsgesellschaft, Leipzig, 1931, p. 240.

[55] E. W. Blank and M. L. Willard, $J. Chem. Ed.$, **10**, 109 (1933).

[56] J. Reilly and W. N. Rae, $Physico-chemical Methods.$ 3rd ed., Vol. I, Van Nostrand, New York, 1939, p. 470. For the technique at low temperatures, see W. Biltz $et al.$, $Z. physik. Chem.$, **A151**, 1 (1930)

B. PYCNOMETERS

Ordinary liquid pycnometers (Fig. 1, types A, B, C) can be used for solids. The principle of the method is practically the same as that already discussed for volumenometers. In the pycnometric method, the volume of the solid is more accurately found by determining the changes in *weight* when the vessel is successively filled with a liquid of known density, solid plus air, and solid plus liquid. It is advisable to determine the density of the immersion liquid with the same pycnometer in the usual way.

With due precautions, an accuracy of about ± 0.0005 in d_{solid} can be achieved, using several grams of solid. The pycnometer tends to give for solids values of d which are too small. The principal drawback to the pycnometric method is the difficulty of completely removing all the air or moisture trapped by the solid. To minimize this effect, the liquid in contact with the solid should be boiled under low pressure for 10 or 15 minutes. The addition of wetting agents is sometimes necessary; and it may also be desirable to provide special means for agitating the solid.[57] A valuable discussion of this occlusion effect and of other sources of error in the pycnometric method is given by Wulff and Heigl.[58] Baxter and Hawkins[59] have described the technique to be used with extremely hygroscopic solids.

Sample Determination

The following example illustrates the operations and calculations involved in the pycnometric method when 4th place accuracy is required. The techniques of filling with liquid and adjusting the volume are the same as those described on pages 82 *et seq.*

With a pycnometer of type C (Fig. 1), a sample of granular diphenyl is measured in the following way, using water as the displacement liquid. Here, as for liquids (page 88), the unprimed symbol, W, *e. g.*, W_2, refers to the *true* (corrected to vacuum) weight.

(1) Weight of Pycnometer Filled with Liquid $(W_1 + W_{tare})$.—The pycnometer is filled to the top with pure liquid (water) at 25° C. and weighed, using a tare. The air density in the balance room, D_{air}, is 0.00115 g./ml. At the rest point, the balance is loaded as follows:

Left pan	*Right pan*
Tare (*true* weight = W_{tare})	Pycnometer completely filled with liquid
$+$	(*true* weight = $W_{pyc.} + W_{L0}$)
W_1' grams of brass weights	

Apparent weight difference $W_1' = 11.7865$ g.

[57] E. L. Gooden, *Ind. Eng. Chem., Anal. Ed.*, **15**, 578 (1943).

[58] P. Wulff and A. Heigl, *Z. physik. Chem.*, **A153**, 187 (1931).

[59] G. P. Baxter and C. F. Hawkins, *J. Am. Chem. Soc.*, **38**, 266 (1916).

In order to correct W_1' for the buoyancy effect of air according to equation (23), we must know the volume of liquid, V_p, contained by the full pycnometer. [The corrections to W_1' and W_4' due to the buoyancy effect of the volume V_p will practically cancel out in the calculation of d_{solid} (compare Eqs. 23 and 39) if the air density remains constant. However, a change in D_{air} of as much as 5% can occur in the laboratory. Therefore the effect of V_p should be included in the calculation of the buoyancy when 4th place accuracy is required.]

The value of V_p can be estimated with more than sufficient accuracy from the uncorrected weights W_1' and W_2', given below. From equation (21): $V_p = W_{L0}/d_L$. But $W_{L0} \approx W_1' + (W_{\text{tare}} - W_{\text{pyc.}})$ from (31), assuming $W_1' = W_1$. Substituting $(W_{\text{tare}} - W_{\text{pyc.}}) \approx - W_2'$ from equation (32), assuming $W_2' = W_2$, we have $W_{L0} \approx W_1' - W_2'$ and $V_p \approx (W_1' - W_2')/d_L$. In certain cases, e. g., where $W_2 < 1$ g., $W_{\text{solid}} > 1$ g., and $d_{\text{solid}} < 3$ g./ml., it is permissible, for 4th place accuracy, to neglect W_2' and use simply $V_p \approx W_1'/d_L$ in correcting both W_1' and W_4' for the effect of V_p.

We estimate in this case that $V_p \approx (11.79 - 1.21)/0.997 = 10.62$ ml. Substituting in equation (23):

True weight difference $W_1 = W_1' + \left(10.62 - \dfrac{11.79}{8.5} \right) 0.00115$

$$W_1 = 11.7865 + 0.0106 = 11.7971$$

It is evident that:

$$W_1 + W_{\text{tare}} \equiv 11.7961 + W_{\text{tare}} = W_{\text{pyc.}} + W_{L0} \qquad (31)$$

The above and subsequent corrections of the weights W' for the buoyant effect of air may be omitted, i. e., W' used for W, if only 3rd place accuracy is required. (2) *Weight of Empty Pycnometer* $(W_2 + W_{\text{tare}})$.—The liquid is removed and the pycnometer dried and weighed, using the same tare. Again $D_{\text{air}} = 0.00115$. At the rest point the balance is loaded as follows:

Left pan	*Right pan*
Tare (*true* weight $= W_{\text{tare}}$)	Empty pycnometer (*true* weight $=$
$+$	$W_{\text{pyc.}}$)
W_2' grams of brass weights	

Apparent weight difference $W_2' = 1.2059$ g.

If one uses W_2' for W_2 in equation (39), the error in d_S is less than 0.03% when $W_2' \lessgtr 1$, $W_3 > 2$ and $d_S < 3$. Thus the value $W_2 = 1.2059$ is sufficiently accurate.

It is evident that:

$$W_2 + W_{\text{tare}} \equiv 1.2059 + W_{\text{tare}} = W_{\text{pyc.}} \qquad (32)$$

(3) *Weight of Pycnometer Partially Filled with Solid* $(W_3 + W_{\text{tare}})$.—About 2 grams of the solid diphenyl are put into the dry, empty pycnometer, which is now weighed,

using the same tare. Again $D_{air} = 0.00115$ g./ml. At the rest point the balance is loaded as follows:

Left pan	Right pan
Tare (*true* weight = W_{tare})	Pycnometer partially filled with solid
+	(*true* weight = $W_{pyc.} + W_S$)
W_3' grams of brass weights	

Apparent weight difference $W_3' = 3.5521$ g.

The buoyancy correction is applied according to a modified form of equation (23) in the form:

$$W = W' + \left(\frac{W_S}{d_S} - \frac{W'}{8.5}\right) D_{air}$$

by estimating the density of the solid to be $d_S = 1.18$ g./ml. and by estimating the weight of solid to be $W_S \approx W_3' - W_4' = 2.35$ g. The true weight difference is:

$$W_3 = 3.5521 + \left(\frac{2.35}{1.18} - \frac{3.55}{8.5}\right) 0.00115$$

$$W_3 = 3.5521 + 0.0018 = 3.5539$$

It is evident that:

$$W_3 + W_{tare} \equiv 3.5539 + W_{tare} = W_{pyc.} + W_S \tag{33}$$

If a rough value of d_S (accurate to $\pm 2\%$) is not available, it may be found with more than sufficient accuracy by making a preliminary calculation identical with the one in the above example, except that weights W_1', W_2', W_3', and W_4' are not corrected to vacuum, *i. e.*, by the use of the values of W' in equation (39).

(4) *Weight of Pycnometer Completely Filled with (Solid + Liquid)* $(W_4 + W_{tare})$.— The solid in the weighed pycnometer is covered with water and the air removed by placing the pycnometer inside a tube which is evacuated while the solid is vigorously agitated. A simple calculation with the vapor pressure of diphenyl (~ 0.03 mm. at 25° C.) shows that a negligible quantity (0.1 mg.) of the solid is lost by evaporation, provided not more than about 150 ml. of saturated gas escapes from the pycnometer. Assuming the free volume inside the tube to be 15 ml., it is therefore safe to repeat the evacuation about ten times, stopping each time when boiling of the liquid occurs. The liquid is then brought to the top at 25° C., leaving W_L ($< W_{Lc}$) grams of liquid in the pycnometer, which is now weighed using the same tare. The air density has changed to $D_{air} = 0.00120$. At the rest point the balance is loaded as follows:

Left pan	Right pan
Tare (*true* weight = W_{tare})	Pycnometer completely filled with (solid +
+	liquid)
W_4' grams of brass weights	(*true* weight = $W_{pyc.} + W_S + W_L$)

Apparent weight difference $W_4' = 12.1416$ g.

The buoyancy correction is applied according to equation (23) in the form:

$$W_4 = W_4' + \left(V_p - \frac{W_4'}{8.5} \right) D_{air} = 12.1416 + \left(10.62 - \frac{12.14}{8.5} \right) 0.00120$$

where the volume contained by the pycnometer, $V_p = 10.62$ ml., from page 100.

$$W_4 = 12.1416 + 0.0110 = 12.1526$$

It is evident that:

$$W_4 + W_{tare} \equiv 12.1526 + W_{tare} = W_{pyc.} + W_s + W_L \qquad (34)$$

Pycnometric Formula for d_S.—The fundamental equation for the calculation of the density, d_S, of the solid is:

$$d_S = W_S/V_{DL} \qquad (35)$$

(see Eq. 30), where V_{DL} is the volume corresponding to W_S grams of the solid. The value of V_{DL} can be found from the true weight W_{DL} of liquid which would have been displaced if W_S grams of the solid had been put into the completely liquid-filled pycnometer and from its known density, d_L:

$$V_{DL} = W_{DL}/d_L \qquad (36)$$

But it is evident from equations (31) to (34) that:

$$W_{DL} = W_{L_0} - W_L = (W_1 - W_2) - (W_4 - W_3) \qquad (37)$$

where all the values of W refer to *true* (vacuum-corrected) weight differences. From equations (32) and (33):

$$W_S = W_3 - W_2 \qquad (38)$$

Substituting equation (36), (37), and (38) into (35), we have the pycnometric formula for the density d_S in terms of the four corrected weight differences obtained in the above four operations:

$$d_S = \frac{W_3 - W_2}{W_1 - W_2 + W_3 - W_4} \cdot d_L \qquad (39)$$

where W_1, W_2, W_3, and W_4 are defined above under (*1*), (*2*), (*3*), and (*4*), respectively. Substituting the appropriate numerical values for the above example of diphenyl, the following density value[52] is obtained:

$$d_4^{25} = \frac{3.5539 - 1.2059}{11.7971 - 1.2059 + 3.5539 - 12.1526} \cdot 0.99707 = 1.175_0 \text{ g./ml.}$$

For third place accuracy, one uses corresponding *uncorrected* weights (W') in equation (39) and applies the correction[59a] $0.0012 (1 - d_S/d_L)$.

3. Buoyancy Methods

The application of Archimedes' principle (page 91) furnishes the most precise and reliable way of measuring solids. All of these buoyancy meth-

---

[59a] J. Johnston and L. H. Adams, *J. Am. Chem. Soc.*, **34**, 568 (1912).

ods, except the hydrostatic weighing method, are somewhat limited by the necessity of finding a liquid mixture in which the solid does not rapidly or appreciably dissolve.

A. FREE FLOTATION

When a solid neither rises nor falls through a liquid in which it is submerged, the densities of the solid and the liquid are equal. It is then only necessary to determine the density of the liquid. The method is, of course, limited to those solids for which can be found an immersion medium of sufficient density. The upper limit of d for liquids is about 3.3 grams per milliliter, which is sufficiently high to include most organic solids. There are several ways of applying the free flotation method. All have the advantage that crystals having inclusions of gases or liquids may be easily detected and rejected, since they will, in general, float in a medium which is not dense enough to float the more perfect ones.

Precision Technique of Wulff and Heigl.—Wulff and Heigl[58] have described a useful apparatus based on the original free flotation method of Retgers.[60] By arranging for temperature control to $\pm 0.02°$, for transfer of the liquid to the pycnometer without danger of evaporation, and by other improvements, these authors were able to measure the densities of crystals weighing 0.1 mg. with an accuracy of $\pm 0.005\%$. The composition of the liquid mixture was changed continuously by the addition of one component and by the carefully regulated flow of dry air, which serves to mix the liquids and to evaporate the more volatile component. When the solid particles have zero velocity, as shown by observation with a telescope, the liquid is forced into the attached pycnometer by air pressure.

Centrifuge Method.—The convenience and speed of Retgers' method can be increased by subjecting the solid particles to an increased gravitational field. In addition, this allows measurements on very small samples.

Bernal and Crowfoot[61] describe the application of the centrifuge to this purpose. A two-component liquid mixture, made up to about the proper density, is added to a few particles of the solid in a centrifuge tube and then centrifuged at 2000–4000 r.p.m. for a few minutes. Some of the heavier or the lighter component is added to the mixture, depending on whether the crystals have fallen or risen in the tube. This is repeated until the suspended particles do not appreciably move when centrifuged. At this point, $d_{solid} = d_{liquid}$. A sample of the liquid is removed and measured to ± 0.001. In this way, Bernal and Crowfoot found the density of $C_{21}H_{16}$

---

[60] J. W. Retgers, *Z. physik. Chem.*, **3**, 289 (1899).
[61] J. D. Bernal and D. Crowfoot, *Nature*, **134**, 809 (1934).

$(d = 1.244)$ with an accuracy of ±0.002, using only 0.05 mg. of sample. A higher accuracy is possible when larger crystals and a more powerful centrifuge are used.[52]

Temperature Variation Method.—The temperature of the immersion liquid, which is controllable to $\pm0.001°$, can be changed until the solid just floats. This method is convenient for a large number of accurate determinations on samples which have nearly the same density. Hutchison and Johnston[62] have used it to detect density differences as small as 1×10^{-6}. The coefficient of expansion of the immersion liquid, as well as its density, must be known or measured.

B. HYDROSTATIC WEIGHING

The convenient, rapid method (see page 91) of finding apparent loss in weight by weighing a solid first in air, then immersed in a liquid, can be applied to a wide variety of samples. For large homogeneous specimens it can give results with a higher accuracy ($\sim0.001\%$) than any other method. If the sample is a powder, it is placed in a cup suspended from the balance arm by a fine platinum wire. The hydrostatic method, like the pycnometric, has the advantage that the immersion liquid may have any density smaller than that of the solid. Moreover, a saturated solution of the solid may be used as the immersion liquid. The latter should have low viscosity and surface tension. Care must be exercised to prevent air bubbles from being trapped by the sample or the cup. The density of the solid, d_S, is calculated from the relation:

$$d_S = \frac{W_0}{W_0 - W_L} \cdot d_L \tag{40}$$

where d_L refers to the density of the liquid and W_0 and W_L to the weight of solid in a vacuum and in the liquid, respectively. Using a cup of true weight W_C, the corrected value of W_L is $(W_L' - W_C - B' + B_{CL})$, where weights W_L' balance the immersed sample + cup and $B' = V_W d_{air}$ (see page 86) is the buoyancy of W_L'; $B_{CL} = (W_C - W_{CL})$, i. e, B_{CL} is the buoyancy of an immersed cup weighing W_{CL} in the liquid. An identical immersed tare, used opposite the cup, eliminates the correction B_{CL}.

The method is especially convenient when the weighings are made with a torsion microbalance.[58, 63] Suitable balances of this type are available commercially.[64] For samples of 5 to 25 mg., the Berman density balance,

[62] C. A. Hutchison and H. L. Johnston, *J. Am. Chem. Soc.*, **62**, 3165 (1940).

[63] H. Berman, *Am. Mineral.*, **24**, 434 (1939).

[64] *Baird Associates*, Cambridge, Mass. (Berman density balance); *Fisher Scientific Co.*, Pittsburgh, Pa.; *Will Corporation*, Rochester, N. Y.

equipped with weighing pans and wire suspension, is very satisfactory. It gives an accuracy of as high as 0.2% on 25-mg. samples. The effect of surface tension is cancelled out by letting an extension of the wire dip into the liquid while weighing in air. This principle might also be applied to the hydrostatic weighing method for liquids (see page 91). When samples as large as 500 mg. are available, the accuracy can be increased to about 0.02% by using an ordinary microbalance for the weighing in air, while still using the less accurate but more convenient torsion balance for the weighing in liquid. In this case the relative error ($\nabla d/d$) in the density is given by:[58]

$$\frac{\nabla d_S}{d_S} = \frac{1}{W_0} \cdot \frac{d_S}{d_L} (\nabla W) \tag{41}$$

where ∇W is the error of the weighing in the liquid. With a suitable torsion balance, samples of 500 mg. can be weighed with an error of only about 0.1 mg. It is evident from equation (41) that the density of the immersion liquid should be as great as possible.

When using the torsion balance, it is worth while to inspect the sample under the microscope, since the required number of crystal fragments is relatively small. Any fragments showing inhomogeneities are rejected.

V. GUIDE FOR THE SELECTION OF METHODS

Table II is designed to facilitate the selection of methods best suited to various types of problems. It is clear that such a table cannot include all possible problems and therefore should be used mainly for purposes of orientation. In most cases, a detailed comparison of various methods should be undertaken before a selection is made.

TABLE II

RECOMMENDED METHODS FOR VARIOUS SPECIAL PROBLEMS

Conditions required	Method recommended	Maximum precision, g./ml. ($d \approx 1$)	Described on page
PURE LIQUIDS			
Rapidity	Stopper pyc. (type B)	$\pm 5 \times 10^{-5}$	77 / 84
High precision	Capillary pyc. (type D)	$\pm 5 \times 10^{-6}$	79 / 84
SOLUTIONS OR PURE LIQUIDS			
Volatile and/or hygroscopic component	Bicapillary pyc. (type E or F)	$\pm 5 \times 10^{-6}$	80 / 84
Rapidity, routine	Electrodensitometer or	$\pm 5 \times 10^{-3}$	93
	Mohr-Westphal balance	$\pm 5 \times 10^{-3}$	91
	or balanced column	$\pm 5 \times 10^{-4}$	96

TABLE II (Continued)

SOLUTIONS OR PURE LIQUIDS

Conditions required	Method recommended	Maximum precision, g./ml. $(d \approx 1)$	Described on page
Precision, routine, rapidity	Hydrostatic weighing or falling drop	$\pm 2 \times 10^{-6}$ $\pm 1 \times 10^{-5}$	91 94
Comparison, highest precision	Magnetic float	$\pm 2 \times 10^{-8}$	93
Small concn. changes, routine, precision	Temperature of flotation	$\pm 1 \times 10^{-7}$	93
Closed system, routine	Helix	$< 10^{-6}$	92
High or low pressure	Balanced column	$\pm 5 \times 10^{-4}$	96
High temperature	Pipette pyc.	$\pm 1 \times 10^{-4}$	97
Various temperatures	Dilatometer or hydrostatic weighing	$\pm 1 \times 10^{-6}$ $\pm 2 \times 10^{-6}$	89 91
Small amounts (<20 mg.)	Pipette pyc. or falling drop	$\pm 1 \times 10^{-4}$ $\pm 1 \times 10^{-5}$	97 94

SOLIDS

Rapidity	Volumenometer	$\pm 1 \times 10^{-2}$	98
Highest precision, small amounts	Flotation	$\pm 5 \times 10^{-5}$	103
Comparison precision, routine	Temperature of flotation	$\pm 1 \times 10^{-6}$	104
Powdered samples ($d >$ or < 3 g./ml.)	Pyc. type B or C	$\pm 5 \times 10^{-4}$	79 99
Large crystals	Hydrostatic weighing	$\pm 1 \times 10^{-5}$	104
Small amounts	Centrifuge	$\mp 1 \times 10^{-4}$	103
Small amounts ($d >$ or $<$ 3g./ml.), rapidity	Hydrostatic weighing, torsion microbalance	$\pm 5 \times 10^{-4}$	104

General References

Alber, H. K., "Systematic Qualitative Organic Microanalysis. Determination of Specific Gravity," *Ind. Eng. Chem., Anal. Ed.*, **12**, 764–767 (1940).

Blank, E. W., and Willard, M. L., "Micro-density Determination of Solids and Liquids," *J. Chem. Education*, **10**, 109–112 (1933).

Daniels, F., Mathews, J. H., and Williams, J. W., *Experimental Physical Chemistry*. 3rd ed., McGraw-Hill, New York, 1941, pp. 94–97, 321–325.

Drucker, C., in Ostwald-Luther: *Physiko-chemische Messungen*. 5th ed., Akadem. Verlagsgesellschaft, Leipzig, 1931, pp. 81–98, 218–245.

Reilly, J., and Rae, W. N., *Physico-chemical Methods*. 3rd ed., Vol. I, Van Nostrand, New York, 1939, pp. 30–64, 465–505.

Timmermans, J., *Chemical Species*. Chemical Pub. Co., New York, 1940.

Timmermans, J., and Martin, F., "The Work of the International Bureau of Physical-Chemical Standards. I. Methods and Apparatus," *J. chim. phys.*, **23**, 733–746 (1926).

Wulff, P., and Heigl, A., "Methods of Density Determination of Solid Substances," *Z. physik. Chem.*, **A153**, 187–209 (1931).

CHAPTER IV

Determination of
SOLUBILITY

ROBERT D. VOLD AND MARJORIE J. VOLD

University of Southern California

I. GENERAL

The solubility of compounds is a property of great importance with a wide variety of applications: Appropriate solvents furnish media for reactions; differential solubility relations offer one of the most useful means for the isolation and purification of substances; a study of the solutions one compound forms with others provides information about its molecular structure and the nature and extent of intermolecular forces; solubility tests are one of the bases of systematic qualitative analysis, etc.

It is fortunate that so useful a property as solubility is in many cases easy to measure with adequate precision. This chapter is intended to serve as a working guide for making determinations of solubility and interpreting the results in a wide variety of cases.

1. Definition of Solubility

Solubility may be defined as the capacity of two or more substances to form spontaneously one with the other without chemical reaction a homogeneous molecular or colloidal dispersion. This definition is sufficiently condensed to warrant explanation. We first note that the state of the dispersion is not limited; it may be gaseous, liquid, crystalline, mesomorphic, or amorphous. A colloidal dispersion of a water-insoluble dye in an aqueous soap solution, or of a swollen polymer such as rubber in benzene, is just as much a solution as is alcohol in water. Secondly, we require that the dispersion be formed spontaneously, so that it would be possible to devise a means of obtaining useful work from the process—in other words, the formation of the solution is accompanied by a decrease in thermodynamic free energy. But free energy change due to chemical reaction, as in the "solution" of base metals in acid, is ruled out. Finally, we recognize that the capacity of any system of substances to form a solution has definite limits. These limits find their most concise expression in the phase rule of Gibbs:

$$F + P = C + 2$$

where F is the number of degrees of freedom in a system of C components with P phases. For two components and two phases (solid and liquid, two liquids, or two solids) under the pressure of their own vapor and at constant temperature, F equals zero. If one of the phases consists solely of one component, $i.$ $e.$, is a pure substance, the quantitative measure of solubility is a single number, $viz.$, the amount of the substance (solute) which is contained in saturated solution in a unit amount of the other component (solvent). For any case in which F is zero, a $definite$ $reproducible$ $solubility$ $equilibrium$ can be reached. The measure of solubility in this general case is the set of numbers giving the composition of each of the phases at the given temperature. Complete representation of the solubility relations requires determination of the phase diagram, which gives the number, composition, and relative amounts of each phase present at any temperature in a sample containing the components in any specified proportion.

2. Units for Expressing Solubility

Solubilities are expressed in various ways, $e.$ $g.$, in g. of solute per 100 g. or 100 cc. of solvent, in g. of solute per 100 g. or 100 cc. of solution; and in mole of solute per l. of solution. Table I illustrates the differences between the first four expressions.[1] Interconversion of these values is simple if the respective densities are known. Solubility in g. per 100 cc. solvent or solution is equal to solubility in g. per 100 g. solvent or solution divided by the

---

[1] A. Seidell, $Solubilities$ of $Organic$ $Compounds.$ 3rd ed., Vol. II, Van Nostrand, New York, 1941.

density of the solvent or the solution, respectively. Solubility in g. per 100 g. solution, S_A, is related to solubility in g. per 100 g. solvent, S_C by the formula:

$$S_C = S_A/(100 + S_A)$$

Weight fraction (g. solute per g. solution) or weight per cent (100 × weight fraction), and mole fraction (moles solute per mole solution) or

TABLE I

SOLUBILITY OF VARIOUS COMPOUNDS
EXPRESSED IN DIFFERENT UNITS

Compound	Solvent	Temp., ° C.	Solubility			
			g./100 g. solvent	g./100 cc. solvent	g./100 g. soln.	g./100 cc. soln.
Tartaric acid	50% by wt. ethanol in water	25	88.6	80.9	47.0	55.7
o-Nitrophenol	Ethanol	30.2	60.58	47.32	41.03	41.00
l-Leucine	Water	25	2.397	2.390	2.341	...

mole per cent (100 × mole fraction), can be interconverted without knowledge of the respective densities. The following formulas refer to a system of n components in which W_i is the weight fraction of the i component, M_i its molecular weight, and N_i its mole fraction:

$$N_i = W_i/M_i \left(\sum_{x=1}^{n} W_x/M_x \right)$$

$$W_i = N_iM_i/ \sum_{x=1}^{n} N_xM_x$$

Occasionally it is useful to employ an unconventional unit for the sake of plotting solubility results on a readable graph. For example, McBain[2] takes as units for calculating a "fractional proportion" one mole of potassium oleate, one mole of potassium chloride and 1000 grams of water.

3. Typical Solubility Relations and Their Utility in Organic Chemistry

A. PURIFICATION BY RECRYSTALLIZATION

Differences in the solubility of two compounds in a given solvent as a function of temperature can be used to effect a more or less complete separation in which the less soluble compound is readily produced in pure form. The physicochemical basis for this kind of separation is made evident by

[2] J. W. McBain, in *Colloid Chemistry*, edited by J. Alexander. Vol. I, Chemical Catalog Co., New York, 1926, p. 137.

figure 1, which shows two hypothetical solubility curves. Suppose, for
example, that it is desired to separate compound *I* from compound *II*,
which is contained in *I* to the extent of about 20%. Fifty grams of the
mixture, containing 40 g. of *I* and 10 g. of *II* will dissolve completely in
100 g. of solvent when heated to 45° C. Upon cooling to room temperature, 20°, *II* will remain entirely in solution, while 31 g. of *I* will crystallize
out, since its solubility at 20° is only 9 g. per 100 g. solvent. Thus, pure *I*

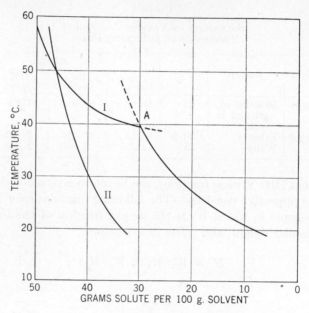

Fig. 1.—Typical solubility curves.

is obtained in a 77.5% yield by one recrystallization. The residual material, 10 g. of *II* and 9 g. of *I*, can be dissolved in 25 g. of solvent at 45°;
and 6.75 g. of pure *I* will separate out when the temperature is again reduced to 20°. A third recrystallization from the minimum weight (22.2 g.)
of solvent required to dissolve the 10 g. of *II* at 45° yields only an additional 0.25 g. of *I*, so that the maximum separation obtainable when working between 45° and 20° with this solvent gives pure *I* in a 95% yield and
II of about 83% purity. In this elementary example, complete independ-
ence of the two curves has been assumed, the possibility of coprecipitation
is neglected, and the problem of washing the crystals of pure *I* free from the
solution containing a considerable amount of *II* is ignored.

   The solubility curve for compound *I* is not smooth: the inflection at
point *A* indicates either that there are two allotropic forms of *I* between

which a transition occurs at 39.5° C. or that I forms one or more solvates with this solvent. It would be necessary to ascertain whether or not the solid formed at room temperature is pure compound I before using the product.

B. FRACTIONATION OF MIXTURES BY SALTING OUT

The separation of many biochemical preparations, particularly proteins and protein complexes, is carried out by the addition of successive amounts of some salt, for example, ammonium sulfate or potassium citrate, to a buffered solution of the protein mixture in aqueous solution. This technique likewise serves to indicate the number of components present in a complex mixture. For example, Jameson[3] has used this method to study the effects of kidney disorders on the blood serum proteins. Potassium citrate was added to a given solution, the protein precipitate was filtered off, and the protein and salt concentrations of the filtrate were determined by analysis. When the results were plotted, the curve of protein content *vs.* salt content showed a series of changes in slope, the segments corresponding to different protein components.

C. EXTRACTION EQUILIBRIA

The separation of the components of a mixture, particularly of a desired product from a complex reaction mixture, by extraction with a solvent of limited miscibility with the reaction solvent is a further broad example of the use of solubility relations in organic chemistry.

Extraction equilibria have also found application in determinations of the extent of molecular association and dissociation. For a substance which is present in molecular dispersion in each of two immiscible solvents, the distribution equilibrium is given by

$$C_1/C_2 = K$$

where C_1 is the concentration of substance in solvent 1, C_2 its concentration in solvent 2, and K a constant equal to the ratio of the solubilities of the substance in the two solvents. Any reaction which affects the molecular concentration of the substance in either solvent will alter the form of the relation. Thus for dimer formation in solvent 1, the relation is:

$$(1/_4 K_d + \sqrt{1/_8 K_d + C_1/K_d})/C_2 = K$$

where C_1 is the stoichiometric concentration of the substance in solvent 1, C_2 the concentration in solvent 2, and K_d the association constant for dimer

---

[3] E. Jameson, *Cold Spring Harbor Symposia Quant. Biol.*, **6**, 331 (1938).

formation. Again, if the substance is a weak acid partly dissociated in solvent 1, the form of the distribution equilibrium is:

$$(C_1 - K_a/2 + \sqrt{K_a^2/4 + K_aC_1})/C_2 = K$$

where K_a is the acid dissociation constant and the other symbols have the same significance as before.

An example of the use of extraction measurements to determine the equilibria in one solvent is found in their use by McBain and Eaton[4] to determine the extent of hydrolysis of aqueous solutions of potassium laurate from the amount of lauric acid extractable by benzene at various concentrations of potassium laurate solution in water.

D.   SOLUBILITY AS A CRITERION OF PURITY

While constancy of solubility on repeated crystallization, together with constancy of other physical properties, such as m.p., b.p., vapor pressure, etc., has long been recognized as a criterion of purity, Sørensen[5] and others have developed a sensitive test for the purity of a protein preparation, based on solubility measurements. If the protein preparation consists of a single pure substance it must have a solubility in a given solvent, usually a buffered salt solution, which is constant at constant temperature and independent of other variables, in particular, of the amount of residual solid phase. Accordingly, several suspensions are made up containing increasing amounts of protein per unit amount of solvent. After standing sufficient time for saturation to occur, the suspensions are filtered and the total protein contents of the filtrates determined, usually by analysis for protein nitrogen. A graph is constructed of protein nitrogen per ml. suspension against protein nitrogen per ml. filtrate. From the shape of the curve the nature of the impurity can be determined (*i. e.*, whether it is soluble or insoluble, present in the preparation in simple admixture or as a solid solution, etc.) and, in some cases, the amount of the impurity. A specific example is given among the typical cases discussed at the end of this chapter.

E.   IDENTIFICATION AND CHARACTERIZATION OF COMPOUNDS

The qualitative solubility behavior of organic compounds toward a selected group of solvents is the basis of one of four general procedures used for the systematic identification of unknown compounds.[6] The solvents

[4] J. W. McBain and M. Eaton, *J. Chem. Soc.*, **1928**, 2166.

[5] S. P. L. Sørensen and M. Høyrup, *Compt. rend. trav. lab. Carlsberg*, **12**, 213 (1917).

[6] R. L. Shriner and R. C. Fuson, *Systematic Identification of Organic Compounds.* 2nd ed., Wiley, New York, 1940.

employed for such general classifications are usually water and ether, as representatives of "polar" and "nonpolar" solvents, dilute solutions of acid and base, and, finally, more concentrated acids.   More elaborate systems based on the use of a sequence of organic solvents are employed only in special cases.   In general, the solubility relations of substances are too specific to permit a division of compounds into mutually exclusive small classes.

F.   SOLUBILITY IN THE STUDY OF INTERMOLECULAR FORCES[7]

The mutual solubility of two substances has long been used as a qualitative measure of the extent of the interaction between their molecules,

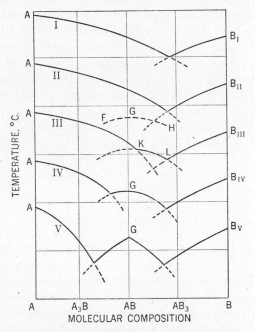

Fig. 2.—Solubility curves for varying degrees
of compound formation.[8]

varying from simple departure from the laws of ideal solution (Raoult's law, Henry's law) to a genuine formation of a compound between the solvent and the solute.

Figure 2 shows how the solubility of a substance A will vary in a series of

[7] J. H. Hildebrand, *Solubility*.   1st ed., Chemical Catalog Co., New York, 1924. 2nd ed., Reinhold, New York, 1936.

[8] J. Kendall, A. W. Davidson, and H. Adler, *J. Am. Chem. Soc.*, **43**, 1481 (1921).

different solvents, B_I to B_V, exhibiting gradually increasing compound formation with A in the liquid state.[8] In this diagram, temperature is plotted against the molecular composition of the saturated solution. The point A represents the same temperature throughout; *viz.*, the melting point of A. "Curve I indicates the ideal system AB_I where compound formation is entirely absent...Curves II to V illustrate the successive changes which occur in the diagram as compound formation increases. In curve II, the compound is so highly dissociated that its solubility curve, FGH, never enters the stable region of the diagram. In curve III, compound formation is somewhat more extensive and the solubility curve of the compound AB_{IV} possesses a limited stable interval KL; in curve IV, this interval has expanded sufficiently to exhibit a maximum point, G (in other words, the compound AB_{IV} is stable at its melting point). In curve V, finally, the compound AB_V is not dissociated at all into its components in the solution, the system consisting of two simple systems of the type shown in figure 1 compressed into a single composition range."

Marvel, Copley, and coworkers[9] have used the solubility of compounds containing hydrogen in solvents containing amine, hydroxyl, and similar groups as a measure of the extent of hydrogen bond formation. Such relatively simple interpretations of the complex phenomena of solubility, while attractive, are not always lasting. Thus the interpretations of Bancroft and coworkers[10] of the solubilities of various substances in mixtures of water and other solvents in terms of the association of water to simple polymers has been largely abandoned.

G.   SOLUBILITY RELATIONS OF HIGH POLYMERS[11−14]

High polymers show a behavior toward solvents quite different from that of substances with smaller molecules. Some, notably chain polymers, swell continuously in certain solvents until finally a homogeneous solution is formed. There is no saturation equilibrium and no numerical value of solubility. Rather, at a given temperature, liquids may be classed sharply as solvents or nonsolvents for the particular polymer. For some solvents, a critical temperature exists above which "solubility" of the polymer is

[9] M. J. Copley, E. Ginsberg, G. F. Zellhoefer, and C. S. Marvel, *J. Am. Chem. Soc.*, **63**, 254 (1941).

[10] W. D. Bancroft and F. J. C. Butler, *J. Phys. Chem.*, **36**, 2515 (1932).

[11] H. Mark and R. Raff, *High Polymeric Reactions.* Interscience, New York, 1941, p. 25.

[12] K. H. Meyer, *Natural and Synthetic High Polymers.* Interscience, New York, 1942, pp. 9, 25.

[13] J. N. Brønsted and K. Volquartz, *Trans. Faraday Soc.*, **35**, 576 (1939).

[14] G. V. Schulz and B. Jirgensons, *Z. physik. Chem.*, **B46**, 105, 137 (1940).

unlimited and below which it is negligible. Other polymers, notably space and net polymers, swell to a limited extent in various solvents but no molecular dispersion forms in the equilibrated solvent.

The behavior of a given polymer toward various standard solvents, as water, liquid ammonia, formamide or formic acid, strong acids, concentrated solutions of certain salts, hydrocarbons, halogenated hydrocarbons, esters, ketones, etc., is used as a means of identification of unknown samples.[12]

The amounts of nonsolvent required to precipitate a polymer from its solution in a miscible solvent, at varying polymer concentrations, can be used as a method for estimation of the molecular weight of the polymers.[14]

4. Accuracy in Measurements

The accuracy required of a given measurement of solubility varies considerably with the use to be made of the data. For qualitative identification of compounds, the simple observation that some dissolves in a given solvent usually suffices. For example, Shriner and Fuson[6] require that 0.1 g. of solute dissolves in 3 cc. of solvent for a "positive" result in any given solubility test. At the other extreme, if the results are to be used to establish the order of solubility of a series of closely related compounds for comparison with the predictions of some theory of their solution, the accuracy must be such that errors have no conceivable effect on the order cited. Happily, when adequate care is taken to secure real equilibrium between the saturated solution and the saturating phase, precise analysis of the phases is frequently possible with very little extra effort, which should certainly be expended. An over-all accuracy of about 0.5% is not difficult to obtain except, perhaps, in very special cases.

5. Compilations of Data

The most useful (English) compilation of solubility data is probably that of A. Seidell.[15] Some data can be found in the *International Critical Tables*[16] and in Landolt-Börnstein.[17] Qualitative observations on the solubility of compounds for which no quantitative data are available may frequently be found in Beilstein.[18] In *Chemical Abstracts*, a search should be made under "name of compound, sol'y of," rather than under "solubility." In

[15] A. Seidell, *Solubilities of Organic Compounds*. 3rd ed., Vol. II, Van Nostrand, New York, 1941.

[16] *International Critical Tables*. McGraw-Hill, New York, 1926.

[17] Landolt-Börnstein, *Physikalisch-chemische Tabellen*. 5th ed., Springer, Berlin, 1923–1936.

[18] F. K. Beilstein, *Handbuch der organischen Chemie*. 4th ed., Springer, Berlin, 1928–1941.

scarching for the solubility of a particular substance, freezing point data should not be overlooked because they give directly the solubility of the given solid in the other components at the freezing temperature.

6. General Precautions in Measurements

A. EQUILIBRIUM

Since solubility is an equilibrium phenomenon, experimental effort is first directed to the attainment of saturation. The most satisfactory experimental criterion to adopt is the concordance of results obtained when the final state is reached from both undersaturation and supersaturation. Only when equilibrium has been assured by such a dual approach can the experimenter be certain that the accuracy of his measurement is correctly given by the precision of its component parts: the measurements of *temperature* and *concentration* and the *purity of the materials*.

The approach to equilibrium from undersaturation is accomplished, obviously, by mixing solvent and solute at the temperature of the measurement. Supersaturated solutions can generally be prepared by mixing solvent and solute at a higher temperature and then cooling to the temperature of the measurement.

It may be experimentally impractical to approach equilibrium from both sides in some particular case. Very slightly soluble solids are frequently very slow to reach equilibrium from the side of undersaturation. On the other hand, many supersaturated solutions are very slow to deposit the excess, even in the presence of seed crystals. When either of these cases is encountered, the experimenter is obliged to use as evidence of equilibrium the finding that no further change of concentrations occurs for longer times of equilibration.

The length of time to be allowed varies from case to case and must be determined experimentally. Nevertheless, the following generalizations may prove useful. Measurements of rate of solution[19] confirm the theory[20] that a thin layer surrounding the crystals first becomes saturated and that transfer of material from this layer to the bulk of the solution occurs by a diffusion process. Consequently, solution will occur more slowly in solvents of higher viscosity, even with the same efficiency of stirring. Likewise, heat increases the rate of solution in the same way it affects diffusion coefficients. A corollary is that, under similar experimental conditions, substances of low diffusion velocity will dissolve more slowly than substances with high diffusion coefficients. Again, since diffusion velocity is proportional to the concentration gradient, more soluble substances tend to dis-

---

[19] C. V. King, *J. Am. Chem. Soc.*, **57**, 828 (1935).
[20] A. A. Noyes and W. R. Whitney, *Z. physik. Chem.*, **23**, 689 (1897).

solve faster than less soluble ones. The operation of some of these factors in a particular case is shown in table II.

TABLE II

INFLUENCE OF VARIOUS FACTORS ON THE RATE OF SOLUTION
OF MAGNESIUM IN ACETIC ACID[a]

Stirring speed, r.p.m.	Rate of solution[b] in 0.0275 M acetic acid	Rate of solution in 0.0275 M acetic acid with 0.6 M sugar to increase viscosity
1200	0.448	0.264
1000	0.378	0.230
600	0.273	0.150
300	0.179	0.103

[a] C. V. King, *J. Am. Chem. Soc.*, **57**, 828 (1935).

[b] k of the equation: $dx/dt = k \cdot A/V \cdot (a - x)$, where dx/dt is moles of magnesium dissolved per unit time, A the surface area of the magnesium cylinder, V the volume of solution, a the final magnesium concentration, and x the concentration at time t.

B.   TEMPERATURE CONTROL

Since the solubility of almost all substances varies with temperature, this variable must be carefully controlled during the entire time of the measurement within limits which are determined by the desired precision and the magnitude of the temperature coefficient of solubility of the particular system being studied. For example, picric acid is soluble in methyl alcohol to the extent of 13.8 g. per 100 g. solvent at 0° C., and of 21.1 g. per 100 g. solvent at 21.1°. Assuming a linear variation between these limits, temperature control with ±0.05° is sufficient for measurements precise within about 0.2%. However, for m-nitrobenzoic acid in benzene, the same temperature fluctuation could cause an error of up to about 2.5%. Not only must control of temperature be maintained throughout the period of equilibration, but also during separation of the saturated solution for analysis. This is most easily accomplished by allowing the contents of the solubility flask to settle and removing the solution through a pipette attached to a suitable filter (cotton, glass wool, asbestos pulp, etc.). Figure 3 shows an arrangement for accomplishing the separation and at the same time securing a known volume of solution at the temperature of the experiment. Several portions of solution should first be withdrawn and discarded to satisfy any possible capacity of the filter to sorb solute from the saturated solution.

In general, because of its higher heat capacity, a liquid bath is much to be preferred to an air thermostat. In a water bath using a heating element with sufficiently small "lag" (i. e., that cools off rapidly when current is cut off and vice versa), adequate stirring, and a sufficiently sensitive thermo-regulator, a temperature control to within ±0.01° or even better can be obtained near room temperature. Moreover, if stirring is satisfactory, temperature gradients can be eliminated so that all parts of the solubility apparatus and its contents are really at the temperature read on a correct thermometer hung anywhere in the thermostat.

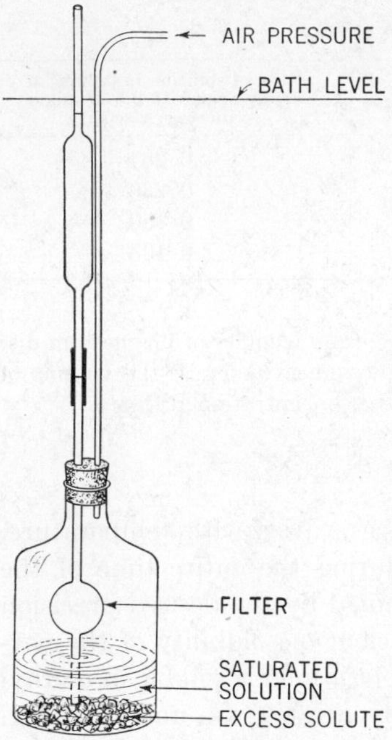

Never use a thermometer which has not been calibrated against known thermometric standards, for any purpose whatsoever. The authors are aware of (albeit unusual) cases in which thermometers purchased from reputable sources have been found to be wrong by 10–20° C.

At high temperatures, and in an air bath at any temperature, gradients are difficult to avoid, and the fluctuations of the temperature about its mean value are likely to be large. Figure 4 shows a thermoregulator circuit the authors have for years found to be satisfactory at temperatures up to 150° C. in either liquid or air baths. The parts can be obtained from any good scientific supply house for much less than the cost of a preassembled thermostat unit. E, T, and H are sockets into which are plugged lead wires to the 110-volt source, the thermoregulator, and the bath heater (500 watts to match other quoted characteristics). R_I and R_C are two variable resistances (50 ohms, 200 watts, and 10 ohms, 150 watts, respectively) in parallel with each other and in series with the heater. C is a 0.1 microfarad condenser. R is a 15,000-ohm carbon resistor in parallel with T. A is the armature of an alternating-current relay capable of carrying about 6 amperes.

Figure 5 gives the authors' recommendation for the arrangement of apparatus within the thermostat. It is suggested that commercially obtainable heaters contained in flexible copper tubing be bent into a convenient shape. A loop passing all the way around the walls of the thermostat close to the bottom of the tank is most desirable. The stirrer blades, S, should be so turned that they lift the liquid from bottom to top. Circulation may be improved by surrounding the stirrer with cylindrical baffle C.

Fig. 3.—Assembly of equipment for separating saturated solution from excess solute at constant temperature.

C. STIRRING

Stirring the contents of the solubility apparatus or rocking the apparatus as a whole to insure mixing its contents thoroughly serves to eliminate any

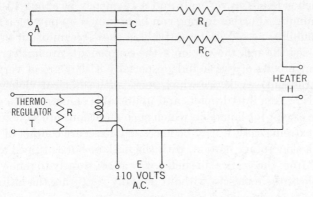

Fig. 4.—Thermoregulator circuit.

temperature gradients and also to reduce the time required to attain saturation. Such mixing is virtually indispensable in any accurate determination of solubility. But agitation should not be so violent as to produce foam.

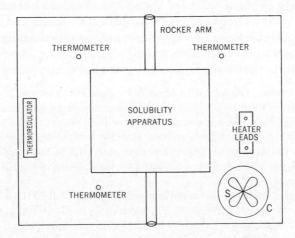

Fig. 5.—Arrangement of equipment in thermostat.

Some proteins undergo irreversible denaturation[21] under such conditions; some detergent materials are concentrated in the foam by adsorption to

21 H. B. Bull and H. Neurath, *J. Biol. Chem.*, **118**, 163 (1937).

such an extent that the phenomenon has been used as a method for their purification.

Sufficient agitation for a system composed of solid and liquid can usually be achieved by attaching the apparatus to a rocking device with a 120° arc (60° on each side of the vertical) and a frequency of about 10–30 oscillations per minute. Further mixing can be obtained by putting a marble inside the solubility vessel. Alternatively, a slow stream of air or other gas may be passed through the system if the components are not very volatile. The efficient mixing of two liquids, especially if they are of very different density, is difficult. A device which rocks with sufficient violence to keep both liquids broken into droplets and in unstable emulsion with each other is desirable except for liquids in which such emulsions are slow to separate. In fact, in extreme cases it may be necessary to secure contact of two liquid phases by a slow rotary motion, with the flask or bottle tipped at an angle of about 5° from the vertical in such a way as constantly to renew the liquid on each side of the meniscus without actually rupturing the latter.

D. PURITY OF MATERIALS

The effect on results of measuring the solubility of an impure solute in an impure solvent may be either negligible or very great. No measurement is of any value unless the nature and amount of impurities are considered, i. e., unless the chemical nature of the substance to which the figures apply is known. Analyses must always be made of both solute and solvent, but there is considerable leeway for the exercise of the experimenter's judgment as to how rigorously purification must be carried out. The following examples illustrate the considerations governing minimum purity acceptable:

(1) In measuring the solubility of anhydrous sodium stearate in alcohol, both solute and solvent must be very dry, since in the presence of even small amounts of water the equilibrium phase is not anhydrous sodium stearate but a stoichiometric hydrate.[22] If 1 g. of anhydrous sodium stearate is equilibrated with 1000 g. of ethyl alcohol, the latter must contain less than about 0.07% moisture if the equilibrium solid is not to be entirely converted to $C_{17}H_{35}COONa \cdot 1/8 \, H_2O$, the lowest reported hydrate.

(2) The solubility of succinic acid in absolute acetone[10] at 40° C. is 7 g. per 100 g. solvent, while for acetone containing 5% water it is 13 g. per 100 g. solvent. For acetone adulterated with 5% carbon tetrachloride or methyl, ethyl, or propyl alcohol, the solubility of succinic acid is 6.2 g. per 100 g., 9.3, 8.0, and 7.5 g., respectively. From these figures one can readily calculate (assuming a linear mixture rule) how pure the acetone must be if the measured solubility is to be correct within any given precision. The differences just cited are not extraordinarily large, al-

---

[22] M. J. Buerger, L. B. Smith, A. de Bretteville, Jr., and F. V. Ryer, *Proc. Natl. Acad. Sci. U. S.*, **28**, 526 (1942).

though the effect of chemically similar impurities, as toluene in benzene, would be expected to be small. Thus the solubility of *m*-nitroaniline in benzene is diminished by only 0.6% for a contamination of benzene with 5% toluene.

(*3*) The effect of impurities in a solute on the solubility of the solute in a pure solvent is a complex one, depending on the solubility of the impurity in both solute and solvent. One example is discussed fully on page 129, since this effect has found application as a criterion of purity, particularly in the field of protein chemistry.

E. ANALYSIS OF PHASES

As has already been pointed out, a complete description of solubility includes the weight of solute per unit amount of solvent at a given temperature in equilibrium with a second phase of *known composition*. It is thus necessary to determine the nature of the equilibrium solid phase. This may be done by direct analysis, by crystallographic observations, by taking its melting point alone and in mixture with the original solid, or in other ways. This analysis of the solid is often very simple to carry out, but in exceptional cases can be extremely difficult.

F. PARTICLE SIZE

There has been a great deal of discussion[23-27] concerning the variation of solubility with the size of solid particles, the reality of the phenomenon, its magnitude, and its possible effect on measurements of solubility. If sufficient time is allowed for aging of freshly precipitated solids, and for Ostwald ripening (solution of small particles and growth of large ones), the whole effect is of no major importance to solubility measurements. Similarly, while it is true that crystals with lattice distortions produced by mechanical strain are more soluble than perfect crystals, the effect is both of second order and transient. In fact, in order for either effect to be observed one must employ very sparingly soluble substances (*e. g.*, barium sulfate) to slow down the Ostwald ripening. However, if the particles are small or tend to be dispersed in the solution by some wetting agent, special care must be used in separating the supernatant fluid for analysis. A very fine filter may serve; or in some instances centrifuging can be used to settle fine dispersions of solid in saturated solution. If the particles are sufficiently fine, spurious results may be obtained due to formation of a colloidal suspension.

[23] J. Willard Gibbs, *Scientific Papers.* Vol. I, Longmans, Green, London, 1906, p. 315.

[24] A. Hulett, *Z. physik. Chem.*, **37**, 385 (1901); **47**, 357 (1904).

[25] M. L. Dundon and E. Mack, Jr., *J. Am. Chem. Soc.*, **45**, 2479 (1923); M. L. Dundon, *ibid.*, **45**, 2658 (1923).

[26] D. Balarew, *Z. anorg. allgem. Chem.*, **145**, 122 (1925).

[27] I. M. Kolthoff and C. Rosenblum, *J. Am. Chem. Soc.*, **56**, 1264 (1934).

II. PRACTICAL PROCEDURES

1. Solubility of Stable Solids in Liquids

A. ANALYTICAL METHOD

Crystalline Solids of Moderate Solubility; Nonvolatile, Mobile Solvents.[28]—Weigh out crudely four samples of the solid of a size which will not dissolve completely at the given temperature in the volume of solvent contemplated. Place the samples in each of four flasks or cylinders, and pour in the solvent until the flasks are about two-thirds full. Stopper tightly. Rubber caps such as are sold for infants' nursing bottles placed over suitably protected cork stoppers have been found leakproof by the authors under moderate conditions of temperature and pressure. The solid should consist partly of fine and partly of coarse crystals.

Heat two of the samples well above the final temperature of measurement in order to approach equilibrium from the side of supersaturation, since most substances have a positive temperature coefficient for solubility. Place all four flasks on a suitable rocking device in such a way that they are completely submerged in the thermostat. After equilibrium seems likely to have been reached, discontinue agitation and set the flasks upright in the thermostat to facilitate settling of the excess solid to the bottom of the cylinder. If the flask has a long neck and the bath temperature is not very different from room temperature, the cap may be allowed to project above the bath to facilitate removal of the saturated solution. In general, however, some such arrangement as that shown in figure 3 is desirable.

Weigh samples of the solution which had a known volume at the temperature of the experiment. This procedure provides data for interconversion of units, and is very important. Then analyze the solution for solute content by any convenient procedure. All four results should agree within the precision called for in the determination, and there must be no significant difference between the pair originally supersaturated and the pair originally undersaturated.

Obtain a sample of the solid by filtering the residue, and examine a crystal under a hand magnifier or a low-power microscope. If any doubt exists as to its identity with the original, free a sample from the excess solution by rapid washing on a filter with fresh solvent or a more volatile solvent miscible with the first, and analyze the residue for solute content, or take a melting point of it alone and in admixture with the original.

Crystalline Solids in Volatile Liquids.—The procedure described above need not be unsatisfactory for solvents of moderate volatility. If the

---

[28] J. Reilly and W. N. Rae, *Physico-chemical Methods*. 3rd ed., Vol. I, Van Nostrand, New York, 1939, p. 589.

vapor pressure of the solvent is considerable (say 50–100 mm. Hg at the temperature of the thermostat), allow time for the air space in the flasks to become saturated with vapor before stoppering.   Better still, partially evacuate the flasks through a glass tube inserted through the stopper and provided with a stopcock or rubber tube and screw clamp for subsequent closure.   (Pinch clamps leak.)

However, when the vapor pressure is high (1 atm. or more), some type of solubility bomb must be employed to hold the solution and deliver a filtered sample. A suitable solubility bomb has been designed by Schroeder, Berk and Gabriel.[29]

Very Slightly Soluble Solids.—If a solid is very slightly soluble, the approach to equilibrium from the side of undersaturation may be very slow.   It can be hastened by preparing the solid in the form of a very fine powder by means of grinding or rapid precipitation.   In such cases a physicochemical method of analysis of the saturated solution may be desirable.

Very Viscous Solvents or Solutions Which Gel, etc.—In these cases as well as those in which the solubility changes so rapidly with temperature that filtration is accompanied by deposition of solid from the solution (owing to heat absorbed in vaporizing the solvent during filtration), it is probably wise to use the synthetic method described below.

Rapid Procedure.—Occasionally it is desirable to make a large number of solubility determinations with no great precision, for example, in characterizing the solvent characteristics of a newly prepared liquid.   Thus Trimble[30] reports the solubility of over 200 organic and inorganic substances in commercial furfural.

The following procedure may be used advantageously.   Place the solvent and solute in wide-mouth test tubes of about 50-ml. capacity, two for each solute.   Heat the tubes in a beaker of water to a temperature above that of the determination, but not high enough to dissolve all the solid.   Then chill one member of each pair to a temperature below that of the determination until considerable solid has crystallized out.   Stopper all the tubes tightly and rock in a thermostat with their lips above the surface of the bath liquid.   Place a small shaped filter such as a Soxhlet thimble in each and allow the saturated solution to filter in.   Analyze a weighed volume of the liquid so obtained by any convenient method.

Methods of Analysis.—The simplest procedure for the analysis of a saturated solution of a nonvolatile material is evaporation of the solvent. This involves considerable risk of mechanical loss and is seldom employed in accurate work.

    [29] W. C. Schroeder, A. A. Berk, and A. Gabriel, *J. Am. Chem. Soc.*, **59**, 1783 (1937).
    [30] F. Trimble, *Ind. Eng. Chem., Ind. Ed.*, **33**, 660 (1941).

In addition to strictly chemical methods based on the reactions of the particular solute, a number of physical methods of analysis are available. Many of these are described elsewhere in this volume. Some have a special advantage in that suspended solids do not interfere; others are particularly applicable to dilute solutions, others to microsamples, etc. *Optical* methods include: refractometry; colorimetry, including nephelometry; polarimetry; and interferometry. *Electrical* methods involve conductance measurements; electromotive force measurements; and polarography. In *density* determinations, pycnometers of various types are used directly, or flotation methods (*e. g.*, "hydrometry") are employed. Still another physical method of analysis uses *radioactive indicators*.

B.   SYNTHETIC METHOD

The so-called synthetic method (Hill's[31] "plethostatic," *i. e.*, constant-composition, method) consists in determining the temperature at which solution takes place on heating a sample of known composition. The procedure is simple and can be made very precise, particularly in cases in which the solubility does not change rapidly with increasing temperature. Since the composition is known with any desired accuracy, the precision of the measurement is limited only by the change in the solubility over the uncertainty range, sometimes as small as $0.1°$, in the measurement of the temperature of complete solution.

In theory, equilibrium can be approached from both supersaturation and undersaturation by observing both the temperature at which the first crystals separate as the solution is cooled and that at which the last crystal disappears on heating. In practice, undercooling is generally experienced, and only the approach from the side of undersaturation is practical. On the other hand, the separation of a single liquid solution into two liquid phases is accompanied by little, if any, undercooling; furthermore, the second phase frequently separates as a readily visible turbidity of finely divided droplets which are uniformly dispersed and easily observed.

Directions for the method follow. Weigh the desired amount of solvent and solute into a test tube with walls heavy enough to withstand the pressure developed by heating the solvent to the appropriate temperature. Seal the tube. This is the only satisfactory way to keep the composition constant. Prepare the sample for observation by obtaining the solid phase as a finely divided crystal mass readily dispersed throughout the liquid by gentle agitation. This can be accomplished by heating to effect complete solution, and then chilling rapidly. Heat the prepared sample very slowly, certainly no faster than $0.5°$ per minute, and note the tempera-

---

[31] A. E. Hill, *J. Am. Chem. Soc.*, **45**, 1143 (1923).

ture at which the last trace of crystal disappears. Avoid a large vapor space in the tube; test whether vaporization of the solvent causes an increase in actual concentration of the solute.

The method can also be adapted to a microscopic scale, using 1-mg. samples observed under a microscope.[32]

2. Solubility of Solids Decomposing to Vapors

In the determination of the solubility of a solid which decomposes reversibly, one of the products being gaseous, a difference is experienced between

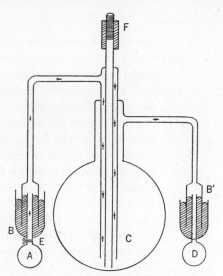

Fig. 6.—Apparatus for solubility measurement at constant gas pressure.[33]

results at constant pressure of the gas and results at the vapor pressure of the system. The synthetic method is limited to the latter case, in general, though it would not be impossible to design an apparatus operating at constant pressure and employing this method.

A. SYNTHETIC METHOD

The procedure described above can be used without modification. If the vapor pressure is high, the vapor space must be kept small enough so that changes in composition due to decomposition are not appreciable.

---

[32] R. D. Vold and M. J. Vold, *J. Am. Chem. Soc.*, **61**, 808 (1939). R. D. Vold, *J. Phys. Chem.*, **43**, 1213 (1939).

[33] A. C. Walker, U. B. Bray, and J. Johnston, *J. Am. Chem. Soc.*, **49**, 1235 (1927).

If the vapor pressure is low enough, *i. e.*, less than about 1 atm., the type of apparatus (Fig. 6) used by Walker, Bray, and Johnston,[33] to study the equilibrium between carbonate and bicarbonate ions may prove convenient. The gas is introduced through intake manifold A, regulating stopcock E, and mercury seal B, into the top of equilibration flask C. It passes down through the annular space surrounding sampling tube F, and is sucked out by a suitable pump attached to exhaust manifold D, which is connected with a manometer. The gas stream serves also as a stirrer for the contents of the flask.

C.   MICROSYNTHETIC METHOD

When only small quantities of solute or solvent are available, the authors prefer a synthetic to an analytical method because less handling of ma-

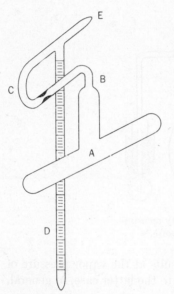

terial is required and the chance of mechanical loss is thereby reduced. Samples can be prepared in capillary tubes and the heating and observations conducted in a furnace mounted on the stage of a microscope.[32] Alternatively, Menzies[34] describes an apparatus (Fig. 7) in which he determined the complete solubility curve for strontium chloride in deuterium water, using only 1 ml. of solvent, over 90% of which was recovered at the end of the experiments. A is the solubility vessel containing the solid under investigation. D is a reservoir of solvent whose amount is known from the graduation on the tube. It is introduced by distillation (without ebullition) from a flask sealed on at E. The solvent used in any given experiment is distilled from D to A through trap C, which is closed during determinations by melting a pellet of silver iodide–chloride mixture above the constriction in U tube C, and allowing it to run into the constriction.

Fig. 7.—Apparatus of Menzies.[34]

3.   Mutual Solubility of Two Liquids

A.   ANALYTICAL METHOD

The procedure consists essentially of two operations: securing equilibrium between the two liquid phases by sufficiently long equilibration, with the customary precaution of approach to the final state from both

[34] A. W. C. Menzies, *J. Am. Chem. Soc.*, **58**, 934 (1936).

sides (*i. e.*, higher and lower temperature); and obtaining samples of each layer at the temperature of the experiment.

Measure out the desired volumes of the two liquids into two suitable containers which can be tightly stoppered. If either liquid has an appreciable vapor pressure, allow the vessels to stand uncovered for several minutes before stoppering, or reduce the pressure inside after stoppering by means of an aspirator or other suitable pump connected through the stopper to a tube and screw clamp arrangement. Place one vessel in a beaker of cold water and agitate thoroughly. Place the second in hot water and agitate. Then submerge the two in a thermostat at the (intermediate) temperature of the determination and rock mechanically for a suitable time interval. With adequate mixing, if the liquids are not too viscous, equilibrium should be reached in a few minutes. However, if the liquids tend to emulsify, the only permissible agitation is a gentle rotation renewing the liquid near the surface without ever rupturing the meniscus separating the two liquids. In such a case, several hours may be required to establish equilibrium.

To secure samples for analysis, allow the vessels to come to rest in an upright position with their stoppers barely projecting above the surface of the bath. If distillation occurs because of the temperature gradient thus established along the neck of the flask, leave the vessels completely submerged, but so arranged that they can be raised without disturbing the liquid layers. The samples desired can be taken from the top layer very easily by means of a pipette. A sample of the bottom layer can also be secured; maintaining a slight air pressure on the pipette as it is lowered through the top layer into the bottom layer prevents contamination. Alternatively, a graduated pipette with the tip sealed by a thin-blown glass membrane can be used to sample the lower layer, the membrane being broken against the bottom of the vessel. Weigh known volumes of the two layers to obtain the data needed for expressing the results in any units which may subsequently be desired.

Use any convenient procedure to determine the composition of the layers. If the necessary calibrations have been made, physical methods such as measurements of refraction or density are the simplest.

When separation occurs readily into two liquid layers, each of moderate volume, the authors prefer the analytical method described above. Many other procedures have been developed, a few of which are briefly outlined in the following sections.

B. SYNTHETIC METHOD

The synthetic method for a liquid–liquid system differs from that described for a solid–liquid system only in that the temperature of incipient separation into two phases is determined as the isotropic, single-phase liquid solution is cooled. Minute droplets of the second phase begin to form throughout the formerly homogeneous system and give it a cloudy appearance. The temperatures of appearance of the cloud, on cooling, and of its disappearance, on heating, are usually the same within experimental error, which is difficult to reduce below 0.1° C. However, instances of real discrepancies of up to 3° have been reported.[35] A single experiment gives no information about the composition of the second phase. To determine the composition of both phases at any given temperature a series of experiments must be performed so that the complete solubility curve can be constructed.

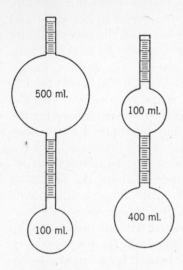

Fig. 8.—Solubility flasks.

Sometimes no readily visible cloud is formed. If a dye can be found whose color differs in the two phases, a minute amount dissolved in the solution may change color sharply when the second phase separates out. Klobbie[36] used this effect successfully in studying the system diethylether–water. To increase the visibility of the cloud the authors have placed the sample in a heavy-walled tube held in a horizontal position. A wire net-work is viewed through the tube which acts as a lens. Distortion or disappearance of the image shows when a second phase began to form. In the special cases in which the separating phase is liquid crystalline rather than liquid, observation through crossed polaroid plates renders its appearance conspicuous.

C. THE THERMOSTATIC METHOD OF HILL[31]

In this procedure, the volumes of the two layers are determined accurately in specially designed flasks (Fig. 8). The flask size to be used is determined in preliminary experiments in graduated cylinders. From two parallel experiments with different initial weight ratios of the two liquids, it is possible to calculate the composition and the density of each layer. The calculation is exact, involving only the phase rule principle that the compositions of the layers must be the same for the two experiments at the same temperature.

[35] H. S. Davis, *J. Am. Chem. Soc.*, **38**, 1166 (1916).
[36] E. A. Klobbie, *Z. physik. Chem.*, **24**, 615 (1897).

D. THE THERMOSTATIC METHOD OF HERZ[37]

To obtain a rough measure of the solubility of one liquid in another at room temperature, the one liquid may be added to the other dropwise from a burette, with continuous shaking; the first excess will give the whole liquid in the flask a cloudy appearance.   This procedure is frequently used also in ternary liquid systems.

A refinement is reported by Sobotka and Kahn,[38] who used as indicator particles minute, jagged crystals insoluble in the first liquid.   The slightest excess of the second liquid rapidly dissolved the indicator particles, converting them from jagged crystals into rounded droplets of a different color.   Results for the solubility of various esters in water are given to three significant figures.

III. INTERPRETATION OF RESULTS

The following specific examples illustrate a few of the many applications of solubility measurements.

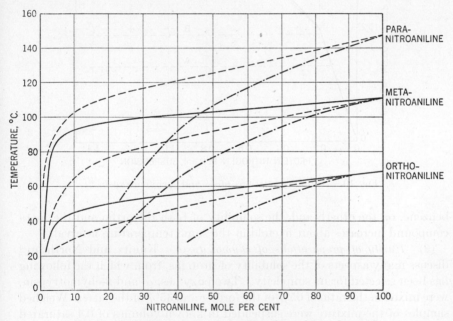

Fig. 9.—Solubilities of the nitroanilines in various solvents.[39]

———, solubility in carbon tetrachloride; -----, solubility in benzene;
—·—·—·—, solubility in acetone.

[37] W. Herz, *Ber.*, **31**, 2669 (1898).
[38] H. Sobotka and J. Kahn, *J. Am. Chem. Soc.*, **53**, 2935 (1931).
[39] A. R. Collett and J. Johnston, *J. Phys. Chem.*, **30**, 70 (1926).

(1)   *Solubility of o-, m-, and p-nitroaniline in various solvents.*[39]   Some
of the results of measurements of the solubility of these compounds in various solvents are represented in figure 9.   The synthetic method used by
Collett and Johnston was particularly suitable, since all the solvents are
fairly volatile.   The results are said to be precise within 0.5%.

There is an immediate practical consequence of this work: carbon
tetrachloride is shown to be the best solvent of those tried for a separation
of the ortho and meta isomers.   The solubility of the ortho compound in
carbon tetrachloride increases by a factor of 140 in the temperature interval from 25–60° C., while that of the meta compound only doubles.   In

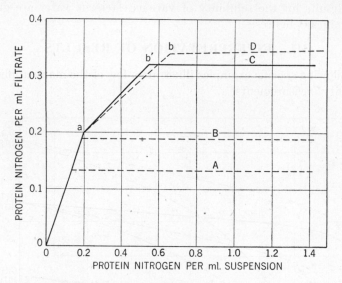

Fig. 10.—Solubility relations of α- and β-chymotrypsin.[40]

benzene, on the otherh and, the solubility of both the ortho and the meta
compound increases about fivefold in the same temperature interval.

(2)   *Purity of preparations of chymotrypsin.*   Kunitz and Northrop[40]
discuss many aspects of the solubility of proteins, from which the following
has been selected for its simplicity.   Two enzymes, α- and β-chymotrypsin,
were mixed in the ratio of 65% of the former and 35% of the latter.   Weighed
samples of the mixture were suspended in known volumes of 0.4 saturated
ammonium sulfate solution buffered to pH 4.0;   after equilibration the
solutions were filtered and analyzed for total protein nitrogen.   The results
are plotted in curve D of figure 10.   This curve can be analyzed to show that

⁴⁰ M. Kunitz and J. H. Northrop, *Cold Spring Harbor Symposia Quant. Biol.*, **6**, 325
(1938).

α- and β-chymotrypsin do not form solid *solutions* with each other. If, on the other hand, the absence of solid solution is known, the relative amounts of the two compounds in the solid *mixture* can be deduced in the following way: As the amount of solid sample of the two mixed enzymes is progressively increased, all of it will dissolve until one of the components is present in excess of its solubility. Thereafter, only the other component will dissolve in increasing amount, and the slope of the curve of protein nitrogen per ml. of filtrate against that per ml. of suspension will decrease. Experimentally, this occurs at point *a*, where 0.2 mg. of protein nitrogen is found per ml. of filtrate. Since the solubility of the alpha component alone (given by curve *A*) is 0.13 mg. of protein nitrogen per ml., the remaining 0.07 mg. must have come from the beta component, which is therefore present in the mixture to the extent of 0.07/0.2 × 100, or 35%. When both components are present in excess of their solubilities, the protein nitrogen of the filtrate should be constant and equal to the sum of the solubilities of the two components—this is shown by curve *C* beyond point *b*. The experimental deviation shown by curve *D* indicates a lack of purity in the preparations used. It can be readily shown that, for a solid mixture of two components, the slope of segment *ab* is equal to the percentage of the less abundant component in the mixture. Experimentally, this value was found to be 0.31, instead of the correct value 0.35. Generally, curves of the type in figure 10 show whether or not a given compound is pure, and, under certain conditions,[40] the amount of impurity present.

(*3*) *Dependence of the solubility of some polystyrenes on molecular weight.* It has already been pointed out that the solubility relations of high polymers differ significantly from those of substances with smaller molecules. Most liquids can be classed either as solvents or as nonsolvents for a given type of polymer. When a solvent and a nonsolvent are miscible, addition of small quantities of the nonsolvent to a solution of polymer in the solvent liquid produces no visible change until, at a certain concentration, complete precipitation occurs over a very narrow range of solvent composition. It has been shown that the ratio of nonsolvent to solvent at incipient precipitation (precipitation value = γ) is a function of the concentration of the polymer and its average molecular weight or degree of polymerization:

$$\gamma = (a - \ln C)/b \text{ (for a constant molecular weight)}$$

$$\gamma = A + B/P \text{ (for a given polymer concentration)}$$

where C is the polymer concentration, P its average degree of polymerization, and a, b, A, and B empirical constants not independent of each other. Schulz and Jirgensons[41] have shown that these equations adequately repre-

[41] G. V. Schulz and B. Jirgensons, *Z. physik. Chem.*, **B46,** 105 (1940).

sent the experimental results, for instance, those obtained with some polystyrenes in mixtures of benzene and ethyl alcohol (Fig. 11).

The relation between solubility and degree of polymerization is a very useful one, since it provides a direct measure of mean particle size. It may also serve as a means of control in polymerization reactions, and has

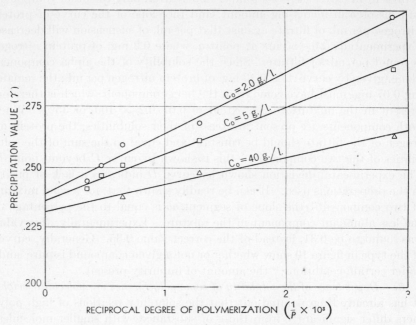

Fig. 11.—Precipitation values for polystyrenes of different degrees of polymerization at various concentrations in mixtures of ethyl alcohol with benzene.[41]

been used successfully to prepare polymer fractions that are fairly homogeneous in size.[42]

[42] R. M. Fuoss, *J. Am. Chem. Soc.*, **63**, 2401 (1941).

General References

Akerlof, G., *J. Am. Chem. Soc.*, **57**, 1196 (1935).

Beilstein, F. K., *Handbuch der organischen Chemie.* 4th ed., Springer, Berlin, 1928–1941.

Bowden, S. T., *The Phase Rule and Phase Reactions. Theoretical and Practical.* Macmillan, New York, 1938.

Cohn, E. J., and Edsall, J. T., *Proteins, Amino Acids and Peptides.* Reinhold, New York, 1943.

Findlay, A., *The Phase Rule and Its Applications*. Longmans, Green, New York, 1935.

Hildebrand, J. H., *Solubility*. 2nd ed., Reinhold, New York, 1936.

Hill, A. E., *J. Am. Chem. Soc.*, **45**, 1143 (1923).

Hill, A. E., and Loucks, C. M., *J. Am. Chem. Soc.*, **59**, 2094 (1937).

International Critical Tables. McGraw-Hill, New York, 1926.

Kolthoff, I., and Rosenblum, C., *J. Am. Chem. Soc.*, **56**, 1264 (1934).

Landolt-Börnstein, *Physikalisch-chemische Tabellen*. 5th ed., Springer, Berlin, 1923–1936.

Lassar-Cohn, *Organic Laboratory Methods*. English translation by Oesper. Williams & Wilkins, Baltimore, 1928.

McBain, J. W., *Advances in Colloid Science*, Vol. 1. Interscience, New York, 1942.

Mark, H., and Raff, R., *High Polymeric Reactions*. Interscience, New York, 1941.

Meyer, K. H., *Natural and Synthetic High Polymers*. Interscience, New York, 1942.

Menzies, A. W. C., *J. Am. Chem. Soc.*, **58**, 934 (1936).

Moll, W. L. H., *Kolloid-Beihefte*, **49**, 1, (1939).

Nelson, O. A., and Haring, M. M., *J. Am. Chem. Soc.*, **59**, 2216 (1937).

Northrop, J. H., *Crystalline Enzymes*. Columbia Univ. Press, New York, 1939.

Ostwald-Luther, *Physiko-chemischer Messungen*. Akadem. Verlagsgesellschaft, Leipzig, 1931; Fifth Edition by C. Drucker, Dover Publications, New York, 1943.

Othmer, D. F., White, R. E., and Trueger, E., *Ind. Eng. Chem.*, *Ind. Ed.*, **33**, 1240 (1941).

Reilly, J., and Rae, W. N., *Physico-chemical Methods*. 3rd ed., Van Nostrand, New York, 1939.

Schulz, G. V., *Z. physik. Chem.*, **184**, 1 (1939).

Seidell, A., *Solubilities of Organic Compounds*. 3rd ed., Vol. II, Van Nostrand, New York, 1941.

Shriner, R. L., and Fuson, R. C., *Systematic Identification of Organic Compounds*. 2nd ed., Wiley, New York, 1940.

Symposia on Quantitative Biology. Vol. VI, Cold Spring Harbor, L. I., N. Y., 1938.

CHAPTER V

Determination of
VISCOSITY

H. Mark, *Polytechnic Institute of Brooklyn*

I. INTRODUCTION

The viscosity of liquids and solutions is a quantity comparatively easy to measure but rather difficult to interpret from the molecular point of view.

For the last two decades attempts have been repeatedly made[1,2] to correlate the viscosity of organic liquids, such as hydrocarbons, polyesters, etc., with the size and shape of the molecules of the substance. An empirical equation was proposed by Flory[3] which relates with fair accuracy the molecular weight of chainlike, kinked molecules of an homologous or polymer-homologous series to the viscosity of the pure liquid (or melt) and to the temperature. An empirical equation has also been proposed by Staudinger[4] to correlate the viscosity of a dilute solution of organic poly-

---

[1] Wilhelm Ostwald—Viscosimeter. Compare E. Hatschek, *Die Viskosität der Flüssigkeiten.* Steinkopff, Dresden and Leipzig, 1929.

[2] Compare E. Ott, ed., *Cellulose and Cellulose Derivatives.* Interscience, New York, 1943, particularly the contributions of M. L. Huggins and H. M. Spurlin.

[3] P. J. Flory, *J. Am. Chem. Soc.,* **62**, 1057 (1940).

[4] H. Staudinger, *Die hochmolekularen organischen Verbindungen.* Springer, Berlin, 1932. See also: H. Staudinger and H. Warth, *J. prakt. Chem.,* **155**, 261 (1940); H. Staudinger and K. Fischer, *ibid.,* **157**, 19, 158 (1941).

mers with the average molecular weight of the dissolved material.   This
equation has succeeded in some cases and failed in others.   It has recently
been replaced by more reliable expressions, based on the investigations of
Alfrey,[5] Bartovics,[5] Baker,[6] Flory,[7] Fordyce,[8] Fuller,[6] Fuoss,[9] Heiss,[6]
Hibbert,[8] Huggins,[10] Mead,[9] Meyer,[11] and van der Wijk.[11]

At present, it is a general assumption that viscosity measurements of
liquids and solutions containing chainlike molecules of low and high
molecular weight can contribute valuable information on the size (or
average size) of the molecules of the material under investigation.

II.   DEFINITIONS

The *viscosity* of a liquid system (melt or solution) can be defined as the
force per unit area necessary to maintain a unit velocity gradient between
two parallel planes kept at a unit distance apart.

$$\eta = \tau/(dv/dx) \tag{1}$$

where τ = force per unit area acting parallel to the planes = shearing force
in dynes per cm.^{2}; dv/dx = velocity gradient perpendicular to the plates,
in cm. sec.$^{-1}$; and η = viscosity in g. cm.$^{-1}$ sec.$^{-1}$.

The absolute unit of viscosity is the poise, defined as the viscosity of a
material which requires a shearing force of 1 dyne per cm.^{2} to maintain a
velocity gradient of 1 cm. per sec. between two planes 1 cm. apart.   This
unit is named after the French physician, J. L. M. Poiseuille, who, in 1846,
published a very careful and exhaustive study[12] of the flow of liquids
through narrow capillaries.   Table I shows the viscosities of several liquid
systems in poises; these values vary between 10^{-3} and 10^2 poises.

Viscous flow is a frictional phenomenon; and therefore viscosity can
also be expressed by the kinetic energy converted into heat per unit of
time and volume, divided by the square of the velocity gradient:

$$\eta = q/(dv/dx)^2 \tag{2}$$

where q = kinetic energy transformed into heat in ergs per sec. per cm.^{3}

[5] T. Alfrey, A. Bartovics, and H. Mark, *J. Am. Chem. Soc.*, **65**, 2319 (1943).

[6] C. S. Fuller, W. O. Baker, and J. H. Heiss, Jr., *J. Am. Chem. Soc.*, **63**, 3316 (1941).

[7] P. J. Flory, *J. Am. Chem. Soc.*, **65**, 372 (1943).

[8] R. Fordyce and H. Hibbert, *J. Am. Chem. Soc.*, **61**, 1912 (1939).   E. Lovell and
H. Hibbert, *ibid.*, **62**, 2140 (1940).

[9] R. M. Fuoss and D. J. Mead, *J. Phys. Chem.*, **47**, 59 (1943).

[10] M. L. Huggins, *J. Am. Chem. Soc.*, **64**, 2716 (1942).

[11] K. H. Meyer and A. van der Wijk, *Helv. Chim. Acta*, **18**, 1067 (1935); **19**, 218
(1936).

[12] J. L. M. Poiseuille, *Mém. Savants Étrangers*, **9**, 433 (1846); see E. C. Bingham,
Fluidity and Plasticity, McGraw-Hill, New York, 1922, pp. 331–338.

TABLE I

VISCOSITIES AND FLUIDITIES OF SOME LIQUIDS AND SOLUTIONS

System	Temp., ° C.	Viscosity, poises	Fluidity, rhes
n-Pentane	0	0.003	330
Water	0	0.018	55
Glycol	0	0.022	45
Butanol	0	0.052	19
Octane	0	0.071	14
Olive oil	0	1.38	0.72
60% Sugar in water	0	2.4	0.42
Glycerol	20	8.3	0.12
Castor oil	10	25	0.04
15% Cellulose acetate in acetone	40	85	0.012

Fluidity, defined as

$$\varphi = 1/\eta \tag{3}$$

is measured in reciprocal poises or "rhes" (from the greek *rhein*, to flow). Its dimension is cm.-sec. g.$^{-1}$.

III. APPARATUS AND CONDITIONS FOR VISCOSITY MEASUREMENTS

Many methods exist for measuring viscosity[1, 13-15]; but for the organic chemist, who usually encounters systems of viscosities between 10^{-2} and 10^2 poises, one method is superior to all the others by virtue of its simplicity and accuracy, the measurement of the rate of flow of a liquid through a capillary under constant pressure. This was successfully used in early investigations by Bingham,[13, 14] Couette,[16] Hagen,[17] Hagenbach[18] and Poiseuille,[12] and has more recently been virtually standardized by the capillary viscometers of Ostwald[1] and of Ubbelohde.[19] The method is generally employed to determine the viscosity of a given liquid *relative* to that of a standard substance. For pure liquids or melts, a well-known fluid of similar viscosity is used as a standard; for solutions, the measured viscosity is usually referred to that of the solvent.

Figure 1 illustrates the principle employed in the design of the Ostwald

[13] E. C. Bingham, *J. Am. Chem. Soc.*, **46**, 959 (1913).

[14] E. C. Bingham, *J. Am. Chem. Soc.*, **43**, 302 (1910).

[15] R. Houwink, *J. prakt. Chem.*, **157**, 15 (1940).

[16] M. Couette, *Ann. chim. phys.*, **21**, 433 (1890).

[17] G. Hagen, *Ann. Physik*, **46**, 413 (1839).

[18] E. Hagenbach, *Ann. Physik*, **109**, 385 (1860).

[19] L. Ubbelohde, *Handbuch der Chemie und Technologie der Öle*, **1**, 340 (1908). For more special designs, see *Ind. Eng. Chem., Anal. Ed.*, **9**, 85 (1937).

viscometer.[19a]   An accurately measured (pipette) volume of the standard liquid is placed at a carefully controlled temperature in the wide arm of the U-shaped tube, and is then sucked through the capillary until its meniscus is somewhat above mark A.   The liquid flows back under its own weight.   The time, t_0, required for the meniscus to fall from A to B is measured by an accurate stop watch.   The viscosity, η_0, of the standard is then given by:

$$\eta_0 = C\rho_0 t_0 \tag{4}$$

where η_0 is the known viscosity of the standard substance and ρ_0 is the known density of the standard substance, both at the temperature of the experiment. C is the calibration constant of the instrument, which can be determined from equation (4).   The procedure is then repeated, exactly as performed the first time, with the liquid to be investigated and the result is expressed as:

$$\eta = C\rho t \tag{5}$$

where ρ is the density of the liquid and t the time observed in the second experiment.   Dividing equation (5) by (4), one obtains

$$\eta = \eta_0(\rho t/\rho_0 t_0) \tag{6}$$

which expresses the unknown viscosity η in terms of the known viscosity η_0, the two densities involved, and the measured efflux times.

Several conditions must be met to permit an accurate measurement of viscosity.   These conditions are discussed in the following sections.

1.   Flow Characteristics of the Liquid

In order to apply the methods described and to use the quantity η as defined in equations (1) and (2), the system must be a Newtonian liquid, i. e., the rate of shear must be proportional to the shearing stress.   This condition is obtained or very nearly obtained for all dilute solutions of organic substances or polymers if the concentration is below about 1% and the flow is sufficiently slow.   Most organic liquids having viscosities below 100 poises also behave as Newtonian fluids if the temperature is sufficiently above the melting point and the flow sufficiently slow.

In general it seems advisable so to choose the dimensions of the instrument (length and diameter of the capillary) and the standard liquid that both t_0 and t are between 100 and 200 seconds.   The optimum volume of the liquid is between 2 and 5 ml.   However, microviscometers have been devised which use as little as 0.5 ml. of liquid.[19b]

[19a] For special designs, see, for example, M. R. Cannon and M. R. Fenske, *Ind. Eng. Chem., Anal. Ed.*, **10**, 297 (1938).

[19b] Compare E. Hatschek, *Die Viskosität der Flüssigkeiten.*   Steinkopff, Dresden and Leipzig, 1929.

2. Purity of the Liquid

It is very important that both liquids be as free as possible from dust, filter fibers, or any other impurity which may jam the capillary and hinder the flow. Measurements repeated in different instruments are the best means of demonstrating errors arising from this source.

3. Temperature Constancy

Viscosity changes very rapidly with temperature. It is therefore essential to carry out all viscosity measurements in a thermostat which can be controlled to about $\pm 0.1°$ C.

4. Pressure Constancy

The flow of the liquid through the capillary of the U tube in figure 1 does not take place under strictly constant pressure, but under an average pressure. If the pipette is not filled with the liquids at the same temperature at which the measurements are carried out, a different thermal expansion of the two liquids which are being compared will cause different average pressures under which they flow.

5. Kinetic Energy and Surface Tension Effects

The pressure driving the liquid through the capillary is not entirely available for overcoming the viscosity. A portion of the energy is expended in accelerating the liquid in the various parts of the (Ostwald) viscometer. The reduction of the effective pressure can be calculated and a correction applied.[20] However, results of good accuracy can be obtained without this by choosing a standard liquid the viscosity of which is approximately the same as that of the system under consideration. The inherent error is much greater when comparing liquids (or solutions) of low viscosity than it is when comparing liquids of high viscosity, other factors being equal.

Capillary effects may cause a reduction in the effective pressure and similarly introduce an error in the measurement.[21] It is, therefore, advisable to compare liquids of similar surface tension.

Equation (6) requires not only the viscosity of the standard liquid and the efflux times as measured during the experiments, but also the densities ρ_0 and ρ. In most cases these either will be known or can be obtained without difficulty. To avoid the use of density data, however, another instrument may be employed. Figure 2 shows the Ubbelohde viscometer[19]

[20] E. C. Bingham, *Fluidity and Plasticity*. McGraw-Hill, New York, 1922, pp. 17 *et seq.*

[21] G. Jones and H. J. Fornwalt, *J. Am. Chem. Soc.*, **60**, 1683 (1938).

in which flow takes place under a carefully controlled air pressure. A measured volume of liquid is introduced into the instrument at a given temperature in such a way that one meniscus is somewhat above a, the other somewhat below b'. Then the liquid is slowly moved from the ball

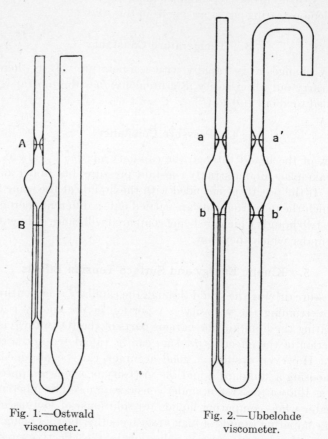

Fig. 1.—Ostwald
viscometer.

Fig. 2.—Ubbelohde
viscometer.

between a and b to the sphere (of identical size) between a' and b'. The time which elapses between the passing of the meniscus through b' and a' is measured. If the pressure is kept constant, the viscosity of the liquid under consideration is given by:

$$\eta = \eta_0(t/t_0) \tag{7}$$

where t and t_0 are the efflux times for the two liquids and η_0 is the viscosity of the standard substance. It has been found advantageous to work with times between 100 and 200 seconds.

Table II gives actual measurements of the viscosity of a polystyrene solution in toluene. First the standard value was determined twice, then four measurements of the solution, two measurements of the solvent, four measurements of the solution, and again two measurements of the

TABLE II

POLYSTYRENE FRACTION DISSOLVED IN TOLUENE

Volume concentration, 0.24%; temperature, 26.5° C.

Substance	Time, sec.	Substance	Time, sec.
Pure solvent	67.2	Pure solvent	67.0
Pure solvent	67.6	Solution	81.0
Solution	81.4	Solution	81.2
Solution	81.6	Solution	80.8
Solution	80.8	Solution	81.4
Solution	81.2	Pure solvent	67.2
Pure solvent	67.4	Pure solvent	67.6

Average t_0 for pure solvent = 67.33 seconds
Average t for solution = 81.18 seconds
$\eta_{sp.} = (t - t_0)/t_0 = 13.85/67.33 = 0.206$

solvent. The final value is therefore an average of 14 individual observations and can be considered sufficiently accurate and reliable for most purposes.

IV. INTERPRETATION OF THE RESULTS

Evaluation of the experimental results must take into account whether one is investigating a liquid or a solution.

1. Pure Liquids or Melts

Very early attempts were made[13, 14, 22-24] to correlate the viscosity of a liquid with the structure of the molecules of which it is composed; and—as is usual in organic chemistry—homologous series were first investigated. The aim was to find something like an "atomic" or "group" viscosity characteristic for certain atoms or atomic groups with the aid of which one could build up the viscosity of the whole molecule. This would be an obvious analogy to atomic and group refraction and to atomic or group polarization, which, to a certain extent, show a rather satisfactory additive behavior. Thorpe and Rodger[24] found, in fact, that in a homologous series each additional CH_2 group contributes an increment to the

[22] R. Przibram and A. Hanell, *Sitzber. Akad. Wiss. Wien*, **78**, 113 (1878); **80**, 17 (1879).
[23] L. Rellstab, *Transpiration homologer Flüssigkeiten.* Bonn, 1868.
[24] T. E. Thorpe and J. W. Rodger, *Proc. Roy. Soc. London*, **A60**, 152 (1896).

viscosity. However, these increments are not constant; they depend upon the number of CH_2 groups already present, upon the end groups, and upon the temperature. Bingham[13, 14] later very extensively studied the correlation between viscosity and molecular constitution. He pointed out that the fluidity (reciprocal viscosity) is better suited for an investigation of this kind. In comparing different members of an homologous series at constant fluidity (instead of constant temperatures), he found that the increments for the CH_2 group were more regular than previously observed.

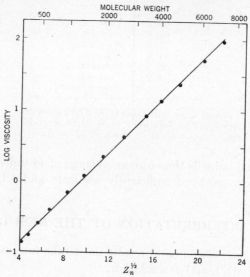

Fig. 3.—Relation between melt viscosity and molecular weight of polyesters.

However, as soon as one abandons the restriction on homologous series and attempts to correlate in a more general way viscosity (or fluidity) with chemical constitution, it becomes clear that it is a very complicated problem and that no definite statements can be made at present. This is perhaps not surprising, because viscosity depends not only upon the size and shape of the molecules of the liquid, but also very clearly upon their mutual interaction by van der Waals' forces.

Eyring and his collaborators[25] have recently shown that the viscosity of liquids can be very successfully correlated with other physical properties of the material such as compressibility, heat of fusion, entropy of fusion, etc.; but no general direct link has yet been established between viscosity and the chemical constitution of organic substances. There seems to be,

[25] R. E. Powell, E. A. Roseveare, and H. Eyring, *Ind. Eng. Chem., Ind. Ed.*, **33**, 430 (1941). R. E. Powell, C. R. Clark, and H. Eyring, *J. Chem. Phys.*, **9**, 268 (1941).

however, one case, in which the weight of the molecules of a liquid or melt can be determined with fair accuracy from viscosity measurements. Flory[3] observed that the molecular weights of linear polyesters can be correlated with their viscosity by the following equation:

$$\log \eta = A + BM^{1/2} - C/T \tag{8}$$

where η = viscosity in poises at temperature T; M = weight average molecular weight; and A, B, and C = constants characteristic for a given polymer homologous series. Equation (8), which was first established as an empirical relationship, conforms—as Flory[3] points out—with Eyring's theory of viscosity and with the assumption of linear, flexible, randomly kinked macromolecules.

Figure 3 illustrates how closely equation (8) represents the molecular weights of polyhexamethyleneglycol adipates over a range from 200 to 8000. Table III contains the values for the three constants A, B, and C as far as they have been determined to date.

TABLE III

VALUES OF A, B, AND C IN EQUATION (8) FOR A FEW HIGH POLYMERS[a]

Substances	T, ° C.	A	B	C
Decamethylene sebacate	109	−1.429	1760	0.1108
Decamethylene adipate	109	−1.435	1800	0.1144
Decamethylene succinate	109	−1.37	1870	0.112
Diethylene adipate	109	−1.213	1840	0.0992

[a] All figures from P. J. Flory, *J. Am. Chem. Soc.*, **62**, 1057 (1940).

2. Solutions

It was early recognized, and first expressed by Berl[26] and Biltz,[27] that a general relation exists between the viscosity of a solution and the molecular weight of the solute. However, no mathematical formulation of this relation was given until Staudinger[4] proposed his well-known viscosity rule, choosing for the comparisons not the viscosity η_c of a solution with concentration c, but the relative increase of the viscosity η_0 of the solvent due to the presence of the dissolved material. This is given by:

$$\eta_{sp.} = (\eta_c - \eta_0)/\eta_0 \tag{9}$$

and is called the *specific viscosity*. Kraemer,[28, 29] and recently particularly

[26] E. Berl, *Z. ges. Schiess- u. Sprengstoffw.*, **5**, 82 (1910).
[27] W. Biltz, *Z. physik. Chem.*, **73**, 481 (1910); **83**, 625, 683 (1913).
[28] E. O. Kraemer, *Ind. Eng. Chem., Ind. Ed.*, **30**, 1200 (1938).
[29] E. O. Kraemer and W. D. Lansing, *J. Phys. Chem.*, **39**, 153 (1935).

Huggins,[10] have shown that this specific viscosity, even in very dilute solutions, depends upon the concentration, c, of the solute according to:

$$\eta_{sp.} = Ac + Bc^2 \tag{10}$$

c being expressed in units of grams of solute per 100 ml. of solution. This unit of concentration is used throughout the chapter. Plotting $\eta_{sp.}/c$ against c yields a straight line with the intercept A and the slope B. A represents the limiting value of $\eta_{sp.}/c$ at infinite dilution. According to Huggins, equation (10) becomes:

$$\eta_{sp.}/c = [\eta] + k'[\eta]^2 c + \ldots \tag{11}$$

where $[\eta]$ is the intrinsic viscosity, defined by Kraemer[28] as:

$$[\eta] \equiv \left(\frac{\ln \eta_r}{c}\right)_{c=0} = \left(\frac{2.303 \log_{10} \eta_r}{c}\right)_{c=0} \tag{12}$$

where η_r is the relative viscosity $= \eta_{sp.} + 1$. It is evident from equation (11) that the intrinsic viscosity is identical with the value of the ratio, $\eta_{sp.}/c$, at infinite dilution. This means that $[\eta]$ both determines the intercept and influences the slope, as already observed by Staudinger[4] and recently confirmed by Schulz and Blaschke,[30] Kemp and Peters,[31] and others. The constant, k', is characteristic of a certain solute–solvent system.

The Staudinger rule postulates that the molecular weight of a high polymer is directly proportional to the specific viscosity of its dilute solution:

$$\eta_{sp}/c = K_i M \tag{13}$$

where K is a constant. At infinite dilution, equation (13) reduces to:

$$[\eta] = K_i M \tag{14}$$

Eq. (13) has been, and is being, widely used to estimate the order of magnitude of the molecular weight of high polymers. It has proved to be useful in some cases, but has failed seriously in others. It should be emphasized that K_m values as reported by Staudinger and coworkers are given in *Grundmolar*, *i. e.*, weight concentration in grams per liter divided by the molecular weight of the repeating unit of the polymer. Therefore K_i of equations (13), (14), (15), and (16) is proportional to, but not identical with, Staudinger's K_m constant.

Recent more systematic studies have shown that two improvements are necessary to establish a quantitative correlation between intrinsic viscosity and molecular weight.

[30] G. V. Schulz and B. Jirgensons, *Z. physik. Chem.*, **B46**, 105 (1940). G. V. Schulz and F. Blaschke, *J. prakt. Chem.*, **158**, 130 (1941).

[31] A. R. Kemp and H. Peters, *Ind. Eng. Chem., Ind. Ed.*, **33**, 1263 (1941); **34**, 1192 (1942).

(a) In the domain of comparatively small molecular weights (up to about 6000 or 8000) Meyer and van der Wijk,[11] Hibbert and Fordyce,[8] Fuller, Baker, and Heiss,[6] and Fuoss and Mead[9] have shown that equation (14) must be replaced by:

$$[\eta] = K_i M + K_0 \tag{15}$$

Instead of a single constant, K_i, two characteristic constants, K_i and K_0, are needed for each solute–solvent system. Table IV gives the constants known to date expressed in concentration units of gram per 100 milliliters.

If the molecular weight of a linear polymer in this range is to be determined, it is therefore best to measure the specific viscosity at a low concentration (c around 1.00 g. per 100 ml.) and to compute M from equation (15) with the aid of the two constants, K_0 and K_i, as taken from table IV.

TABLE IV

VALUES OF K_i AND K_0 FOR A FEW HIGH POLYMERS

IN THE EQUATION: $\left(\dfrac{\ln \eta_r}{c}\right)_{c=0} = K_i M + K_0$

System	T, ° C.	K_i	K_0
Polyoxyethylene glycol in carbon tetrachloride[a]	20	0.83×10^{-5}	0.034
Polydecamethylene glycol adipate in diethyl succinate[b]	79	1.25×10^{-5}	0.042
Same polymer in chlorobenzene[b]	25	2.12×10^{-5}	0.060
Same polymer in chlorobenzene[b]	79	1.87×10^{-5}	0.032
n-Paraffins in carbon tetrachloride[c]	25	10.40×10^{-5}	0.011

[a] R. Fordyce and H. Hibbert, *J. Am. Chem. Soc.*, **61**, 1912 (1939).
[b] P. J. Flory and P. B. Stickney, *J. Am. Chem. Soc.*, **62**, 3032 (1940).
[c] K. H. Meyer and A. van der Wijk, *Helv. Chim. Acta*, **18**, 1067 (1935).

It should be emphasized that all high polymers are mixtures of molecules having different degrees of polymerization. Therefore, M in equations (8), (13), (14), and (15) represents only an average value of the actual molecular weight distribution curve. If equation (15) is used, this average is identical with the weight average molecular weight of Kraemer.[28]

(b) In the domain of high degrees of polymerization (molecular weights above 10,000), Alfrey,[5] Bartovics,[5] Flory,[7] Houwink,[15] Huggins,[2, 10] Schulz,[30] and others[32] have found that (14) must be replaced by:

$$[\eta] = K M^a \tag{16}$$

where K and a are two constants characteristic of a given solute–solvent system. Table V contains values for K and a as available to date. If the molecular weight of a linear polymer in this range is to be obtained, it is

[32] H. Mark, *Z. Electrochem.*, **40**, 449 (1934); see also in *Der feste Körper*, S. Hirzel, Leipzig, 1938.

best to determine $\eta_{sp.}/c$ at four or five concentrations (c between 0.2 and 0.8 g. per 100 ml.), to draw the straight line given by equation (11), and

TABLE V

VALUES FOR K AND a FOR A FEW HIGH POLYMER SOLUTIONS*

System	$T, °C.$	K	a
Nitrocellulose in acetone[a]	27	3.8×10^{-5}	1.0
Cellulose acetate in acetone[b]	25	9.1×10^{-4}	0.67
Polyisobutylene in diisobutylene[c]	20	3.6×10^{-4}	0.64
Polystyrene prepared at 60° C. in toluene[d]	30	1.2×10^{-4}	0.71
Polystyrene prepared at 120° C. in toluene[d]	30	5.4×10^{-4}	0.81
Polystyrene prepared at 180° C. in toluene[d]	30	9.8×10^{-5}	1.1
Polymethylmethacrylate in acetone[i]	30	1.6×10^{-4}	0.67
Polyvinyl acetate in acetone[e]	30	2.8×10^{-4}	0.67
Polyvinyl alcohol in water[e]	30	5.9×10^{-4}	0.67
Poly-ε-aminocaprolactam in concentrated sulfuric acid[e]	20	2.5×10^{-4}	0.67
Poly-ε-aminocaprolactam in 40% sulfuric acid[e]	20	2.4×10^{-4}	0.51
ω-Polyhydroxyundecanoic acid in chloroform[f]	25	3.2×10^{-5}	1.0
Cellulose in cuprammonium oxide[g]	25	1.8×10^{-3}	0.72
Polyvinyl chloride in cyclohexanone[h]	25	1.1×10^{-5}	1.0
Polyvinylchloride acetate in cyclohexanone[i]	60	....	1.10
Copolymer of butadiene and styrene in toluene[j]	25	4.4×10^{-4}	0.67
Amylose in ethylenediamine[k]	25	....	1.5

* The K values are all computed under the assumption that the concentration of the solution is expressed in g. solute per 100 ml. of solution. Some articles (or abstracts of them) do not clearly indicate which units were used for the computation of the intrinsic viscosity. In such cases, the table contains only the value for a, which does not depend upon the unit in which the concentration is expressed.

[a] See the comprehensive article by M. L. Huggins, *Ind. Eng. Chem., Ind. Ed.*, **35**, 980 (1943). According to H. Mosiman, *Helv. Chim. Acta*, **26**, 61, 369 (1943), and N. Gralén, *Inaugural Dissertation*, Uppsala, 1944, the value of a for nitrocellulose in acetone is somewhat smaller than 1.0.

[b] A. Bartovics and H. Mark, *J. Am. Chem. Soc.*, **65**, 1901 (1943). More recent measurements of A. M. Sookne, W. Badgley and M. Jelling (unpublished) indicate that the value of a for cellulose acetate in acetone is somewhat larger than 0.67.

[c] P. J. Flory, *J. Am. Chem. Soc.*, **65**, 372 (1943).

[d] T. Alfrey, A. Bartovics, and H. Mark, *J. Am. Chem. Soc.*, **65**, 2319 (1943). The values given in this table deviate from those in the paper partly because other units of concentration are used, and partly because Drs. R. Spencer and L. R. Drake of the Dow Chemical Company have recently improved the calculation. The author is indebted to Drs. Spencer and Drake for this communication and has used their values in table V.

[e] A. Matthes, *J. prakt. Chem.*, **162**, 245 (1943).

[f] W. O. Baker, C. S. Fuller, and J. H. Heiss, Jr., *J. Am. Chem. Soc.*, **63**, 3313 (1941).

[g] Computed form data of N. Gralén, *thesis*, Uppsala, 1944; see also N. Gralén and T. Svedberg, *Nature*, **152**, 625 (1943).

[h] D. J. Mead and R. M. Fuoss, *J. Am. Chem. Soc.*, **64**, 277 (1942).

[i] Unpublished measurements by P. M. Doty, V. Auerbach and M. Jelling at the Polytechnic Institute of Brooklyn.

[j] H. Staudinger and K. Fischer, *J. prakt. Chem.*, **157**, 19 (1940).

[k] J. F. Foster and R. M. Hixon, *J. Am. Chem. Soc.*, **66**, 557 (1944).

[l] H. Staudinger and W. Warth, *J. prakt. Chem.*, **155**, 261 (1940).

to locate $[\eta]$ by extrapolation. If the value of k' is known, a viscosity determination at a single concentration suffices to determine $[\eta]$. With the value for $[\eta]$ and the appropriate constants K and a taken from table V, the molecular weight can be computed from equation (16).

Again, it should be emphasized an average value is obtained which, in the case of $a = 1$, is identical with Kraemer's weight average molecular weight. If a is either smaller or larger than one, the average is a somewhat complicated value, which Flory has termed the *viscosity average molecular weight*.

As far as our present knowledge goes, it seems that equation (16) permits the determination with rather fair accuracy of the viscosity average molecular weights of many high polymers over a wide degree of polymerization range.

General References

Bingham, E. C., *Fluidity and Plasticity.* McGraw-Hill, New York, 1922.

Hatschek, E., *Die Viskosität der Flüssigkeiten.* Steinkopff, Dresden and Leipzig, 1929.

Mark, H., *Der feste Körper.* S. Hirzel, Leipzig, 1938.

Ott, E., ed., *Cellulose and Cellulose Derivatives.* Interscience, New York, 1943

Staudinger, H., *Die hochmolekularen organischen Verbindungen.* Springer, Berlin, 1932.

Ubbelohde, L., *Handbuch der Chemie und Technologie der Öle,* **1**, 340 (1908).

CHAPTER VI

Determination of
SURFACE AND INTERFACIAL TENSION

WILLIAM D. HARKINS, *University of Chicago and Universal Oil Products Co.*

SECTION ON **Parachor** by GEORGE W. THOMSON, *Ethyl Corporation*

I. INTRODUCTION

The region in which two phases meet is designated in general as an interface, and an interface between a gaseous and another phase may be con sidered specifically as a surface, although this term, as commonly used, indicates any type of interface. Although interfaces are at most only a few molecules thick, they are present in many systems, for example in the human body, where they are no less important than the phases which they inclose. There are many factors which make the energy of surfaces of paramount importance. Whenever material passes from one phase to another, it must all pass through the surface or interface, so the surface plays an important part in such phenomena as vaporization and condensation. In processes such as adsorption, diffusion through an interface, photoelectric or thermo-ionic emission of electrons, adsorption accompanied by catalysis, and reactions in nonhomogeneous systems, the material passes either through or into or out of surface regions. Moreover, the study of friction, lubrication, and adhesion involves the study of surface energy.

The surface even becomes of greater importance as the volume which it incloses becomes very small. The possession of a large surface with a small volume is the principal characteristic of the phenomena which are classed together as colloidal. Thus, a colloid is distinguished by the fact that the surface energy has a value which is an appreciable fraction of the molecular kinetic energy of the dispersed phase. For example, if one milliliter of water is sprayed into spherical droplets 0.01μ (10^{-6} cm.) in diameter, the superficial area of the droplets is 600 square meters. The free surface energy for this area at ordinary temperatures is about 2.18×10^8 ergs or 10.5 calories, while what is sometimes called the total energy of the surface would be about 16.6 calories, or one-third as much as the kinetic energy of vibration of the water molecules.

The importance of interfaces arises also from their abundance. Most solids, including cast iron, steel, stone, etc., consist of small crystals, each of which is bounded by an interface. These exist around every cell in the plant or animal body, around the nucleus or nuclei of each cell, around the fibrils, nuclei, nucleoli, chromosomes, genes, and other subdivisions of cells, and on both sides of each membrane. The examination under the microscope or ultramicroscope proves, too, that so-called homogeneous fluid systems, such as air, water, etc., actually contain an enormous number of minute interfaces. In Sugden's parachor (page 201), the surface tension is combined with data on density to give a function of considerable interest in connection with structural problems.

II. GENERAL CONSIDERATIONS

1. Reality of Surface Tension and Some Thermodynamic Relations

Some more recent writers depart from the older methods of thought, and introduce surface tension as hypothetical, or fictitious. That there is a true mechanical tension in the surface of a liquid is shown by many phenomena, and is demonstrated very simply by the Dupré frame (Fig. 1), in which a film of soap solution is stretched on a vertical rectangular framework of wire. The lower horizontal wire is free to move, and, provided the friction is sufficiently small, will move upward if the total tension, t, of the soap film is greater than the weight, W (which includes that of the wire), and downward if W is the greater. If γ represents the surface tension of the film per cm. and l the length of its attachment to the movable wire, then, since the film has two surfaces, the length of the boundary between the two surfaces and the wire is $2l$, and

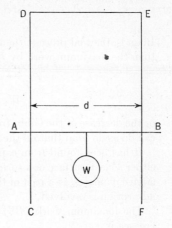

$$\gamma = t/2l \qquad (1)$$

If l is 5 cm. and t is 250 dynes, then $\gamma = 25$ dyne cm.$^{-1}$ Now if the wire is pulled downward 10 cm. $(= d)$, while γ remains constant (which may occur if the total area, Σ, of the surface of the soap film is sufficiently large, and the concentration of the soap sufficiently high), then, the area of the surface increases by 100 cm.^{2}, and the work done, $i.\ e.$, the increase of free surface energy, is $t \times d = 250 \times 10 = 2500$ ergs or 25 erg cm.$^{-2}$

Fig. 1.—Dupré frame.

In isolated system, any actual change is accompanied by an increase of entropy. The problem of the type of change is simplified by a consideration of two thermodynamic functions used by Gibbs:

$$A = E - TS \text{ (Helmholtz free energy)} \qquad (2)$$

and:

$$F = (E + PV) - TS = H - TS = A + PV \text{ (Gibbs free energy)} \qquad (3)$$

in which E is the internal energy of the system and S, its entropy. By differentiation:

$$dA = dE - TdS - SdT \qquad (2a)$$

$$dF = dE - TdS - SdT - PdV - VdP \qquad (3a)$$

At a constant temperature, a change of a system from one state to another increases the Helmholtz free energy by:

$$\Delta A = \Delta E - T\Delta S \qquad (4)$$

and if the process is reversible, then:

$$Q = T\Delta S \text{ since } Q/T = \Delta S \qquad (5)$$

so:

$$\Delta A = \Delta E \qquad (6)$$

By the first law of thermodynamics,

$$W = -\Delta E \tag{7}$$

where W is the *maximum work* which can be obtained from the system in the particular change; or the work done by the system equals its decrease of internal energy, and, therefore:

$$-\Delta A = W \tag{8}$$

In an isothermal process, the net work obtained at a constant pressure (W_p) is less than the maximum work by $P\Delta V$:

$$W_p = W - P\Delta V \tag{9}$$

$$W_p = -\Delta F = W - P\Delta V \tag{10}$$

or the decrease of the Gibbs free energy gives the maximum work which the system can do aside from that on the surroundings at constant pressure.

It has been found from experience that thermodynamic equations are valid for either a clean surface or a surface covered by an insoluble film without including the adjacent phases as a part of the system. It is obvious that this cannot be true if adsorption is involved.

The maximum work (dW) for a system when its area (Σ) is increased or decreased is:

$$dW = -\gamma d\Sigma - pdv \tag{11}$$

where γ is the surface tension. If the process is isothermal and reversible:

$$dA = -dW \tag{12}$$

and:

$$dF = \gamma d\Sigma + vdp \tag{13}$$

So, if p is constant,

$$(\partial F/\partial \Sigma)_{p,T} = \gamma \tag{14}$$

and

$$(\partial F/\partial \Sigma)_{p,T}\, d\Sigma = \gamma d\Sigma \tag{15}$$

The heat content or enthalpy, H, is defined by:

$$H = E + pv \tag{16}$$

so

$$dH = dE + pdv + vdp \tag{17}$$

From equation (3):

$$H = F + ST \tag{18}$$

or

$$dH = dF + TdS + SdT \tag{19}$$

In changes in the area of a surface, it is convenient to designate by small letters any change of energy for a unit increase of area. Thus:

$$h = (\partial H/\partial \sigma)_T \tag{20}$$

From the first and second laws of thermodynamics it may be shown very simply that:

$$h = \gamma - T\left(\frac{\partial \gamma}{\partial T}\right)_{p,\Sigma} = \gamma + l \tag{21}$$

where $l = - T (\partial/\partial T)_{p,\Sigma}$ is the latent heat of the surface. Equation (21) may be obtained directly from (19), since the entropy, s per unit area is given by:

$$s = -(\partial \gamma/\partial T)_{p,\Sigma} \tag{22}$$

Let the internal or total surface energy per cm.² be designated by ϵ, then:

$$\epsilon = (\partial E/\partial \Sigma)_{p,T} \tag{23}$$

For a system at constant pressure, equation (17) gives:

$$\epsilon = h - p\,\Delta v \tag{24}$$

Now the change of volume of a liquid when its area increases by 1 cm.² at constant p and T is extremely small, and is negligible as compared with the value of h, so:

$$\epsilon \cong h \equiv \left[\gamma - T\left(\frac{\partial \gamma}{\partial T}\right)_{p,\Sigma}\right] \tag{25}$$

while not absolutely true, is correct within the limits of error of the most accurate experimental work.

Consider a bar of liquid one square centimeter in cross section (Fig. 2). Let this be pulled apart in a plane (area = 1 cm.²) The work done *on* the system is:

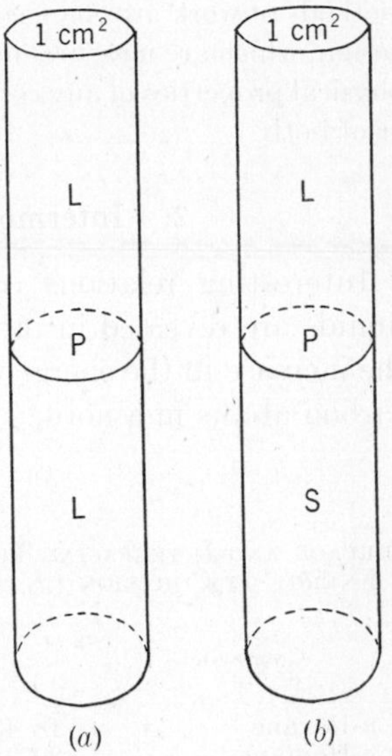

$$w_c = 2\gamma \tag{26}$$

and the increase of energy of the system is:

$$\Delta E = \Delta H = 2h = 2\epsilon \tag{27}$$

Fig. 2.—(a) If a cylinder of liquid 1 sq. cm. in cross section is pulled apart at the plane P, the work done (w_c is equal to twice the free surface energy of the liquid, which is 2γ); (b) if the liquid is pulled away to give a clean surface of the solid, the amount of work done is ($W_A = \gamma_S + \gamma_L - \gamma_{SL}$), since the surface of the solid and that of the liquid are formed and the interface between them disappears.

While the work required to pull a liquid apart, given by the work of cohesion, w_c, is twice the free surface energy or surface tension of the liquid, the work required to separate an organic liquid, b, from water or from mercury, etc., is:

$$w_A = \gamma_a + \gamma_b - \gamma_{ab} \tag{28}$$

and:

$$\epsilon_A = h_a + h_b - h_{ab} \tag{29}$$

Actually, a and b can represent any pair of liquids or a liquid and a solid though the methods of work are changed very greatly if a solid is involved. Cohesion and adhesion, which are measures of intermolecular action, are among the most important physical properties of any condensed system, whether it consists of liquids, of solids, or of both.

2. Intermolecular Forces in Organic Liquids

Interesting relations concerning the intermolecular forces in organic liquids are revealed in table I. As the first example, there is given below the increase in the energy of interaction due to an increase of the number of carbon atoms in a normal hydrocarbon molecule from 7 to 14. All energy

TABLE I

SURFACE AND INTERFACIAL TENSION (γ = FREE SURFACE ENERGY) AND WORK AND
ENERGY OF COHESION (w_C, ϵ_C) AND OF ADHESION (ϵ_C, ϵ_A) TO WATER AT 20° C.

Compound	γ	γ_i	w_C	w_A	ϵ	ϵ_i	ϵ_A	$S_{b/a} = w_A - w_{C(b)}$
n-Hexane	18.43	. .	36.86	. .	. .	. .	. .	3.0
n-Heptane	20.24	52.55	40.48	40.44	49.9	74.3	92.8	0.0
n-Octane	21.77	. .	. .	43.76	50.2	. .	. .	. .
n-Tetradecane	26.51	54.17	53.02	45.09	52.6	72.2	97.7	−7.93
n-Hexadecane	27.46	54.84	54.92	43.36	53.2	75.7	94.8	−9.56
Benzene	28.90	34.96	69.92	66.74	69.0	51.7	134.0	9.0
Carbon tetrachloride	26.70	45.05	53.40	54.45	62.9	73.9	106.0	1.1
Ethylene bromide	38.80	37.20	77.60	74.40	78.2	68.8	126.4	−3.2
Heptylic acid	28.14	7.54	56.28	93.40	52.6	19.2	150.5	37.1
n-Octyl alcohol	27.53	8.53	55.06	91.80	50.5	−3.0	164.6	35.7
sec-Octyl alcohol	26.28	9.24	52.56	89.90	50.4	−2.6	170.1	37.3

values are in erg cm.$^{-2}$ (1) The work of cohesion, w_C, increases from 40.5 to 53.0 erg cm.$^{-2}$ or by 31%. (2) The total energy of cohesion, ϵ_C, increases from 100 to 105, or by only 5%. The value of w_C is a much poorer measure of the intermolecular energy than ϵ_C, so the molecular interaction *per unit area* is increased only slightly (5%) by increase of molecular length (doubling). (3) The work of adhesion toward water, w_A, increases from 40.5 to 45 or by 10%, while the energy of adhesion, which represents the adhesion more exactly, increases from 92.8 to 97.7 or by 5.3%. The percentage increase in the energy of adhesion is the same, within the limits of experimental error, as that in the energy of cohesion, and both increases are small.

Values are not available for the effort of chain length on the cohesion and adhesion for alcohols or acids. However, a comparison of the values for

n-heptane and n-octyl alcohol gives the following interesting results: (*1*)
The value of w_C is 40.5 for the hydrocarbon and 55 for the alcohol, while
w_A is 40.5 for the hydrocarbon and 91.8 for the alcohol. Thus w_C is increased by 36%, but w_A by 127%, or the effect of the hydroxyl group in increasing the work of cohesion is small, but that of adhesion very large.
(*2*) The value of ϵ_C is 100 for n-heptane and almost the same, 101, for n-
octyl alcohol, but ϵ_A increases from 93 to 165, so the introduction of the
hydroxyl group increases the molecular interaction by 77%.

The spreading coefficient, S, for an organic liquid on water is given by:

$$S_{b/a} = \gamma_a + \gamma_b - \gamma_{ab} = w_A - w_{C(b)} \tag{30}$$

This is designated as the initial spreading coefficient. If it is positive, the
pure, dry, organic liquid will spread over the clean surface of water.

The extremely important relation emerges that the introduction of the
highly polar —OH group into a hydrocarbon has very little effect on the cohesion in the liquid, but a very great effect upon the adhesion toward
water and also toward quartz, titanium dioxide (anatase), barium sulfate,
and other polar solids. The molecular interaction between water and
organic compounds which contain —OH and —COOH groups, and groups
which contain nitrogen and hydrogen, is increased considerably by the
hydrogen bonding which occurs. In molecular interactions toward metals,
halogen atoms in organic compounds exhibit much larger values than
hydroxyl groups.

3. Errors in Surface Tension Determinations

Although the determination of the surface tension is fundamentally
simple, the history of the methods employed for this purpose may be described as a comedy of errors. The errors were made: (*1*) in the experimental methods, and (*2*) either in the fundamental theory or in the theory
of the corrections. In general, if one of these errors was avoided, the other
was embraced, so that even in practically all of the best work between
1896 and 1916 errors of 3% were made. In the poorer work, the error rose
to 15 or 20% or even more, and was often especially high in the determination of interfacial tension.

These errors had two principal causes: (*1*) The use, in the capillary
height methods, of a lower meniscus which was entirely too small. Since
the results of this method were commonly taken as standards, the error
thus introduced was reflected in the results obtained by other methods, as,
for example, the drop weight method. Therefore, most of the surface tensions published during the period mentioned above were about 3% low.
This error was detected by the writer in work done with Haber in 1909, and
was pointed out to Richards, who, in 1916, published the first extensive

highly accurate work on surface tension. (2) A much more serious error was introduced by the use of an incorrect theory of certain of the methods employed. In the case of at least the two most commonly used methods, those of the drop weight and the ring, the error in the theory was brought about by the neglect of the principle of similitude, one of the relations of general dimensional theory.

4. Principle of Similitude

For the surfaces of liquids the principle of similitude may be stated in the following form. All static liquid surfaces of revolution have the same shape, which is independent of the nature of the liquid and its surface tension, whenever the necessary dimensionless variables are kept so that each has constant value for all the surfaces concerned.

Capillary Constant.—It was noted more than a century ago that, when a very fine capillary tube was used, the product of the radius, r, of any tube by the capillary height, h, is very nearly constant. The relationship may be written as $rh = a^2$, where a^2 is the capillary constant. Now r and h are linear dimensions, so a also represents a linear dimension, and the quantity, r/a, which finds extensive use in the theory of the shapes of surfaces, is dimensionless. It has been shown by Harkins that the linear quantity, $V^{1/3}$, where V represents the volume, may be used in place of a, and $r/V^{1/3}$ substituted for r/a. This has the great advantage that, in methods which use the drop weight or shape, the bubble pressure or a ring, V, is obtained directly, while, to obtain a, it is necessary to calculate by successive approximations.

Capillary Height Method.—The height to which a liquid rises in a narrow capillary tube above a plane liquid surface outside is determined by the surface tension and the angle of contact. The shape, S, of the meniscus is, however, for any diameter of tube a function of r/a, and of θ, the angle of contact:

$$S = f(r/a, \theta) \tag{31}$$

or, for a zero angle of contact:

$$S = f(r/a) \tag{32}$$

Drop-Weight Method.—The principle of similitude applies to any drop of liquid which hangs with its surface in contact with the sharp edge of a plane, circular, horizontal tip with a vertical cylindrical wall, such as is used in the drop-weight method. The shape of any such drop depends only on r/a and h/a, where h is the height of liquid which would give the pressure, p, caused by the curvature at the bottom of the tip. Now $r/V^{1/3}$ can be used in place of r/a; and this is much more simple, since V is the volume of the drop. Thus, the shape S of all drops is the same if $r/V^{1/3}$ and $h/V^{1/3}$ have the same value, so:

$$S = f(r/V^{1/3}, h/V^{1/3}) \tag{33}$$

$$S = f(r^3/V, h/V^{1/3}) \tag{34}$$

The stability of the hanging drop depends upon its shape, so the shape of the drop of maximum size which can hang from the tip is dependent alone upon either r^3/V, or h^3/V. Thus, for the maximum drop:

$$S_m = f_1(h^3/V) \tag{35}$$

or:

$$S_m = f_2(r^3/V) \tag{36}$$

It is more convenient to use the latter of these equations. The weight of any drop which hangs is given by:

$$W = Mg = 2\pi r\gamma \cdot f(r^3/V, h^3/V) \tag{37}$$

and the weight of the maximum drop by:

$$W_m = Mg = 2\pi r\gamma \cdot f(r^3/V) \tag{38}$$

Now if the maximum weight is exceeded by only a very slight amount, it is found by experience that, for a drop of this definite shape (when the process occurs slowly), a *definite* fraction of the whole drop (*e. g.*, this could be 0.8963 in a certain case) falls, and leaves the residue (0.1037 in this case) hanging from the tip as a residual drop. Thus, for the drop which falls with infinite slowness, the weight is given by the equation:

$$W_f = Mg = 2\pi r \cdot f'(r^3/V) \tag{39}$$

It is shown later that, in the theory of the shape of a drop, r/a and h/a are preferable to $r/V^{1/3}$ and $h/V^{1/3}$.

Ring and Bubble-Pressure Methods.—The application of the principle of similitude to these methods is given as a part of the discussion of the development of these particular methods.

III.   METHODS AND APPARATUS

1.   Choice of Method

It is important, when work is to be begun upon a problem which involves the determination of surface or interfacial tension, to choose that particular method which will give the best results with the least effort. There is no single *best method*. The following outline may be helpful in the choice.

(1) Single Liquids:

(a) *Capillary Height.*—For highest accuracy, but slow for surface tension.   Not as satisfactory for interfacial tension as method (b).

(b) *Drop Weight.*—Best general method for both surface and interfacial tensions if both accuracy and speed are considered. *May be used with a single drop*, which may be very small.

(c) *Ring Method.*—Very fast and quite accurate for surface tension, but not properly tested for interfacial tension.   However, the same corrections apply.

(d) *Bubble Pressure.*—As now used, a moderately good method for surface tension; improved greatly by the use of a single bubble, though no work has been published in which this has been done.

(e) *Hanging Drop.*—At present the least accurate of the five methods.   Theory, developed partly by Lohnstein[1] and more completely by Freud and Harkins,[2] but has not yet been applied.

(2) Solutions:

(a) *Drop Weight.*—The best method for surface and interfacial tension if long time effects are not involved.

(b) *Ring Method.*—Excellent for surface tension, even if time effects are involved.

(c) *Sessile Bubble or Sessile Drop.*—The best method if extremely long time effects are involved (sessile bubble preferred when applicable).

2. Capillary Height Method

A. THEORY

As an absolute method, the determination of surface tension by a measurement of capillary height depends upon the very simple relations made evident by figure 3. A narrow tube, T, of known constant internal diameter dips into the liquid in a vessel or tube, V, so wide that the large meniscus is not raised appreciably by capillarity.   There is then a hydrostatic equilibrium between the liquid in V and the part of T below dotted line AB.   Provided the gas and vapor around the tube are of negligible density, the whole weight of the liquid in T above this line must be held up by the surface tension of the upper meniscus.   If the liquid wets the wall of the glass tube and the angle of contact between the liquid and the glass is zero

---

[1] T. Lohnstein, *Ann. Physik*, **20**, 237, 606 (1906); **22**, 1030 (1906).

[2] B. B. Freud and W. D. Harkins, *J. Phys. Chem.*, **33**, 1217 (1929).

there will be a vertical duplex film of water, at equilibrium about 25 Å. thick, on the glass which exerts a pull along a length equal to the circumference of the tube, or to $2\pi r$. The pull of a film of this length is $f = 2\pi r\gamma$ and this tension supports the liquid in T.

The weight of this liquid up to line CD (Fig. 3) at the bottom of the meniscus is $W = \pi r^2 h_1\rho$, where ρ is the density of the liquid. The total weight supported by the surface tension of the liquid is this weight plus that of the meniscus, W'. Thus the force upward is:

$$f_u = 2\pi r\gamma \tag{40}$$

and that downward is:

$$f_d = \pi r^2 h_0 g + W' \tag{41}$$

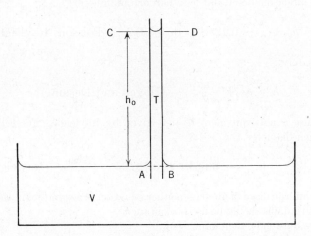

Fig. 3.—Capillary height method.

At equilibrium, therefore, $f_u = f_d$ or:

$$\gamma = {}^1/_2\, rh_0 g\rho + W'/2\pi r = {}^1/_2\, rh_0 g + mg/2\pi r \tag{42}$$

where m is the unknown, very small mass of liquid in the meniscus. If the capillary tube has an extremely small internal diameter, then W' is negligible and:

$$\gamma = {}^1/_2\, rh_0 g\rho \tag{43}$$

If the vapor around tube T has an appreciable density ρ_0, then a part of the weight of the liquid is balanced hydrostatically by the vapor, and equation (41) becomes:

$$f_d = 2\pi r^2 h_0 g(\rho - \rho_0) + gv(\rho - \rho_0) \tag{44}$$

in which v is the volume of the meniscus (i. e., of the liquid above line CD). Equation (42) is changed by this density correction to:

$$\gamma = {}^1/_2\, rh_0 g(\rho - \rho_0) + gv(\rho - \rho_0)/2\pi r \tag{45}$$

It is simpler to add to the height, h_0, a small height h', which when multiplied by πr^2 gives the volume, v, of the meniscus, and to consider a total height $h = h_0 + h'$. With capillary tubes of small diameter such as those generally used for the determination of surface tension, $h = r/3$ (valid with water for $r < 0.2$ min.):

$$h = h_0 + r/3 \tag{46}$$

and:

$$\gamma = {}^1/_2\, rhg(\rho_l - \rho_v) \tag{47}$$

where h indicates $h_0 + r/3$, l liquid, and v vapor. For interfacial tension:

$$\gamma = {}^1/_2\, rhg(\rho_{l_1} - \rho_{l_2}) \tag{48}$$

For tubes of larger diameter, but less than one millimeter:

$$h = h_0 + \frac{r}{3} - 0.1288\,\frac{r^2}{h_0} + 0.1312\,\frac{r^3}{h_0^2} \text{ (Poisson, Rayleigh)} \tag{49}$$

or, approximately:

$$h = h_0 + \frac{a^2 r}{3a^2 + r^2} \text{ (Hagen and Desains)} \tag{50}$$

This expression is not equivalent to that given by Rayleigh. For tubes of considerably larger diameter, $r/a > 4.3$:

$$1.4142\,\frac{r}{a} - \ln\frac{a}{h_0} = 0.6648 + 0.19785\,\frac{a}{r} + \frac{1}{2}\ln\frac{r}{a} \text{ (Rayleigh)} \tag{51}$$

For tubes of intermediate diameters, neither equation is accurate and the tables of Bashforth and Adams should be used to obtain h'.

The surface tension is, therefore:

$$\gamma = {}^1/_2\, rhg(\rho - \rho_0) \tag{52}$$

B. APPARATUS

If sufficient liquid is available an apparatus similar to that shown in figure 4, gives excellent results. The general form is that used by Richards and Carver,[3] with the fundamentally important addition of an overflow trap by Young, Gross, and Harkins.[4] Certain factors which are important in the construction of the apparatus and in the measurement of the surface tension are outlined below.

The large tube should have a diameter of about 8 cm., should be of uniform bore, and should have a wall of uniform thickness without optical de-

[3] T. W. Richards and E. K. Carver, *J. Am. Chem. Soc.*, **43**, 827 (1921). T. W. Richards and L. B. Coombs, *ibid.*, **37**, 1657 (1915).

[4] P. L. K. Gross, "The Theory of Atomic Collisions, the Determination of a Standard for Surface Tension Measurements." *Ph.D. thesis*, University of Chicago, 1926.

fects. To avoid these defects, Harkins, Brown, and Davies used a very
heavily gold-plated apparatus of rectangular horizontal cross section, with
a front and back of optical glass. This apparatus was provided with two
capillaries instead of one. Harkins and Jordan[5] used another modification
in which smaller quantities of liquid can be measured (Fig. 5). The large
lower meniscus should be not too close to either end of the large tube, since
this is distorted at the ends. To accomplish this without the use of an ex-

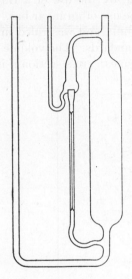

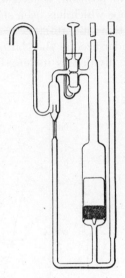

Fig.   4.—Capillary
height apparatus of
Richards and Carver
as modified by Young,
Gross and Harkins.[4]

Fig. 5.—Capil-
lary height ap-
paratus of Har-
kins and Jor-
dan.[5]

cessive amount of liquid, the lower half of the tube is largely filled by a glass
bulb which has a flat top. In general the capillary tube is longer than is
shown in the figure.

A suitable diameter for the capillary tube is of the order of 0.5 mm., although a slightly smaller diameter might be better for organic liquids.
The cross section should be as nearly circular as possible, and the bore and
wall thickness should be as uniform as possible. Great care is well employed in selecting capillary tubes of the most uniform bore to be found in
a very large amount of tubing. The determination of the capillary height is
the most accurate surface tension method, and any error in the value of the

⁵ W. D. Harkins and H. F. Jordan, *J. Am. Chem. Soc.*, **52**, 1751 (1930).

diameter of the capillary tube at the position of the meniscus introduces an
error of the same percentage magnitude in the value of the surface tension.
For this reason, it is important to have a method, such as that of Young,
which makes possible obtaining the radius of the capillary at any position.

Almost the whole length of the capillary is filled with very pure mercury.
The weight of the mercury is determined as that of the tube with mercury
less that of the tube.   The length of the column of mercury, while in a
horizontal position, is measured to 0.001 mm. by the use of a traveling
microscope which has been standardized by the use of an invar bar.   That
used in this laboratory is graduated to 0.01 mm., and was ruled in Paris
and standardized at the National Bureau of Standards.   The volume of the
mercury, divided by its length, would give the mean cross section if it were

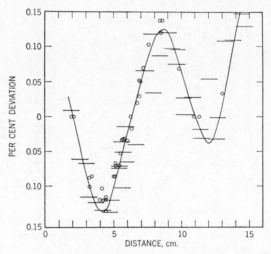

Fig. 6.—Capillary height method correction for
variation in diameter of capillary tube.

not for the volume of two menisci.   Next, a column of mercury of approximately half the initial length is used.   On placing this anywhere in any
part of the tube occupied by the initial column, the mean radius of the
initial section not now occupied by mercury is given by:

$$r = [(m_1 - m_2)/\pi\rho(l_1 - l_2)]^{1/2} \tag{53}$$

In practice, the mean radius of each end of the section of the capillary to be
used is determined in this way.   If, for example, this useful section is 12
cm. in length, the procedure gives the mean diameter of each end of about
6 cm. length, when this is the length not occupied by mercury.

Next, a bead of about 1.2 cm. in length is introduced and weighed.   This is then moved from one end of the tube to the other in more or less uniform steps of 0.6 cm., and each length is measured.   The departure of the length of this bead for any 1.2-cm. section from the mean length of the same bead for that particular half of the tube gives the correction to be applied to the mean diameter of the half-tube to obtain the mean diameter for the 1.2-cm. section.   These deviations are plotted as chords as a function of the length of the tube.   A smooth curve is drawn through positions near the centers of the chords in such a way that the areas inclosed by the curve lines perpendicular to the chord at its ends, and the chord itself, are equal (Fig. 6).   The percentage correction which corresponds to any desired position on the capillary is given by the corresponding point on the curve.

C.   WATER AS A STANDARD

In 1919, Harkins, Brown, and Davies carried out an extensive series of measurements by the capillary height method on the surface tension of water, and obtained a value of 72.800 dyne cm.$^{-1}$ at 20° C.   Other values

TABLE II

EXPERIMENTAL AND CALCULATED VALUES FOR THE SURFACE TENSION OF WATER (GROSS, YOUNG, AND HARKINS)[a]

$t°$ C.	γexp.	γcalc.	$\Delta\gamma$
0.20	75.658	75.652	.006
4.99	74.962	74.982	− .020
10.02	73.255	74.262	− .007
20.00	72.785	72.781	.004
40.20	69.571	69.588	− .017
60.00	66.233	66.220	.013

[a] P. L. K. Gross, "The Theory of Atomic Collisions, the Determination of a Standard for Surface Tension Measurements."   *Ph.D. thesis*, University of Chicago, 1926.

for this quantity by accurate workers and the same method are: Richards, 72.72; Domke, 72.72; and Volkmann, 72.80.   In later work Gross,[4] under the direction of Young and Harkins, obtained the value 72.804, but in a still later (1926), more extensive, investigation obtained 72.785 dyne cm.$^{-1}$, which is only 0.02% lower than the value of Harkins and Brown[6] The following equation was found to express the experimental values within the limits of error of the experimental work:

$$\gamma_{H_2O} = 75.680 - 0.138t - 0.0_5356t^2 + 0.0_647t^3 \tag{54}$$

The values involved are given in table II.   These values should serve as a standard for work on surface tension.   For benzene, $\gamma^{65} = 28.88$.[3,6]

[6] W. D. Harkins and F. E. Brown, *J. Am. Chem. Soc.*, **41**, 499 (1919); **38**, 248 (1916).

D. CAPILLARY HEIGHT METHOD AT INTERFACES

Interfacial tensions are of extreme importance in connection with colloids and biological systems. The principles involved in making the determinations by the capillary height method are no different than those in the preceding section as applied to surface tension. The whole difference from the experimental standpoint is that the upper liquid must have its upper surface the upper opening in the capillary tube. The method is more sensitive than at a surface, since the capillary height for a given diameter of capillary may be five to twenty times greater. This makes it essential to observe the following precautions: (1) The diameter of the lower meniscus must be even greater for interfacial than for surface tensions. (2) In interfacial work the angle of contact is not known to be always zero.

For the determination of interfacial tension, the apparatus of Harkins and Jordan[5] (Fig. 5), but with a much longer capillary and larger tubes is suitable. Obviously grease should not be used on the stopcock. If the oil has a higher density than the aqueous phase, the capillary should be just to its bottom with the aqueous phase and then the large tube should be partly filled with the oil, while the top of the apparatus should be filled with water. The general principle to heed is that, since water wets glass better than an oil, the glass always be wet first by the aqueous phase. The capillary height method is used so seldom for interfacial tension that a detailed description will not be given, but a paper by Harkins and Humphery[7] should be consulted for further information. They describe an apparatus which gives results of high accuracy without the use of a cathetometer.

3. Methods Depending on Shape of Drops

Two well-known methods for the determination of the surface tension of liquids have their basis in the theory of the shape of drops which hang from a horizontal tip, with a sharp edge and a circular cross section. These are: the method of the hanging or pendant drop; and the "drop-weight" method. At present, neither is an absolute method, but the theory of the pendant drop has been developed by Bashforth and Adams, by Lohnstein, and by Freud and Harkins, and only a simple numerical calculation is needed to change this from an empirical to an absolute method. However, at least at present, the drop-weight method is one of the two most accurate of known surface tension methods, while that of the pendant drop gives a low degree of precision.

The equation of Laplace is:

$$p_1 - p_2 = \gamma(1/R_1 + 1/R_2) \tag{55}$$

---

[7] W. D. Harkins and E. C. Humphery, *J. Am. Chem. Soc.*, **38**, 228 (1916).

where R_1 and R_2 are the radii of curvature of the surface at any point in the surface and p is the pressure on the concave side at that point.   The equations presented below are given for the sole purpose of exhibiting the type of problem involved;   those interested in the details should consult the original paper.[2]

$$y''/(1 + y'^2)^{3/2} + y'/x(1 - y'^2)^{1/2} = 2(h - y)/a^2 \qquad (56)$$

or:

$$du/dx + u/x = 2(h - y)/a^2 \qquad (57)$$

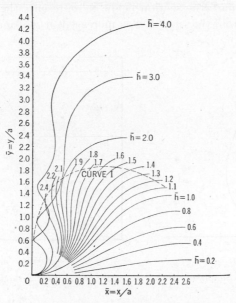

Fig. 7.—Profiles of hanging drops.   Expansion
by Taylor's theorem of:

$$\bar{y}''/(1 - \bar{y}'^2)^{3/2} + \bar{y}'/\bar{x}(1 - \bar{y}'^2)^{1/2} = 2(h - \bar{y})$$

It is sufficient to say that this equation is nonintegrable, but may be solved by integration in series by the use of Taylor's theorem.

If the forces acting on a horizontal section of the drop are equated, it is found that:

$$2\pi x u V = V g \rho = \pi x^2 (h - y) g \rho$$

$$V = \int_0^y \pi x^2 dy = \pi x u a^2 - \pi x^2 (h - y) \qquad (58)$$

where V is the volume of liquid below any horizontal plane which intersects the drop, x and y are the coordinates with the bottom of the drop as origin and the axis of symmetry as the y-axis, u is the sine of the angle between the tangent to the profile and the horizontal, and h is the height of liquid which would give pressure p at the vertex of the drop.

If, in figure 7, a horizontal (iso-$\bar{h}$) line is drawn from any point on any curve to the vertical $\bar{h}$-axis, the curve below the line gives a section of the (half) drop, and the length ($\bar{x}$) of this line gives the radius of the circular tip from which it hangs in terms of $\bar{x}$. The actual radius, $x = r$, is given by:

$$r = x = a\bar{x} \tag{59}$$

If the horizontal line is drawn from the intersection of any profile with curve I (broken line), the section below it represents the maximum drop which can hang from the tip. If $\bar{h}$ is increased, it will increase in volume

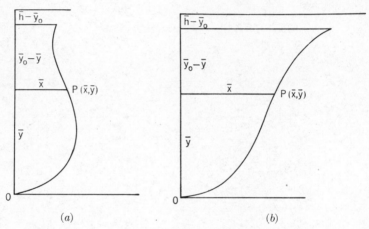

Fig. 8.—Shapes of drops: (a) with neck and (b) without neck.

and will form a neck, with the result that a certain fraction of the maximum drop will fall. If R/a or $R/V^{1/3}$, or R^3/V, were zero, the whole drop would fall; so, with tips of extremely small radius, practically the whole drop falls.

Equation (58) contains two constants, a and h, but these may be reduced to one by the substitution of $a\bar{x}$, $a\bar{y}$, $a\bar{h}$, and $a^3\bar{V}$ for x, y, h, and V, respectively, which makes one set of curves express the shapes for all hanging drops, whether in vapor or in a second liquid. Figure 7 shows that there are two types of profiles: one in which $\bar{y}$ continuously increases with $\bar{x}$, and one in which there are one or more constrictions or necks. It should be noted that the shape of the drop is determined by the pressure at the vertex of the drop when the pressure is given by $\bar{h} = h/a$, the height of the liquid which would give this pressure divided by the square root, a, of the capillary constant. Here, $a = (2\gamma/g\rho)^{1/2}$. Figure 8 exhibits two shapes as a function of $\bar{h}$, $\bar{y}$, and $\bar{x}$. Here $P_{(\bar{x},\bar{y})}$ is any point P on the surface of the drop, with coordinates x and y with reference to the vertex (0) of the drop, $\bar{y}_0$ is the ordinate of the bottom of the circular tip, $\bar{h}$ is the height which represents the pressure in the drop at its vertex. This represents the actual height minus the capillary height in the capillary tube which admits water to the tip.

A. DROP-WEIGHT METHOD

If the drop which hangs at the end of a tip were cylindrical and of the same diameter as the tip, it is evident that the maximum weight of drop which could be supported would be exactly equal to the weight of the liquid

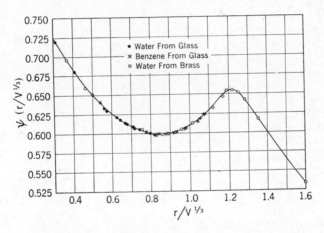

Fig. 9.—Drop-weight corrections. Fraction of ideal drop which falls *vs.* ratio of tip radius to cube root of volume of drop.

upheld in a capillary tube of the same diameter. This is because, in both cases, the force of surface tension acts on a line $2\pi r$ long, so the force is $2\pi r\gamma$, or:

$$W = mg = 2\pi r\gamma \qquad (60)$$

Both observation and theory indicate that, on tips of ordinary size, only a fraction of the drop falls, so the weight of the drop which falls must be less than that given by equation (60). (*Note*: For values of $r/a > 0$, even the weight of the hanging drop is less than $2\pi r\gamma$, since the surface of the liquid is not vertical where it meets the edge of the tip.) However, as the tip is made smaller, the *fraction* which falls becomes larger and larger, and extrapolation of the curve to zero diameter indicates that here all of the drop falls, or the hanging and the falling drop have the same weight. Both the theory of the preceding section and the extrapolation of experimental values show that equation (60) gives the correct weight of the drop when r/a or $r/V^{1/3}$ is zero.

A drop of the weight $(2\pi r\gamma)$, given by equation (60), has been designated by Harkins and Brown[6] as the *ideal drop*. The fraction of the ideal drop which falls was determined by them in an extensive series of experiments in which four pure liquids were dropped from 15 glass and 20 brass or Monel

TABLE III

EXPERIMENTAL VALUES FOR DROP-WEIGHT CORRECTIONS[a]

V/r^3	F	$\pm^\circ/^\circ$	V/r^3	F	$\pm^\circ/^\circ$
	0.159	..	2.3414	0.26350	0.1
5000	0.172	..	2.0929	0.26452	0.05
250	0.198	..	1.8839	0.26522	0.05
58.1	0.215	..	1.7062	0.26562	0.05
24.6	0.2256	..	1.5545	0.26566	0.05
17.7	0.2305	0.3	1.4235	0.26544	0.05
13.28	0.23522	0.25	1.3096	0.26495	0.1
10.29	0.23976	0.2	1.2109	0.26407	0.1
8.190	0.24398	0.15	1.124	0.2632	0.15
6.662	0.24786	0.15	1.048	0.2617	0.15
5.522	0.25135	0.15	0.980	0.2602	0.15
4.653	0.25419	0.15	0.912	0.2585	0.15
3.975	0.25661	0.15	0.865	0.2570	0.2
3.433	0.25874	0.15	0.816	0.2550	..
2.995	0.26065	0.15	0.771	0.2534	..
2.637	0.26224	0.1	0.729	0.2617	..
0.692	0.2499	..	0.541	0.2430	..
0.658	0.2482	..	0.512	0.2441	..
0.626	0.2464	..	0.483	0.2460	..
0.597	0.2445	..	0.455	0.2491	..
0.570	0.2430	..	0.428	0.2526	..
			0.403	0.2559	..

[a] W. D. Harkins and F. E. Brown (given in *International Critical Tables*, Vol. IV, McGraw-Hill, New York, 1928).

metal tips. The fraction of the ideal drop which falls is given by the ordinates of the curves in figure 9. While any value of $r/V^{1/3}$ may be used in a determination of surface tension, those between about 0.7 and 0.9 give the best results. Now the form of the maximum, stable hanging drop is a function either of r/a or of $r/V^{1/3}$, and the form of the maximum hanging drop determines the fraction, $f(r/V^{1/3})$ or $f_1(r/a)$, which falls. Thus the weight, W, of the drop which falls is:

$$W = 2\pi r\gamma \cdot f(r/V^{1/3}) = 2\pi r\gamma f_1(r/a) \qquad (61)$$

so, since $W = mg$:

$$\gamma = mg/2\pi r \cdot f(r/V^{1/3}) = mg/2\pi r \cdot f_1(r/a) = mg\varphi/2\pi r = mg/r \cdot F \qquad (62)$$

If the vapor is dilute, it is simplest to let m represent the weight in grams of one drop as weighed in air. Now, since the drop, as it hangs, is also in air, no additional correction for buoyancy need be made. To determine the surface tension of a liquid, it is only necessary to determine the mass of one drop, calculate its volume, V, by dividing by a roughly determined density, also in air, calculate V, multiply by $1/r^3$, look up the value of F in the table and multiply this by mg/r. The density of the liquid is involved only in determining the value of the correction, which is not very sensitive to density differences.

Apparatus and Technique.—The forms of the drop-weight apparatus described first are those designed to give a precision of 0.02 to 0.03% with pure liquids which are not too volatile. The apparatus may be greatly simplified, and very greatly reduced in cost, if a precision of 0.3%, which is better than the average of published values by all methods, is considered satisfactory. Such an apparatus consists merely of an inverted U of capillary tubing, three weighing bottles, and two glass tubes.

The cross section of an accurate drop-weight apparatus is shown in figure 9. For work of high precision, the apparatus is supported by a heavy iron rod one inch in diameter held upright by a heavy iron tripod which rests upon a concrete pier. During a determination, the box is suspended in the water of a thermostat from its outside support. The most important part of the apparatus is the tip,

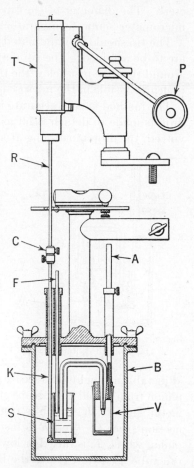

Fig. 10.—Drop-weight apparatus.

shown in figures 10 and 11. This is made from a straight, heavy-walled, capillary tube of Pyrex glass. The end of the tube is ground off until it is a plane perpendicular to the length of the tube by the use of Carborundum. A piece of the same tube, only a few millimeters in length, is then sealed on the end by a mixture of beeswax and rosin or another suitable cement. The tube is then clamped in a precision lathe, and rotated in one direction, while the tube is cut round to the proper diameter near the end by a wheel of fine Carborundum which rotates at high speed in the opposite direction. It is then polished by rouge, on sealing wax or pitch, while still rotating in the lathe. The end is not polished. A tip ground in this way should have an edge which appears perfectly sharp under a magnification of 40 diameters. The diameter of the tip is measured by a microscope moved by a micrometer screw (comparator).

The tip should be illuminated properly if measurements of high accuracy are to be attained. The tip may be inverted, black paper used as a collar around the tube just below the tip, and the light adjusted until a sharp edge is clearly visible in the microscope.

The method is very accurate if the following conditions are met: (1) the drop is made to detach itself as slowly as possible; (2) if a solution is involved, the drop must hang at as nearly full extension as possible until the process of adsorption is completed, i. e., equilibrium is attained; and (3) with very volatile liquids, additional precautions should be taken as described later. It is important that the drop not be pulled over by suction, since this may disturb the equilibrium with the vapor. It is also important that the drop hang in the saturated vapor at almost full size until equilibrium is attained. For this purpose, a method of control of the drop devised by Harkins, Gross, and Harkins[8] is used. The supply bottle, S, in figures 10 and 11, which contains the phase under investigation, is made adjustable in height. To secure good adjustment, a stand with a ratchet and pinion from an old microscope stand is used. The supply bottle is held by a metal support, K, which is fastened to a metal rod, R, by means of connection piece C. Rod R is fastened to movable bar T. By turning P, a pinion wheel, T, is raised or lowered and the height of S thus regulated. F is a tube used to regulate the height of the liquid in the supply bottle, S, which is raised to start the formation of the drop, and is then lowered. Next, it is adjusted to such a height as to give the largest possible stable drop. The bottom of the largest stable drop is located by the position of the cross hair of a short-focus telescope which has been carefully adjusted by an earlier trial. The period during which the drops are suspended at full extension may usually be varied from three to six minutes per drop without any perceptible variation in the weight of the drop which falls. For some very dilute solutions, this suspension time must be greatly lengthened.

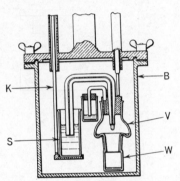

Fig. 11.—Drop-weight apparatus for volatile liquids.

---

[8] H. N. Harkins and W. D. Harkins, *J. Clin. Investigation*, **1**, 263 (1929).

In some cases, depending upon the vapor pressure and other factors, probably chiefly upon the difference between the temperature of the room and that of the thermostat, it was found necessary to cool V, which contains the liquid for saturating the vapor phase, before adjusting the apparatus in the thermostat, in order to prevent distillation into W while the desired temperature was being reached.

For determination of the drop weight of a very volatile liquid such as carbon disulfide, it was found necessary to devise a special type of vent tube, which is shown in figure 11.   Instead of having a vent hole through the brass tube and stopper (to which V is attached), a brass tube was soldered to the stopper, connecting with a small vent hole.   The other end of the brass tube passed through another stopper provided with a vent hole. This second stopper supported a small weighing bottle containing just enough carbon disulfide so that its surface stood slightly above the outlet of the brass tube.   In this way, the loss by vaporization from the bottle in which the drops are being collected is almost entirely eliminated, and more constant drop-weight results can be obtained than otherwise.   (Any remaining correction due to vaporization loss is taken care of by determining the difference in weight between 30 drops and 5 drops of the liquid obtained under exactly similar conditions, according to the procedure of Morgan.) The box, B, and the stand which carries the ratchet and pinion are clamped to separate iron stands in order that the drops may not be shaken by the adjustment of the height of bottle S.

After the dropping tip has been cleaned, V is fitted on to the glass or brass stopper and W is fitted on to V.   The supply bottle which rests on K is put into place.   Support K is temporarily prevented from slipping through the tube attached to the roof of the box by collar C.   By fastening C at the proper distance along K, the level of the liquid in S may be adjusted to stand a few millimeters above the level of the tip surface from which the drops fall.   By the application of suction at the end of the vent tube, enough liquid is forced into the capillary tube to fill it completely up to the tip surface where the drops are formed.   Due to capillary forces, the liquid will remain in the capillary tube as long as desired.   If the level of the liquid in S is not properly adjusted as described above, the liquid in the capillary will siphon back into S, or else drops will siphon over from S into W, neither of which is desired until the apparatus has been in the thermostat long enough to attain the proper temperature.   The vent-tube weighing bottle is next adjusted on its stopper.   After attaching the lower part of the box B by means of the wing nuts shown in the diagram, the apparatus is immersed in the thermostat.   The apparatus is then leveled, the microscope stand is lowered into place, and rod R is connected to K by means of C.   In moving C to the end of K, care should be taken not to permit the liquid in the capillary tube to siphon out. After the apparatus has been in the thermostat the proper length of time, the drop formation is started by turning pinion wheel P, thus raising S.

In almost all work the simple weighing bottle, W (Fig. 10), is attached directly to the stopper which supports the tip. The auxiliary upper section, V (Fig. 11), is used in the determination of the surface tension of solutions such that the concentration may change by evaporation. Before the determination is begun, the annular depression in V, which is actually larger and deeper than is shown, is filled with the solution so that the weighing bottle may be filled by the vapor of the solution before the first drop is formed.

B.   A DROP-WEIGHT–VOLUME METHOD AT INTERFACES

The drop-weight method is directly applicable to the determination of the interfacial tension of oils or mercury against an aqueous phase, but for general use the drop-weight–volume method as used in this laboratory is usually preferable. The apparatus is shown in figure 12.[7] It is supported in the thermostat by a metal or hard rubber back. After equilibrium has been established, the aqueous phase is put into pipette $ABCD$. The tip is then placed under the surface of the other phase, which is in a vessel (not shown) supported in F. The edge of the aqueous phase is drawn exactly to the end of the capillary at the tip, and the reading of the meniscus of this phase above the bulb of the pipette is taken. Suction is applied carefully at G, and drops are pulled off until the meniscus falls to the scale below the bulb. From the volume thus obtained, the surface tension may be calculated by equation of the preceding section, which takes the form:

$$\gamma = V(\rho_1 - \rho_2)g/2\pi r \cdot f(r/V^{1/3})$$
$$= V(\rho_1 - \rho_2)g\varphi/2\pi r = [V(\rho_1 - \rho_2)g/r] \cdot F \qquad (63)$$

The corrections involved are the same as those of the drop-weight method as given in table III.

It may be noted that the phase which best wets the tip should be the one to be dropped either downward or upward into the other phase—if upward, the capillary must be bent so that the face of the tip is upward instead of downward. Thus, an aqueous phase is dropped downward into an organic phase of lesser density, or upward into one of higher density. If sufficient care is taken, this apparatus gives accurate results since the detachment of the drop is a slower process in dropping into a liquid than into a vapor. The pressure–height can be adjusted much better by the use of either of the devices shown in figure 13 or figure 14. In the former, the height may be adjusted with great sensitivity because of the presence of a glass spring, C.

The coiled glass tube, C, was made from a single length of ordinary 4-mm. glass tubing by heating, drawing, and winding it around a hot asbestos cylinder. The coil has 16 turns, a diameter of $3^3/_4$ inches and an approximate internal volume of 5 ml. It may be pressed together until only a couple of inches high or else stretched to a height of 14 inches or more, without any appreciable change of internal volume. The upper end of the coil is sealed to pipette B, while the lower end is sealed to a capillary tube ending with a dropping tip, T (diameter, 0.9888 cm.). The best diameter depends upon the value of $R/V^{1/3}$.

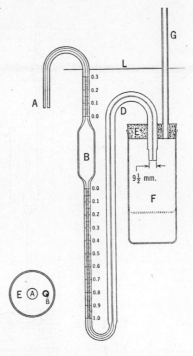

Fig. 12.—Drop-weight volume apparatus for interfacial tension (Harkins and Humphery).

The mechanism for raising or lowering the pipette consists of a wheel and shaft, W, and a rack, R, and pinion, P (encased). By raising the pipette the speed of drop formation is increased, and by lowering it, the speed is decreased. Scale Q acts as a guide for adjusting the level of the liquid in the pipette. Thus, for any desired speed of drop formation the liquid level should stand at a certain height as indicated by the scale. These simple manipulations give complete control of the drops and eliminate the necessity of using the more difficult method of control by suction. Other parts are: M, metal plate; S, glass stopper; V, vent tube; and Z, screw.

The apparatus represented by figure 14, as devised by Adinoff and Harkins[9] of this laboratory, accomplishes the same result in another way. The pipette, E, and the graduated tubes, E' and E'', are connected by glass tubing to capillary M, which leads to dropping tip H, as in the apparatus of Harkins and Humphery. Parallel to this, a wider tube, F, is attached. At the top of tube F is attached a very fine capillary tip, G.

At the beginning of the experiment, water is drawn from F into G by suction. Because of capillary action it remains there after the suction is removed, even though the level of the water in E' is somewhat below it. The small oil–water interface at the dropping tip is then adjusted to the

[9] B. Adinoff, "Thermodynamics of Hydrocarbon Surfaces." *Ph.D. thesis*, Univ. of Chicago, 1943.

reference position (described below) and the level of the water in E' read. Then, by slight air pressure at B, the water is forced out of capillary H into F. During the formation and detachment of the required number of drops, B is kept open to the atmosphere and the level of the water in F is kept constant by applying either suction or pressure at A. When the

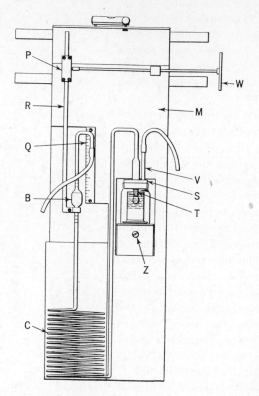

Fig. 13.—Apparatus for interfacial tension
(Harkins).

proper number of drops has fallen, the water is again drawn up to the initial level in H, the interface is adjusted to the reference position, and the level in E'' read. Since the position of the interface and the amount of water in F are the same at the beginning and end of the experiment, the volume of the drops is the difference between the two readings.

The receiving vessel, I, is constructed in such a way as to remove these difficulties. As each drop of water falls, the water phase, W, overflows through side arm L into the larger vessel, K, from which it is removed through N from time to time by air pressure through C or suction through

N.   Thus, the level of the liquid in I remains constant.   The edge of ground glass joint J is coated with high-melting paraffin to prevent the entrance of any water from the thermostat, since it is considered inadvisable to have any grease present in the system.   The paraffin used does not soften appreciably below 70°.

In regard to the reference position of the interface, it was found that the most reproducible position of the interface was obtained by the reflection

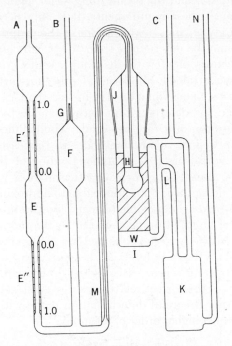

Fig. 14.—Apparatus of Adinoff and Harkins
for interfacial tension.

of a light placed in front of and below the dropping tip.   It is also advisable to place the telescope slightly below the tip, so that the surface of the tip is visible.   Under these conditions, the reflection pattern varies considerably with very small changes in volume when the interface is forced into the capillary of the dropping tip.   As long as the light, the telescope, and the tip are kept in the same position, the position of the interface can be reproduced so that the level of the water in E changes by an amount which represents less than 0.001 ml.   It was also found that forcing the water out of capillary G and pulling it back in again did not change the reading to any observable extent.   Thus, the difference in the volume of water in the apparatus could be determined to 0.001 ml., which was as close as the graduations could be read.

As in the determination of surface tension, the drops are extended to nearly full size by suction, and then allowed to detach themselves under the influence of gravity only. The point of extension is chosen so that the remainder of the drop forms in about 20 seconds.

It is often necessary, in industrial work, to determine the surface or interfacial tension *quickly*, and sometimes only *small quantities of material* are available. To meet these requirements, it is only necessary to use what seems to be entirely obvious modifications of the drop method. Thus, the surface tension may be determined from the weight of a single drop, and often with an accuracy of a few tenths of a per cent. After the proper temperature has been attained, an essential procedure with any method, a single drop may be taken from the tip in less than two minutes; so the time is short, and the determination may be made by the use of only a few drops or one drop of a rare material. Similar modifications may be made in the drop-weight–volume method. In this case, a micropipette is employed. The surprising lack of understanding of the drop method is illustrated by an altogether incorrect criticism by a well-known worker, who stated that the method is not applicable to approximate or commercial work because it would be impossible to spend five minutes per drop and still obtain the several hundred drops essential to the method. Evidently he had in mind the altogether erroneous method of the drop number, that is, counting the usually large number of drops in a certain volume. Commonly, the results are given in terms of the drop number, with the statement that this gives the correct relative values—a statement which is very far from the truth. A careful determination made with one drop gives a result of a very much higher order of accuracy.

4. Ring Method

It is probable that the ring method is at present more widely applied than any other for the determination of surface tension. The method is extremely rapid, very simple, and when properly applied may give an accuracy as high as $\pm 0.25\%$. One very experienced worker in this laboratory considers that, with pure liquids and great care, he can attain a precision of $\pm 0.1\%$.

As now used, the method depends upon a determination of the maximum pull necessary to detach a circular ring of circular wire from the surface of a liquid, with an angle of contact of $0°$, as determined by a good balance. The use of a ring for this purpose seems to have been suggested by Timberg (1887). Until 1926, the theory of this method was developed so imperfectly that not even a single value obtained by its use was included in

International Critical Tables (Vol. IV, 1928).   This method is based upon the fundamental work of Harkins, Young, and Cheng,[10] who showed that the incorrectness of the theory up to that time was due to the neglect of the principle of similitude (pages 156–157).

A.   APPARATUS

For accurate work a chainomatic balance may be used, while a du Noüy torsion balance may be employed for work of low accuracy.   With either it

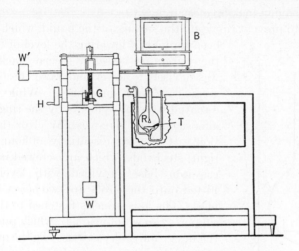

Fig. 15.—Apparatus for determination of surface tension by the ring method.[11]

is better to raise the balance, and thus pull the ring away from the surface of the liquid, than to lower the liquid, which may give rise to waves or ripples in its surface.   If this is inconvenient, the vessel which contains the liquid whose surface tension is to be determined may be floated on any suitable liquid (*e. g.*, mercury).   The surface of this latter liquid is lowered gradually by flow through a tube in order to detach the ring.

In the use of the du Noüy tensiometer, the platform supporting the vessel which contains the liquid should be discarded, and the instrument should be supported by a small jack which, in this laboratory, cost $2.50.   A fine pointed end should be fastened on the end of the rod which supports the ring, and another very fine point set opposite this, by a support from the frame, at the null point of the balance.   The apparatus as sold is very crude

[10] W. D. Harkins, T. F. Young and Lan Hua Cheng, *Science*, **64**, 333 (1926).
[11] W. D. Harkins and H. F. Jordan, *J. Am. Chem. Soc.*, **52**, 1751 (1930).

with respect to the observation of the zero point. If a chainomatic balance is used, the apparatus of Harkins and Jordan[11] may be employed, constructed as described below (Fig. 15).

The balance, B, sensitive to 0.05 milligram, was adapted for the work by removing the left pan and boring directly under it in the base of the balance a small hole through which an aluminum rod connected the ring, R, with the beam of the balance. The right-hand pan was replaced by a very light aluminum pan in order that the momentum of the beam and pan might be reduced to a minimum. The pan rest was disconnected, as it was found to be troublesome in making measurements.

In order to prevent ripples in the surface of the liquid, which might have

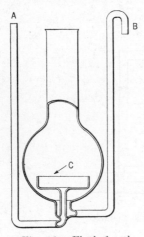

Fig. 16.—Flask for the liquid used in determining surface tension by the ring method.

been formed by lowering the level of the liquid or the containing vessel, a special "jack" (Fig. 15) was devised to lower and raise the balance with great ease and smoothness. While this is not essential to measurements by the ring method, it almost entirely removes any error due to vibration. It consists essentially of four heavy, upright, steel rods, which are screwed into a heavy, cast-iron base provided with leveling screws. Fitted onto these rods are two heavy bronze castings. The lower one is fastened to the rods, and supports the set of gears, G, which raise and lower the upper movable casting. To the upper casting are attached the balance platform and its counterweight. Frictional effects are reduced to a minimum by a delicate counterbalancing of weights throughout. For example, the balance is counterbalanced by movable weight W'. These and the casting which supports them are, in turn, counterbalanced by weight W. This is connected to the upper casting by a steel piano wire which runs over a stationary pulley. The smoothness of operation is also increased by reducing the bearing surface of the movable casting to a minimum. The balance platform is provided with two large, oval-shaped openings through which passes the rod connecting the ring with the balance beam. The balance is lifted by turning handle H. The glass trough, C, is used to hold the solution.

The flask used in the measurements is shown in figure 16. The principle of the design is to provide a means of overflowing the surface in order to prevent surface contamination. The flask was constructed by sealing a cup, C, 7.5 centimeters in diameter and one centimeter or less high near the bottom of a two-liter flask, and by replacing the neck with a longer and wider one.   The liquid is introduced into side arm A and the excess withdrawn through B.

The rings were made of platinum–iridium wire containing 10% iridium, to give the wire stiffness, and were constructed by bending the wire around a brass rod turned down to the exact inner diameter desired, and welding the ends of the wire together with a spot welder.   This had to be done with extreme care or the wire flattens at the spot of the weld.   The stirrups were then welded on to the top or side of the ring, and all protuberances and unevenness removed with a fine file and emery paper.   In four of the rings, made with fine wire, silver solder was used instead of welding.   The loop at the top of the stirrup was made in the form of an ellipse with the least possible radius of curvature at the uppermost part so that the ring would always hang in the same position.   All the rings with radii greater than 0.8 centimeter were made with two stirrups whose planes were at right angles to each other.   Suitable rings of four-centimeter circumference may be purchased from the *Central Scientific Company*.

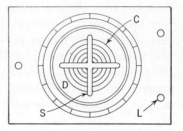

Fig. 17.—Apparatus for measurement of the diameter of the rings.

Since the correction factor, γ/p or F (see page 182), is a function of the variable, R/r, it is necessary to have very accurate measurements of the radii of the wires of which the rings are made, as well as of the radii of the rings.

The diameters of the rings may be measured by a screw micrometer carrying a microscope with a magnification of ten diameters.   In order to make precise measurements, it is necessary to illuminate the ring from below, and the method used is as follows: A reading glass about two and one-half inches in diameter is mounted in a hole in the top of a box, and within the box at the principal focus of the lens is placed a 100-watt lamp painted black with the exception of a spot about one centimeter in diameter.   This provides, for practical purposes, a point source, with parallel light coming through the lens.   Above the lens and about two inches away from it is placed the leveling table containing the ring.   This is constructed as is shown in figure 17.   It may be leveled with leveling screws, or, with the leveling screws removed, may be attached to a microscope by removing the microscope platform.   In the top of a circular hole in the table is mounted a transparent celluloid disk, D, roughened with emery paper.   The disk has two slits cut in it at right angles to each other, S, through which the stirrups are passed, and on it are scratched a series of concentric circles, C, to aid in centering the ring.   The holes, L, are used to fasten the disk in position. Measurements on the rings are made across twelve evenly spaced diameters from the outer edge of the ring on one side to the inner edge on the other. Readings are taken at the point at which the cross hair, which is previously made perpendicular to the direction of travel, becomes tangent to the edge of the ring.

The measurements of the radii of the wires were made with a microscope with a magnification of ten diameters and provided with a micrometer eyepiece. This was calibrated by comparison with an invar scale made in Paris and standardized by the National Bureau of Standards. One division on the micrometer screw head corresponds to 0.0001 centimeter at this magnification. In these measurements, the leveling table was attached to the microscope in place of the microscope platform by means of a special adapter, and the illumination from below was used as in the previous measurements. In place of the celluloid disk, a piece of bond paper was stretched over the top of the cylinder. In order to make the ring appear very black and the edges sharp, a narrow strip of thin cardboard with a slit very slightly wider than the diameter of the wire was slipped under the wire to cut down the extra light. This method gives excellent illumination; and precise measurements of the wire can be made in this manner. Measurements at twelve different, evenly spaced points on the ring were made and the average of these was used.

B. TECHNIQUE

The experimental technique employed by Harkins and Jordan[11] is described since it gives excellent results, though it is obvious that, in many cases, some of the details may be modified. The flask (Fig. 16) used to hold the liquid should be cleaned by methods described earlier in connection with other methods. In order to level the ring, it is suspended over the plane surface of a small, gold-plated brass table, fitted with leveling screws, and polished to a mirror finish on top. This is made level by a small, right-angle level, and the ring is lowered to within one-half millimeter of the top of the table. By sighting between the top of the table and the ring in two mutually perpendicular directions, and by looking at the ring and its mirror image at the same time, considerably less than 30' of tilt can be determined. The stirrup of the ring is bent until the plane of the ring appears to be perfectly horizontal. The ring is then cleaned by heating to red heat in a flame. In the case of three or four of the rings in which the stirrups were silver-soldered to the ring, the ring was cleaned by dipping it into warm cleaning solution, rinsing it thoroughly in conductivity water, and drying it at some distance above a gas flame.

The flask is then put in position under the balance (Fig. 15) so that the plane of the inner cup is as nearly horizontal as possible. The ring is connected to the left-hand stirrup of the balance beam by a jointed aluminum rod composed of links about two inches in length.   On its end is a hook, the inner circumference of which is beveled to a knife edge to allow free motion of the stirrup loop over it.   An inverted Erlenmeyer flask with a hole about one centimeter in diameter blown in the bottom is placed over the top of the measuring flask to prevent evaporation.

The weight of the ring suspended in air is determined and taken as the zero weight.   The cup in the flask is overflowed with plenty of liquid to insure a clean surface, and enough liquid is withdrawn through side arm A (Fig. 16) to cause the liquid in the cup to become level instead of concave upward.   With large rings, the initial surface is made slightly convex up-

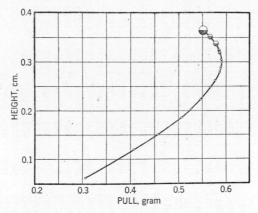

Fig. 18.—Variation of the pull on a ring with its
height above the surface of a liquid.[11]

ward, to such an extent that the outer part of the surface becomes plane when the ring is lifted to the height of detachment.   The balance is lowered until the ring meets the liquid, and then is slowly raised while weights are added to determine the approximate maximum pull.   In this procedure, the addition of weights to the pan is made with the beam rest supporting the beam as in ordinary weighing, and during the addition of weight by the chain the rest is lowered only enough to allow the pointer to swing three divisions in either direction.   The final addition of weight by the chain and the raising of the balance are so regulated as to keep the pointer always at the scale zero.   In check determinations, the beam of the balance is raised and lowered again when the pull is about 10 milligrams less than the maximum to insure its proper position, and the additional weight is added very slowly.   When the maximum weight is reached, the balance pointer suddenly swings to the left and the liquid may or may not become detached

TABLE IV

CORRECTION FACTORS (F) FOR THE RING METHOD[a]

R^3/V	$R/r = 30$	32	34	36	38	40	42	44	46	48	50	52	54	56	58	60
0.30	1.012	1.018	1.024	1.029	1.034	1.038	1.042	1.046	1.049	1.052	1.054					
.31	1.006	1.013	1.018	1.024	1.028	1.033	1.039	1.041	1.044	1.046	1.049					
.32	1.001	1.008	1.012	1.019	1.023	1.028	1.033	1.035	1.039	1.041	1.045					
.33	0.9959	1.003	1.008	1.014	1.018	1.024	1.028	1.030	1.035	1.036	1.040					
.34	.9913	0.998	1.003	1.010	1.014	1.019	1.023	1.026	1.031	1.032	1.036					
.35	.9865	.993	0.999	1.006	1.008	1.015	1.019	1.022	1.026	1.027	1.031					
.36	.9824	.989	.995	1.002	1.005	1.010	1.015	1.018	1.022	1.024	1.027					
.37	.9781	.985	.991	.998	1.001	1.006	1.011	1.014	1.018	1.020	1.024					
.38	.9743	.981	.987	.995	0.998	1.003	1.007	1.010	1.015	1.017	1.020					
.39	.9707	.977	.983	.991	.994	0.9988	1.004	1.007	1.011	1.013	1.017					
.40	.9672	.974	.980	.986	.991	.9959	1.000	1.004	1.008	1.010	1.013	1.016	1.018	1.020	1.021	1.022
.41	.9636	.970	.976	.983	.987	.9922	0.997	1.001	1.005	1.007	1.010	1.013	1.015	1.017	1.019	1.019
.42	.9605	.968	.973	.980	.984	.9892	.994	0.998	1.002	1.004	1.007	1.010	1.013	1.014	1.016	1.017
.43	.9577	.964	.970	.977	.981	.9863	.991	.995	.999	1.001	1.005	1.007	1.010	1.011	1.014	1.014
.44	.9546	.961	.967	.974	.979	.9833	.988	.992	.997	0.998	1.002	1.005	1.007	1.009	1.011	1.011
.45	.9521	.959	.965	.971	.976	.9809	.986	.990	.993	.996	0.9993	1.002	1.004	1.006	1.009	1.009
.46	.9491	.956	.962	.969	.973	.9779	.983	.987	.991	.994	.9968	1.000	1.002	1.004	1.006	1.007
.47	.9467	.954	.960	.966	.971	.9757	.980	.985	.988	.992	.9945	0.998	1.000	1.002	1.004	1.005
.48	.9443	.951	.957	.963	.968	.9732	.978	.983	.986	.989	.9922	.995	0.997	0.999	1.002	1.003
.49	.9419	.949	.955	.961	.966	.9710	.976	.981	.984	.987	.9899	.993	.995	.997	1.000	1.001
.50	.9402	.946	.952	.959	.964	.9687	.973	.978	.981	.985	.9876	.991	.993	.995	.997	.9984
.51	.9378	.944	.950	.956	.961	.9665	.971	.976	.979	.983	.9856	.989	.991	.993	.995	.9965
.52	.9354	.942	.948	.954	.959	.9645	.969	.974	.977	.981	.9836	.987	.989	.991	.994	.9945
.53	.9337	.940	.946	.952	.957	.9625	.967	.972	.975	.979	.9815	.985	.987	.990	.992	.9929
.54	.9315	.938	.944	.950	.955	.9603	.965	.970	.974	.977	.9797	.983	.986	.988	.990	.9909
.55	.9298	.936	.942	.948	.953	.9585	.964	.968	.972	.975	.9779	.981	.984	.986	.988	.9892
.56	.9281	.934	.940	.946	.951	.9567	.962	.966	.970	.974	.9763	.980	.982	.984	.986	.9879
.57	.9262	.932	.939	.944	.949	.9550	.960	.964	.968	.972	.9745	.978	.980	.983	.984	.9861

.58	.9247	.930	.938	.942	.947	.9532	.958	.963	.966	.970	.9730	.976	.979	.981	.982	.9842
.59	.9230	.929	.935	.940	.946	.9515	.956	.961	.965	.968	.9714	.975	.977	.979	.981	.9827
.60	.9215	.927	.933	.939	.944	.9497	.954	.959	.963	.967	.9701	.973	.976	.978	.979	.9813
.62	.9184	.924	.930	.936	.041	.9467	.951	.956	.960	.964	.9669	.970	.973	.975	.976	.9784
.64	.9150	.921	.927	.932	.938	.9439	.948	.953	.957	.961	.9643	.968	.970	.972	.973	.9754
.66	.9121	.918	.925	.930	.935	.9408	.946	.950	.954	.959	.9614	.965	.967	.969	.971	.9728
.68	.9093	.915	.921	.927	.932	.9382	.943	.948	.951	.956	.9590	.963	.965	.967	.968	.9703
.70	.9064	.912	.919	.924	.929	.9352	.940	.945	.949	.953	.9563	.960	.962	.964	.966	.9678
.72	.9037	.910	.916	.921	.927	.9328	.937	.943	.946	.951	.9542	.957	.960	.962	.964	.9656
.74	.9012	.907	.913	.919	.924	.9303	.935	.940	.944	.949	.9519	.955	.958	.960	.962	.9636
.76	.8987	.905	.911	.916	.922	.9277	.933	.938	.942	.947	.9497	.953	.956	.958	.860	.9616
.78	.8964	.902	.908	.914	.920	.9258	.930	.936	.939	.944	.9475	.951	.954	.956	.958	.9598
.80	.8937	.900	.906	.912	.918	.9280	.928	.933	.937	.942	.9454	.949	.952	.954	.956	.9581
.82	.8917	.898	.904	.909	.915	.9211	.926	.931	.935	.940	.9436	.946	.950	.952	.954	.9563
.84	.8894	.895	.902	.907	.913	.9190	.924	.929	.933	.938	.9419	.944	.949	.951	.953	.9548
.86	.8874	.893	.900	.905	.911	.9171	.922	.927	.932	.936	.9402	.942	.947	.949	.951	.9534
.88	.8853	.891	.858	.903	.909	.9152	.921	.926	.930	.934	.9384	.940	.945	.947	.950	.9517
.90	.8831	.889	.896	.902	.907	.9131	.919	.924	.928	.933	.9367	.939	.943	.946	.948	.9504
.92	.8809	.887	.894	.900	.905	.9114	.917	.922	.926	.931	.9350	.937	.942	.945	.947	.9489
.94	.8791	.885	.892	.898	.904	.9097	.915	.920	.925	.929	.9333	.936	.940	.943	.945	.9476
.96	.8770	.883	.890	.896	.902	.9074	.914	.919	.923	.928	.9320	.934	.939	.942	.944	.9462
.98	.8754	.882	.888	.894	.900	.9064	.912	.917	.922	.926	.9305	.933	.937	.940	.943	.9452
1.00	.8734	.880	.886	.892	.899	.9047	.910	.916	.920	.925	.9290	.929	.936	.939	.941	.9438
1.05	.8688	.875	.882	.888	.895	.9007	.906	.912	.916	.921	.9253	.925	.932	.936	.938	.9408
1.10	.8644	.871	.878	.885	.891	.8970	.903	.908	.913	.917	.9217	.922	.929	.933	.935	.9378
1.15	.8602	.867	.875	.981	.888	.8937	.900	.905	.910	.914	.9183	.920	.926	.930	.933	.9352
1.20	.8561	.864	.871	.878	.885	.8904	.897	.902	.907	.911	.9154	.916	.923	.927	.930	.9324
1.25	.8521	.860	.868	.875	.882	.8874	.893	.899	.904	.908	.9125	.914	.920	.924	.927	.9300
1.30	.8484	.856	.864	.871	.879	.8845	.891	.896	.901	.905	.9097	.911	.917	.921	.925	.9277
1.35	.8451	.853	.861	.869	.876	.8819	.888	.893	.898	.903	.9068	.906	.915	.919	.922	.9253
1.40	.8420	.850	.858	.866	.873	.8794	.885	.891	.896	.900	.9043	.909	.913	.916	.920	.9232
1.45	.8387	.847	.855	.863	.871	.8764	.883	.888	.893	.898	.9014	.906	.910	.914	.918	.9207

(Continued)

TABLE IV (continued)

CORRECTION FACTORS (F) FOR THE RING METHOD

R³/V	R/r=30	32	34	36	38	40	42	44	46	48	50	52	54	56	58	60	65	70	75	80
1.50	0.8356	.844	0.853	0.861	0.868	0.8744	0.881	0.886	0.891	0.895	0.8995	0.904	0.908	0.912	0.916	0.9190				0.9382
1.55	.8327	.841	.850	.858	.866	.8722	.878	.883	.888	.893	.8970	.901	.906	.910	.914	.9171		0.928	0.933	.9365
1.60	.8297	.839	.848	.856	.863	.8700	.876	.881	.886	.891	.8947	.899	.904	.908	.912	.9152	0.922	927	931	.9354
1.65	.8272	.836	.845	.853	.861	.8678	.874	.879	.884	.889	.8927	.897	.902	.906	.910	.9133	921	925	930	.9341
1.70	.8245	.834	.843	.851	.859	.8658	.872	.877	.882	.886	.8906	.895	.900	.904	.909	.9116	919	924	929	.9328
1.75	.8217	.831	.840	.849	.857	.8638	.870	.875	.880	.884	.8886	.893	.898	.902	.907	.9097	918	922	927	.9317
1.80	.8194	.829	.838	.847	.855	.8618	.868	.873	.878	.882	.8867	.891	.896	.900	.905	.9080	916	921	926	.9305
1.85	.8168	.827	.836	.845	.853	.8596	.866	.871	.876	.881	.8849	.889	.895	.899	.903	.9066	915	919	925	.9291
1.90	.8143	.824	.834	.843	.851	.8578	.864	.869	.874	.879	.8831	.888	.893	.897	.902	.9047	913	917	923	.9281
1.95	.8119	.822	.832	.841	.849	.8559	.862	.867	.872	.877	.8815	.886	.891	.895	.900	.9034	912	914	922	.9270
2.00	.8098	.820	.830	.839	.847	.8539	.860	.865	.870	.875	.8798	.884	.890	.893	.899	.9016	910	911	920	.9247
2.10	.8056	.816	.826	.835	.843	.8502	.856	.862	.867	.872	.8768	.881	.886	.890	.895	.8991	908	909	917	.9226
2.20	.8015	.812	.822	.831	.839	.8464	.853	.858	.864	.869	.8738	.879	.883	.887	.892	.8962	905	907	915	.9206
2.30	.7976	.808	.818	.828	.835	.8428	.849	.855	.861	.866	.8710	.876	.880	.884	.890	.8935	903	904	913	.9185
2.40	.7936	.804	.814	.824	.832	.8393	.846	.852	.857	.863	.8680	.873	.878	.882	.887	.8910	900	902	910	.9166
2.50	.7898	.800	.811	.820	.828	.8360	.843	.849	.854	.860	.8651	.870	.875	.879	.884	.8884	898	900	908	.9145
2.60	.7861	.797	.807	.817	.825	.8325	.840	.846	.851	.857	.8624	.868	.872	.877	.882	.8859	895	898	906	.9126
2.70	.7824	.793	.803	.813	.822	.8291	.836	.843	.848	.854	.8598	.865	.870	.874	.880	.8837	893	896	904	.9107
2.80	.7788	.790	.800	.810	.818	.8260	.834	.840	.846	.852	.8570	.862	.867	.872	.877	.8813	891	894	902	.9089
2.90	.7752	.786	.796	.806	.815	.8230	.831	.837	.843	.849	.8545	.860	.865	.870	.875	.8790	889	892	900	.9068
3.00	.7716	.783	.793	.803	.812	.8200	.828	.834	.841	.846	.8521	.858	.863	.868	.873	.8770	887	890	899	.9049
3.10	.7677	.779	.790	.800	.809	.8170	.825	.832	.838	.844	.8494	.855	.860	.866	.871	.8750	885	888	897	.9030
3.20	.7644	.776	.787	.797	.806	.8140	.822	.829	.835	.842	.8472	.853	.858	.864	.869	.8730	883	886	895	.9012
3.30	.7610	.772	.783	.793	.803	.8113	.820	.827	.833	.840	.8449	.851	.856	.862	.866	.8710	881	884	893	.8993
3.40	.7572	.769	.780	.790	.800	.8083	.817	.824	.831	.837	.8424	.849	.854	.860	.864	.8688	879		892	.8974
3.50	.7542	.766	.777	.788	.798	.8057	.814	.822	.829	.835	.8404	.847	.852	.858	.862	.8668	877			

from the ring; but any attempt to raise the balance—to bring the pointer back to zero—causes detachment of the liquid. The maximum weight is that required to make the pointer suddenly move to the left, and which cannot be compensated for by raising the balance without detachment of the liquid from the ring.

Dorsey[12] has suggested that many workers, particularly those using the du Noüy tensiometer, might be measuring the pull of a film of liquid upon the ring rather than the maximum pull of the surface of the liquid. It was therefore considered important to study the variation of the pull on the ring with the distance it is raised above the free surface of the liquid. The values, which are shown graphically in figure 18, are given in table IV.

As the ring is pulled out of the liquid, the pull on it increases to a maximum and then decreases. It is at once evident that there is no danger of measuring any other than the maximum pull with the balance, with the technique used, since great difficulty was experienced is measuring points beyond the maximum. After the maximum pull has been reached, the balance pointer swings to the left and can be made to return only by decreasing the weight by 15 or 20, milligrams, when it swings quickly to the right and remains there. During this time, its motion is restricted by the beam rest to one division in either direction from the scale zero. In order to make any measurements of even low precision beyond the maximum, it is necessary to attach a stop which would allow the pointer to swing from zero to a point one-half scale division away in one direction at a time. The weight that would just suffice to make the pointer leave zero in one direction, and then the weight to make it leave in the other direction, are both determined. In this way, the limits of the pull on the ring are determined for those heights which are above the height of maximum pull.

It was noticed, particularly in the case of the smaller rings, that the liquid column had a tendency to adhere to the ring and be pulled out into a film after the pointer had swung to the left, signifying that the maximum pull had been reached. If, however, the beam rest was further released from under the balance beam, the liquid broke. Until the maximum pull was reached the edge of the liquid meniscus appeared to be attached to the ring.

C.   CALCULATION

In early work in which this method was used, the false assumption was made that the pull of the surface tension is vertically downward upon the inner side of the wire of diameter r where the ring has a diameter R', and also upon the outer side of the wire where the ring has a diameter $R' + r$

[12] N. E. Dorsey, *Science*, **69**, 187 (1929).

Thus, the total pull, P, which is equal to the weight of liquid, Mg, suspended, should be, if this assumption were correct:

$$P = Mg = 2\pi\gamma R' + 2\pi\gamma(R' + r) = 4\pi\gamma(R' + r/2) = 4\pi\gamma R \quad \text{(wrong)} \quad (64)$$

where R is the mean radius of the ring. This is equivalent to the assumption that the ring holds up a hollow cylinder of liquid, with vertical walls of radii R' and $R' + r$, and with a weight equal to that upheld inside a capillary tube of a radius equal to twice that of the ring. This idea did not take into account the fact that the surface of the liquid is not vertical where it is in contact with the wire.

The pull, P, under static conditions, is determined by the shape, S, of both the surface outside and that inside the ring. These shapes are dependent upon the angle of contact between the liquid and the surface of the ring. However, in no case has the angle of contact between the surface of a liquid and the properly cleaned wire been found to be other than zero when the maximum pull upon the ring is attained.

Harkins, Young, and Cheng[10] considered that the size of the surfaces outside and inside the ring is determined mostly by the size of the ring, R, and that its shape is determined by the surface tension and density of the liquid, the radius of the ring, R, and of the wire, r, and certain other variables. In order to determine the form of the functional relation, they used the principle of similitude (page 156), which, in this case, indicates that the shape of each surface supported by the pull of the ring depends entirely, when at rest, upon a few simple dimensionless variables. These are: (1) the ratio, R^3/V, of the cube of the radius of the ring to the volume of the liquid; (2) the ratio, R/r, of the radius of the circular ring to the radius of the circular wire of which it is made; and (3) the ratio, h^3/V, of the cube of the pressure height to the volume of liquid which the ring supports. Thus, the shape, S, is given by equation (65) or (66):

$$S = f(R^3/V, R/r, h^3/V) \tag{65}$$

$$S = \varphi(R/a, R/r, h/a) \tag{66}$$

The surface tension is a function of the shape, and, therefore, of these same variables, and its value is given by:

$$\gamma = Mg/4\pi R \cdot f_1(R^3/V, R/r, h^3/V) \tag{67}$$

Since the volume upheld by the ring becomes a maximum at a certain definite shape for which the value of h^3/V is determined by the values of R^3/V and R/r, this term may be omitted (Eq. 68 or 69):

$$\gamma = (Mg/4\pi R) \cdot f(R^3/V, R/r) \tag{68}$$

$$\gamma = (Mg/4\pi R) \cdot \gamma/p = Mg/4\pi R \cdot F \tag{69}$$

The values of F may be determined experimentally be determining the true surface tensions of various liquids by the capillary height or drop-weight methods, and comparing with the values of p as shown in the above equation, as was done by Harkins and Jordan,[11] or they may be calculated from the shapes of the curves obtained theoretically by Freud and Freud[13] in another paper from this laboratory.

The values of the correction factor, F, which is γ/p, are given in figure 19 as a function of R^3/V and of R/r. Here V is the volume of liquid raised above the level of the plane surface of the liquid by the maximum pull of

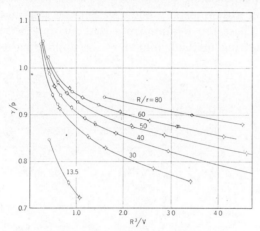

Fig. 19.—Correction factors (F) for the ring method for surface tension.[11]

the ring. It is equal to the mass, M, of the liquid, as determined by the balance (the M of Eq. 67, 68, or 69) divided by its density, ρ, or:

$$V = M/\rho \qquad (70)$$

The values of F are listed in table IV, which may be used by linear inter-polation. If many determinations are to be made by a single ring, it is advisable to plot a correction curve for the ring. This is more linear if log F is plotted as a function of log (R^3/V). Also $g/4\pi R$ may be incorporated in the correction:

$$\varphi = g/4\pi R \cdot F \qquad (71)$$

so that:

$$\gamma = M\varphi \qquad (72)$$

[13] B. B. Freud and H. Z. Freud, *J. Am. Chem. Soc.*, **52**, 1772 (1930).

The difficulties involved in making precise measurements by the ring method may be overcome very simply. Any rigorous theory of the ring method would require: (1) that the wire of the ring lie in one plane; (2) that the plane of the ring be horizontal; (3) that the vessel containing the liquid under investigation give an area large enough that any curvature of the free surface of the liquid be not great enough to affect the shape of the liquid surface raised by the ring; (4) that the surface of the liquid be free from wave motion; (5) that there be no motion of the ring except an extremely slow upward motion; (6) that, since there should be no evaporation and consequent cooling of the surface, the liquid be in a vessel immersed deeply in a thermostat; and (7) that the ring be circular and of circular wire. These are requirements that are inherent in the proper technique of the ring method, and must be approximated as nearly as possible.

TABLE V

ERROR DUE TO TIPPING OF RING[a]

(Ring 12, $R = 1.8277$, $r = 0.20986$)

Angle, α	α^2	p	Δp	Error, %
0.00	0.00	84.05	0.00	0.00
1.10	1.21	83.61	0.44	0.52
1.62	2.62	83.20	0.85	1.01
2.10	4.42	82.73	1.32	1.57

[a] W. D. Harkins and H. F. Jordan, *J. Am. Chem. Soc.*, **52**, 1751 (1930).

The most important source of error arises from the ring not being horizontal. This was investigated in a quantitative way by measuring the pull on a ring when tipped by various amounts. The stirrup was bent so the plane of the ring was not horizontal, and the difference in height between the two sides was measured with a cathetometer. From this, the angle made between the plane of the ring and the horizontal was calculated. The data, which are given in table V, are illustrated in figure 20.

It is seen from the graph of the data that, for small angles such as are likely to be encountered in practice, the error introduced is proportional to the square of the angle. Δp is, therefore, expressed by the equation:

$$- \Delta p = k\alpha^2 \tag{73}$$

In the present case, the equation holds for angles not greater than 1.5°, and k has the value 0.36. From the graph it may be seen that, for the error due to this source to be less than 0.1%, the angle of tip must be less than 0.47°, and for an angle of 1°, the error introduced is 0.43%.

The effect of the curvature of the meniscus and the size of the vessel was studied by making measurements of water contained in crystallizing dishes of various sizes. The crystallizing dish was placed on a glass desiccator triangle in a two-liter beaker, and overflowed from the top, thus insuring

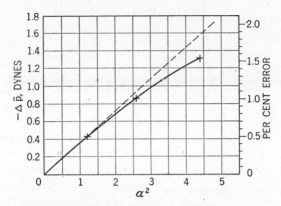

Fig. 20.—Error in the ring method caused by tipping the ring. α^2 is the square of the angle of deviation from the horizontal.[11]

uniformly clean surfaces. To prevent evaporation, the top of the beaker was covered with a plate of glass in which a hole was bored. Measurements could not be made when the diameter of the dish was less than seven centimeters, as the curvature of the meniscus was so great as to cause the ring to cling to the side of the dish. The data are given in table VI. A diameter

TABLE VI

EFFECT OF CURVATURE OF MENISCUS ON MAXIMUM PULL ON THE RING[a]

(Ring 12)

Diameter of dish, cm	7	8	9	10	12
p	83.96	84.03	84.08	84.05	84.06

[a] W. D. Harkins and H. F. Jordan, *J. Am. Chem. Soc.*, **52**, 1751 (1930).

of more than seven centimeters is satisfactory for the measurement of surface tension for the smaller rings, but with larger rings or in the measurement of interfacial tension the diameter should be larger.

The error caused by not having all the wire in the same plane cannot be measured quantitatively with any accuracy, and this may be an important source of error. A ring not in a plane gives a consistently lower pull, and is one of the troublesome factors in measurements with larger rings made of fine wire. In straightening the wire, a small brass plate was used in which a groove was cut. The ring was set on the plate with the portion of the ring to be straightened across the groove, and was then tapped gently with a small brass rod rounded at the end. While this method was not entirely satisfactory, it was the best of a number that were tried.

5. Bubble-Pressure Method

A. GENERAL

The surface tension of a liquid can be determined from the maximum pressure in a bubble, as, for example, at the bottom of a circular capillary tube. The method was suggested in 1851 by Simon,[14] and the first correct theory of the formation of bubbles was published by Cantor,[15] although his equations for the manometric pressure were not exact.

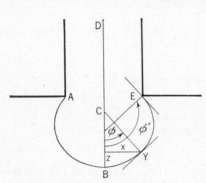

Fig. 21.—Bubble at the lower end of a capillary opening.

Equations for the calculation of the surface tension have been given by a number of workers. That of Schroedinger,[16] approved by Verschaffelt:[17]

$$\gamma = \frac{\bar{p}r}{2}\left[1 - \frac{2}{3}\frac{r}{h} - \frac{1}{6}\left(\frac{r}{h}\right)^2 \cdots \right]$$

(74)

is valid if r/h is small, but for larger values the tables of Bashforth and Adams[18] should be used. The symbols in equation (74) and below are: r = radius of tip. ρ = density of liquid (or denser phase). ρ' = density of gas (or less dense liquid). p = pressure difference (at varying depths) on the two sides of the bubble wall. $\bar{p}$ = maximum pressure difference between the inside and outside of the bubble at the face of the tip. b = radius of curvature at the vertex of the bubble or meniscus. j = height of vertex of bubble above the face of the tip, so, in the bubble, j is negative. $h = \bar{p}/(\rho - \rho')g$, is the "ideal" height read on a manometer. This is the height when the manometer contains the liquid the surface tension of which is being measured, and when the face of the tip is at just the level of the plane surface of the liquid outside the tip; meniscus corrections should be applied to the manometer; these are given in the section on the capillary

---

[14] M. Simon, *Ann. chim. phys.*, **33**, 5 (1851).

[15] M. Cantor, *Ann. Phys.*, **47**, 399 (1892).

[16] E. Schroedinger, *Ann. Physik*, **46**, 410 (1915).

[17] J. E. Verschaffelt, *Commun. Leiden*, Suppl. No. 42d (1918).

[18] F. Bashforth and J. C. Adams, *An Attempt to Test the Theories of Capillary Action.* Cambridge Univ. Press, London, 1883.

height method on pages 159–160. x = horizontal coordinate for a point on the surface of the bubble. ϕ and ϕ' = angles shown in figure 21. A is the contact of bubble with inside edge of tip; B is the vertex of the bubble; and X and Z are abscissa and ordinate, respectively, of point Y with respect to B. D is the vertical axis of tube and bubble; ϕ is the angle between the vertical axis and normal to the surface at Y; ϕ is the same for normal at E; and C is the intersection of normal at Y with the vertical axis. Hg equals the height measured on the manometer, provided this contains the liquid the surface tension of which is being determined, and at the same temperature.   If the tip is below the plane surface of the liquid, the depth is subtracted from the manometric height.

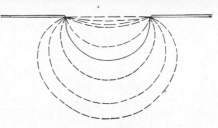

Fig. 22.—Bubble formation under a thin plate.

The bubble-pressure method has not been applied in its most accurate form, that is, in a way prescribed by the theory.   However, if what is measured is actually the maximum pressure, as by the use of a single, very slowly growing bubble, the method should be one of the best, and, for certain purposes, the most convenient of all methods for the determination of surface tension. The method gave inexact values in the work of Jaeger;[19] and, while the results of Sugden[20] are more accurate, his method has not been tested with sufficient thoroughness to make certain that it is reliable.   The errors are due to the fact that his method is kinetic, whereas the theory is that of a static procedure.

A correct bubble-pressure method, as described on pages 194–199, should be of particular value for the determination of the surface tensions of molten salts, and of liquid metals, for which the data are at present much less accurate than for other liquids.   The method has the obvious disadvantage that it cannot be used in a vacuum.

Before the bubble-pressure method is used for the determination of surface tension, the investigator should become familiar with the phenomena exhibited in the *expansion of a bubble*.   These were revealed by the work of Frese,[21] Hoffman,[22] and Tripp[23] under the direction of Young.

[19] F. M. Jaeger, *Z. anorg. chem.*, **101**, 1 (1917).

[20] S. Sugden, *J. Am. Chem. Soc.*, **121**, 858 (1922); **125**, 29 (1924).

[21] T. F. Young and F. G. Frese, *private communication.*

[22] M. Hoffman, "Pressure as a Function of the Shapes of Liquid Surfaces." *M.S. thesis*, Univ. of Chicago, 1926.

[23] H. P. Tripp, "Maximum Bubble Pressure Method for Measurement of Surface Tension." *Ph.D. thesis*, Univ. of Chicago, 1934.

Figure 22 illustrates the form as calculated produced by increasing the pressure in bubbles under a circular hole in a plate of infinitesimal thickness. In experimental work, for obvious reasons, this is replaced by a thicker plate with a hole with a sharp edge (preferably the sharp edge is at the bottom). Here, the upper, broken straight line shows the form of the surface under zero pressure, where $\phi' = 0$. If pressure is applied to the gas and not to the liquid, the other lines represent the form of the meniscus or bubble as p is increased, the continuous curve giving the form for $\phi' = 90°$. At higher pressures, the bubble expands to higher values of ϕ', and the form of the bubble below the plate now becomes identical with that below the tube, so $\phi' = \phi$.

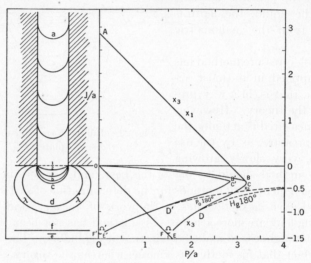

Fig. 23.—Relation between pressure, P/a, and height, J/a, of vertex of meniscus, a to b, or bubble b, c, d, λ. Positions 1, 2, 3, do not occur if the liquid wets the tube, but occur with a hole in a thin plate (Fig. 22). The maximum pressure, P/a, from which the surface tension is calculated, occurs at c and is equal to $\bar{x} = P/a$ at C. At B, ϕ' is 80°; at C, the pressure is at a maximum; at D the value of ϕ' is 180°, Ω is the last point which can be calculated from the tables of Bushforth and Adams; and at F (and f), the volume of the bubble is infinite.

Let P_0 represent the pressure difference between the two sides of any bubble or meniscus at its vertex, then the curve $OB'F'$ (Fig. 23) represents the P_{10} of a bubble formed underneath the thin plate: OB from 0° to 90°, $B'D'$ from 90° to 180°, and $D'F'$ the further expansion of the bubble. Portion $B'F'$ obviously gives also the relations for a bubble below a tube as well as below a plate. Line OF gives the change in pressure in the liquid itself (at the vertex) as the depth increases. Obviously, this is linear.

Since the tube used for the formation of the bubbles is a fine capillary, the liquid rises to a height h if the gas pressure at the meniscus, a, is zero. This height is designated in figure 23 by J/a. The diagram which constitutes the right-hand side of the figure gives the pressure, which is zero at A, on the x-axis. As the meniscus is pushed down the tube to b by an increase (linear) of pressure it remains the same shape. Shapes *1*, *2*, and *3*, are not exhibited, since these occur with the thin plate but not with a tube, which gives a contact angle of zero with respect to the liquid.

After the linear increase of pressure along AB is ended at B (position b), the meniscus changes into a bubble. The pressure now increases more slowly, until the bottom of the bubble reaches c and below this decreases as the bottom of the bubble is pressed down. Thus the value of x at c gives the maximum pressure, p/a, which the bubble can give, and this is what should be measured.

The use of j/a, p/a, $\bar{p}/a$, etc., instead of j, p, and $\bar{p}$, etc., depends upon the principle of similitude (page 156), since, for a given r/a, all bubbles have the same shape for a given p/a, and also for a given $\bar{p}/a$. Thus, any number of bubbles which give the same maximum values of $\bar{p}/a$ have the same shape if r/a and D/a are the same. Similar applications of the principle of similitude are fundamental in connection with the drop-weight and ring methods.

The pressure in the bubble below the tube is the pressure difference between gas and liquid (P_0 at the vertex of the bubble) plus the hydrostatic pressure, J (given by OF since its slope is unity). Thus, any point on curve $OBCEF$ has a value of x = $x_{OF} + x_{OB'C'E'F'}$ at any value of J/a or, since $p/a = x$:

$$p_{OBCEF} = p_{OB'C'E'F'} + p_{OF} \qquad (75)$$

The pressure change throughout the history of a bubble formed on a capillary tube can be traced on curve $ABCD\Omega F$. Portion AB represents the depression of the meniscus in the tube. When the upper edge of the meniscus reaches the tip of the tube, the pressure has the value at B. The shape is now represented by curve b, figure 23. As more gas is forced in and the vertex is depressed further, the pressure rises less rapidly than hitherto. When the bubble attains shape c, the pressure has reached a maximum value shown at C. As more gas is forced in, the expansion is so rapid that the pressure decreases. During this expansion, ϕ' increases further and the bubble attains shape d when ϕ' reaches 180°. The pressure is now shown at D. When more gas is added, ϕ' can no longer increase because of the horizontal surface of the tip. The circular line of contract now begins to increase in diameter, and the pressure follows course DEF. Point F represents the pressure and depth of a bubble of infinite volume. The curvature at the vertex of such a bubble is zero, and the pressure is therefore due solely to j/a. F is therefore on the line having the slope of minus one. According to an equation of Verschaffelt which is to be discussed later, the depth of the bubble passes through a maximum at point E (bottom at e). The radius of curvature of this bubble of maximum depth cannot be zero; and the pressure in such a bubble must be greater than j. Point E therefore lies to the right of OF.

During the third stage, when $\phi' = 180°$, the forms of all bubbles having a given circle of contact will be identical and the pressure will likewise be the same. Curve DEF therefore is representative of any bubble whose circle of contact is greater than the bore of the tube. The maximum pressure (point C) occurs when dHg/dj is zero. This point is reached when:

$$dp_0/dj = dj/dj = 1 \qquad (76)$$

in other words—the slope of $OB'F'$ is unity as at C'.   Figure 24 exhibits the effect of a change of the size of the tip or, more exactly, of r/a, on the relations shown in figure 23.

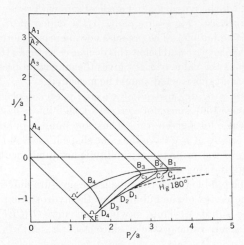

Fig. 24.—Effect of the radius of the orifice of the tip or, more generally, of r/a, on the relations exhibited in figure 23.   The curves from *1* to *4* correspond to values of r/a of 0.3081, 0.3386, 0.4021, and 1, respectively.

B.   APPARATUS, MEASUREMENT, AND CALCULATIONS

The tip on which the bubble is to be formed is prepared by grinding off the end of a piece of capillary tubing in such a way as to give a smooth surface perpendicular to the walls.   The interior diameter, measured by a comparator, should be as nearly the same in different directions as is possible, and may have a diameter as low as 0.008 cm.; but if too small it is difficult to obtain an accurate measure of the diameter.

This face of tip is leveled while the tube is in a convenient support, and the liquid whose surface tension is to be measured is brought up around it by raising the U tube in which it is contained.   The arm of the U tube which contains the liquid may be narrow (*ca.* 1.5 cm. in diameter) and the other wide (*ca.* 4.5 cm.) and will require 75 to 90 ml. of liquid.   The amount may be decreased by using a narrower "wide tube," and by estimating the capillary rise in this tube when the pressure is calculated.   This introduces a difficulty in that the level varies more rapidly during the formation of the bubble, but the variation may be estimated.

The upper part of the capillary tube is connected with a manometer gage of U shape or some other form.   The diameter of the manometer tubing may be 0.4 cm.   It should be connected to a pressure generator.   Tripp[23] employed 5 cm. of rubber tubing of an internal diameter of 0.4 cm., pinched by a small vise with a screw which had 80 threads to the inch, in order to regulate the pressure. The depth of immersion of the tip is considered as its depth below the plane surface of the liquid in the wider arm of the U tube, as measured by a cathetometer.

Equation (74) may be written:

$$a^2 = hr \left[1 - \frac{2}{3} \frac{r}{h} - \frac{1}{6} \left(\frac{r}{h} \right)^2 \right] \tag{77}$$

($a^2 = hr$, for a capillary height with a different h), which is valid if r/h is small. For larger values, the tables of Bashforth and Adams[18] may be used. They give the equation:

$$p = g(\rho - \rho')Z + C = \gamma(1/R_1 + 1/R_2) \tag{78}$$

where Z is zero at the apex of the bubble, or $c/\gamma = 2/b$, where $b = R_1 = R_2$.

$$p = 2\gamma/b + Z_g(\rho - \rho') \tag{79}$$

This pressure would be exerted by a column of liquid of height:

$$h = p/g(\rho - \rho') = (2T/gb(\rho - \rho')) + Z \tag{80}$$

but:

$$2\gamma/g(\rho - \rho') = a^2 \tag{81}$$

Hence:

$$h = (a^2/b) + Z \tag{82}$$

as found by Sugden.[20]

Multiplication by r/a^2 gives:

$$hr/a^2 = r/b + rZb/aba \tag{83}$$

Bashforth and Adams[11] use a β, which they define by:

$$\beta = g(\rho - \rho')b^2/\gamma \tag{84}$$

which determines the shape of bubble, or this may be written as equation (85) or (86):

$$\beta = 2b^2/a^2 \tag{85}$$

$$b/a = \sqrt{\beta/2} \tag{86}$$

Now:

$$r/b = r\sqrt{2/\beta}/a \tag{87}$$

so:

$$hr/a^2 = r/b + rZ\sqrt{\beta/2}/ab \tag{88}$$

Sugden rearranges this and defines a quantity, X, by the equation, $X = a^2/h$, so:

$$\frac{r}{a^2/h} = \frac{r}{X} = \frac{r}{b} + \frac{r}{a}\frac{Z}{b}\sqrt{\frac{\beta}{2}} \tag{89}$$

This discussion is based on that of Young and Frese,[21] who show that, for any chosen value of r/a, there will be a number of values of r/X corresponding to a series of values of β, $i.$ $e.$, to a series of values of ϕ, since β is a function of ϕ for any selected liquid. In equation (78), a value is assigned to r/a, say unity. Then $r/b = \sqrt{2/\beta}$. Now assign a value of 6 to β. If this value of r/b, which is really x/b in the tables, is found in the tables, the corresponding angle may be calculated, and likewise the z/b for this angle. Then, knowing r/b, Z/b, and β, r/X may be calculated from equation (79). As the next step, a value of 6.5 is assigned to β, and another value for r/X is obtained. By repetition of this method, a table is constructed for some chosen value of r/a. An example will make the meaning clear (Table VII). From the table it is seen that as angle ϕ increases, r/X, which is proportional to h (see Eq. 79), likewise increases and passes through a maximum. A series of minimum values can be calculated for X/r in this way for a range of values of r/a; from them, by interpolation, a table (Table VIII) was calculated by Sugden.

TABLE VII[a]

VALUES OF r/b, Z/b, r/X AND ϕ AS A FUNCTION OF β AT $r/a = 1.0$

β	r/b	Z/b	r/X	ϕ
6	0.5772	0.6756	1.7479	147.1
6.5	0.5546	0.6640	1.7519	152.6
7.0	0.5346	0.6514	1.7536	157.5
7.5	0.5165	0.6384	1.7528	162.1
8.0	0.5000	0.6254	1.7508	166.5

[a] T. F. Young and F. G. Frese, *private communication.*

The surface tension may be calculated from table VIII or by the direct use of the tables of Bashforth and Adams.[18] Now:

$$h = a^2/X + l \tag{90}$$

where l is the depth of the tip. Let $h_0 = h - l = a^2/X$, since:

$$a^2 = h_0 X \tag{91}$$

Assume first that $X = r$, and calculate a^2, and from this r/a. From table VIII, the value of X/r may be obtained, and from this the value of X, which from $a^2 = h_0 X$ gives a new value of a^2. By successive approximations, the correct value of a^2, and thus of γ is obtained.

In *Sugden's method*,[20] which is less accurate than Young's method of the single bubble, two tubes with tips of widely varying diameters are used, and the bubbles are pulled through the apparatus by means of a mercury aspirator attached to a manometer filled with tinted absolute alcohol. An improved bubbler was recently described by Quayle and Smart (Fig. 25).[24]

TABLE VIII

MINIMUM VALUE OF X/r FOR VALUES OF r/a FROM 0 TO 1.50[a]

r/a	0.00	0.01	0.02	0.03	0.04	0.05	0.06	0.07	0.08	0.09
0.0	1.0000	0.9999	0.9997	0.9994	0.9990	0.9984	0.9977	0.9968	0.9958	0.9946
0.1	0.9934	.9920	.9905	.9888	.9870	.9851	.9831	.9809	.9786	.9762
0.2	.9737	.9710	.9682	.9653	.9623	.9592	.9560	.9527	.9492	.9456
0.3	.9419	.9382	.9344	.9305	.9265	.9224	.9182	.9138	.9093	.9047
0.4	.9000	.8952	.8903	.8853	.8802	.8750	.8698	.8645	.8592	.8538
0.5	.8484	.8429	.8374	.8319	.8263	.8207	.8151	.8094	.8037	.7979
0.6	.7920	.7860	.7800	.7739	.7678	.7616	.7554	.7493	.7432	.7372
0.7	.7312	.7252	.7192	.7132	.7072	.7012	.6953	.6894	.6835	.6776
0.8	.6718	.6660	.6603	.6547	.6492	.6438	.6385	.6333	.6281	.6230
0.9	.6179	.6129	.6079	.6030	.5981	.5953	.5885	.5838	.5792	.5747
1.0	.5703	.5659	.5616	.5573	.5531	.5489	.5448	.5408	.5368	.5329
1.1	.5290	.5251	.5213	.5176	.5139	.5103	.5067	.5032	.4997	.4962
1.2	.4928	.4895	.4862	.4829	.4797	.4765	.4733	.4702	.4671	.4641
1.3	.4611	.4582	.4553	.4524	.4496	.4468	.4440	.4413	.4386	.4359
1.4	.4333	.4307	.4281	.4256	.4231	.4206	.4181	.4157	.4133	.4109
1.5	.4085	..	..	..	..	..	..	..	..	..

[a] S. Sugden, *The Parachor and Valency*.   Routledge, London, 1930, Table 80, p. 219.

The quantity of liquid is adjusted so the tips are two to three millimeters below the surface.   The stopcock leading to the wider tip is closed, and the bubbles pulled through the narrow tip at about one per second.   The maximum pressure is recorded.   Then the stopcock is opened and the maximum pressure again noted.   The difference in the maxima is H', and this may be converted to accord with the density of the liquid being measured:

$$H = H' \cdot \rho_{manometer}/\rho_{liquid} \qquad (92)$$

The calculation is made in exactly the same way as exhibited before for a single tube, as follows: Let r_1 and r_2 be the radii of the tubes, h_1 and h_2 the pressures, measured in centimeters of the liquid concerned, which are required to liberate bubbles, and l the depth to which each tube is immersed. Then, from equation (91):

$$h_1 = a^2/X_1 + l, \qquad h_2 = a^2/X_2 + l \qquad (93)$$

[24] O. R. Quayle and K. O. Smart, *J. Am. Chem. Soc.*, **66**, 937 (1944).

Therefore:

$$H = h_1 - h_2 = a^2(1/X_1 - 1/X_2) \tag{94}$$

or:

$$a^2 = H/(1/X_1 - 1/X_2) \tag{95}$$

The use of this equation and the table are best explained by means of an example. With an apparatus similar to that described on page 197, the

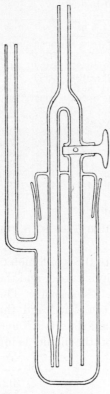

following values were found by Sugden[24a] for benzene at 20°: $r_1 = 0.007525$ cm., $r_2 = 0.0600$ cm., $H = 6.81$ cm. of water at 15° $= 7.755$ cm. of benzene at 20° C.

As a first approximation, take, $X_1 = r_1$, $X_2 = r_2$. Then $a^2 = 7.755/116.2 = 6.675$ sq. mm. Using this value of a^2 to calculate r_1/a and r_2/a, it is found that $r_1/a = 0.029$ and $r_2/a = 0.232$. From table VIII, the corresponding values of X/r are: $X_1/r = 0.9994$ and $X_2/r = 0.9649$, whence $X_1 = 0.007522$ and $X_2 = 0.0579$. Putting these values in equation (95), $a^2 = 6.703$ sq. mm.

A further application of this method of successive approximations gives the same result for a^2.

At 20° C., for benzene, $D - d = 0.8771$ and $g = 981$ cm. per sec.² from which $\gamma = 28.84$ dynes per cm.

This method of calculation is accurate for any size of tube giving values of r/a covered by table VIII. It is, however, very tedious when a large number of results have to be dealt with; and a much simpler method can be used if the values of r_1 and r_2 fall within certain limits. In practice, tubes of radii less than 0.005 cm. are difficult to use, since they are readily blocked by dust particles; on the other hand, tubes of radii greater than 0.010 cm. give pressures which are

Fig. 25.—Sugden apparatus[24] as modified by Quayle.

small and cannot be measured accurately. The radius of the wide tube is conveniently fixed at between 0.100 and 0.200 cm. For tubes of these radii and liquids with values of a^2 greater than 3 mm.², it is found that the surface tension may be calculated by the simple empirical formula:

$$\gamma = AP \left(1 + 0.69r_2 \frac{gd}{P}\right) \tag{96}$$

[24a] S. Sugden, *The Parachor and Valency*. Routledge, London, 1930, p. 220.

Here, A is, for the apparatus, a constant which is determined chiefly by the radius of the smaller tube, but also by that of the larger one, and P is the difference in pressure required to liberate bubbles from the two tubes, expressed in dynes per cm.[2] This simple expression, when tested by comparison with the more accurate method, using equation (95) and table VIII, is found to be accurate to one part in 1000 within the limits stated above. It is, therefore, amply accurate, since the errors of Sugden's two-tube method are usually considerably larger (about one in 200).

The *precautions* listed below are essential if a stream of bubbles is used. If a single bubble is observed only (*1*) is important:

(*1*)   The outside diameter of the tip should not be too large, *i. e.*, the wall of the capillary should be thin at the tip.

(*2*)   If the method of observation of a single bubble is not employed, and that of many bubbles is adopted, a rate of flow of from 35 to 60 bubbles per minute seems to avoid the fluctuations of pressure found at lower rates and also at higher rates.

(*3*)   If the frictional resistance in the tip is too high, the pressure required to liberate a stream of bubbles is greater than that to overcome the surface tension. This condition is easily detected, since the maximum pressure varies with the rate of flow. With too small a frictional resistance, the bubbles are liberated in groups of two or more, and the gage may oscillate through several tenths of a millimeter or more. The tube which connects the gage to the tip should be free from constrictions, since they may give an excess of pressure on the gage.

(*4*)   If the diameter of the gage or the volume of the system is too small, there may be a decrease in pressure when the bubble escapes and the true maximum pressure may not be attained.

Since the precautions which must be observed in order to obtain accurate results are much more simple if a single bubble, rather than a stream of bubbles, is observed, it seems obvious that the method which uses the variation of pressure in a single bubble is preferable. It is essential that enough bubbles be released from the tip to insure a clean liquid–gas interface before the observation of a single bubble is begun. Young, who has done a considerable amount of work on bubble-pressure methods, considers that the use of single bubbles should give better results than that of a stream of bubbles. The maximum pressure should be measured for each of 10 or more bubbles.

6.   Concluding Remarks

A.   ABSOLUTE METHODS

In the section on the "Choice of Method" (pages 157 *et seq.*) the relative accuracy of certain methods is indicated. Now that the theory of the shapes of surfaces has been given some consideration, a further discussion should be profitable, since the suitability of the method for the particular purpose for which it is to be used is as important as the experimental technique applied.

Methods may be considered as "absolute" if the complete theory of the method has been developed to such a state that there is agreement between the theory and the experimental results. The theory of the capillary height method is so simple that it is easily shown that it involves no possibility of error, except in the meniscus correction, which can be made so small as to be almost negligible. The theory of the shape of a small meniscus is developed to such an extent that the total error due to the theory is less than that in the extremely accurate experimental work which has been done. This is the best illustration of an "absolute" method.

The ring method may also be considered as absolute, since the theory of Freud and Freud[13] and the experimental values of Harkins and Jordan[11] have been found to agree. However, with pure liquids, the error in the use of this method is greater than in extremely careful work by the capillary height method.

B. METHODS NOT DESCRIBED*

Pendant-Drop.—The theory but not the practice of the pendant-drop method is presented on pages 164–168. This method is less accurate than any of those described above. As used at present, it is a relative method, but it might become absolute if the theory of Bashforth and Adams,[18] or of Freud and Harkins[2] were to be applied.

Small Drops.—The drop is formed, the pressure in it measured, and the form of the drop determined, either directly or by the use of an enlarged photograph. The surface tension is calculated from the curvature at the point where the pressure is measured, and is independent of the contact angle. The method is equally applicable to bubbles or drops, and to surface or interfacial tension. This applies to the method of large drops also.

Larger Drops.—The general method is the same with the exception that the drops are too large to permit an accurate measurement of pressure. All that is necessary is to make two measurements of linear dimensions so selected as to allow a moderately accurate calculation of the surface tension. Before this method is chosen it is well to consider a statement by Dorsey.[12] "All such determinations are based upon a departure of the surface from a spherical form. . . . . This indicates the limitations of the method; it rests upon the precise measurement of quantities which in other methods enter only as corrective terms."

---

* See also *General References*, p. 209.

In view of the above statement about a method which depends upon the measurement of a static drop, it might seem that the drop-weight method, which involves motion, should be even less accurate.   However, actually it is very much more accurate than the pendant-drop method. The form of a drop which hangs from the sharp edge of a horizontal circular tip is, as shown earlier, very exactly determined by the dimensionless quantities, h/a and r/a (page 165), while, for the maximum stable drop, it is determined by r/a alone.   It has been found by an extensive series of experiments that the fraction of the ideal drop which falls is also determined with considerable exactness, provided the drop detaches itself with the slowness attained in the best experimental technique.   Thus, the form of the pendant drop and the weight of the drop which falls are determined quite exactly by the dimensionless quantities.   In the determination of the surface tension by the pendant-drop method two linear measurements related to the shape are used, while in the drop-weight method the weight is utilized.   This difference causes the latter method to be much the more accurate.   The drop-weight method, unlike that of the pendant drop, does not depend upon a departure from the spherical shape. The shape enters into the correction factor—$f(r/a)$, $f(r/V^{1/3})$, or F—but this may be chosen for values of r/a such that this factor is almost independent of r/a.   All of these relationships give the drop-weight method a high degree of accuracy, and the pendant-drop method a low degree of accuracy.

Sessile Bubbles or Drops.—This method involves the same general considerations as that of the pendant drop or bubble, but it is the best method if very slow time effects are involved.   The form of a drop which rests upon a horizontal plane plate, or of a bubble under the plate, is observed.   The use of the bubble is much to be preferred, since a series of bubbles can be blown under the plate and thus a clean surface obtained which keeps clean very much better than that of a drop.   The only practical use of the method of the sessile bubble is in the measurement of the surface tension of solutions of detergents and other substances which exhibit the same aging phenomenon.   The surface tension of dilute solutions of these substances may decrease with the age of the surface for a period of many hours, and, according to some investigators, for a period even of weeks.

The Pull on a Vertical Plate.—The pull on a vertical plate as measured by a balance (Wilhelmy method) is described in its differential form on pages 218–222.   The use of the nondifferential form has been greatly limited by the fact that the depth of immersion of the plate must be known with considerable accuracy.

IV. PARACHOR

The correlation of physical properties with structure would be greatly simplified if some truly "additive" property could be discovered (see page 672.)   The value of this property for any compound would be obtained by simply adding the contributions of the atoms and the structural linkages in the compound.   Molecular volume, critical volume and *nullpunkts-volume* (molecular volume extrapolated empirically to absolute zero) possess, to a certain extent, this property of additivity, but not nearly to the same extent as that function of the surface tension and density of the liquid known as parachor.   However, recent studies[25, 33, 34] have shown that even the parachor is not quite as completely additive as was first believed. Additional interference terms are necessary to explain the various effects of structure and present indications are that the use of the parachor for deciding between possible structures is not as reliable as was originally expected.

In 1923, MacLeod[26] discovered empirically that the fourth root of the surface tension, γ, is proportional to the difference between the liquid and vapor densities, $D - d$, and that the proportionality constant for non-associated liquids is very little affected by temperature up to about 30° C. below the critical temperature.   Sugden[27] multiplied the ratio of $\gamma^{1/4}$ to $(D - d)$ by the molecular weight and termed the product the *parachor*, that is, comparative volume $[P]$.   The defining equation for the parachor at any given temperature is thus:

$$[P] = M\gamma^{1/4}/(D - d) \tag{97}$$

where γ = surface tension in dynes per centimeter, D = liquid density in grams per cubic centimeter, d = vapor density in grams per cubic centimeter, at the same temperature and at the vapor pressure of the liquid, and M = molecular weight.   It is of interest to note that the unit of the parachor is not that of molecular volume, but is gram$^{1/4}$ cm.^{3}/sec.$^{1/2}$ mole. The exponent, $1/4$, has no foundation in theory, but has been found to maintain the parachor constant over a considerable temperature range for a variety of compounds.

There is some rational basis for the parachor in that the compounds are compared under similar conditions of surface tension.   This is supposedly equivalent to a comparison of the molecular volumes under equal compression by the intermolecular forces.   However, the choice of a fourth

[25] A. I. Vogel *et al.*, *J. Chem. Soc.*, **1938**, 1323; **1940**, 171, 1528; **1943**, 16.
[26] D. B. MacLeod, *Trans. Faraday Soc.*, **19**, 38 (1923).
[27] S. Sugden, *J. Chem. Soc.*, **1924**, 1177.

root in the formula and the inclusion of the density of the vapor as a correction to the density of the liquid are not explained by the above rationalization.   The exponent, $1/4$, is a good compromise for all the compounds measured, but for an individual compound the parachor may show better constancy at different temperatures with a slightly different value of the exponent.

In modern work, surface tension is usually determined at several different temperatures so the effect of temperature on the parachor can be observed.   Thus, for typical nonassociated liquids such as the paraffin hydrocarbons, the effect of temperature is small, as can be seen from table IX. For a typical associated liquid such as ethyl alcohol, the parachor increases from 124.2 at $-57°$ to 131.0 at 200° C.   In general, the more associated the liquid the greater is the increase of the parachor with temperature.

TABLE IX

EFFECT OF TEMPERATURE ON PARACHOR OF NONASSOCIATED LIQUIDS[a]

Hydrocarbon	20° C.	30° C.	40° C.	50° C.
n-Hexane	270.8_4	270.7_0	270.8_0	..
n-Heptane	311.3_4	311.2_1	311.3_6	310.5_8
n-Octane	351.1_3	350.9_6	351.2_8	351.0_0
n-Nonane	391.1_4	391.0_9	390.9_9	..
n-Decane	431.2_4	431.1_4	431.4_8	..
n-Undecane	470.5_6	470.8_6	471.0_8	..
n-Dodecane	510.1_4	510.7_6	510.8_6	..

[a] O. R. Quayle, R. A. Day, and G. M. Brown, *J. Am. Chem. Soc.*, **66**, 938 (1944).

For the calculation of parachor values, the density of the vapor, d, is frequently neglected because it is relatively small, although for accurate work it should be included.   At room temperatures, a calculation from the ideal gas laws is perfectly satisfactory, using available vapor pressure data or even a rough approximation from a Cox chart[28] or similar method.   At higher temperatures, the following correlations[29] for estimating the density of the vapor are convenient:

$$\log (d/d_b) = 5(T/T_b - 1) \tag{98}$$

$$d_b = 0.0122M/T_b \tag{99}$$

where d = density of vapor in grams per cubic centimeter, d_b = d at normal boiling point in grams per cubic centimeter, T = absolute temperature in degrees K., T_b = absolute normal boiling point in degrees K., and M = molecular weight.

[28] G. Calingaert and D. S. Davis, *Ind. Eng. Chem.*, **17**, 1287 (1925).
[29] G. E. Boyd and L. E. Copeland, *J. Am. Chem. Soc.*, **64**, 2540 (1942).

1. Calculation from Atomic and Structural Values

A large amount of work has been devoted to the determination of the best values of the atomic and structural parameters, and of the magnitude of additional terms to correct for deviations from additivity. The accuracy of surface-tension measurements has increased so much since Sugden's pioneer work that discrepancies which would have been of the order of experimental error 20 years ago must now be taken into account. Vogel[25] and several other modern workers have deferred analysis of their parachor values until a better set of atomic and structural values based on the newer measurements are obtained. For most organic compounds which

TABLE X

SUGDEN'S PARACHOR VALUES

Carbon	4 8	Sulfur	48.2
Hydrogen	17.1	Fluorine	25.7
Nitrogen	12.5	Chlorine	54.3
Phosphorus	37.7	Bromine	68.0
Oxygen	20.0	Iodine	91.0

Double bond	23.2
Triple bond	46.6
3-Membered ring	16.7
4-Membered ring	11.6
5-Membered ring	8.5
6-Membered ring	6.1
Esters	− 3.2
Coordinate linkage	− 1.6
Singlet linkage	−11.6

are not highly associated, experimental parachors[30] are constant to about ±0.5 unit over a 30° temperature range. Hence, the calculated values should reproduce the experimental data to this accuracy.

The values are calculated by adding the atomic contributions for each atom in the compound together with certain structural contributions of which the most important are the presence of rings and unsaturated bonds and possibly other types of bonds according to the system used.[31] The atomic and structural equivalents vary from system to system. Sugden's system is the least complicated. The constants are given in table X.[27]

---

[30] All experimental parachor values not otherwise credited have been taken from "A List of Parachors," *Brit. Assoc. Advancement Sci. Rept.*, **1932**, 265.

[31] For examples, see: T. W. Gibling, *J. Chem. Soc.*, **1941**, 299; **1942**, 661; **1943**, 146. S. A. Mumford and J. W. C. Phillips, *J. Chem. Soc.*, **1928**, 155; **1929**, 2112; *Ber.*, **B63**, 1818 (1930). R. Samuel, *J. Chem. Phys.*, **12**, 157 (1944). N. S. Bayliss, *J. Am. Chem. Soc.*, **59**, 444 (1937). J. Reilly and W. N. Rae, *Physico-chemical Methods*, 3rd ed., Van Nostrand, New York, 1939, pp. 109–113.

For example, the parachor of ethylamine is calculated as follows:

$$
\begin{aligned}
2\,C &= 2 \times 4.8 = & 9.6 \\
7\,H &= 7 \times 17.1 = & 119.7 \\
N &= & 12.5 \\
\hline
C_2H_5NH_2 & & [P] = 141.8
\end{aligned}
$$

The observed value[32] is 139.9 ± 0.3, a fairly good check. Only single bonds are involved in this example. Other types of linkages must be specially accounted for by means of the constants shown in table X. For example, the parachor of either ethyl acetate or methyl propionate is calculated as follows:

$$
\begin{aligned}
4\,C &= 4 \times 4.8 = & 19.2 \\
8\,H &= 8 \times 17.1 = & 136.8 \\
2\,O &= 2 \times 20.0 = & 40.0 \\
\text{Double bond} & = & 23.2 \\
\text{Esters} & = & -3.2 \\
\hline
& & [P] = 216.0
\end{aligned}
$$

The experimental values are:

Methyl propionate................ 215.0
Ethyl acetate.................... 216.6.

A few other similar comparisons are:

Methyl valerate.................. 292.5
Ethyl butyrate.................. 293.7
Propyl propionate................ 295.3

Methyl propyl ketone............. 238.0
Diethyl ketone.................. 236.8

Methyl butyl ketone.............. 276.6
Ethyl propyl ketone.............. 277.3.

The effect of structural isomerism is shown by the following examples:

Ethyl butyrate................... 293.7
Ethyl isobutyrate................ 292.9

Ethyl valerate................... 332.1
Ethyl isovalerate................ 331.9

Propyl butyrate.................. 333.8
Propyl isobutyrate............... 332.6.

---

[32] E. Swift, Jr. and C. R. Calkins, *J. Am. Chem. Soc.*, **65**, 2415 (1943).

It will be noted that there appears to be a small but definite effect of structure. This effect was considered to be of the order of the experimental error in Sugden's work and accordingly was neglected. However, in view of the greatly increased accuracy of determinations of surface tension, more exact methods of calculation are now justified. The comprehensive studies of Mumford and Phillips[33] and Gibling[34] analyze these recent values of parachors and provide improved sets of fundamental values. Gibling probably gives the best available system. It takes into account the small increase in the parachor of the CH_2 group as the number of carbon atoms increases, and assigns parachor values to groups rather than to single atoms (see page 679). In this way, most of the "interference" effects are handled satisfactorily.

2. Use for Determination of Structure

The parachor has been used to decide between several possible structural formulas of an organic compound. Sugden's parachor value for six-membered rings was determined largely from data on cyclohexane derivatives. Using this value, the calculated values for aromatic compounds are in excellent agreement with the concept that the benzene ring contains three double bonds, as shown below for benzene itself:

$$
\begin{array}{rcl}
6\,C = 6 \times 4.8 = & 28.8 \\
6\,H = 6 \times 17.1 = & 102.6 \\
\text{6-Membered ring} = & 6.1 \\
\text{3 double bonds} = 3 \times 23.2 = & 69.6 \\
\hline
C_6H_6 \qquad [P] = & 207.1 \\
\text{Experimental value} = & 206.2
\end{array}
$$

It is precisely on this point that the various systems for calculating the parachor fail, since the use of a somewhat different set of fundamental atomic and structural constants may reverse the decision as to the most probable structure for a given compound.

Samuel[35] gives excellent examples of such comparisons in a comprehensive review of the whole problem. The determination of the structure of the azide group by means of the parachor is frequently given as an example of the success of the method. The various possible structures and the corresponding parachors calculated from values suggested by Sugden and by Samuel (figures in *italics*) are:

---

[33] S. A. Mumford and J. W. C. Phillips, *J. Chem. Soc.*, **1928**, 155; **1929**, 2112; *Ber.*, **B63**, 1818 (1930).

[34] T. W. Gibling, *J. Chem. Soc.*, **1941**, 299; **1942**, 661; **1943**, 146.

[35] R. Samuel, *J. Chem. Phys.*, **12**, 157 (1944).

$$-N\underset{N}{\overset{N}{\big\langle}}\;\;\parallel \qquad -N{=}N{\equiv}N \qquad -N{\rightleftharpoons}N{\equiv}N \qquad -N{=}N{\rightarrow}N$$

77·4	107·3	82·5	82·3
84·6	*77·3*	...	...

Since the mean experimental parachor value of the azide group is 77.2, Sugden ascribed a ring structure to the group, while Samuel's values indicate an open-chain structure. Pauling and Brockway[36] have shown from electron diffraction measurements that methyl azide has an open chain, so that Sugden's parachor calculation supports the wrong structure.

Similar considerations of other compounds show that the parachor should be used with great discrimination for distinguishing between different possible structures of a molecule.[35]   However, within the limits of accuracy of the schemes mentioned above, the calculation of parachors has provided a convenient starting place for the prediction of physical properties.   Meissner and Redding[37] have used with considerable success Sugden's parachors and normal boiling points for the estimation of critical properties.   A similar and more extensive study by Herzog[38] uses the parachor calculation methods of Mumford and Phillips.[33]

The parachor may be used to predict the surface tension of mixtures. Katz and coworkers[39, 40] have shown that the surface tension of three binary mixtures at temperatures up to 90° C., and pressures up to 100 atmospheres can be predicted within the experimental error by the formula:

$$\gamma^{1/4} = [P_1]\left(\frac{D}{M_L}x_1 - \frac{d}{M_V}y_1\right) + [P_2]\left(\frac{D}{M_L}x_2 - \frac{d}{M_V}y_2\right) \qquad (100)$$

where γ, D, d, and M have the same meaning as above, x is the mole fraction of the constituent in liquid phase, y is the mole fraction of the constituent in vapor phase, $[P]$ is the effective parachor of the component, and L denotes the liquid, and V the vapor phase.   For the methane–propane and nitrogen–butane mixtures, the "effective parachors" of the constituents are the same as the parachors of the pure compounds, but for the nitrogen–heptane system, from 0 to 10 mole per cent nitrogen, the effective parachor of nitrogen is only 41 as compared with 60, the value for pure nitrogen.

[36] L. Pauling and L. B. Brockway, *J. Am. Chem. Soc.*, **59**, 13 (1937).

[37] H. P. Meissner and E. M. Redding, *Ind. Eng. Chem., Ind. Ed.*, **34**, 521 (1942).

[38] R. Herzog, *Ind. Eng. Chem., Ind. Ed.*, **36**, 997 (1944).

[39] C. F. Weinaug and D. L. Katz, *Ind. Eng. Chem., Ind. Ed.*, **35**, 239 (1943).

[40] G. J. Reno and D. L. Katz, *Ind. Eng. Chem., Ind. Ed.*, **35**, 1091 (1943).

3. Conclusions

The parachor is a useful additive function but not a reliable tool for deciding between different possible structures. For a critical analysis of its theoretical background the excellent review by Reilly and Rae[41] is recommended. The book by Sugden[42] is by now of more interest for its historical value than for its discussions of the use of the parachor for determining structure. Probably the best analysis of the structural and atomic constants is that of Gibling,[34] referred to above.

---

[41] J. Reilly and W. N. Rae, *Physico-chemical Methods*, 3rd ed., Van Nostrand, New York, 1939, pp. 109–113.

[42] S. Sugden, *The Parachor and Valency*. Routledge, London, 1930.

General References

SHAPES OF SURFACES

Bakker, G., *Kapillarität und Oberflächenspannung*. Akadem. Verlagsgesellschaft, Leipzig, 1928.

Bashforth, F., and Adams, J. C., *An Attempt to Test the Theories of Capillary Action*, Cambridge Univ. Press, London, 1883.

Freud, B. B., and Freud, H. Z., *J. Am. Chem. Soc.*, **52**, 1772 (1930).

Freud, B. B., and Harkins, W. D., *unpublished data*.

Desains, M., *Ann. chim. phys.*, **51**, 417 (1857).

Laplace, P. S., *Méchanique Céleste*, Volume IV, Supplement to Book X, pp. 1 to 65 and second part, pp. 1–78 (1805).

Lohnstein, T., *Ann. Physik*, **20**, 237, 606 (1906); **22**, 1030 (1906).

Strutt, R. J. (Lord Rayleigh), *Proc. Roy. Soc. London*, **A92**, 184 (1915)

SURFACE TENSION

Capillary Height Method

Ferguson, A., *Proc. Phys. Soc. London*, **36**, 37 (1923); **44**, 511 (1932).

Harkins, W. D., and Brown, F. E., *J. Am. Chem. Soc.*, **41**, 499 (1919).

Jones, G., and Ray, W. A., *J. Am. Chem. Soc.*, **59**, 187 (1937).

Richards, T. W., and Carver, E. K., *J. Am. Chem. Soc.*, **43**, 827 (1921).

Richards, T. W., and Coombs, L. B., *J. Am. Chem. Soc.*, **37**, 1656 (1915).

Drop-Weight Method

Gaddum, J. H. (method of Harkins and Brown modified for less than 0.5 ml.), *Proc. Roy. Soc. London*, **B109**, 114 (1931).

Harkins, W. D., and Brown, F. E., *J. Am. Chem. Soc.*, **41**, 499 (1919).

Pendant Drop

Hauser, E. A., *Colloidal Phenomena.*   McGraw-Hill, New York, 1939, p. 231.

Ring Method

Harkins, W. D., and Jordan, H. F., *J. Am. Chem. Soc.*, **52,** 1751 (1930).

Sessile Bubble

Tartar, H. V., Sivertz, V., and Reitmeier, R. E., *J. Am. Chem. Soc.*, **62,** 2377 (1940).

General Methods

Adam, N. K., *Physics and Chemistry of Surfaces.*   Oxford Univ. Press, New York, 1942.

Dorsey, N. E., *Natl. Bur. Standards Sci. Papers*, **21,** No. 540 (1926).

PARACHOR

Reilly, J., and Rae, W. N., *Physico-chemical Methods.*   3rd ed., Van Nostrand, New York, 1939.

Sugden, S., *The Parachor and Valency.*   Routledge, London, 1930.

CHAPTER VII

Determination of
PROPERTIES OF MONOLAYERS
AND DUPLEX FILMS

WILLIAM D. HARKINS, *University of Chicago and Universal Oil Products Company*

I. INTRODUCTION

The behavior of monomolecular layers, usually designated as monolayers, of organic substances upon an aqueous subphase can be investigated by means of a film balance.[1] Since many organic molecules stand upright upon the surface in their most tightly packed (condensed) monolayers, it is often possible by a few minutes' work with an extremely simple appara-

---

[1] H. Devaux, *Proc.-verb. Soc. Phys. Nat. Bordeaux*, Nov. 19, Dec. 3 (1903); Jan. 7, Apr. 14 (1904); Mar. 28(1912). *J. phys.*, **3**, 450 (1904); **2**, 699, 891 (1912). *Ann. Rept. Smithsonian Inst.*, **1913,** 261.

tus to obtain a moderately good knowledge of the length of the molecule. This is found by dividing the volume of the liquid or solid put on the surface of the water by the smallest area to which the monolayer can be compressed without collapse. If, from its method of preparation, it is considered that the molecule is linear, and if its elementary composition is known, the length of the molecule gives an idea of its approximate molecular weight. For example, in a laboratory of the rubber industry, it was desired to obtain some knowledge of the molecular weight of one of the compounds used. By 15 minutes' work on the film balance, after this had been set up, a molecular weight of about 700 was reported, while many weeks later the organic laboratory found the value to be 670.

If the molecular weight is known, the molecular area can be determined. From the length and area of the molecules, and the surface potential of the film, it is sometimes possible to decide between two or more probable structures proposed by organic chemists. For example, both x-ray investigations and measurements of monolayers have been utilized in determining the structure of the sterols and certain hormones. A few special cases are cited later (pages 239–243). If the greatest thickness to which a monolayer can be compressed is about 4.5 Å., the organic molecules lie flat on the surface,[2] since this is about the diameter of the (ellipsoidal) hydrocarbon chain. Protein films are in general thicker than this, even at low film pressures, but are sufficiently thin to indicate that the molecules lie flat on the surface.

While this chapter describes apparatus which is designed to give high accuracy in the investigation of monolayers of oil on water, moderately good accuracy may be attained when devices of the utmost simplicity are used, provided the precautions described here are taken whenever possible. Thus the vertical film balance described on page 218 is extremely simple since it may consist merely of a cheap pulp balance, a wire, and a microscope slide. In addition to this, all that is needed is a meter rule, a rectangular Pyrex dish with a level edge, a few barriers of glass, metal, or paraffined paper, and a pipette to measure the solution of the oil. Devaux[1] states: "Films of oil tell us with the greatest nicety of the discontinuity of matter, and the dimensions of molecules. They also give us valuable information as to the field of molecular action. For our observations we will find that there is no need of complicated apparatus; basins, paper, threads of glass, a pipette, a sieve with some talc powder, and finally some oil and benzol suffice for the greater part of the experiments. As to measuring instruments, a double decimeter will do, although its divisions be a million times greater than the diameter of the molecules. Though it seems like

---

[2] W. D. Harkins, E. F. Carman, and H. E. Ries, *J. Chem. Phys.*, **3**, 692 (1935).

measuring microbes with a surveyor's chain, we will see that the measures
. . . can be made with great precision, because of a very remarkable pecu-
liarity of films of the thickness of one molecule."

II.   GENERAL CONSIDERATIONS

The most valuable apparatus used for the investigation of the properties
of monolayers is the film balance.   Actually this designation may be applied to *any apparatus* which determines the difference between the surface

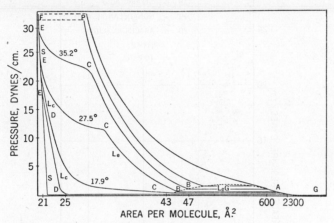

Fig. 1.—General phase diagram for a monolayer below its
critical temperature for the formation of a liquid expanded (L_e)
film.

tension (γ_0) of the clean surface of the subphase and that of the surface
when covered by a film (γ_f).   The film pressure (π) is defined as this difference, or

$$\pi = \gamma_0 - \gamma_f \tag{1}$$

The use of this equation is not restricted to aqueous subphases.   If the
subphase is a solid, it is customary in this laboratory to write it as follows:

$$\pi = \gamma_s - \gamma_f \tag{2}$$

The justification for the designation of the difference between two surface tensions as a pressure lies in the close correlation which is thus obtained between the behavior of two- and three-dimensional systems.   For
example, at high-molecular areas, monolayers on water obey the gas law:

$$\pi\sigma = kT \tag{3}$$

in which σ is the area per molecule and k is the same (Boltzmann) constant
as that for a three-dimensional gas ($k = 1.371 \times 10^{-16}$ erg deg.$^{-1}$).   Re-

cently, Jura and Harkins found this equation is valid for monolayers of nitrogen or of water on titanium dioxide (anatase) or of n-heptane on certain metals, etc. Not only is this true, but in addition the two-dimensional $\pi - \sigma$ and $\pi - \sigma - T$ diagrams resemble very closely those for three-dimensional systems.

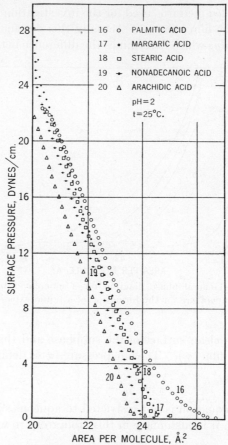

Fig. 2.—Relations in the liquid condensed (L_c) or (ED) region of figure 1. Monolayers of the various acids.

Before the film balance is described, it is well to consider the types of phases which may be revealed by its use in the determination of the pressure–area relationships.[3] The usual phase diagram is given in figure 1. As has been stated, the monolayer is a perfect gas at extremely high areas,

---

[3] W. D. Harkins and L. E. Copeland, *J. Chem. Phys.*, **10**, 276 (1942).

G, and changes into an imperfect gas at lower areas.   If at 27.5° C. a very dilute monolayer of pentadecylic acid is compressed, the vapor film begins to condense into a liquid state at a molecular area of about 1000 A.², but is not completely condensed until the area is reduced to 45 Å.² Through all this region, L_eG, the monolayer is heterogeneous, as can be shown by variations in the surface potential as indicated by an electrode which is moved to different positions above the surface (pages 222, 236).   Since the

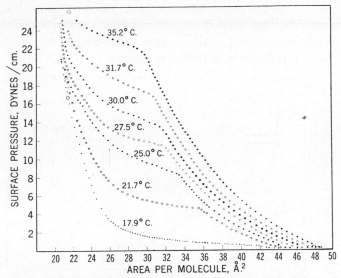

Fig. 3.—Intermediate (L_i) and liquid expanded (L_e) regions of figure 1 for pentadecylic acid.

pressure remains constant while the molecular area is varied, condensation of the monolayer from the gaseous to the liquid state is a change of the first order, just as it is in three dimensions.   During a reduction in area from 45 to 30.5 A.², there is no change of phase.   This phase, BC, which is coherent, like a liquid, was discovered by Labrouste[4] and was designated by Adam[5] as the liquid expanded (L_e) phase.   It is characterized by a $\pi - \sigma$ curve which is like that for a gas in that it has nearly the form of an equilateral hyperbola, but differs from a gas in that the axes are at an area considerably above a zero molecular area and below a zero film pressure.

At C, this phase transforms into what has been designated by the writer as the intermediate liquid phase, L_i by a transition of the second order,

[4] H. Labrouste, *Ann. phys.*, **14**, 164 (1920).

[5] N. K. Adam, *Proc. Roy. Soc. London*, **101**, 452 (1922).   N. K. Adam and G. Jessop, *ibid.*, **112**, 362 (1926).

i. e., without a latent heat. The intermediate phase is characterized by an extremely high compressibility, and a large heat of expansion, especially near point C. Near D, however, the compressibility and the heat of expansion decrease rapidly, so that both these become small in the liquid condensed, L_c phase, ED (Fig. 2). The most condensed phase, EF, is commonly considered as a two-dimensional solid; but since it does not always exhibit all the characteristics of a three-dimensional solid, it is designated in figure 1 as the S phase. This, in certain cases, as with normal long-chain alcohols may be an LS phase, which exhibits the low compressibility of a solid film and the high fluidity of a liquid film. If the S or solid phase melts, no heat is absorbed, so this is also a transition of the second order. The effect of temperature is exhibited in figure 3.

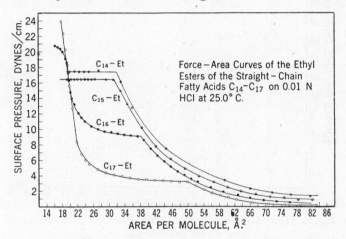

Fig. 4.—Phase diagram for a temperature (25° C.) above the critical temperature for the formation of a liquid expanded (L_e) film. The transition gaseous to intermediate film is second order for ethyl palmitate and margarate. The myristate and pentadecylate exhibit collapse.

The vaporization of a solid, condensed liquid, or expanded film is a transformation of the first order—that is, there is a discontinuity in the area of the film with respect to pressure, and there is also a latent heat of vaporization. All the other ordinary phase changes in monolayers are second-order transformations—that is, there is no discontinuity in the area and no latent heat of change, but there are discontinuities in the heat capacity and in the compressibility. In a third-order change, there are none of the above discontinuities, but there is a discontinuity in the derivative of the specific heat with respect to temperature. The system of classifying phase changes according to their order is due to Ehrenfest.[6]

Until recently it could have been stated that all transitions between liquid phases, or between liquid and solid phases in films, are second or third order. Thus, with a

[6] P. Ehrenfest, *Proc. Acad. Sci. Amsterdam*, **36,** 153 (1933).

decrease of one in the number of dimensions it was found that there was a general increase of one in the order of the phase changes.   However, a new LS phase, discovered by Harkins and Copeland,[3] exhibits a first-order change between itself and the liquid condensed phase, over a limited range.   Thus, the order of the phase transitions in two-dimensional systems are:

$$LS \rightleftharpoons L_c, \text{ first, or at higher temperatures second, order}$$
$$LS \rightleftharpoons S, \text{ second order}$$
$$S \rightleftharpoons L_c, \text{ second order}$$
$$L_c \rightleftharpoons L_i, \text{ third order}$$
$$L_i \rightleftharpoons L_e, \text{ second order}$$
$$L_i \rightleftharpoons G, \text{ second order}$$
$$L_e \rightleftharpoons G, \text{ first order}$$

The LS phase is highly condensed and has the compressibility of the S phase, but exhibits an extremely great variation in viscosity, which may be lower than that of the liquid condensed film from which it is formed.   Harkins and Jura[7] recently discovered two distinct *condensed* phases of nitrogen and also of water on the surfaces of high melting solids; a gaseous phase is found at low pressures.

Figure 1 (page 213) represents films which are below the critical temperature for the transition between gaseous, G, and liquid expanded, L_e, monolayers.   In the same range of temperatures, certain esters, of the same general order of chain length, are above this temperature,[8] as shown in figure 4.   These exhibit *vaporization* of the intermediate *liquid*, L_i, *without a latent heat of vaporization*, to form, by a second-order transition, a highly compressed vapor film.

III.   FILM BALANCE

1.   Original Apparatus

The first film balance was devised by Pockels[9] in 1891.   She used a long, rectangular trough filled with water to the brim.   The surface of the water was made clean by "sweeping" or "scraping" with a barrier which consisted of a transverse sheet of metal 1.5 cm. wide resting on the edges of the trough. In the earliest work the surface tension of both the clean and the film-covered water was obtained by determining, by means of an ordinary balance, the force necessary to pull from the surface either a small disk (6 mm. in diameter) or a large ring (114 mm. in circumference).

The measurements of film pressure may be made more exact if the difference between the two surface tensions is determined directly, as in the

[7] W. D. Harkins and G. Jura, *J. Chem. Phys.*, **11**, 430 (1943).

[8] W. D. Harkins and E. Boyd, *J. Phys. Chem.*, **45**, 21, 38 (1941).

[9] Agnes Pockels, *Nature*, **43**, 437 (1890); **48**, 152 (1893).

film balance of Lord Rayleigh,[10] which makes use of the Wilhelmy[11] slide. This apparatus gave excellent results, since, with a monolayer of stearic acid the area at which the film pressure began to rise rapidly corresponded to 22.1 Å.[2] at 15° C., while the most recent value, as determined in this laboratory, is about 21 Å.[2], when a minute amount of calcium ion is present in neutral water, presumably the kind of water used for this early work.

2. Vertical Film Balance

The simplest, most generally applicable, and probably most accurate film balance is that in which the surface tension exerts a downward pull upon the vertical face of a sheet of glass or other suitable material, as in the surface tension method of Wilhelmy.[11]   Because of its inherent difficulties, this surface tension method is not in use, but it was found by Harkins, Myers, and Anderson[12] that these difficulties disappear if no attempt is made to determine the surface tension (γ) itself, and the principle of the vertical pull is used in the development of a balance which measures π directly.

For work of ordinary accuracy, the vertical film balance can be assembled and put in use by any chemist in a very short time.   Both apparatus and technique are extremely simple.   The fundamental part of the apparatus is a microscope slide, or a large (thinner) rectangular microscope cover of glass or quartz, or a sheet of platinum–iridium.   This is hung from one arm of a balance, as shown in figure 5.   The trough should be rectangular and may be made of brass or stainless steel, or it may consist of a large, rectangular, Pyrex glass dish, in which case it may be necessary to grind the edges to make them more level.   Both the edges of the trough and the barriers are paraffined with paraffin free from polar groups.   The surface of the water is swept several times;   then the clean slide is lowered into it, after which it is swept still more by barriers put nearly in contact with the slide on both sides.   If the film is insoluble, it is then spread on the surface, and the film pressure, π, is given directly by the deflection of a beam of light as read on a scale at a distance of several meters.

The vertical film balance exhibits the following advantages over the horizontal type commonly used:

(1) It is much cheaper for any given accuracy.

(2) It is much simpler and may be installed in a few minutes, because an ordinary balance and a microscope slide give results of high degree of accuracy.

(3) It is specially useful in studies of the effects of metal ions, because the slide,

[10] Lord Rayleigh, *Phil. Mag.*, **5**, 48 (1899).

[11] L. Wilhelmy, *Ann. Physik*, **119**, 177 (1863).

[12] W. D. Harkins and T. F. Anderson, *J. Am. Chem. Soc.*, **59**, 2189 (1937).

trough, and barriers can all consist of quartz so that the solution and its surface come in contact with quartz alone.

(4) In a simple form it will give the film pressure of a soluble film, while the use of the horizontal types involves the very elaborate movable partition of the *PLAWM** trough of McBain.

It is easy to give the method a very high sensitivity, since all that is required is to make the slide or slides very thin. With wide sheets of glass of the thickness of microscope cover glasses, surface pressures as low as

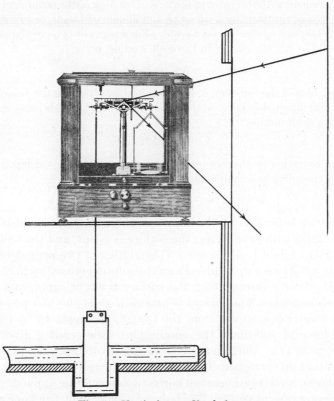

Fig. 5.—Vertical-type film balance.

0.003 dyne per cm. may be measured. With thinner sheets, 0.001 dyne per cm. or even less could be detected. This should make feasible determining the molecular weights of certain film-forming substances by the use of the two-dimensional gas law.

If the slide or sheet is w cm. wide and t cm. thick, the perimeter, p, is $2(w + t)$ and the downward pull of the surface tension is $2(w + t)\gamma$ or $2p\gamma$. Let W be the appar-

* Named after *P*ockels, *L*angmuir, *A*dam, *W*ilson, and *Mc*Bain.

ent weight in grams of the slide partly immersed in water. If the surface tension is reduced by the spreading of a film the slide rises, but if W is kept constant the decrease in the downward pull, F_d, of the surface tension must be compensated for by a decrease in the buoyancy, F_u, of the submerged portion of the slide, or:

$$\Delta F_d = \Delta F_u \tag{4}$$

$$2p \, \Delta\gamma = \rho \; ptw \; \Delta h \tag{5}$$

where ρ is the acceleration of gravity, and h is the change in height of the slide measured by the use of a cathetometer. In practice it is much simpler to mount a galvanometer mirror with its center in the axis of rotation of the beam, and to observe the deflection of the beam by a telescope and illuminated scale, or to use a beam of light and observe its deflection on a scale. For a segment of a circular scale, Δh, is proportional to ΔS, the change in the scale reading, or:

$$-p \, \Delta\gamma = k \, \Delta S \tag{6}$$

where the value of the constant, k, is determined by observing the values of ΔS associated with different weights on the balance pan with the slide immersed in water which has a clean surface.

$$k = -\rho \, \Delta M / \Delta S \tag{7}$$

Thus, the reduction in the surface tension, $-\Delta\gamma$, which is the film pressure π, caused by spreading and compressing the film, is:

$$\pi = - \Delta\gamma = k \, \Delta S / 2p \tag{8}$$

In the determination of the film pressure of a soluble substance, the trough is filled with pure water, the surface is swept, and the scale reading on the beam of light is set to zero. Then either of two procedures may be followed: (1) The solute is added and the solution stirred until the concentration is uniform throughout; the surface is swept again, and the scale reading, taken when equilibrium is attained, gives the film pressure. (2) The pure water is removed from the trough, and replaced by exactly the same volume of solution; the equilibrium scale reading gives the film pressure, as in (1). Surface-active solutes are often present at such great dilutions that no corrections for differences of density are needed, but with more concentrated solutions such corrections should be applied.

In a second type of vertical film balance a slide, hung from one end of the balance beam, is suspended in clean water, and another slide, from the other end of the beam, is suspended in the solution.

It is extremely simple to convert the vertical film balance into a recording form, as was done by Dervichian,[13] who used the light beam of figure 5 to record the pressure on a rotating cylinder covered by photographic paper, which also recorded the motion of the barrier which compressed the monolayer. This is a remarkably good apparatus for use in the very rapid

---

[13] D. G. Dervichian, *J. Chem. Phys.*, **7**, 932 (1939).

compression of a monolayer in studies of time effects.   In this laboratory, the compression has been made to go at a constant rate by the use of a synchronous motor, and film pressures have been recorded by a method devised by Gordon.[14]   This is suitable for recording changes for long or short periods; it is described in the following section:

The adaptibility of the vertical film balance for different types of work may be illustrated by its use by Harkins, Gordon, and Copeland[14] in investigations of film penetration, a phenomenon studied extensively by Schulman.[15]

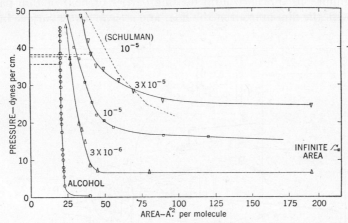

Fig. 6.—Penetration of a monolayer of cetyl alcohol by sodium cetyl sulfate.   The numbers on the curves, as 3×10^{-5} on the top curve, represent the concentration of the detergent in moles per liter.   The area per molecule is that of the alcohol.   The broken line represents the work of Schulman at 10^{-5} molar concentration of sodium cetyl sulfate.

This phenomenon is exhibited by many biological compounds of considerable interest, but has been investigated most thoroughly (Schulman) in the case in which soluble sodium cetyl sulfate molecules penetrate insoluble films of cetyl alcohol.   This may give rise to a great increase of film pressure.   By allowing the penetration to occur and then compressing the film every minute, Schulman obtained the broken curve of figure 6, when the subphase contained 3×10^{-5} molar sodium sulfate, while our data obtained at equilibrium are represented by the extremely different middle curve.   From the irregularities in the curve, Schulman developed the idea that compounds are formed with either one or three molecules of sodium cetyl sulfate to one of the alcohol.   However, our curves show no such irregularities.

Since the attainment of equilibrium had been found to be extremely slow for some

[14] W. D. Harkins, S. Gordon, and L. E. Copeland, Publ. No. 21, A. A. A. S., Washington, D. C., p. 79.

[15] J. H. Schulman and E. K. Rideal, *Biochem. J.*, **27**, 1581 (1933); *Proc. Roy. Soc. London*, **B122**, 29, 47 (1937); J. H. Schulman and A. H. Hughes, *Biochem. J.*, **29**, 1236, 1243 (1935).

of the points, a motion picture camera was operated by a clock to give an exposure every five minutes overnight, and to photograph, with this interval, a line of light on the long scale of the apparatus. This gave each film pressure with a good degree of accuracy. It is obvious that much shorter time intervals can be employed for changes which have a faster rate, but in this special case 120 points for a 10-hour interval were sufficient to define the curve.

3. Horizontal Float Balance

Langmuir[16] used a horizontal floating barrier or float of thin paraffined paper with the film in front of the float and a clean water surface back of it

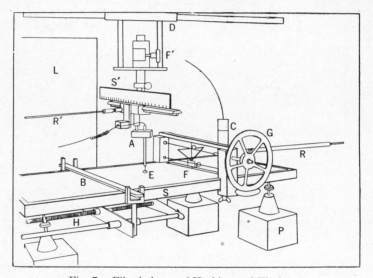

Fig. 7.—Film balance of Harkins and Fischer.[18]

in order to determine the difference between the two surface tensions, γ_0 and γ_f. This float pressed on two nearly vertical rods attached to an ordinary balance. The film was kept from flowing around the ends of the float by two jets of air which, together with the insensitivity of the balance *when arranged in this way*, prevent this from being an accurate instrument. It is therefore no longer in use.

Adam adopted the floating barrier, or "float," but used very thin strips of gold or platinum, set edgewise in the surface, to join the ends of the float to the walls of the trough and thus prevent the film from spreading over the clean surface.

This general type of apparatus was developed in this laboratory by Har-

---

[16] I. Langmuir, *J. Am. Chem. Soc.*, **39**, 1848 (1917).

kins and Freud[17] and is shown in figure 7 as modified by Harkins and Fischer.[18]   This apparatus is controlled entirely from outside an air thermostat.   In figure 7, S is the trough, F the float, B the barrier, and H a screw of 1-mm. pitch for measuring the change of area.   The graduated circle and vernier G, for measuring the amount of rotation of the end of the torsion wire, is turned by rod R.   On the newer models, G is outside the end of the thermostat. C is the calomel electrode, and E is the polonium–silver electrode used to determine the surface potential.   It may be moved to any position over the film by rod R' which, by pushing and pulling, moves a long tube, D, and, by turning a pinion, moves the support of the electrode

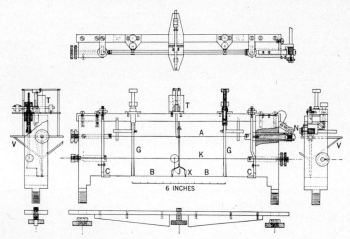

Fig. 8.—Details of film balance of Harkins and Myers.[19]

transversely to different positions along scale S'. L is a grounded box (of metal) which contains the Compton electrometer.   The air thermostat around the apparatus is constructed of metal, and its glass window is covered with wire gauze which, together with the metal of the thermostat, is grounded. F' is used to raise or lower electrode E.

The horizontal type of torsion film balance, as designed by Harkins and Richard Kittle, instrument maker of the laboratory, is shown in figure 8. This fits the trough and is held to it firmly by a transverse bar underneath the trough.   The balance beam, which is suspended on the principal torsion wire of phosphor–bronze, is cut from a sheet of magnesium–aluminum alloy, but the wires, X, which give it loose contact with the float of paraffined gold or copper, are of platinum–iridium.   Just above the center of the upper

[17] B. B. Freud, *Ph.D. thesis*, Univ. of Chicago, 1927.

[18] W. D. Harkins and E. K. Fischer, *J. Chem. Phys.*, **1**, 852 (1933).

[19] W. D. Harkins and R. J. Myers, *J. Chem. Phys.*, **4**, 716 (1936).

Fig. 9.—Film balance and air thermostat of Harkins and Myers.[19]

Fig. 10.—End of thermostat, with controls.

bar of the balance is a mechanism used to lift beam T at all times when it is not in direct use.   On the left and right are supports, G, which keep the float in place when it is not in use.   The extremely thin ribbons of gold or platinum which connect the ends of the float to the side supports are visible in the figure (C).   One end of the principal torsion wire, A, which supports the balance beam is turned by gear N, which is turned by a rod (shown in Fig. 9) extending outside the operating end of the thermostat.   The mirror, supported on the finer torsion wire K, is attached to the float by quartz fiber J.   Supports G (Fig. 8) hold the float in place when it is not in use. A rod, whose height is adjusted by a screw head, rests against the top of the float; and the part of the support below the float is kept in place by means of a spiral spring at the top.

The apparatus of Harkins and Myers,[19] which is enclosed in a glass box with a metal bottom and surrounded by an air thermostat, is shown in figures 9 and 10.   A barrier (Fig. 9) is seen in place as used for compressing a monolayer to a low area.   The metal (often glass is used) barriers used for sweeping the surface of the water are shown on shelves at each end of the trough.   The controls are placed outside of the end of the thermostat shown in figure 10. A White double potentiometer (not shown) is used to determine the temperature of the surface of the water and of the air just above it.

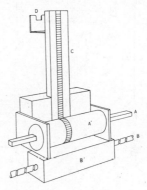

Fig. 11.—Sweeping mechanism.

Single junctions of copper–constantan, enclosed in very fine thin glass tubes, are used, one in the surface and one just above the surface.   The area of the film is the distance between the tops of the inside longitudinal walls of the trough, when measured *along the surface of the liquid*, multiplied by the distance between the barrier and the float, or, with the "vertical" type of balance, between the two barriers used to confine the film.   The distance between these barriers is determined by the number of turns of a steel rod with threads of 1 minute per turn. The number of full turns is read from a counter outside the thermostat, which is operated by a lever on the end of the rod. The sweeping mechanism consists of one metal yoke (Fig. 11) on each side of the trough.   Each of these has a depression, D, which fits any one of the stainless steel or glass rods, with a square $1/4$-inch cross section, which are used as barriers.   Turning screw B propels the square rod which rests in slot D, and sweeps the surface of the aqueous phase, while turning rod A raises or lowers D (and the rod) by the rack-and-pinion mechanism.   The two pairs of rods, A and B, are below the level of the trough (Fig. 12), one in front of, and one behind, the trough. They are turned by a handle outside one end of the thermostat. The pitch of the screw is 1 cm. per turn. A plentiful supply of paraffined barriers is kept on rods above each end of the trough, and any one of these may be picked up by the pair of

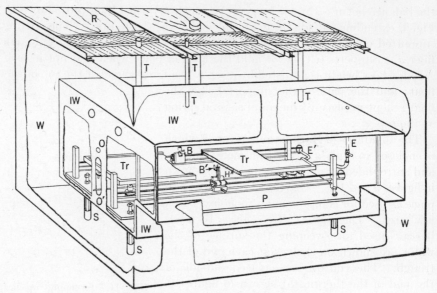

Fig. 12.—Arrangement of thermostat.

yokes and either deposited in position for measurement of the length of the film, or used for sweeping as many times as is desired. This can all be done without opening the thermostat. After the film is spread the thermostat may be closed by an insulating window, and it is not necessary to see what is going on because all operations may be carried on by controls outside.

4.   Temperature Control

A large part of the work on surface films, as reviewed in a book such as that of Adam, was done without the use of a thermostat; and the writer has been told that thermostats are not used for film balances in one of the largest English laboratories devoted to a study of surface chemistry. It cannot be denied that excellent work on some of the topics of this subject may be done in this way; also, direct manual control is used in much good work. It is evident, however, that such methods cannot give high accuracy. Obviously the worker should construct the simplest apparatus which will give the requisite accuracy for all of the work he is to undertake, but many investigations are made worthless by the use of apparatus or techniques unsuited for the particular purpose.   The following methods of temperature control, or lack of it, have been used:

(1) The apparatus and trough are used without any type of temperature control and without an enclosure.   This leads to errors due to vaporization at the surface, as well as to changes of temperature.

(2) An enclosure is used, but this is opened to sweep, to move the barriers, and to adjust the apparatus.

(3) The bottom of the trough is put into contact with the water of a thermostat. It should be recognized that the temperature of the surface of the water in the trough will not be that of the thermostat unless a cover over the trough is used and is kept closed.

(4) The trough is enclosed in an air thermostat and the latter is kept closed during the operations.   Even this is far from perfect unless: (a) a trough with a hollow bottom is used, with water at the correct temperature flowing through it; (b) the air around the trough is kept saturated, but not supersaturated, with water vapor.

(5) For measurements on the energy relations of films, and in general for the most accurate work, the box or chamber which contains the apparatus is completely submerged in the liquid of a large thermostat.   Such a thermostat is described below.

A *totally enclosed thermostat* constructed by Harkins and Copeland (Fig. 12) takes into account the fact that it is much more difficult to adjust and maintain constant, to a high degree of accuracy, the temperature of the surface than of the inside of a body of water, and that the radiation which strikes the surface should be of the proper temperature.   The inner copper box, 112 × 66 × 41 cm., which contains the film balance is surrounded on all sides by a solution of ethylene glycol, held by a much larger copper box insulated on the outside by one inch of hard foam rubber covered by aluminum foil.   The window in front (not shown) is hollow; through it the solution from the thermostat is pumped continually in order to keep the temperature the same as that of the main body of liquid.   The latter is cooled, when desired, by a copper coil through which is passed a solution of ethylene glycol chilled by an adjacent refrigerating machine.   For higher temperatures, a heated solution of the glycol is pumped through copper coils in the thermostat.   The apparatus was designed for temperatures from −30° to +70° C., or slightly higher.   At temperatures below zero, the films are spread on salt solutions.

The controls used in the operation of the apparatus are passed through copper tubes, which prevent liquid from entering the inner box or chamber. The controls are operated by rods which turn, so packing may be used to keep the air of the room from entering the box.   If the "vertical" film balance is in use, the wire which supports the slide must be left free.   The trough and film balance are upheld by three supports resting on a heavy steel plate, P, which is supported by four steel legs passing through holes in the bottom of the thermostat without contact and resting upon a concrete pier below.   In order to eliminate vibration the (heavy) thermostat does not rest on this pier, but is supported by heavy angle irons which stand outside the pier on the concrete floor.   Thus the vibrations due to stirring the liquid in the thermostat are not transmitted to the trough and film balance.   In figure 12, Tr is the trough of stainless steel and H is the hollow bottom through which water flows from the thermostat.   The hollow is divided into four sections (not shown). B and B' (details in Fig. 11) are used to move the barriers for sweeping (shown in Fig. 10a) and for picking up and putting in the place the barrier used for compressing the film (as shown in Fig. 9 but not in Fig. 12); O are the openings for control; T, tubes for the wires of vertical film balances or the torsion wires of viscometers; W, the copper wall of the thermostat; IW, inner wall; and R, one-inch, hardened foam rubber, which covers the entire thermostat.

Since two, or even three, film pressures may need to be determined simultaneously, the thermostat is constructed in such a way as to provide for the controls for one horizontal and two vertical film balances, and two of these are kept ready for use.   In determinations of the viscosity of films by the slit or the canal method, the difference between the two film pressures should be kept constant, and the higher (or lower) pressure should be determined independently.

The air in the inner chamber is kept close to saturation by passing a gentle stream of clean air through wash bottles which contain the same solution as that in the trough.   These are submerged in the liquid of the thermostat; and this air is carried into the inner chamber by a tube of rubber and glass.   The top of the thermostat is completely covered, except for the small openings for wires for viscosity determinations, etc., by a metal-lined cover of wood, which is covered in turn by one inch of hard foam rubber.   The walls are insulated by foam rubber of the same thickness. A large mercury regulator, which operates a heater by a vacuum-tube relay circuit, and efficient stirring keep the thermostat at a temperature constant to $\pm0.001°$ C.

5.   Spreading the Film and Determination of Area

The largest errors commonly found in reports of work on the pressure–area relations of monolayers are those in the molecular area due to impurities in the organic material or to poor technique in spreading the film. The technique whereby the substance is placed on the surface to form a monomolecular film varies with the nature of the film.   Most oils, if they do not contain too high a proportion of polar groups, may be spread from solutions in pentane and hexane mixtures or in benzene.   When the polar nature of the molecule becomes so high that the substance is not soluble in pentane–hexane mixtures, the spreading may be effected from other mixed solvents.   Mixtures of hydrocarbon and ethyl alcohol, and hydrocarbon and chloroform, have been used.   A mixture of water and isoamyl alcohol has proved suitable for the formation of monomolecular films of proteins. Aside from its solvent power for the film-forming substance, the spreading liquid should possess a high spreading coefficient and a high volatility. Preferably it should be insoluble in the underlying aqueous solution upon which the film is spread.

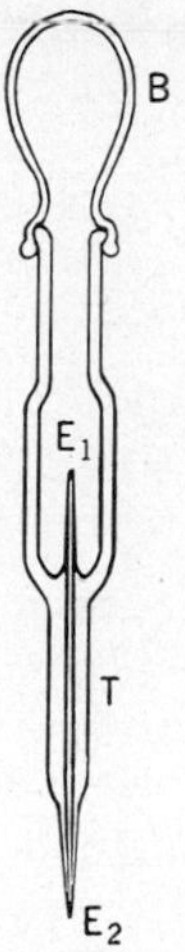

The accurate determination of the molecular area involves: (1) weighing the pure solid or liquid to a sufficient percentage accuracy;   (2) careful measurement of the total volume of the solution; and, most difficult of all, (3) an accurate knowledge of the volume of the usually volatile solution put on the surface of the water.   For this purpose a *volumetric pipette* is found to be suitable, provided the temperature is known accurately.   A pipette (Fig. 13) devised by the writer has been found to give excellent results because it defines very definitely the volume used and also minimizes error due to volatilization of the solution.   The liquid is held at a constant volume *by means of two fine capillary tips.*   By use of rubber bulb B, pipette T is completely filled from E_1 to E_2 with the solution of the film-forming substance in a volatile, nonsoluble, organic liquid such as hexane. The ends, E_1 and E_2, are very fine capillaries;   and the solution can be brought exactly to the ends by touching end E_2 very lightly and quickly by a small piece of filter paper.

Fig. 13.— A pipette for spreading mono- layers.

The method of application of the solution to the surface may need to be varied for different types of work.   For example, in investigations of the penetration of insoluble monolayers by soluble substances, *e. g.*, of films of cetyl alcohol by sodium cetyl sulfate, the procedure is as follows when the vertical film balance is used, and is practically the same with the horizontal type: The zero of the balance is determined with water in the trough.   The correct amount of sodium cetyl sulfate is then added and the solution is stirred until the concentration is considered to be uniform throughout.   With the extremely dilute solutions used, this gives a very slight change of density.   The surface of the solution is then swept rapidly several times; and finally a barrier is placed on each of the two sides of the slide and close to it.   As these barriers are in the process of rapid separation from each other, drops of a hexane solution of cetyl alcohol are continually caused to fall upon the surface close to each retreating barrier. This gives a much more uniform mixed film than the methods usually employed, since the alcohol and hexane have a much higher film pressure than the fresh surface of a sodium cetyl sulfate solution.

Proteins have been spread by various methods. Thus, aqueous solutions and also solutions of proteins in water and isoamyl alcohol have been

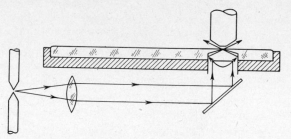

Fig. 14.—Arrangement of ultramicroscope.

used. Gorter and Grendel[20] introduced a method in which a somewhat concentrated solution is dropped from the least possible height upon the surface of the water, while Rideal and others coat a quartz fiber with paraffin and then with protein. This is put into contact with the surface

Fig. 15.—Appearance of a collapsed monolayer of egg albumin under the dark-field ultramicroscope.

of the water and the protein allowed to spread. The loss in weight is determined by a microbalance.

Whenever there is any doubt as to the monomolecular nature of any film, it is examined by a *microscope* with a dark-field condenser screwed

[20] E. Gorter and F. Grendel, *Biochem. Z.*, **192**, 431 (1928).

into the bottom of the trough and focused on the film (Fig. 14), according to the technique of Zocher and Stiebel.[21]   If the film is monomolecular, the optical field is empty, except for dust particles which are easy to recognize.   A photograph of a partly collapsed film of egg albumen taken by this method is represented by figure 15.[22]

6.   Viscosity and Rigidity of Monolayers

The viscosity of a monolayer is often the property which is the most sensitive of all to a change of phase, and the viscosity and rigidity are among the most important properties of biological films and membranes.

A.   CANAL VISCOMETER

The simplest method for determining the viscosity of a monolayer is to allow it to flow through a slit or a canal between two areas.   In figure 16,

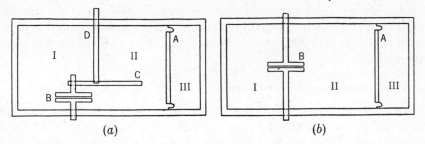

(a) (b)

Fig. 16.—Trough with canal (or slit) viscometer.

A is the float of the film balance. B the barrier with canal, I initially a clean water surface, II the film-covered surface, and III a clean water surface.   The difference of pressure between II and I is kept constant by moving barrier D in figure 16a or B in figure 16b.   It is obvious that the horizontal or the vertical type of film balance may be used.   The pressure of film I may be kept constant by the use of a piston oil, but it is much better to use a movable barrier (not shown) which automatically keeps the pressure, π, constant.   The barrier is moved by a device actuated by a film balance of the vertical type.

The correct theory of the canal viscometer, as given by Harkins and Kirkwood,[23] is expressed by the following in which η is the viscosity coefficient of the film, η_0 is that of the subphase, a and h are the width and

[21] H. Zocher and F. Stiebel, *Z. physik. Chem.*, **147A**, 401 (1930).

[22] G. E. Boyd and W. D. Harkins, *Ind. Eng. Chem., Anal. Ed.*, **14**, 496 (1942).

[23] W. D. Harkins and J. G. Kirkwood, *J. Chem. Phys.*, **6**, 53, 298 (1938).

depth of the rectangular canal, α is the film pressure gradient $(f_2 - f_1)l$, π = 3.14159, and A is the area flux:

$$\eta = \frac{\alpha a^3}{12A} - \frac{a\eta_0}{\pi} \qquad (9)$$

The first term of this equation was developed earlier by Myers and Harkins,[24] and shows that the power of the a^4 of the Poiseuille law for three-dimensional viscosity is reduced by unity to a^3 when the number of dimensions is reduced by unity. As is self-evident, the second term, which represents the effect of the viscosity of the subphase upon the flow of the film, contains the first power of the width, a, of the canal. The difficult point in the theory was that which gave a most simple result, *i. e.*, that the denominator is π ($= 3.14159$).

A slit may be used instead of a canal, but the theory of its use has not been developed correctly. A slit may be defined as a canal of negligible depth, h. The use of a slit was introduced by Bresler, Talmud, and Talmud.[25] It has been shown by Nutting and Harkins[26] that the greatest difficulty in this method is that involved in the choice of the materials of the walls of the canal or slit, since some materials allow a slip of the film along the walls.

B. TORSION OSCILLATION VISCOMETER

An easier but much less sensitive method for determining the viscosity of a film consists of the use of a horizontal circular ring or disk, which merely touches the surface. The ring is supported by a torsion wire hung from a support above the film. In figure 17, the trough and this support, A, but not the ring or scale, S, are viewed from above. I and III are the clean water surfaces; II is the film-covered surface; and A is the torsion pendulum bob supported by phosphor–bronze wire. The ring or disk carries a small mirror which focuses a beam of light on a scale of circular section. Two air jets which act on a vane, fastened above the ring, set the system in vibration. If the pressure on the film is kept constant, the amplitude of the oscillation decreases with each successive swing, and the logarithm of the amplitude plotted as a function of the number of swings gives a straight line whose slope gives a viscosity which is a composite of the viscosity of the film and that of the water associated with it. In the clean surface of water, the slope of this straight line is smaller. If λ is the logarithm of the ratio of successive amplitudes and $\Delta\lambda$ gives the difference in the

---

[24] R. J. Myers and W. D. Harkins, *Nature*, **140**, 465 (1937).

[25] S. E. Bresler, B. A. Talmud, and D. L. Talmud, *Physik. Z. Sowjetunion*, **4**. 864 (1933).

[26] G. C. Nutting and W. D. Harkins, *J. Am. Chem. Soc.*, **62**, 3155 (1940).

value of the logarithmic decrement between water and water covered by the film, then:

$$\eta = \Delta\gamma_{10} \frac{2.3I}{2P} \left(\frac{1}{a^2} - \frac{1}{b^2} \right) \tag{10}$$

where I is the moment of inertia of the ring and rigidly attached material, P is the period, a is the radius of the ring or disk, and b is that of an outer guard ring. It is apparent that the viscosity, η, obtained for the film has a value which depends upon a somewhat arbitrary method for making al-

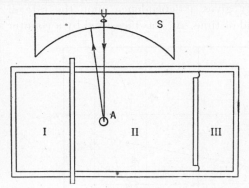

Fig. 17a.—Arrangement of torsion oscillation viscometer.

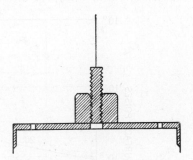

Fig. 17b.—Design of torsion pendulum bob A of figure 17a, supported by phosphor bronze wire.

lowance for the dragging along of the water underneath the film by the motion of the film. Nevertheless, the viscosities obtained in this way for liquid films exhibit just the logarithmic relation toward increase of pressure predicted by general theories of the liquid state. In other respects, η seems to represent almost perfectly the true viscosity of the film, even though it may have a magnitude which is somewhat different from that determined by use of a canal. The design of the ring is shown in figure 17b.

C. TORSION ROTATION VISCOMETER

Fourt and Harkins[27] have determined the viscosity of films from the measurement of the torque required to maintain a uniform rate of rotation of the ring or disk described above. The shaft of an electric clock is used as the upper suspension; and the twist between the two ends of the torsion is measured by two beams of light reflected from mirrors mounted on the support of the wire and on the axis of the ring, respectively. These are focused on the same scale and give a single line when the shaft is not in ro-

[27] L. Fourt and W. D. Harkins. *J. Phys. Chem.*. **42**, 897 (1938).

tation.   The torsion constant, τ dynes per radian, may be determined by
the method of oscillations.   The torque may be obtained by timing the
interval, t, between the passage of the two beams of light past a fixed mark.
If the viscosity of the film is Newtonian, independent of the rate of shear,
the equation for viscosity does not include a term for the rate of rotation of
the ring.   If Δt is the change in the interval produced by the film, the
viscosity is given by:

$$\eta = \frac{\tau \,\Delta t}{4\pi}\left(\frac{1}{a^2} - \frac{1}{b^2}\right) \tag{11}$$

Anomalous viscosity or plasticity gives a dependence upon the rate of
shear.   In later work, the interval of time, Δt, was measured by a counter

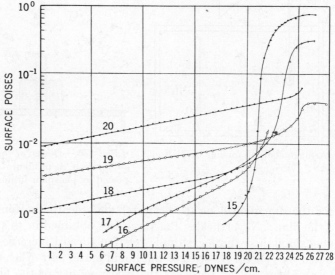

Fig. 18.—Viscosity–pressure relations of monolayers of the
normal long–chain paraffin acids: pentadecylic 15, palmitic 16,
margaric 17, stearic 18, nonadecanoic 19, arachidic 20.

started when the first beam of light passed a photocell, and stopped when
the second beam fell upon the counter.   The method of the rotating ring
should be used if the flow of the film is of the plastic type.

The effects of pressure and variation of chain length upon the viscosity
of monolayers are exhibited in figure 18.   Relations are shown for the normal long-chain paraffin acids.   Up to pressures of 21 to 25 dyne cm.$^{-1}$, the
monolayers are in the liquid condensed state.   On increase of pressure
above this point, the viscosity rises with extreme rapidity, especially very
near the second-order transition to the S state.   The L_c phase exhibits
Newtonian viscosity, $i.\ e.$, the viscosity is independent of the rate of shear,

while the S phase has a non-Newtonian viscosity. The acids with 16 and 17 carbon atoms are too close to the liquid expanded state to have entirely normal viscosities in the liquid condensed state. For those with 18, 19, and 20 carbon atoms, the value of $\Delta \log \eta$ is the same between 18 and 19 as between 19 and 20 carbon atoms. The most important relations are:[28]

(1) From the lowest pressures investigated up to 18 dynes per cm. or more the logarithm of the surface viscosity is proportional to the film pressure, or

$$\log \eta = \log \eta_0 + kf \qquad (12)$$

for all the acids containing from 16 to 20 carbon atoms.

(2) The viscosity of the liquid films increases rapidly with the length of the hydrocarbon chain.

(3) The liquid or low-pressure condensed films exhibit a Newtonian viscosity.

(4) The viscosity of the "plastic" (or high-pressure condensed) films decreases with the length of the hydrocarbon chain.

(5) Films designated as "plastic" exhibit a non-Newtonian viscosity, that is, the viscosity varies with the rate of shear.

(6) The film viscosity begins to increase more rapidly than corresponds to equation (12) at a pressure considerably lower than that of the sharp kink in the film pressure–area curve. Also, the rise in viscosity between the low-pressure condensed film and the high-pressure condensed film is larger the shorter the hydrocarbon chain of the fatty acid.

It should be noted that the viscosities in the S phase are given only for those acids which contain an *odd* number of carbon atoms in the molecule. Those with an even number of carbon atoms form unstable S monolayers, though the alcohol films are stable in this phase.

IV. SURFACE POTENTIAL

If the surfaces of two metals are separated slightly by a gas, and if the gas is sufficiently ionized, a potential known as the contact potential, V, is developed between the surfaces. This can be measured by the use of an electrometer of small capacity. This and other methods for the determination of contact potential were developed by Lord Kelvin.[29] If one of the metals is replaced by water, made electrically conducting by an electrolyte, a potential is still found. If a monolayer is allowed to flow under the electrode, this difference of potential is changed by an amount which may vary from a few millivolts to a volt. This change is designated as the surface potential (ΔV) of the monolayer.

[28] E. Boyd and W. D. Harkins, *J. Am. Chem. Soc.*, **61**, 1188 (1939).

[29] Sir Wm. Thomson, Lord Kelvin, *Contact Electricity of Metals. Vol. VI, Mathematical and Physical Papers*, Cambridge Univ. Press, London, 1911, pp. 110–145. See also Righi, *J. phys. radium*, **7**, 153 (1888).

The first measurements of surface potential were made in 1883 by Bichat and Blondlot,[30] and later by other workers.[31]   The method used by Kenrick[31] was to allow the reference liquid to flow down over the inner wall of a moderately large glass tube placed with its axis vertical, and to allow the second liquid to flow from a fine glass tip in a narrow jet down this axis. The two solutions were connected through calomel electrodes to a quadrant electrometer.   It is claimed by both Kenrick and Frumkin[31] that this method gives satisfactory results for aqueous solutions of inorganic electrolytes and for not too dilute solutions of derivatives of the hydrocarbons.

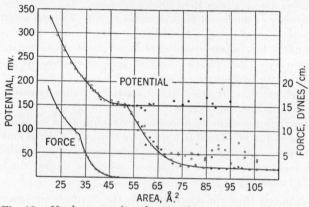

Fig. 19.—Nonhomogeneity of a monolayer of myristic acid.[18]

The errors inherent in the method of the "dropping electrode" are discussed by Williams and Vigfusson.[32]

Unfortunately, the values of the surface potentials as determined for similar systems by different observers did not exhibit a good agreement. In an attempt to obtain better values, Guyot and Frumkin independently[33] developed a method in which the potential is determined between a metal coated with a radioactive substance, such as polonium, and a solution. The method of Guyot and Frumkin was used by Frumkin and Williams[34] and by Schulman and Rideal.[35]   The development of this method did not,

[30] Bichat and Blondlot, *J. phys. radium,* **11,** 548 (1883).

[31] F. B. Kenrick, *Z. physik. Chem.,* **19,** 625 (1896).   M. J. Guyot, *Ann. Phys.,* **2,** 506 (1924).   A. Frumkin, *Z. physik. Chem.,* **111,** 190 (1924); **116,** 485 (1925).   Garrison, *J. Phys. Chem..* **29,** 1517 (1925).   A. Buhl, *Ann. Physik,* **84,** 211 (1927); **87,** 877 (1928).

[32] J. W. Williams and V. A. Vigfusson, *J. Phys. Chem.,* **35,** 348 (1931).

[33] M. J. Guyot, *Ann. Phys.,* [10] **2,** 506 (1924).   A. Frumkin, *Z. physik. Chem.,* **116,** 485 (1925).

[34] A. Frumkin and J. W. Williams, *Proc. Natl. Acad. Sci. U. S.,* **15,** 400 (1929).

[35] J. H. Schulman and E. K. Rideal, *Proc. Roy. Soc. London,* **A130,** 259, 270, 284 (1930).

however, remove the difficulty that the values obtained by different workers, or even by the same worker, on seemingly identical systems were extremely variable.   The researches on surface films which had been carried
on for many years in this laboratory had shown that many films of insoluble
organic substances of the polar–nonpolar type are much less homogeneous
than had usually been supposed in the literature on the subject.   From
this point of view, it was suggested by the writer to Frumkin (Harkins and
Fischer[18]) that his method for the determination of surface potential gives
correct results, but that those who had used it had failed to combine it with
a film balance, so the errors arose from a lack of proper control of the film.

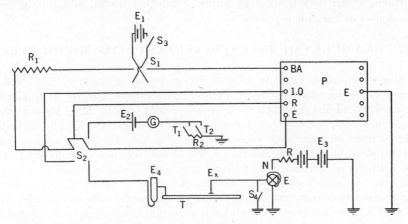

Fig. 20.—Circuit used for determination of surface potential with polonium
electrode and Compton electrometer.

When this suggestion was adopted, the errors disappeared.   Figure 19
shows the lack of homogeneity of a monolayer of myristic acid in the region
in which islands of liquid expanded (L_e) film lie in a sea of gaseous film
(above 52 Å.[2] per molecule).   The lower curve at the higher areas corresponds to the gas phase, and the highest points to the L_e film.

The polonium electrode is prepared by dipping a thin circular disk of
silver, 1 cm. in diameter and soldered to a platinum wire, into an acidic
solution of a polonium salt.   Polonium deposits on the silver.   If the potential over a smaller area is to be determined, the polonium is deposited
electrolytically at the end of a heavy platinum wire, about 2 mm. of which
projects from the end of a glass tube into which it is sealed to make electrical contact with the mercury inside.   One circuit used in this laboratory
is shown in figure 20.   This makes use of a Compton electrometer.   A
vacuum-tube electrometer is also in use in an independent apparatus, the
tube being mounted directly above the electrode.

One method used for moving the electrode over the surface has been shown in figure 7. The electrode should be set at a height of 1–2 mm. above the surface and should be kept dry. The air is made electrically conducting by alpha particles which shoot out of the polonium and produce both positive and negative ions. If polonium is not available, the method of Zisman[36] may be used. This employs an electrode which vibrates about 250 to 1000 times per second. Because the apparatus is much more bulky than that for the polonium electrode, it has been used mostly in this laboratory for the determination of the potentials of built-up films. The vibration of the electrode varies the distance between it and the other surface, which may be that of water or another metal, and thus gives a condenser of variable capacity.

V. EXAMPLES OF INVESTIGATIONS USING MONOLAYERS

Many illustrations might be given of important uses of the film balance and its accessories in investigations in organic and biological chemistry.[37] It application to the study of film penetration has been described on page 221. Measurements made on monolayers of sterols, hormones, and enzymes have added to our knowledge of their structure and behavior. The older formulas for cholestanol, ergosterol, and estriol were such that the models of the molecules indicated that, with the hydroxyl group down, the molecular area could not be less than 54 Å.^{2}, while the newer formulas indicate cross sections of from 35 to 40 Å.^{2} (Fig. 21). In the tightly packed monolayers, the mean areas, determined experimentally, vary from 37 to 44 Å. Bernal, whose x-ray work was important in this connection, pointed out that the molecules are not only too slender, but they are also too long for the old formula to be valid. The surface potentials of some of these substances exhibit remarkable relationships. Thus, that of a condensed film of cholestanol is 400 mv., while with epicholestanol, it is −100 mv. The only apparent difference in the two compounds is the orientation of the hydroxyl group. In the former, it is presumably oriented nearly vertically, with the positive end upward, while in epicholestanol it would seem to have the negative higher than the positive end. The smallness of area of these compounds with four rings and the very small compressibility

[36] W. A. Zisman, *Rev. Sci. Instruments*, **3**, 7 (1932). W. A. Zisman and H. G. Yamins, *Physics*, **4**, 7 (1933). H. G. Yamins and W. A. Zisman, *J. Chem. Phys.*, **1**, 656 (1933).

[37] SUMMARIES: O. Rosenheim and H. King, *Ann. Rev. Biochem.*, **3**, 87 (1934); Kon, *Ann. Rept. Chem. Soc.*, **31**, 206 (1934).

PAPERS ON STEROLS, ETC., IN SURFACE FILMS: J. B. Leathes, *J. Physiol., Proc.*, Nov. 1923; N. K. Adam and G. Jessop, *Proc. Roy. Soc. London*, **A120**, 473 (1928); O. Rosenheim and N. K. Adam, *ibid.*, **A126**, 25 (1929); O. Rosenheim and N. K. Adam, *ibid.*, **B105**, 422 (1929); R. J. Fosbinder, *ibid.*, **A139**, 93 (1933); J. F. Danielli and N. K. Adam, *Biochem. J.*, **28**, 1583 (1934); N. K. Adam, F. A. Askew, and J. F. Danielli, *ibid.*, **29**, 1786 (1935); N. K. Adam, J. F. Danielli, G. A. D. Haslewood, and G. F. Marrian, *ibid.*, **26**, 1233 (1932); J. F. Danielli, G. F. Marrian, and G. A. D. Haslewood, *ibid.*, **27**, 311 (1933); I. Langmuir and others, *J. Am. Chem. Soc.*, **59**, 1406, 1751 (1937).

of their films seem to indicate that the molecules are oriented vertically. The thickest monolayers of d-pimaric and of tetrahydro-d-pimaric acids (Fig. 22) were found by Harkins, Ries, and Carman[38] to be 12 Å., thick or about one-half that of a stearic acid monolayer.

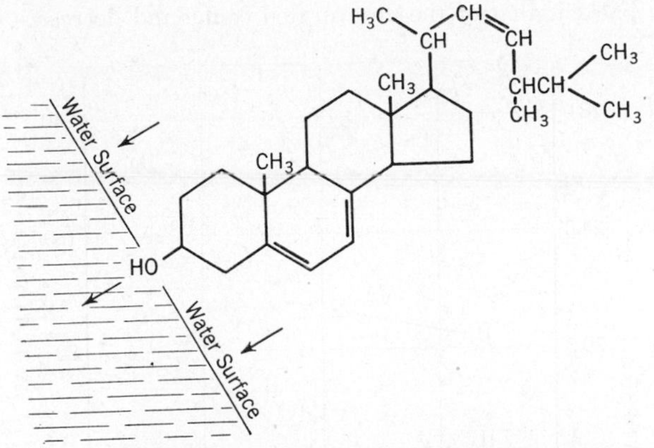

Fig. 21.—Ergosterol molecule as oriented on the side of a drop of water in a tightly packed monolayer.

In figure 23 are given the surface pressure area and surface potential relations for each substance. At zero pressure the extrapolated molecular area of the saturated compound, I, is 54 Å.^{2}, and of the unsaturated, II, 57 Å.^{2}, while at the highest pressure the former is compressed to 47 A.^{2} and the latter to 43 A.^{2} Thus, at a

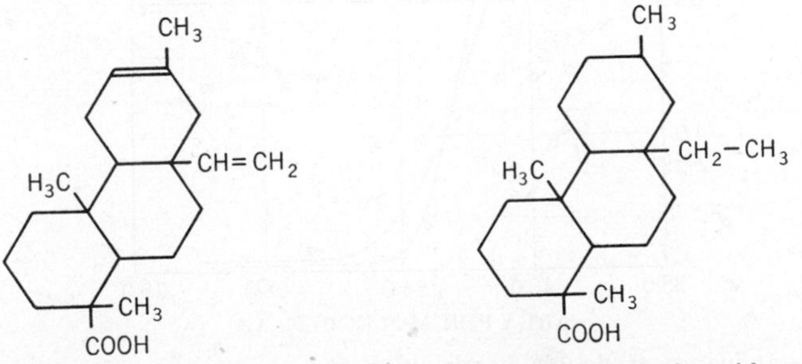

Fig. 22.—(a) d-Pimaric and (b) tetrahydro-d-pimaric acids.

pressure of 5 dynes per cm.$^{-1}$, the molecular areas are equal (51 Å.^{2}), while the compressibility of the monolayer of the unsaturated compound is much higher (0.0100) than that of the saturated compound (0.00681). The molecular area of these substances is somewhat more than twice that of stearic acid. The molecule of d-pimaric acid contains two double bonds, which occur at or near the top of the mole-

[38] W. D. Harkins, H. E. Ries, and E. F. Carman, J. Am. Chem. Soc., (a) 57, 2224 (1935); (b) 58, 1377 (1937).

cule when oriented upright in a tightly packed film. The effect of these double bonds on the surface potential is extremely interesting. Since the surface potential of the unsaturated is less than half that of the saturated compound, the dipoles due to unsaturation are opposed to those of the carboxyl group. Furthermore, while the surface potential of the saturated compound rises as the film becomes more tightly packed, that of the unsaturated compound decreases with packing.

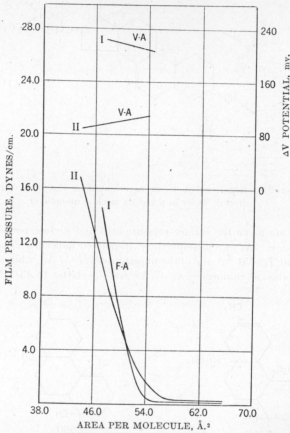

Fig. 23.—Influence of double bonds upon the pressure–area and potential–area relations of the pimaric acids. Curve *I*, tetrahydro-*d*-pimaric acid; curve *II*, *d*-pimaric acid.

The former normal effect is due largely to an increase in the number of dipoles per unit area with pressure. The latter indicates that increased tightness of packing increases the opposition of the dipoles. It has been seen that unsaturation at the top of the molecules increases the tightness of packing at the highest pressure and gives a molecular area of 43 Å.² Molecular models of these compounds gave an area of 42 Å.² for tight packing of vertically oriented molecules. If the carboxyl group had been in position 3, the orientation should have been different; and the molecular models for this case gave an area of 37 Å.², which is much less than that actually found.   At a low film pressure, the unsaturated groups near the top of the molecule change the molecular area in the opposite direction—that is, they cause

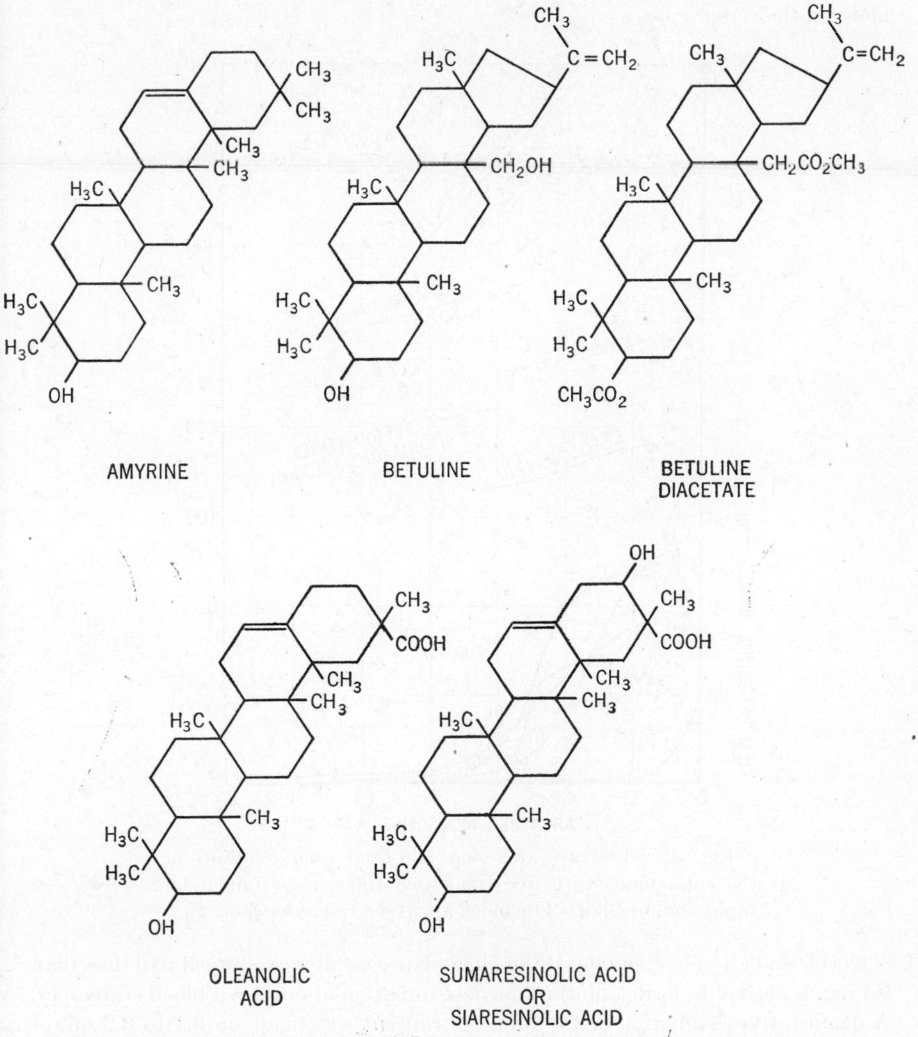

AMYRINE   BETULINE   BETULINE
                                                      DIACETATE

OLEANOLIC   SUMARESINOLIC ACID
  ACID   OR
                          SIARESINOLIC ACID

Fig. 24.—Formulas of compounds which contain a system of five condensed rings.

slight expansion of the film, presumably because the tops of some of the molecules are pulled downward to the water by the dipoles of the unsaturated groups.

A number of compounds with five rings (Fig. 24) investigated by the same workers also exhibited great differences, both in area and surface potential, as the result of

changes in the one, two, or three polar groups present.   This is shown in figure 25.
A decrease of pressure with decrease of area indicates that the film is collapsing.

With measurements on mixtures, the possibility of interaction of film molecules
must be kept in mind.   Often the assumption is made, with insufficient justification, that each molecule occupies an area of the same magnitude as when present
alone on the water surface.

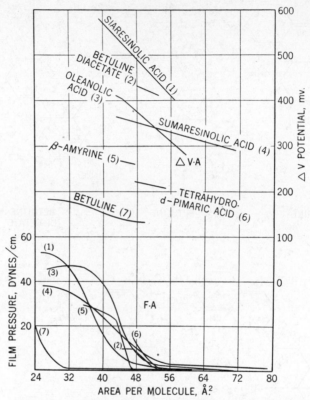

Fig. 25.—Pressure–area and potential area-relations of
the compounds with five condensed rings, as obtained by
rapid compression. For older films, see reference 38b.

Gorter and Grendel[20] employed the film balance as microanalytical tool (less than
0.1 mg. is needed to form a film) in the determination of fat in red blood corpuscles.
A quantitative estimation of the total fat content was made on 0.1 to 0.2 ml. of
blood.   An interesting result of this research is that many mixed films of biologi-
cally interesting compounds such as cholesterol, lecithin, and lipides behave in a
simple additive manner.   The study[39] of films of phthioic acid, $C_{26}H_{52}O_2$, one of the
tubercle acids isolated by Anderson, has given noteworthy results in the elucida-

[39] E. Stenhagen, *Trans. Faraday Soc.*, **36**, 597 (1940).

tion of the probable structure of this compound.   X-ray reflections from multilayer films of the barium salt showed that the length of the molecule was that of a chain of 12 to 14 carbon atoms.   The phthioic acid films differ in behavior from those of known fatty acids.   On water, a highly incompressible film which collapses at an area of 38 Å.^{2} per molecule is formed, in contrast with n-decyl-n-dodecylacetic acid, which forms an expanded film collapsing at about 60 Å.^{2} The surface dipole of this film was much smaller than that found for phthioic acid.   This evidence suggested to Stenhagen the presence of a small alkyl group in the position alpha to carboxyl, because this might account for the observed close packing of the chains.   The most probable formula is that of ethyl-n-decyl-n-dodecylacetic acid.

In exhaustive researches, Clowes and coworkers[40] found that numerous carcinogenic compounds, although not capable of giving coherent films in themselves, interact extensively with sterols in stable monomolecular films.   In some cases the interaction is sufficiently strong to lead to the formation of association complexes.   The association type of interaction, which is especially pronounced when the hydrocarbon–sterol films contain a fat, stearic acid, or a phosphatide as a third component may possibly provide a mechanism whereby the polycyclic hydrocarbons may be bound into and act as a modifying influence in biological structures.

The subject of two-dimensional solutions of nonpolar solutes in polar solvents is in its infancy.   It was discovered by Harkins, Myers, and Fowkes[41] that hydrocarbon oils of high molecular weight, which will not by themselves spread on water may nevertheless be made to spread as a certain percentage of the material in a monolayer of a polar–nonpolar oil.   Numerous two-dimensional solutions of this type were encountered in the work of Clowes.

VI.   MULTILAYERS ON SOLID SURFACES

1.   General Relations

The dimensions of organic molecules may often be determined from the pressure–area relations of their monolayers on water.   The assumption, justified by the results obtained, is that the mean density of the monolayer is that of the three-dimensional liquid.   If many monolayers could be piled up to form a multilayer, the thickness could be determined by optical means.   The deposition of multilayers was accomplished by Blodgett,[42] whose first paper appeared in 1934.   The methods used in this deposition of multilayers and in the study of these monolayers after they are formed are so varied that the original papers by Blodgett should be consulted by those who wish to work in this field.   Only a few of the methods and the most

[40] Summary by G. H. A. Clowes, Publ. No. 21, Am. Assoc. Adv. Sci., Washington, D. C., 1941.

[41] W. D. Harkins and R. J. Myers, *J. Am. Chem. Soc.*, **58**, 1817 (1936); R. J. Myers and W. D. Harkins, *J. Phys. Chem.*, **40**, 959 (1936); F. M. Fowkes, R. J. Myers, and W. D. Harkins, *J. Am. Chem. Soc.*, **59**, 593 (1937).

[42] K. B. Blodgett, *J. Am. Chem. Soc.*, **56**, 495 (1934); **57**, 1007 (1935).

important of the characteristics of these multilayers can be considered here. In general, only highly condensed monolayers can be transferred by this general method. In order to obtain a uniformly deposited monolayer, it is essential that the pressure upon the monolayer on the surface of the aqueous subphase be kept constant. The methods for doing this are indicated later.

The films transferred as monolayers from the surface of an aqueous phase are of three types—X or D, Y or UD, and Z or U—where D indicates that the monolayer is transferred as the slide moves downward, and U, as it moves upward through the surface. The type of deposition obtained is a function of the type of monolayer employed, of the temperature, of the nature of the surface upon which the monolayer is deposited, and of the rate at which the slide is moved. If the monolayer on the aqueous phase is spread as an acid, the pH and the nature of the multivalent positive ion largely determine the deposition. That this should be true is evident when it is considered that the fraction of neutral soap present increases[43] as the pH increases from 2 to 10 or more, and most rapidly between 4 and 8. The hydrophilic character of the films increases in the order $X < Y < Z$, and the type of film deposited is related to the "wettability" of the surface and thus to the contact angle between the surface of the slide and the film.[44] A *small angle of contact*, when measured between the monolayer on the water and that part of the surface of the slide which is moving toward the edge of contact, is favorable to the deposition of the layer on the slide.

In Blodgett's early work, a vertical clean glass slide was partly immersed in a nearly saturated (5×10^{-4} molar) solution of calcium carbonate; and a film of stearic acid was spread on the clean surface of the water. When the slide was withdrawn slowly, it emerged "completely dry" at a pH of 7.5 to 8.0. The surface of this film was both hydro- and oleophobic. At a pH of 6.5 to 7.0, the slide emerged covered with a layer of water, on the surface of which was a monolayer of calcium stearate. The latter adhered to the surface of the glass if the water was removed by evaporation at a low temperature.

Y or UD multilayers are formed from monolayers of barium or magnesium stearate on the surface of water, and with calcium stearate at pH < 7.0 and often between pH 7.0 to 8.5. The layer (U^1) deposited on the first up trip has its —$(COO)_2Ca$ "heads" oriented toward, and the $<CH_3$ groups away from, the glass. The succeeding layers are oriented in opposite directions. Thus the whole multilayer consists of an aggregate of double layers of molecules with their polar groups outward. This is exactly the structure of soap micelles in an aqueous solution of soap, except that the

---

[43] I. Langmuir and V. J. Schaefer, *J. Am. Chem. Soc.*, **58**, 284 (1936).

[44] J. J. Bikerman, *Proc. Roy. Soc. London*, **A170**, 130 (1939).

soap micelles have a layer of water between the polar groups of adjacent double soap layers.

The deposition of Y layers is shown[45] graphically in figure 26.   The plate of glass or metal is first made hydrophobic by covering the surface with ferric stearate and rubbing the warm slide very vigorously with a clean towel, which removes all but a single monolayer.   On the first down trip the first layer deposits in such a way that the polar groups are oriented to-

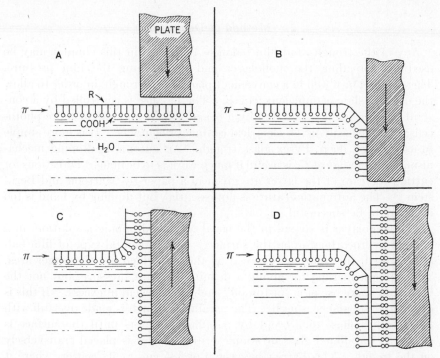

Fig. 26.—Deposition of Y layers.

ward the polar water, but on the first up trip toward the polar groups of the stearate.   Thus a thick multilayer consists of *double* layers of polar–nonpolar molecules with their *like* groups turned toward each other: polar toward polar and nonpolar toward nonpolar.   This structure is found in both Y (UD or DU multilayers) and X or U layers.   That both should give the same structure is made plain if the principles of the molecular orientation theory are considered.   In this connection, a quotation from the first paper on orientation (Harkins, Davies, and Clark,[46] 1917) may be

[45] I. Langmuir, *Proc. Roy. Soc. London*, **A170**, 1 (1939).

[46] W. D. Harkins, E. C. H. Davies, and G. L. Clark, *J. Am. Chem. Soc.*, **39**, 541 (1917).

cited as follows: "at any surface or interface the change which occurs is
such as to make the transition to the adjacent phase less abrupt."

In general it is the molecular forces which determine the orientation of
the molecules in the multilayer, and not the type of deposition.   Thus the
molecules "overturn" when those in the monolayer do not have the same
orientation as that which the multilayer should have.   However, the *density* of the multilayer depends upon the method of deposition and is different in X and Y multilayers.

2.   Method of Deposition

Any of the troughs and film balances described in this chapter may be
used for spreading the monolayer and determining the film pressure.
There should be a well in a convenient place in the trough, in order to allow
the use of a slide of sufficient length.   The balance is controlled by a constant-pressure device operated by a beam of light and one or more photo-
cells, or more easily by an electrical contact or contacts.   It is more simple
to use a large, deep, Pyrex glass trough.   An automatic dipping mechanism, shown in figure 27, is useful if much work is to be done.   Directions for
cutting the cam of the latter are given in a paper by Mattoon and Bernstein.[47]   The automatic feature is not essential, but dipping by hand is too
irregular to be successful.

The monolayer is spread in the usual way by dropping a solution, in a
volatile hydrocarbon, upon the surface.   If a horizontal type of film balance is used, the solution is spread on the end which has the larger area.
The simplest method for giving a definite constant pressure, but not the
best, is to make use of a "piston oil" such as oleic acid in excess.   If this is
done, no film balance is used.   The paraffined trough is made overfull with
the aqueous phase and swept by paraffined barriers until the surface is
clean.   A paraffined glass or stainless steel barrier is placed transversely
on the trough.   This barrier has a gap of 3–5 cm. at its center, where it
does not touch the water.   The monolayer is prevented from passing into
the other end of the trough by a paraffined silk thread which is longer than
the gap and whose ends are fastened at the edges of the gap.   This thread
lies on the surface.   The solution of the monolayer material is now dropped
near the end of the trough, on one side of the barrier, and the piston oil at
the other end of the trough.   If lenses of the piston oil are present and if the
barrier is moved until the silk thread lies loosely in the surface, the pressures of the monolayer and of the piston oil are equal, and dipping may be
begun.   If the silk thread is not much longer than the gap, it is simple to
determine the ratio of the area of that part of the slide upon which the mono-

---

[47] R. W. Mattoon and S. Bernstein, *Rev. Sci. Instruments*, **9**, 125 (1938).

layer is deposited to the decrease in area of the monolayer. In such a measurement, the barrier is moved to keep the silk thread in the same relative position and the same degree of tautness.

Any insoluble, nonvolatile oil which spreads to give a definite film pressure (π) while lenses are still present may be used as a piston oil.   These pressures, in dyne cm.$^{-1}$, are 30 for pure oleic acid, 15 for triolein, and 9 for

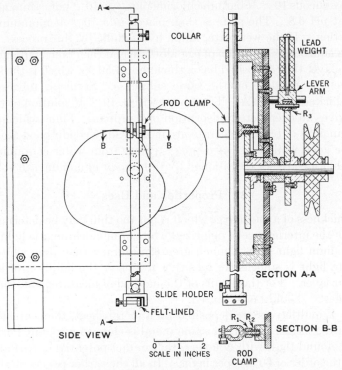

Fig. 27.—Automatic dipping apparatus for the deposition of mono-layers to form multilayers (Mattoon and Bernstein).[47]

tricresyl phosphate. Oxidized lubricating oils spread to give a uniform film which exhibits interference colors that may be calibrated to indicate low film pressures.   Thus, a particular oil appeared as: first-order yellow-red with $\pi = 0$, first-order blue with $\pi = 1.4$, second-order yellow with $\pi = 4$, second-order blue with $\pi = 5.2$, and third-order red with $\pi = 7.0$. A substance of high spreading pressure may be mixed with one which gives $\eta = 0$ to give a piston oil whose pressure depends upon the proportions used.   The following list[48] shows the spreading pressures for various percentages of ethyl myristate mixed with a high-boiling paraffin:

[48] A. Norris and T. W. J. Taylor, *J. Chem. Soc.*, **1938**, 1719.

Ethyl myristate, %.....	0	10.0	16.5	33.0	49.0	65.5	100
F, dynes/cm..........	0	5.0	8.5	11.1	14.7	17.0	20.7

Langmuir and Schaefer[49] have found that the organic film on a solid may be conditioned in such a way as to cause it to adsorb organic substances, which contain polar groups, from their aqueous solutions. This may be done by depositing a Y layer (either D or U), as from a stearic acid monolayer, on aqueous 10^{-4} M barium chloride plus 2×10^{-4} potassium acid carbonate at pH 6.8. The plate is then placed in a 10^{-3} M aluminum chloride solution. If the wet plate, made hydrophilic by this process, is used to stir an aqueous 1% solution of egg albumin and then taken out and dried, the monolayer thus deposited has a thickness of 50 Å., which is the same as that given by catalase on the same subphase. Stanley's tobacco virus gives a thickness of 300 Å. Treatment with a 10^{-3} M solution of thorium nitrate gives an even better adsorption of a protein. Films which contain more than 50% of barium stearate are more readily conditioned than those of stearic acid, while those of copper stearate from water containing 10^{-5} copper chloride are not conditioned by thorium or aluminum salt solutions.

3. Properties and Uses

The thickness of a multilayer which is not too thin may be determined by the use of the interference of polarized white or monochromatic light. The use of sodium light gives a much greater accuracy than does white light, but white light is sufficiently sensitive to detect the addition of a single molecular layer. For the details of the method of measurement, the paper by Blodgett[50] should be consulted.

When Y multilayers are deposited on a metal sheet, the contact potential toward a clean sheet of the same metal is close to zero, but Porter and Wyman[51] found that, with X layers, the contact potential of barium stearate is of the order of 60 mv. per layer. In all the earlier papers on this subject, this potential was attributed to the dipoles of the barium stearate. However, Harkins and Mattoon[52] found that, with a very thin sheet of paraffin on gold which exhibited a practically zero (-30 mv.) contact potential, the first X layer increased the potential to $+5$ volts and the second to $+11$ volts, while dipoles in a single layer have not increased a contact potential by more than one volt. The potential of an X multilayer is due to surface charges, and the equations for the relations between charge and

[49] I. Langmuir and V. J. Schaefer, *J. Am. Chem. Soc.*, **59**, 1762 (1937).

[50] K. B. Blódgett, *J. Phys. Chem.*, **41**, 975 (1937). K. B. Blodgett and I. Langmuir, *Phys. Rev.*, **51**, 964 (1937).

[51] E. F. Porter and P. J. Wyman, *J. Am. Chem. Soc.*, **59**, 2746 (1937); **60**, 1083 (1938).

[52] W. D. Harkins and R. W. Mattoon, *J. Chem. Phys.*, **7**, 186 (1939).

the equations for the relations between charge and potential are given by Harkins and Mattoon. In the deposition of an X multilayer, the film is (partly?) discharged during the down trip and charged again during the up trip (Groetzinger and Harkins[53]).

The principal use of multilayers to the organic or biological chemist is the determination of something related to the dimensions of organic molecules. A simple illustration is given by the work of Harkins, Fourt, and Fourt,[54] who found that catalase deposited by adsorption from aqueous solution on a subphase of barium stearate on chromium gave a thickness of 50 Å. for the first monolayer. A monolayer of (rabbit) anticatalase deposited on the catalase gave a thickness of 50 Å. also, but catalase on anticatalase exhibited a thickness of 10 Å. Anticatalase as the next layer gave 50 Å., and catalase on this 10 Å. Langmuir and Schaefer[55] obtained 14.2 Å. as the thickness of chlorophyll layers at not too high values of π, but at $\pi = 30$, *double layers* were 59 Å. thick at pH of 3 and 5.8, and 68 Å. at a pH of 10. Sobotka and Bloch[56] obtained thicknesses per monolayer in multilayers as follows (in Å.): hemin, 36; protoporphyrin, 36; coproporphyrin III, 30; uroporphyrin-III-octamethyl ester, 32; and phaeophorbide, 32–36, while the standard value for barium stearate is 24.4.

VII. FILM BALANCE FOR FILMS ON SOLIDS[59-67]

1. Equations for Films on Liquids and Solids

While oil films on water are not thicker than one molecular layer except when unstable, adsorbed films of oils, nitrogen, oxygen, etc., may grow to thicknesses of several molecules on the surface of a solid. For example, adsorbed films of water or nitrogen may, on solids, attain thicknesses of the general order of 5 to 10 molecular layers. Even on graphite, generally considered as a hydrophobic solid (contact angle against water $= 85.5°$), the water layer obtains a thickness of three water molecules at $p/p_0 = 0.97$.

It may easily be shown that any apparatus, by means of which an accurate adsorption isotherm can be obtained, may be used as a film balance for films on solids, since from the isotherm it is possible to calculate $\pi = \gamma_0 - \gamma$ where γ_0 is the free surface energy of the solid. That this may be done on the basis of the adsorption equation of Gibbs was suggested by Bangham,[57, 58] whose equations correspond to (13) to (15). The Gibbs equation for a single vapor may be written:

[53] G. Groetzinger and W. D. Harkins, *J. Chem. Phys.*, **7**, 204 (1939).

[54] W. D. Harkins, L. Fourt, and P. C. Fourt, *J. Biol. Chem.*, **132**, 111 (1940).

[55] I. Langmuir and V. J. Schaefer, *J. Am. Chem. Soc.*, **59**, 2075 (1937).

[56] H. Sobotka, Publ. No. **7**, Am. Assoc. Adv. Sci., 1939, p. 54.

[57] D. H. Bangham, *Trans. Faraday Soc.*, **33**, 805 (1937); D. H. Bangham and R. I. Razouk, *ibid.*, **1459**, 1463.

[58] D. H. Bangham and S. Mosallam, *Proc. Roy. Soc. London*, **A166**, 558 (1938).

$$\Gamma = - \left(\frac{\partial \gamma}{\partial \mu}\right)_T = - \frac{1}{RT} \left(\frac{\partial \gamma}{\partial \ln f}\right)_T \tag{13}$$

in which Γ is the surface excess in mole cm.$^{-2}$, μ is the thermodynamic potential, and f is the fugacity. For a perfect gas this becomes:

$$\Gamma = - \frac{1}{RT} \left(\frac{\partial \gamma}{\partial \ln p}\right)_T \tag{14}$$

The case to be considered here is one in which van der Waals' forces alone are operative. Integration of (4) between $p = 0$ and $p = p$ gives:

$$\pi = \gamma_0 - \gamma = RT \int_0^p \Gamma d \ln p \tag{15}$$

The methods used in calculating π, with illustrative values, are given by Jura and Harkins.[59] This equation is applicable to films of nitrogen, butane, benzene, etc., on solids. It is also valid for the adsorption of vapors on water or mercury, though it would be difficult to obtain a large enough area to make it possible to apply the equation.

The remarkable new fact which now emerges[60] is that the same phases which have been found in monolayers on water are also found in films on solids. The equations which characterize these phases are as follows:[61]

Condensed phases:
Compressibility, $k = 1/a\sigma$ $\qquad(16)$
Film pressure, $\pi = b - a\sigma$, where $a = (\partial \gamma/\partial \sigma)_T$ $\qquad(17)$
Vapor pressure, $\ln p = B - A/V^2$ $\qquad(18)$
Intermediate phase:
Compressibility, $k = -a + b/\sigma$ $\qquad(19)$
Film pressure, $\pi = c - \frac{1}{a}(\ln a\sigma - b)$ $\qquad(20)$

Vapor pressure, $\ln p = C + aA/2BV^2 - b/a^2AB \ln \dfrac{aA - bV}{V}$ $\qquad(21)$

Liquid expanded phase:
Compressibility, $k = 1/(a\sigma - b)$ $\qquad(22)$
Film pressure, $\pi = C + a\sigma - b \ln \sigma$ $\qquad(23)$
Vapor pressure, $\ln p = C + aA/BV^2 - b/BV$ $\qquad(24)$

Vapor phase: Equations the same as in three dimensions, but with π substituted for gas pressure, and σ for volume of gas.

In these equations, a, b, A, B, and C are constants and k indicates compressi-

---

[59] G. Jura and W. D. Harkins, *J. Am. Chem. Soc.*, **66**, 1356 (1944).

[60] G. Jura and W. D. Harkins, *J. Chem. Phys.*, **11**, 43 (1943). W. D. Harkins and G. Jura, *ibid.*, 430, 432.

[61] W. D. Harkins and G. Jura, *J. Chem. Phys.*, **12**, 112 (1944). G. Jura and W. D. Harkins, *ibid.*, 114 (1944).

bility, π film pressure, p vapor pressure, and V volume of vapor, under standard conditions.

2.   Determination of Area of Organic Molecules on Solids and of the Area of a Solid

It has been shown by Harkins and Jura[62] that equation (18) may be used to obtain the area of a nonporous or a porous solid by determining the adsorption isotherm of the vapor of a given liquid.   The equation is used in the following form:

$$\log (p/p_0) = B - A/V^2 \tag{18a}$$

If V is plotted as a function of p/p_0, an S-shaped isotherm is obtained, but $\log (p/p_0)$ $vs.$ $1/V^2$ gives a linear plot in the proper range of temperatures.   If $\log (p/p_0)$ is plotted on the y axis (semilogarithmic paper), a straight line of slope $-A$ is obtained.   It is very simple to show that the square roots of slopes A are proportional to the areas of the solids.   If $-A$ is represented by s, then the area, Σ, for one gram of solid is given by:

$$\Sigma = ks^{1/2} = (4.06s^{1/2} \text{ for nitrogen}) \tag{25}$$

in which Σ is the area in square meters per gram if V in equation (18a) represents the volume adsorbed by one gram of material.   The value of the constant, 4.06, was determined by the substitution in equation (25) of the value 13.8 square meters per gram for Σ as determined for a sample of anatase by an absolute method discovered by Harkins and Jura.[67]   The value of s was determined from the adsorption isotherm of this same powder.   Brunauer, Emmett, and Teller[63] have found that, if $p/V(p - p_0)$ is plotted against p/p_0, a straight line is obtained.   From the intercept and slope of this line, they are able to calculate the number, N, of molecules necessary to $complete$ the first monolayer on the surface of a solid.   The same isotherm is used to obtain the area, Σ, of the solid and the number, N, of molecules in the first monolayer.   It is evident in the equation, $\sigma = \Sigma/N$, that σ gives the area per molecule.

It has been found by Harkins and Jura[62] that the areas of nitrogen (N_2) molecules on 102 porous and nonporous solids exhibit areas from a lower value, which is about that calculated from the density of solid nitrogen at its melting point, up to a higher value, about that calculated from the density of liquid nitrogen at its boiling point (Table I).

The values of k in equation (25) are: 4.06 for nitrogen at $-195.8°$ C., 3.83 for water at $25°$, 13.6 for n-butane at $0°$, and 16.9 for n-heptane at $25°$.   This method can be used for the determination of the area of organic molecules in a complete monolayer on the surface of a solid, while the area of these molecules as well as those of nitrogen should vary with the material of the solids.   The only values obtained

[62] W. D. Harkins and G. Jura, $J.$ $Am.$ $Chem.$ $Soc.$, **66**, 1366 (1944).
[63] S. Brunauer, P. H. Emmett, and E. Teller, $J.$ $Am.$ $Chem.$ $Soc.$, **60**, 316 (1938).
[64] W. D. Harkins and G. Jura, $J.$ $Chem.$ $Phys.$, **11**, 560 (1943).
[65] G. Jura and W. D. Harkins, $J.$ $Chem.$ $Phys.$, **11**, 561 (1943).
[66] W. D. Harkins and G. Jura, $J.$ $Am.$ $Chem.$ $Soc.$, **66**, 919 (1944).
[67] W. D. Harkins and G. Jura, $J.$ $Am.$ $Chem.$ $Soc.$, **66**, 1362 (1944).

thus far are 56.6 Å. for n-butane and 64.0 Å. for n-heptane. These values indicate that, if the theory of Brunauer, Emmett, and Teller gives the correct values, the molecules of these organic substances occupy a much higher area than would be expected from the size of the molecules themselves. The area of the solid used in these

TABLE I

AREA OCCUPIED BY NITROGEN MOLECULES ON THE SURFACES OF SOLIDS[a]

Number of solids with N₂ areas between the limits	Area per N₂
2	13.6–13.7
5	13.8–13.9
9 (peak)	14.0–14.1
6	14.2–14.3
2	14.4–14.5
1	14.6–14.7
4	14.8–14.9
12	15.0–15.1
15 (peak)	15.2–15.3
11	15.4–15.5
2	15.6–15.7
4	15.8–15.9
10	16.0–16.1
12 (peak)	16.2–16.3
3	16.4–16.5
1	16.6–16.7
2	16.8–16.9
1	17.0–17.1
102	

[a] W. D. Harkins and G. Jura, *J. Chem. Phys.*, **11**, 432 (1943).

calculations is correct, so the only possible error is that in the theory of Brunauer, Emmett, and Teller which seems to have worked remarkably well with nitrogen. The value obtained with water is 14.8 Å.[2] These three values were determined on the surface of titanium dioxide in the form of anatase, while many different types of solids are used for the work on nitrogen. A value for n-heptane on graphite will be known soon. From these values, it is evident that molecules of the hydrocarbons lie flat on the surface of a solid, even when the monolayer is complete.

General References

Adam, N. K., *Physics and Chemistry of Surfaces*. Oxford Univ. Press, N. Y., 1942.

Harkins, W. D., "Surface Energy and Surface Tension," in J. Alexander, *Colloid Chemistry*, Vol. I, pp. 192–264; "The Surfaces of Solids and Liquids and the Films that Form upon Them: Part I. Liquids," in Vol. V, pp. 12–102, Reinhold, New York, 1926 and 1944; "Part II. Solids and Adsorption" (in press).

Recent Advances in Surface Chemistry and Chemical Physics, Publ. No. 7, 1939; *Surface Chemistry*, Publ. No. 21, Am. Assoc. Adv. Sci., 1943.

FILM BALANCES: Harkins, W. D., and Anderson, T. F., *J. Am. Chem. Soc.*, **59**, 2189 (1937); Harkins, W. D., and Fischer, E. K., *J. Chem. Phys.*, **1**, 852 (1933); Harkins, W. D., and Myers, R. J., *ibid.*, **4**, 716 (1936).

CHAPTER VIII

Determination of
OSMOTIC PRESSURE

R. H. WAGNER, *Eastman Kodak Company*

I. INTRODUCTION

The principal value of the determination of osmotic pressure, aside from the importance of the quantity itself in the fields of biology and physiology, is its relation to the molecular size of substances and associated properties. The osmotic pressure developed by a solution when separated from the solvent by a semipermeable membrane can be measured for a system provided: (*a*) the membrane is strictly impermeable to the solute under consideration but permeable to all other components of the system, and (*b*) electrolytic effects (Donnan equilibria) are considered and correctly evaluated.

The classical work of Morse and coworkers in this country, and of Berkeley and Hartley in England, amply demonstrates that accurate determinations can be made on low molecular weight solutes, but the difficulties involved in the preparation of satisfactory membranes preclude the general use of the osmometric method for the investigation of solutions of molecules of molecular weights less than about 10,000.

On the other hand, the evaluation of the molecular size of polymers of molecular weights exceeding 500,000 involves the extrapolation of data to an intercept value of pressure corresponding to 0.5 mm. or less of water. From a practical point of view, therefore, the osmometry of solutions is limited to molecules or particles having a molecular weight of between 10,000 and 500,000.

In the second section of this chapter, the fundamental osmotic equations are derived, based on the laws of thermodynamics, on the equation describing the behavior of ideal solutions, and on an equation which describes more perfectly the behavior of systems of "nonideal" high-polymeric solutes. These derivations are presented by way of contrast to emphasize that the classical general osmotic equations, of which the so-called van't Hoff equation is a special case, cannot be correctly used, except as a limiting equation, when dealing with high polymers, or in fact, with any system which does not obey Raoult's law.

The salient points of the final osmotic pressure equation applicable to polymers are briefly dealt with; a concrete example of the practical use of the formulation is given. This procedure, which is followed throughout the chapter, should be of value in aiding the experimentalist in understanding fully and clearly the use of the equations. The latter part of the second section deals with the effect of the Donnan equilibrium on the osmometry of charged polymers. This is intended as a guide for those dealing with charged polymers in order that serious errors due to inadequate consideration of the Donnan effect may be avoided. In the third section, several osmometers are described and recommended according to ease of operation, cost of fabrication, stability of solute, and magnitude of the pressure to be measured.

II. THEORETICAL CONSIDERATIONS

1. General

The existence of a pressure when a solution is separated from the solvent by a semipermeable membrane is thermodynamically due to the difference of the "escaping tendency" or fugacity[1] of a given component (solute or solvent) in the solution phase and in the solvent phase. The ratio of the fugacities of the solvent in these phases is, by definition, the activity, a_1,[2] of the solvent which is related to the partial molal free energy change, $\Delta \bar{F}_1$, the partial molal volume, $\bar{V}_1$, and the osmotic pressure, π, by the equation:

$$\pi \bar{V}_1 = -\Delta \bar{F}_1 = -RT \ln \bar{f}_1/f_1^\circ \equiv -RT \ln a_1 \qquad (1)$$

where R = the gas constant and T = the absolute temperature.

---

[1] G. N. Lewis and M. Randall, *Thermodynamics.* McGraw-Hill, New York, 1923, p. 190.

[2] Throughout this chapter we shall use the subscripts $_1$ and $_2$ to designate the solvent and solute, respectively. In the thermodynamic equations, the notation of Lewis and Randall is used.

The partial molal heat content change, $\Delta\bar{H}_1$, and the partial molal entropy change, $\Delta\bar{S}_1$, which occur when one mole of solvent is transferred from the solvent phase to an infinitely large volume of the solution phase are related to the partial molal free energy change by the Gibbs-Helmholtz equation:

$$\Delta\bar{F}_1 = \Delta\bar{H}_1 - T\,\Delta\bar{S}_1 \tag{2}$$

where $\Delta\bar{H}_1 = \bar{H}_1 - \bar{H}_1^\circ =$ the partial molal heat content change, and $\Delta\bar{S}_1 = \bar{S}_1 - \bar{S}_1^\circ =$ the partial molal entropy change.

For systems which are "ideal" in the sense that they obey Raoult's law the activity of the solvent in the solution phase is related to the mole fraction of the solvent, N_1, and to the mole fraction of the solute, N_2, by the relation:

$$\ln a_1 = \ln N_1 \equiv \ln (1 - N_2) \tag{3}$$

By combining equations (1) and (3), substituting the actual molal volume, V_1, for the partial molal volume, $\bar{V}_1$, and expanding the logarithm into a power series in N_2, we obtain:

$$\pi V_1 = -RT \ln (1 - N_2) = RT(N_2 + \tfrac{1}{2}N_2^2 + \tfrac{1}{3}N_2^3 + \ldots) \tag{4}$$

The mole fraction of the solute is given by the relation:

$$N_2 = \frac{C_2}{\dfrac{V_2}{V_1}\, d_2 + \left(1 - \dfrac{V_2}{V_1}\right) C_2} \tag{5}$$

where $C_2 =$ the concentration of the solute in grams per milliliter, V_1, $V_2 =$ the molal volume of the solvent and solute, respectively, and $d_2 =$ the density of the solute.

Recalling that $V_2 d_2 \equiv M_2$, and combining equations (4) and (5), we have:

$$\pi = RT\left[\frac{C_2}{M_2} + \left(\frac{1}{M_2 d_2} - \frac{V_1}{2M_2^2}\right) C_2^2 + \right.$$
$$\left. \left(\frac{1}{M_2 d_2^2} - \frac{V_1}{M_2^2 d_2} + \frac{V_1^2}{3M_2^3}\right) C_2^3 + \ldots \right] \tag{6}$$

where $M_2 =$ the molecular weight of the solute.

For very dilute solutions, all the terms beyond the first may be neglected and the special case known as van't Hoff's equation is obtained:

$$\pi = RT \cdot C_2/M_2 \tag{7}$$

This equation has been shown experimentally to be applicable to dilute solutions of low molecular weight solutes, *but, except as a limiting equation* (cf. Eq. 13), *it is not applicable to solutions of high polymers* for the very sufficient reason that their behavior is not characterized by equation (3).

To replace equation (3), Flory[3] and Huggins[4-7] have independently derived a function which is applicable to systems consisting of *flexible, long-chain* molecules dispersed in solvents consisting of small molecules. This relation, which includes deviations from so-called ideal behavior, including the heat of mixing contribution ($\Delta \bar{H}_1$, Eq. 2), is:

$$\ln a_1 = \ln V_1 + \left(1 - \frac{\bar{V}_1}{\bar{V}_2}\right) V_2 + \mu_1 V_2^2 \tag{8}$$

where V_1 and V_2 = the volume fraction of solvent and solute, respectively; $\bar{V}_1$ and $\bar{V}_2$ = the partial molal volumes; and μ_1 is an empirical term which characterizes the components of a given system and may be considered to be constant at low concentrations of polymer, *i. e.*, 25 grams per liter or less.[6]

When $\mu_1 = 0$; and $\bar{V}_1/\bar{V}_2 = 1$, $V_1 = N_1$ and equation (8) reduces to equation (3).

By expanding into a power series of V_2, remembering that $V_1 + V_2 = 1$ and taking the partial molal volumes as equal to the actual molal volumes, V_1 and V_2, we have:

$$- \ln a_1 = [V_2 + {}^1\!/_2 V_2^2 + {}^1\!/_3 V_2^3 + \ldots] - V_2 + V_1/V_2 \cdot V_2 - \mu_1 V_2^2 \tag{9}$$

$$- \ln a_1 = (V_1/V_2) V_2 + ({}^1\!/_2 - \mu_1) V_2^2 + {}^1\!/_3 V_2^3 + \ldots. \tag{10}$$

Combining equation (1) with equation (10), remembering that $V_2 = C_2/d_2$ and that $V_1 \equiv M_1/d_1$ and $V_2 \equiv M_2/d_2$, the final relation becomes:

$$\frac{\pi}{C_2} = \frac{RT}{M_2} + \frac{RTd_1}{M_1 d_2^2}\left(\frac{1}{2} - \mu_1\right) C_2 + \frac{RTd_1}{3\,M_1 d_2^3} \cdot C_2^2 + \ldots. \tag{11}$$

or, transposing the third term on the right:

$$\frac{\pi}{C_2} - \frac{RTd_1}{3\,M_1 d_2^3} \cdot C_2^2 = \frac{RT}{M_2} + \frac{RTd_1}{M_1 d_2^2}\left(\frac{1}{2} - \mu_1\right) C_2 + \ldots. \tag{12}$$

where C_2 = the concentration of the solute in grams per milliliter, d_1, d_2 = the density of the solvent and solute, respectively, M_1, M_2 = the molecular weight of the solvent and solute, respectively, R = the gas constant expressed in units consistent with π and C_2, and T = the absolute temperature.

The contribution of the third term on the right in equation (11) may or may not be of importance. It definitely must be considered in any evaluation of the constant, μ_1. For the determination of molecular weight from osmotic pressure data, the third term should be calculated and the effect

[3] P. J. Flory, *J. Chem. Phys.*, **9**, 660 (1941); **10**, 51 (1942).

[4] M. L. Huggins, *J. Chem. Phys.*, **9**, 440 (1941).

[5] M. L. Huggins, *J. Phys. Chem.*, **46**, 151 (1942).

[6] M. L. Huggins, *Ann. N. Y. Acad. Sci.*, **43**, 1 (1942); **44**, 431 (1943).

[7] M. L. Huggins, *J. Am. Chem. Soc.*, **64**, 1712 (1942).

of its exclusion on the extrapolated value observed by graphical methods. Under certain circumstances it will be found to be negligible, but, in general; this will not be the case.   The effect of the third term of equation (11) on data for rubber in benzine is shown in figure 1 and table I, using data of

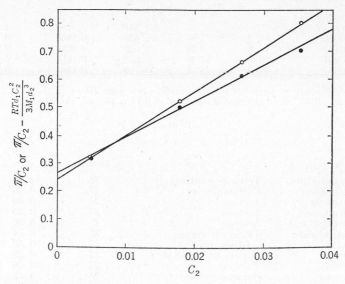

Fig. 1.—Osmotic pressure of rubber in benzine with (black circles) and without (open circles) the third term of equation (11) (*cf.* Huggins[8]).

Caspari.[9]   A molecular weight of 94,000 is indicated when the term is included, whereas a weight of 102,000 is obtained without it.

The intercept of figure 1, which is plotted according to equation (12), is inversely proportional to the molecular weight of the solute, that is:

$$\lim_{C_2 \to 0} \left(\frac{\pi}{C_2} - \frac{RTd_1C_2^2}{3M_1d_2^3} \right) = \frac{RT}{M_2} \tag{13}$$

It is well to point out that only in a monodisperse system, which is generally characteristic of the chromoproteids, *e. g.*, hemoglobin, hemocyanin, etc., in which all the solute particles have the same molecular weight, does the above M_2 represent the true molecular weight.   Most of the so-called linear polymers, whether natural or synthetic, consist of an assemblage of molecules of differing chain length and, therefore, of different molecular weights.   The osmotically determined molecular weight of such systems

[8] M. L. Huggins, *Ind. Eng. Chem., Ind. Ed.*, **35**, 216 (1943).

[9] W. A. Caspari, *J. Chem. Soc.*, **105**, 2139 (1914).

TABLE I
OSMOTIC PRESSURE DATA FOR RUBBER IN BENZINE

$M_1 = 93$; $d_1 = 0.68$; $d_2 = 0.92$; $T = 298°$ K.; $R = 82.07$ ml. atm. per degree

C_2, g. per ml.	h^a, cm.	$\pi \cdot 10^{3b}$, atm.	π/C_2, ml. atm. per g.	$\dfrac{RTd_1C_2^2}{3M_1d_2^3}$	$\left(\dfrac{\pi}{C_2} - \dfrac{RTd_1C_2^2}{3M_1d_2^3}\right)$
Infinite dilution (extrapolated)	..	..	0.240	..	0.260
0.0050	2.2	1.6	0.320	0.002	0.318
0.0179	13.0	9.3	0.520	0.025	0.495
0.0267	24.6	17.6	0.659	0.055	0.604
0.0354	39.4	28.2	0.796	0.096	0.700

[a] In ml. of solution corrected for capillarity. See page 270.
[b] $\pi = hd_s/1033$; d_s = density of solution = 0.74 g. per ml. (av.).

TABLE II
VALUES OF μ_1 FOR VARIOUS SYSTEMS[a]

Polymer	Solvent	Temp., ° C.	μ_1	Ref.
Cellulose triacetate	Tetrachloroethane	24.4	−1.8	11
Cellulose nitrate	Cyclohexanone	27	0.15	12
Cellulose nitrate	Acetone	25	0.30	13
Cellulose nitrate	Acetone	25	0.25	20
Cellulose tributyrate	Acetone	25	0.36	20
Polyvinyl chloride	Tetrahydrofuran	27	0.14	14
Polyvinyl chloride	1,4-Dioxane	27	0.52	14
Gutta-percha	Carbon tetrachloride	27	0.28	15
Gutta-percha	Toluene	27	0.36	15, 16
Gutta-percha	Benzene	25	0.52	8
Balata	Toluene	27	0.36	15
Hydrorubber	Toluene	27	0.45	15
Cyclized rubber	Toluene	27	0.46	15
Rubber	Benzene + 10% ethanol	25	0.26	17
	Carbon tetrachloride	15–20	0.28	18
	Cymene	15–20	0.33	18
	Cyclohexane	6.5	0.33	19
	Tetrachloroethane	15–20	0.36	18
	Chloroform	15–20	0.37	18
	Cumene	15–20	0.38	18
	Light petroleum	25	0.43	8
	Acetylene dichloride	15–20	0.43	18
	Toluene	27	0.43	15, 21
	Benzene	25	0.44	8, 18, 22
Rubber	Amyl acetate	25	0.49	17
	Carbon disulfide	25	0.49	23
	Benzene + 15% methanol	25	0.50	17
	Ether	15–20	0.55	18
Polystyrene	Benzene	5	0.2	24
	Toluene	27	0.44	13
	Ethyl laurate	25	0.47	25
	n-Propyl laurate	25	0.62	25
	Isopropyl laurate	25	0.71	25
	n-Butyl laurate	25	0.74	25
	Isobutyl laurate	25	0.85	25
	Isoamyl laurate	25	0.91	25

[a] M. L. Huggins, *Ann. N. Y. Acad. Sci.*, **44**, 441 (1943).

(See page 259 for references given in table.)

(usually referred to as heterodisperse systems) is the ordinary *number average*, since the colligative properties of solutions depend on the number of particles present rather than on the size of the particles.   The number average molecular weight is expressed analytically by:

$$^n\overline{M} = \frac{\sum\limits_i M_i}{N} \tag{14}$$

where M_i = the molecular weight of the ith particle and N = the total number of particles present.   This average and the relation of it to other averages, such as are obtained by viscosity measurements and ultracentrifuge measurements, were introduced and discussed in detail by Kraemer and Lansing.[10]

The μ_1 constant can be readily calculated from the slope of the plot shown in figure 1, using the second term on the right in equation (12).   The value of the constant appears to depend strongly on the forces operating between the solute and solvent molecules, e. g., solvation.   Other properties and the significance of this quantity have been discussed by Huggins.[6, 7] The values of μ_1 for various systems are collected in table II.

2.   Donnan Membrane Equilibria

When solutions of charged polymers, such as proteins, polyacrylic acid, etc., are measured, the osmotic pressure observed is not entirely due to the undiffusible polymer.   Associated with it are a number of ions of opposite charge which contribute to the observed pressure.   If the polymer is amphoteric and its *net* charge is reduced to zero by the addition of the proper amount of acid or of base, that is, the polymer is made isoelectric, the resultant salt ions will diffuse so that no concentration gradient of the

[10] E. O. Kraemer and W. D. Lansing, *J. Am. Chem. Soc.*, **57**, 1364 (1935); *J. Phys Chem.*, **39**, 153 (1935).

[11] O. Hagger and A. J. A. van der Wyk, *Helv. Chim. Acta*, **23**, 484 (1940).

[12] C. G. Boissonnas and K. H. Meyer, *Helv. Chim. Acta*, **20**, 783 (1937).

[13] G. V. Schulz, *Z. physik. Chem.*, **A176**, 317 (1936).

[14] H. Staudinger and J. Schneiders, *Ann.*, **541**, 151 (1939).

[15] H. Staudinger and K. Fischer, *J. prakt. Chem.*, **157**, 19 (1940).

[16] E. Wolff, *Helv. Chim. Acta*, **23**, 439 (1940).

[17] G. Gee, *Trans. Faraday Soc.*, **36**, 1171 (1940).

[18] E. Posnjak, *Kolloid-Beihefte*, **3**, 417 (1912).

[19] A. R. Kemp and H. Peters, *Ind. Eng. Chem., Ind. Ed.*, **33**, 1263 (1941).

[20] *Unpublished results of the author*.

[21] K. H. Meyer, E. Wolff, and C. G. Boissonnas, *Helv. Chim. Acta*, **23**, 430 (1940).

[22] H. Kroepelin and W. Brumshagen, *Ber.*, **61**, 2441 (1928).

[23] P. Stamberger, *J. Chem. Soc.*, **1929**, 2318.

[24] A. R. Kemp and H. Peters, *Ind. Eng. Chem., Ind. Ed.*, **34**, 1097 (1942).

[25] J. N. Brønsted and K. Volqvartz, *Trans. Faraday Soc.*, **35**, 576 (1939).

ions exists between the polymer solution and the dialyzate. Under these conditions, the observed pressure will be due solely to the polymer.

The reproducibility of osmotic pressure data obtained at the isoelectric point is usually poor, even in the presence of an excess of neutral salt. This may be related to minimum solubility and maximum aggregation known to occur at this point. From a consideration of the Donnan effect, it will be readily understood why reproducibility should be poor in the absence of neutral salt, since the presence of traces of electrolytic impurities (ash) would have a marked effect in producing a spurious pressure, except when the polymer net charge is absolutely identical with zero—a difficult condition to obtain and maintain over periods of time necessary for a determination. It is, therefore, recommended that the hydrogen-ion activity of the solution be maintained (buffered) at a point about one pH unit from the isoelectric point of the polymer under consideration, and that a sufficient concentration of buffer and/or neutral salt be provided to reduce the osmotic contribution due to diffusible ion distribution to an amount equal to 5% or less of the pressure due to the polymer.[26-28] In this way, minor uncertainties in the calculation of the diffusible ion contribution will not vitiate the accuracy of the osmotic pressure of the polymer.

The unequal ion distribution caused by the presence of an undiffusible charged particle was predicted by Gibbs[29] but was first specifically described and experimentally proved by Donnan.[30] Let us consider a simple case in which C_p moles polymer, say gelatin, of effective molar charge, n_p, are dispersed in a salt solution of C_s moles sodium chloride per liter. The value of n_p will depend on the pH of the solution; therefore, we shall specify that the pH be constant. This solution is separated, by a membrane permeable only to water and the salt ions, from another solution consisting also of C_s moles sodium chloride per liter. Then, the electrolyte will diffuse so that at equilibrium the net result is a displacement, δ, of sodium and chloride ions into the dialyzate from the gelatin solution. The distribution at equilibrium is shown as follows, with $n_p C_p$ representing the molar concentration of sodium ions associated with the gelatin:

$$
\begin{array}{rl}
& M \\
C_p = & [\mathrm{G}^{n_p}] \\
n_p C_p = & [\mathrm{Na}^+] \\
(C_s - \delta) = & [\mathrm{Na}^+] \\
(C_s - \delta) = & [\mathrm{Cl}^-]
\end{array}
\quad
\begin{array}{l}
[\mathrm{Na}^+] = (C_s + \delta) \\
[\mathrm{Cl}^-] = (C_s + \delta)
\end{array}
$$

[26] S. P. L. Sørensen, *Compt. rend. trav. lab. Carlsberg*, **12**, 1 (1917). Also *Proteins*, Fleischmann Laboratories, New York, 1925.

[27] F. G. Donnan, *Trans. Faraday Soc.*, **31**, 80 (1935).

[28] G. S. Adair, *Proc. Roy. Soc. London*, **A120**, 573 (1928).

[29] J. W. Gibbs, *Trans. Conn. Acad. Sci.*, **3**, 228 (1876).

[30] F. G. Donnan, *Z. Electrochem.*, **17**, 572 (1911). Also *Chem. Revs.*, **1**, 73 (1924).

The thermodynamic condition for equilibrium is that the product of the activities of the diffusible ions in the gelatin solution be equal to the product of the activities of the ions in the dialyzate, or:

$$(a_{Na^+})_1(a_{Cl^-})_1 = (a_{Na^+})_2(a_{Cl^-})_2 \tag{15}$$

where subscripts 1 and 2 refer to the solution and the dialyzate, respectively. Assuming that the activity coefficients of the ions be taken as unity, we may replace the activities by concentration terms, and equation (15) becomes:

$$[C_s - \delta + n_p C_p][C_s - \delta] = [C_s + \delta]^2 \tag{16}$$

Solving for δ, we have:

$$\delta = \frac{n_p C_p C_s}{4C_s + n_p C_p} \tag{17}$$

The osmotic pressure of the system, $\pi_{obs.}$, will be the sum of the osmotic pressure due to the polymer, π_p (Eq. 11), and that due to the ion distribution, π_i, or:

$$\pi_{obs.} = \pi_p + \pi_i = \pi_p + RT[n_p C_p + 2(C_s - \delta) - 2(C_s + \delta)] =$$
$$\pi_p + RT[n_p C_p - 4\delta] \tag{18}$$

Combining equations (17) and (18), we obtain:

$$\pi_{obs.} = \pi_p + RT \frac{n_p^2 C_p^2}{4C_s + n_p C_p} \cong \pi_p + RT \frac{n_p^2 C_p^2}{4C_s} \tag{19}$$

It should be pointed out that the $n_p^2 C_p^2/(4 C_s + n_p C_p)$ term is the first term of a power series, and since it is small ($\leqq 0.0001$), higher powers of it may be neglected. The approximation involved in equation (19) produces an error of 0.10% or less in π_p, for $C_s \geqq 0.10$ molar.

The analogous equation for sodium sulfate (unibivalent salt) is:

$$\pi_{obs.} = \pi_p + RT \frac{2n_p^2 C_p^2 C_s + n_p^3 C_p^3}{24C_s + 8n_p C_p C_s + n_p^2 C_p^2} \cong \pi_p + RT \frac{n_p^2 C_p^2}{12C_s} \tag{20}$$

Equations (19) and (20) refer to either a positively or a negatively charged polymeric ion.

It should be borne in mind that these derivations apply strictly only at infinite dilution.

The quantities[31] n_p and C_p depend on the molecular weight of the polymer

---

[31] The charge of polymeric ions, n_p, has been discussed by G. S. Adair, *Trans. Faraday Soc.*, **33**, 1106 (1927), and by G. S. Adair and M. E. Adair, *Trans. Faraday Soc.*, **31**, 130 (1935); **36**, 23 (1940). See also Chapter 6 of H. A. Abramson, L. S. Moyer, and M. H. Gorin, *Electrophoresis of Proteins and the Chemistry of Cell Surfaces*, Reinhold, New York, 1942.

which is unknown. Since, however, $n_p \equiv M_2 n_g$ and $C_p = 10^3 \cdot C_2/M_2$, where n_g is the effective charge per gram of polymer, we can write:

$$n_p C_p = n_g C_2 \cdot 10^3 \qquad (21)$$

Provisional values of n_g may be obtained if the amount of acid or base bound at various pH values, the ionization constants, and the total ionizable equivalent of the ionizing group or groups are known. These

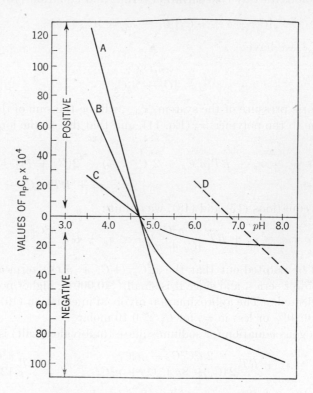

Fig. 2.—The dependence of $n_p C_p$ on pH.
Solid line, gelatin; broken line, hemoglobin. A, 25 g. per liter; B, 15 g. per liter; C, 5.00 g. per liter; D, 25 g. per liter.

values for lime-process gelatin (isoelectric point = 4.8) are shown in figure 2. Also shown in the figure are similar values for hemoglobin calculated by Adair[24] from data of Hastings, Van Slyke et al.[32]

[32] A. B. Hastings, D. D. Van Slyke, J. M. Neill, M. Heidelberger, and C. R. Harington, J. Biol. Chem., 60, 89 (1924).

EXAMPLE: A gelatin solution, of pH 5.3, containing 25 g. of lime-process gelatin per liter and 0.4 mole of sodium chloride per liter, shows an observed osmotic pressure of 10.00 cm. of solution ($d_s = 1.014$ g. per ml.) after correcting for capillarity at 25° C.   The observed pressure in atmospheres is $10.0 \times 1.014/1033 = 9.80 \times 10^{-3}$.   From figure 2, we obtain $n_p C_p = -60 \times 10^{-4}$; and $n_p^2 C_p^2 = 3.6 \times 10^{-5}$; π is in units of atm. and C_p and C_s ($= 0.4$) are in units of moles per liter. $R = 0.08207$ liter atm. per degree.

$$\therefore \pi_i = RT \left(\frac{n_p^2 C_p^2}{4 C_s} \right) = 24.45 \cdot \frac{3.6 \times 10^{-5}}{1.6} = 0.55 \times 10^{-3} \text{ atm.}$$

$$\pi_p = \pi_{\text{obs.}} - \pi_i = (9.80 - 0.55) \times 10^{-3} = 9.25 \times 10^{-3} \text{ atm.}$$

Adair[28, 33] and Adair and Robinson[34] have studied the ion distribution in aqueous hemoglobin systems containing buffers and neutral electrolytes by the measurement of membrane potentials.   The activity of the diffusible ions in the protein solution can be calculated directly from these measurements and a knowledge of the activity of the ions of the dialyzate.   The membrane potentials were determined experimentally as a function of the protein concentration, the salt content being kept constant.   For the hemoglobin system studied,[28] a linear relation was found: $C_p = 0.11\ u$; and, taking $n_p = 8$ (negative), at a pH of 7.8, we have $n_p C_p = 0.88\ u$. $u = f(E_m)$, the membrane potential.   For crystalline serum albumin, the membrane potential–protein concentration function was found to be somewhat more complex[34]; $C_p = 0.010u + 0.050u^2$.

Adair derived the equation:

$$\pi_i = gRT \int_0^u n_p C_p du \tag{22}$$

which is thermodynamically exact, to express the ion pressure contribution as a function of the molar charge, the molar concentration of the polymer, and the membrane potential of the system. g is Bjerrum's so-called osmotic coefficient, i. e., the resultant activity coefficient, of the ions of the dialyzate; $u = E_m F/RT = (11.61/T)E_m$. E_m is the membrane potential in millivolts.   If we express π_i in centimeters of water at 0° C. (taking $g = 1$), equation (22) becomes:

$$\pi_i = 1.013u^2 = 18.35 E_m^2 \tag{23}$$

Calculated values of π_i using E_m values taken from a smooth plot of Adair's experimental data are collected in table III, column 5.

Adair also showed that, when solutions were sufficiently dilute so that

---

[33] G. S. Adair, *Proc. Roy. Soc. London*, **A108**, 627 (1925); **A126**, 16 (1929).

[34] G. S. Adair and M. E. Robinson, *Biochem. J.*, **24**, 1864 (1930).

their membrane potentials amounted to one millivolt or less, the approximation,

$$n_p C_p \cong u \sum_i C_i'' n_i^2 \tag{24}$$

where $\sum_i C_i'' n_i^2$ is twice the ionic strength of the dialyzate, becomes generally applicable. By combining equations (22) and (24), and integrating, we obtain:

$$\pi_i^* = RT \frac{n_p^2 C_p^2}{2\sum_i C_i'' n_i^2} \tag{25}$$

The asterisk is used to differentiate π_i of equation (25) from the same quantity in the more exact equation (23). The example given earlier (page 263) will illustrate the use of this equation. The $\sum_i C_i'' n_i^2$ term is defined by the relation:

$$\sum_i C_i'' n_i^2 = C_1'' n_1^2 + C_2'' n_2^2 + C_3'' n_3^2 + \dots \tag{26}$$

where C_1'', C_2'', $C_3'' \dots$ represent the ionic concentrations in the dialyzate in moles per liter; and $n_1, n_2, n_3 \dots$ are the corresponding valences. If, for example, we consider the dialyzate of the composition given in table III, we have:

Ions	C_i''	n_i	n_i^2	$C_i'' n_i^2$
K$^+$	0.100	1	1	0.100
Cl$^-$	0.100	1	1	0.100
2 Na$^+$	0.122	1	1	0.122
HPO$_4^{--}$	0.0613	2	4	0.245
K$^+$	0.0053	1	1	0.0053
H$_2$PO$_4^-$	0.0053	1	1	0.0053

$$\sum_i C_i'' n_i^2 = 0.578$$

Thus, using this solution instead of 0.4 M sodium chloride, the previous example would yield:

$$\pi_p = \pi_{\text{obs.}} \quad - RT \frac{n_p^2 C_p^2}{2\sum_i C_i'' n_i^2} =$$

$$\left(9.80 \times 10^{-3} - 24.45 \frac{3.6 \times 10^{-5}}{1.156} \right) = 9.04 \times 10^{-3} \text{ atm.} \tag{27}$$

Equation (25), which can be shown to be identical with the approximate forms of equations (19) and (20), based on ideal Donnan distribution, provides a convenient method of obtaining the ion pressure contribution without specific membrane data. These provisional values (π_i^*) compare favorably with the values obtained using potential data and equation (22); see table III, columns 5 and 6.

In the absence of specific membrane data, it would seem justifiable to calculate the ion contribution provisionally by the use of equation (25),

TABLE III

OSMOTIC PRESSURE DATA OF SHEEP HEMOGLOBIN (ADAIR)

Solutions, at 0° C., equilibrated with 0.10 M KCl; 0.0613 M Na$_2$HPO$_4$ and 0.0053 M KH$_2$PO$_4$. pH = 7.8. $\sum_i C_i'' n_i^2$ = 0.578. n_p = −8.0

C_2, g./ml.	$n_p C_p$ $\times 10^4$	E_m, mv.	cm. of water					
			πobs.	π_i	π_i^*	π_p	π_p^*	$\Delta = \pi_p - \pi_p^*$
0.0068	8.15	−0.025	2.58	0.01	0.01	2.57	2.57	0.00
0.0221	26.50	−0.080	8.40	0.12	0.13	8.28	8.27	0.01
0.0290	34.75	−0.110	11.65	0.22	0.24	11.43	11.41	0.02
0.0358	42.90	−0.135	15.15	0.33	0.36	14.82	14.79	0.03
0.0500	60.00	−0.190	20.30	0.66	0.72	19.84	19.78	0.06
0.0800	95.90	−0.305	28.20	1.71	1.81	26.49	26.39	0.10
0.1000	120.0	−0.385	39.00	2.71	2.87	36.29	36.13	0.16
0.1200	144.0	−0.460	54.50	3.88	4.07	50.62	50.43	0.19
0.1550	186.0	−0.600	91.20	6.60	6.90	84.60	84.30	0.30
0.2000	240.0	−0.770	150.00	10.88	11.50	139.12	138.50	0.62

provided this contribution does not exceed 5% of the total pressure observed.   This should be assured, in general, by:

(1) Keeping n_p small but finite.   The solution and the dialyzate should be buffered at about one pH unit from the isoelectric point.

(2) Keeping C_p small.   The polymer concentration of the solution should probably never exceed 25 or 30 grams per liter.

(3) Providing an adequate concentration of neutral and/or buffer salts. In general, it is advisable to have the ionic strength of the solution and of the dialyzate about 0.3 or 0.4 mole per liter.

III.   OSMOMETERS

1.   Membranes

The successful measurement of osmotic pressure depends largely upon the performance of the membrane used in the determination.   The ideal membrane, aside from the obviously necessary condition of semipermeability, should have as high a rate of solvent transference as possible.   The material should be such that it can be obtained or produced with a uniform and reproducible fine structure, and can be used with a wide variety of solvents.

The best membrane material for general use is regenerated cellulose which has never been dried. Commercial cellophane may be obtained[35] in this form, and is probably the most satisfactory material. The material must not be waterproofed and should have a wet thickness (in water) of about 0.004 inch, which corresponds to du Pont's No. 600. This material has been employed successfully for the osmometry of solutes of average molecular weight as low as 6000.[36]   Membranes of regenerated cellulose, produced from cellulose nitrate foils by a process of denitration, can also be used. They are, generally speaking, more permeable than those made of commercial cellophane, although their permeability depends entirely upon the manner of preparation of the original nitrate sheet.[37]   Material of satisfactory permeability may be prepared following the method described by Montonna and Jilk:[38]

"The bottom of a large wide-mouthed bottle was cut off and placed mouth downward in a large tripod.   A desiccator plate was then placed in the bottle.   On this plate was placed a large flat dish, which was filled to a depth of about $3/8$ in. with pure, clean mercury.   A round iron ring, 14 cm. in diameter, constructed from a piece of $1/2$-in. band iron, was then floated on the surface of the mercury.   A piece of wall board into which numerous small holes had been drilled was placed over the top of the bottle.   A small fan, driven by an electric motor at between 200 and 400 r.p.m., was placed about 3 in. above this board so that a small current of air would flow continuously through the bottle and thus materially shorten the time necessary for the evaporation of the solvent.   In preparing a membrane, 45 cc. of Merck's c.p. collodion was run onto the surface of the mercury, inside the iron ring, from a pipet held so that the tip was not over $1/2$ in. above the surface of the mercury. The perforated cover was then put in place and the fan started.   After 2 hrs., the fan was stopped and the membrane removed from the mercury by lifting the iron ring.   The iron ring, to which the membrane was now firmly fastened, was then submerged in distilled water until the membrane broke loose from the ring.   The last traces of the solvent were removed by the water.   The ridge on the periphery of the membrane was next cut off, and the membrane denitrated.   The denitrating solution consisted of 900 cc. of 5 N ammonium hydroxide solution saturated with hydrogen sulfide and 100 cc. of ethyl alcohol.   The membrane, after being submerged in a solution of this composition for 2 hr., was carefully washed with water, carbon disulfide, and acetone, in the order named, and after drying in air for several minutes was ready for use."

---

[35] *E. I. du Pont de Nemours & Co.*, Wilmington, Del.; also *Sylvania Industrial Corporation*, Fredericksburg, Va.; unwrinkled material which has never been dried must be specified.

[36] P. J. Flory, *J. Am. Chem. Soc.*, **65**, 372 (1943).

[37] W. J. Elford, *J. Path. Bact.*, **34**, 505 (1931); *Trans. Faraday Soc.*, **33**, 1094 (1937); cf. also J. D. Ferry, *Chem. Revs.*, **18**, 373 (1936).

[38] R. E. Montonna and L. T. Jilk, *J. Phys. Chem.*, **45**, 1376 (1941).

Both types of regenerated cellulose must be kept wet at all times. If stored for prolonged period, membranes should be immersed in dilute aqueous formaldehyde solution to prevent bacterial action.

They can be conditioned for use with organic liquids by displacing the water with acetone, and displacing the acetone with any desired liquid. It is better to displace the water gradually by washing the foils for 5 or 10 minutes each, in successive aqueous acetone solutions of 25, 50, 75, and 100% acetone. This method does not materially alter the permeability of the membrane.[39]

Occasionally, a membrane for no apparent reason produces very erratic results. This behavior manifests itself in an irregularly shaped equilibrium or time–pressure curve, or in inconsistently low final or equilibrium pressures. The possibility of solute permeation should not be overlooked and should be checked by an analysis of the dialyzate at the conclusion of a determination. The residue obtained by the evaporation of a portion of the dialyzate should not exceed 0.02 mg. per ml. The same membrane can be used for a number of determinations, although it is probably desirable to replace it when measurements are begun on a new system.

2. Apparatus and Their Use

A. STATIC-ELEVATION CELL

In the static-elevation osmometer, the osmotic pressure of the solution is balanced by the liquid column or head developed by the influx of solvent into the solution. This cell has the advantage of being relatively compact, inexpensive to construct, and simple to assemble and operate. Its principal disadvantage is the length of time required for the attainment of equilibrium, which is determined by the time required for sufficient solvent to flow into the cell. It is usually possible, however, to complete a determination in 5 to 8 hours, depending on the system under consideration. This type of osmometer has been used successfully with a number of systems.[9, 33, 40–47]

Modified Schulz Osmometer.—A modification of the Schulz osmom-

[39] J. W. McBain and S. S. Kistler, *J. Phys. Chem.*, **35**, 131 (1931).

[40] H. N. Morse and J. C. W. Frazer, *Am. Chem. J.*, **34**, 28 (1905); **38**, 212 (1907).

[41] J. C. W. Frazer *et al.*, *J. Am. Chem. Soc.*, **38**, 1907 (1916); **43**, 2497 (1921); **45**, 1710 (1923).

[42] N. F. Burk and D. M. Greenberg, *J. Biol. Chem.*, **87**, 197 (1930).

[43] H. B. Oakley, *Trans. Faraday Soc.*, **31**, 136 (1935).

[44] A. Keys and H. Taylor, *J. Biol. Chem.*, **109**, 47 (1935).

[45] J. Bourdillon, *J. Biol. Chem.*, **127**, 617 (1939).

[46] G. V. Schulz, *Z. physik. Chem.*, **A176**, 317 (1936); **B52**, 1 (1942).

[47] G. Gee, *Trans. Faraday Soc.*, **36**, 1162 (1940); **36**, 1171 (1940).

eter[46] shown in figure 3 is recommended for the measurement of pressures from 30 mm. to 300 mm. of solution. This instrument consists of a heavy wall (4 mm.) glass cell, A, and a capillary tube, B, of approximately 0.7-mm. bore, on which may be etched or engraved a 300-mm. scale. The metal portions of the osmometer, consist of a clamp base, C, a clamp yoke, D, and their fasteners, G. They should be fabricated of a noncorrosive material, such as nickel. Nickel-plated brass and 18-8 stainless steel have been found

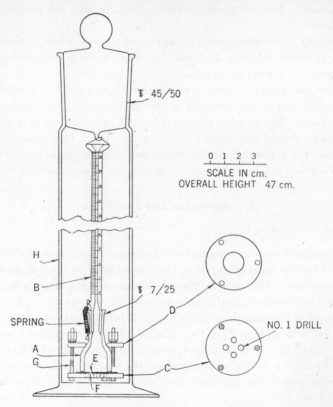

Fig. 3.—Modified Schulz osmometer.

unsatisfactory for aqueous sodium chloride solutions, buffered with phosphate or with phthalate (pH 6.0). For many organic liquids, brass is quite satisfactory. The base should be perforated as shown, using a No. 1 drill. The membrane of the assembled cell is shown at E, resting on a support of fine-texture, ash-free (quantitative) filter paper, F. This paper can be used in as many thicknesses as is necessary to insure a flat and nondeformable support for the membrane.

The technique of assembling the osmometer is very simple. A disk of ash-free filter paper is cut out or punched out to cover the floor of the clamp base.   A hardened, circular, steel punch will be found very useful for cutting both filter paper and membrane disks to the proper size.   The base and the paper are wetted with solvent by immersion in a shallow dish.   A similar disk of membrane is laid on the immersed paper, care being taken not to allow it to become dry.   A clean glass cell, A, is placed on the membrane and the yoke put into position and tightened.   It is not necessary to tighten the yoke excessively—a little more than fingertight is sufficient.

The interior parts of the assembly are rinsed several times with the solution and then completely filled with it.   The solution is then sucked into capillary tube B until it is about half full, and the tube is inserted into the glass joint of the assembly, the excess being allowed to flow out *around* the unseated joint and *not* through the upper end of the capillary tube.   The final position of the capillary meniscus can be adjusted to any level by allowing the solution to flow out through the glass joint in the manner described above.   (If necessary, the liquid can be forced out with a little pressure.)   After the desired level is obtained, the joint is firmly seated and secured with a suitable fastener, such as a light spring.   It is important that no air be trapped inside the osmometer.   Trapping of air can easily be avoided after a little experience with the operation.   The use of ordinary pliers whose jaws were covered with sections of rubber tubing is very helpful in seating and unseating the joint.

The outer surfaces of the assembly are thoroughly washed with solvent to remove all traces of solution (solute) and lowered into the cylinder H containing about 100 ml. of solvent.   This operation will trap some air in the holes of the base which can easily be removed by raising and lowering the inner assembly more or less rapidly while holding the cylinder at an angle of $45°$.   The level of the external liquid or dialyzate is adjusted to a suitable height and the cylinder closed.   In order to obtain a vertical position of the capillary, it is recommended that the inner parts of the osmometer be suspended from the top of the cylinder, as shown in figure 4, or by any other suitable method.   The osmometer should be thermostated to within $\pm 0.1°$ C. of the desired temperature, until no further change in the liquid head is observed.   This head can be read directly by means of a scale on the capillary as shown, or by any suitable device for measuring height, such as a cathetometer.

In regard to the initial positions of the inner and outer liquid levels, it is better to adjust these to about the same height, which should be at or near the bottom of the capillary when dealing with organic solvents.   With aqueous solutions, however, it is essential to begin a determination with the inner meniscus or level near the capillary top, and the outer level at the capillary bottom.   If the approximate magnitude of the final column heights can be estimated, it will be of advantage to adjust the initial level to within a few centimeters of the final value. This, of course, presupposes prior knowledge of the system from previous determinations or from other sources. The error in concentration caused by the influx (or efflux) of solvent during a determination amounts to about 1% in the most extreme case, and is usually considerably less than this.

With this instrument, the equilibrium height observed must be corrected by subtracting the capillary rise of the solution. If a sufficient quantity of solution is available, the most satisfactory procedure will be to measure this rise directly, using the capillary involved without its cell attached. If the quantity of solution is restricted, the surface tension of the solution should be measured, using any of several micromethods[48] and the correction to be applied calculated according to the relation:

$$h_\sigma = 2\sigma \cos \vartheta / r d_s g \tag{28}$$

where h_σ = the capillary rise in cm., σ = the surface tension in dynes per cm., ϑ = the angle of contact between the solution and the capillary wall, which should be zero, r = the radius of the capillary in cm., and g = the acceleration due to gravity = 980 cm. per sec.[2] Cos ϑ will be unity for all liquids which wet glass. The radius of the capillary can be determined by the application of equation (28) using a liquid of known surface tension and contact angle (= 0). The density of the solution (d_s) can be determined by a pycnometer or Westphal balance.[49]

The equilibrium pressures of duplicate determinations usually agree to within a few millimeters or better. Erratic results or poor agreement are usually due to a faulty membrane. It is recommended that check runs be made when work is begun on any new system in order to ascertain the behavior of the membrane and to gage the precision of the results.

A word should be added here about the cleaning of glass. In order to evaluate the capillary correction properly, glass parts must be absolutely clean, especially when dealing with aqueous solutions. The following treatment seems to be adequate:

Immerse all glass parts in a hot 1:1 by volume concentrated nitric–sulfuric acid bath for several hours or overnight. Rinse and immerse in a warm 20% caustic solution for 5 min., rinse, and repeat the acid treatment for 5 min. longer. Rinse thoroughly with distilled water, and avoid all contacts with organic solvents (except when the parts are to be used with these liquids) for drying.

Bourdillon Osmometer.—The osmometer described by Bourdillon[45] is better suited to the measurement of low osmotic pressures, especially

---

[48] L. T. Hallett, *Ind. Eng. Chem., Anal. Ed.*, **14**, 970 (1942).
[49] L. T. Hallett, *Ind. Eng. Chem., Anal. Ed.*, **14**, 968 (1942), for micromethods.

aqueous solutions for which it was originally designed, than is the Schulz instrument. Its design, shown in figure 4, and operation are such as to avoid the necessity of any correction for density and capillarity of the solution. This feature is very important for measurements of low pressure

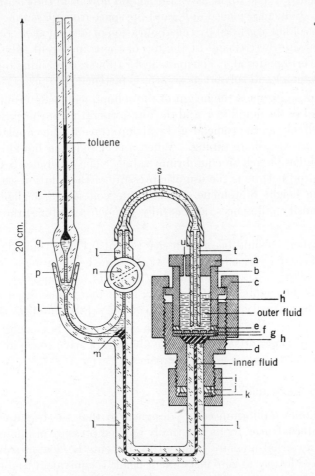

Fig. 4.—The Bourdillon osmometer.[45]

where the magnitude of these corrections may be equal to or greater than the pressure itself. The Bourdillon instrument is designed particularly as a microinstrument, since it uses only 0.2 ml. of solution, at concentrations as low as 0.025 millimole per liter.

The method of assembly and operation may be briefly described as follows: The membrane, *g*, with its perforated supporting plate, *f*, is firmly clamped into place between pieces b and d, using a soft rubber gasket, e, and screw ring c.   With the cell assembly in an inverted position, the chamber, h, is rinsed and filled with solution.   The glass piece, l, is slid into the neck of d until the solution is at position m.   The packing gland assembly, ijk, is then fastened.   The whole assembly should now be in the position shown in figure 4.   Solvent is placed in h', and the space from glass tube t through stopcock n to joint p is filled by the application of suction at p.   No bubble should exist anywhere except at the top of the transparent tube, s, where its presence is immaterial.   The manometer tube, r, containing toluene (for aqueous systems) and solvent as shown, is fastened into place.

With stopcock n open, the height of the column will be determined solely by the height of the liquid in h' and the forces operating at the various interfaces, principally at the toluene–glass–air interface in the capillary, which is 0.2-mm. precision-bore tubing.   When n is closed, the liquid column in r will rise and approach an equilibrium value.   The difference between the final and initial heights is the osmotic pressure of the solution expressed in units of the height of toluene.   This value contains a negligible error, owing to density differences, and is fully compensated for surface tension forces.

The chamber q should be of such size (about 0.1 ml.) that the toluene–water interface remains substantially at the same level during a determination.   The solution–solvent interface at m should be at approximately the same level as the membrane (*cf.* Fig. 4).   These requirements will minimize the error due to density differences between the solution and the solvent.

This instrument was designed for aqueous systems but could easily be adapted to all types of systems.   It is more expensive to build than the Schulz instrument, and is not so compact.

B.   DYNAMIC-EQUILIBRIUM CELL

The dynamic-equilibrium cell is designed so that the osmotic pressure can be counterbalanced by an externally applied pressure of known magnitude.   The external pressure required to prevent the flow of solvent into or out of the solution (at zero instrument head) is equivalent to the osmotic pressure of the solution.   This method is especially advantageous where a rapid determination of the pressure is essential.   Unfortunately, this cell is expensive to construct and requires considerable experience to fill and operate successfully.

The dynamic-equilibrium osmometer was first used by Berkeley and Hartley[50] in their studies of sucrose solutions.   Their results were in excel-

──────────
[50] Earl of Berkeley and E. G. J. Hartley, *Trans. Roy. Soc. London*, **A206,** 486 (1906).

lent agreement with the previous work of Morse and Frazer,[40] who used a static instrument. Sørensen[26] used this method for the determination of the molecular weight of egg albumin.

An improved form of this type of cell, which employed large, flat membranes and required a minimum of solution, was introduced by van Campen[51] in 1931. Several modifications of this cell have been used,[36, 38, 52, 53] but perhaps the best form is the vertical capillary modification of Fuoss and

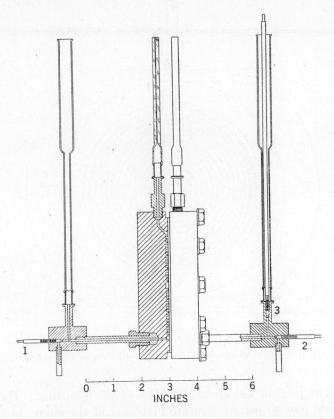

Fig. 5.—Fuoss-Mead dynamic-equilibrium osmometer (complete).[54]

Mead.[54] Their description follows: "The cell [shown in Figs. 5 and 6] consisted of two stainless steel plates, clamped together over the membrane

[51] P. van Campen, *Rec. trav. chim.*, **50**, 915 (1931).
[52] R. O. Herzog and H. M. Spurlin, *Z. physik. Chem.*, **Bodenstein Festband**, 239 (1931).
[53] C. G. Boissonnas and K. H. Meyer, *Helv. Chim. Acta*, 20, 783 (1937).
[54] R. M. Fuoss and D. J. Mead, *J. Phys. Chem.*, 47, 59 (1943).

by means of machine screws at the edge.   The face of each disk had a $^1/_2$-in. flat ring, 5 in. outside diameter; inside this ring was a set of concentric cuts 2 mm. wide and 2 mm. deep, connected by a vertical cut which ran from inlet to outlet of each half-cell.   The faces of the half-cells were ground flat. The membrane was simultaneously the gasket; since the membranes we used were fairly soft, only moderate pressure (a little more than fingertight)

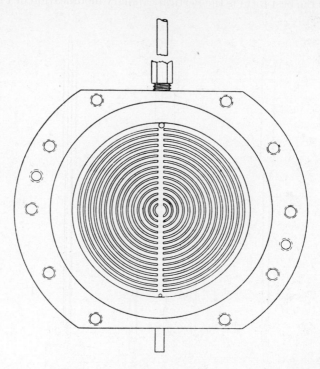

Fig. 6.—Fuoss-Mead osmometer (internal view of half-cell).[54]

was needed to prevent leakage at the edges of the 5-in. ring.   The plates carried guide pins to permit accurate matching of the circles in the two half-cells.   A thermometer was inserted in a boring in one of the plates. After assembly, the osmometer was packed into a basswood box, using cotton waste as a heat insulator. . . .   To the plates were attached filling tubes and measuring apparatus, which projected outside the insulating jacket. . . . After placing a membrane between the two half-cells and tightening the peripheral screws, the two capillaries and the two valve blocks with the filling tubes are locked into place.   Lead washers make these joints liquidtight.   The glass-to-metal seal is at a fernico bushing, which is soft-soldered to the brass valve block.   With valves *1* and *2* closed and valve stem *3* removed, solution is poured into the left-hand tube, while solvent is simultaneously poured into the right one, so that the liquid level rises at about the same rate on both sides of the membrane.   Filling from the bottom of the half-cells in this way eliminates air bubbles.   Then with both sides filled nearly to the top, valves *1* and *2* are opened wide for a few seconds to sweep any entrapped air out of the valve blocks.   (The borings in the valve blocks and connector tubes are $^1/_{16}$-in. in diameter.)   Valve stem *3* is inserted, and valve *3* is closed. . . .   Valve *1* is then opened to drop the meniscus in the solution stand pipe to its desired position.   The height of the meniscus in the left capillary against a vertical steel scale mounted behind both capillaries is read through a telescope, furnished with cross hairs and level.   Then the rate of motion of the meniscus in the right capillary is followed, as will be described later.   The telescope is mounted on a post, where a rack and pinion provide vertical motion.   To raise the meniscus in the right capillary, valve *3* is opened; to drop it, valve *2* is opened.   In the left capillary, the meniscus is lowered by opening valve *1* and raised simply by pouring solution into the open tube.   The essential feature of this design is that the meniscus in the left capillary remains stationary, while the motion of the right meniscus is being followed. . . .   Suppose Δh is the expected difference in pressure.   We set the meniscus in the moving side at a height somewhat greater than $(\Delta h + x)$, where x is of the order of 1 or 2 cm. and corresponds to a whole millimeter mark on the pressure scale. As the meniscus drops through this mark, a stop watch is started, establishing a zero in time.   Readings of the moving meniscus are made at 30-sec. intervals for 6 to 8 min., by which time the meniscus is moving quite slowly. Then a second run is made, starting the meniscus below $(\Delta h - x)$ and starting the timing at a convenient cross mark near $(\Delta h - x)$.   A plot of the meniscus height against time is now a concave-down exponential.   We then plot the half-sum of the rising and falling curves against time; since the curves were started at approximately the same distance from equilibrium, but from opposite sides, the half-sum differs from their mutual asymptote only by small second-order terms.   In practice, the half-sum is constant within several minutes, and determines the desired asymptote directly. . . . The rapidity of convergency of the half-sum depends, of course, on the foreknowledge of Δh; one preliminary run based on merely the order of magnitude of the molecular weight will give a value of sufficient accuracy to use in subsequent runs."

If the vertical capillaries are of equal bore, no surface tension correction is required in the Fuoss-Mead osmometer, *provided* the surface tensions of the solvent and of the solution are not greatly different.

General References

Abramson, H. A., Moyer, L. S., and Gorin, M. H., *Electrophoresis of Proteins and the Chemistry of Cell Surfaces*. Reinhold, New York, 1942.

Bolam, T. R., *The Donnan Equilibria*. Bell, London, 1932. See also *Kolloid-Beihefte*, **39**, 139 (1934).

Ferry, J. D., "Ultrafilter Membranes and Ultrafiltration," *Chem. Revs.*, **18**, 373 (1936).

Lewis, G. N., and Randall, M., *Thermodynamics*. McGraw-Hill, New York, 1923.

CHAPTER IX

Determination of
DIFFUSIVITY

A. L. GEDDES, *Eastman Kodak Company*

I. INTRODUCTION

If a soluble substance is placed in a liquid so that it occupies initially only a part of the available space, it will disperse and, in course of time, will distribute itself uniformly throughout the entire volume at its disposal. This characteristic migratory phenomenon, which acts independently of gravitational and other forces—except the impulses received by collision with neighboring molecules—is called free diffusion. The earliest theoretical treatment of diffusion phenomena is credited to Fick,[1] who, in 1855, introduced his well-known "law" relating diffusion current to concentration gradient. Until recently the development of diffusion theory and methods has not been commensurate with their importance, however, partly because of the failure of Fick's law in the general case and partly because of the difficulties involved in the development of experimental methods of investigation. Fick's equation for linear diffusion, which has been generally used for the computation of diffusion coefficients, has the form:

$$Q = -D \frac{\partial c}{\partial x}$$

---

[1] A. Fick, *Ann. Physik*, **94**, 59 (1855).

where D is the diffusion coefficient for a given substance and is defined as the amount of material which passes a plane of unit area in unit time when under unit concentration gradient. A single linear relation between diffusion current and concentration gradient is thus implied. This is not actually the case, however, as many experimental results have shown, for example, those of Gerlach[2] and Ullmann.[3] Fick's equation may be derived from osmotic theory and thus would be expected to hold only in the limiting condition at infinite dilution. Since D is not a constant for a given material but may be a function of concentration and concentration gradient, it loses its theoretical significance to some extent. In spite of the limitations imposed upon D, however, measurements of diffusivity have a number of important applications, some of which are listed below:

(*1*) Estimation of the size of particles in solution from values of D at infinite dilution, obtained by an extrapolation of experimentally determined values at different concentrations.

(*2*) Qualitative estimation of the charge on, or ionization of, colloidal particles by observing the effect of added electrolyte on the rate of diffusion.

(*3*) Determination of the frictional coefficient of particles moving through a liquid medium. The coefficient thus obtained may be used to determine the molecular weight of the particles from their movement in a gravitational field, or their charge from their movement in an electrical field.

(*4*) Study of solution rates.

(*5*) Study of heterogeneous reaction rates.

(*6*) Development of electrolytic solution theory.

(*7*) Estimation of the porosity of gels.

II. EXPERIMENTAL METHODS AND CALCULATIONS

1. Diffusion in Liquids

Experimental methods for determining diffusivities are essentially of two types, one using free diffusion and the other, diffusion through membranes. Free diffusion methods involve the principle that diffusion takes place through a continuous medium, the diffusing material at the beginning of the experiment being distributed homogeneously on one side of a sharp initial interface. In general, absolute measurements of diffusivity are obtained by the study of free diffusion processes. Membrane diffusion embodies the principle that the material diffuses through a liquid immobilized in the interspaces of a porous diaphragm (usually of fritted glass). In

---

[2] B. Gerlach, *Ann. Physik*, **10**, 437 (1931).
[3] E. Ullmann, *Z. Physik*, **41**, 301 (1927).

this method values are determined relative to those of a material of known diffusivity under certain defined conditions. This method has distinct advantages in that difficulties due to boundary formation, vibrations, and convection, which are of major concern in free diffusion methods, are largely eliminated. The time required for a sufficient transfer of material is short compared with that for free diffusion, with the exception of micro-diffusion methods, because the diffusion may be allowed to take place under a high concentration gradient. Since diffusion is a slow process, this is of considerable importance, particularly in the case of unstable materials such as biological specimens or substances which undergo a change in the state of aggregation on aging. Analytical methods are simplified because the type of apparatus used can be so designed that sufficient quantities of material are available for analysis. The chief limitation of the method, aside from its dependence on a material of known diffusivity for calibration, is that it cannot be used for the investigation of materials, such as basic dyes, which are strongly adsorbed to glass. The fritted glass disk has a large and highly active adsorptive surface. It is also unsuitable for the investigation of polydisperse systems. Also, the method does not lend itself to continuous methods of observation except in special cases where arrangement can be made for analysis *in situ*, such as by electrical conductance.

A. FRITTED GLASS DIAPHRAGM METHOD

The fritted disk method, introduced by Northrup and Anson[4] in 1929, constituted a new development in diffusion technique which has contributed much to the study of diffusion processes. Improvements in the design of the original apparatus have been made from time to time by various workers.[5, 6] The particular apparatus shown in figure 1, which illustrates a method of stirring the liquids, was designed by Mouquin and Cathcart.[7] The disk, through which diffusion may proceed, serves as a permeable membrane between two bodies of liquid, the media on either side being homogeneous in concentration. Convection is essentially absent within the disk but is utilized in the liquids outside to maintain homogeneity. Fritted Pyrex glass disks of suitable dimensions and porosity may be obtained from the *Corning Glass Works*, Corning, N. Y. The disks are supplied sealed in glass tubes which may be shaped to the desired form, as in figure 1. The thickness of the disks should be about 2 millimeters, greater thicknesses not being recommended because the rate of

[4] J. H. Northrup and M. L. Anson, *J. Gen. Physiol.*, **12**, 543 (1929).

[5] J. W. McBain and C. R. Dawson, *Proc. Roy. Soc. London*, **A148**, 32 (1935).

[6] G. S. Hartley and D. F. Runnicles, *Proc. Roy. Soc. London*, **A168**, 401 (1938).

[7] H. Mouquin and W. H. Cathcart, *J. Am. Chem. Soc.*, **57**, 1791 (1935).

transfer of material is thus slowed down unnecessarily. The Corning medium- and fine-grade disks have an approximate maximum pore diameter of 12 and 4 microns, respectively, as measured by the pressure of displacement by air of liquid in the capillary spaces.[8] The pore sizes of Jena disks, grades G3 and G4, as measured in a comparable manner, were found to be 30 and 9 microns, respectively. If disks of very fine porosity are used, experimental difficulties in cleaning and filling the cells are introduced. The use of disks of coarser grade than Corning medium does not hasten the rate of diffusion appreciably, and it does introduce the possibility of bulk streaming of the liquid through the disks when the more dense solution is in the upper compartment. Streaming may be prevented by careful adjustment of the disk to a horizontal position; but this is not possible, of course, when the cell is rotated. Dawson[9] has reported a test for streaming which should be carried out on all disks. It involves the measurement of the diffusivity of a material when the disk is placed and held at an angle of 30° from the horizontal position. If streaming does not occur, the results will compare with those obtained when the cell is in the normal upright position throughout the experiment. The scanty evidence at present appears to argue against the possibility of an appreciable surface transport along the walls of the pores.

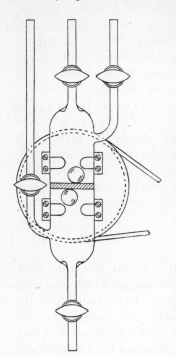

Fig. 1.—Porous-diaphragm diffusion cell.[7]

The apparatus constitutes a closed system which may be completely filled with the liquids. The presence of air is thus prevented, which is an advantage if the materials present are subject to oxidation by atmospheric oxygen. Also, when the compartments are completely filled with liquid, turbulent flow does not occur when the cell is rotated. The interpretation of results is simplified if the volumes on either side of the disk are equal. The cell may be of any desired shape or capacity since the diffusion coefficient does not depend upon the dimensions of the apparatus. Two stopcocks are placed at each end so that either solution can be removed or replenished

[8] F. E. Bartell and H. J. Osterhof, *J. Phys. Chem.*, **32**, 1553 (1928).
[9] C. R. Dawson, *J. Am. Chem. Soc.*, **55**, 432 (1933).

as desired. Stirring is accomplished by means of small glass spheres which move through the liquids when the cell is rotated by the belt and pulley mechanism. Each pair of spheres is so chosen that the density of one is slightly less and the other slightly greater than that of the medium. Indentations are made at the entrance of the tubes to prevent the spheres from stopping the flow of liquid when removing samples. The rotational speed of the cell should be about one revolution per minute. Stirring may not be necessary because gravitational flow will tend to maintain a homogeneous concentration. Mouquin and Cathcart[7] suggest, however, that secondary diffusion layers may build up on the surface of the membrane and introduce a variable factor. Stirring is therefore recommended, particularly in the case of dilute solutions in which the density differences are small. Whether stirring is employed or not, it is important that the same technique be used throughout the calibration and the experiments.

For proper temperature control, the apparatus should be set up in a water bath. The liquids to be used should be at the same temperature as the bath before the apparatus is filled, and it is recommended that one of the upper stopcocks be left open until temperature equilibrium is well established. Care should be taken that all air bubbles are previously removed from the pores of the disk by forcing through a quantity of the deaerated liquid. A preliminary diffusion time of one to four hours, depending upon the diffusivity of the material, should be allowed for a steady state to be set up in the diaphragm. The liquids should then be replaced with a fresh supply, usually of pure solvent on one side of the disk. The time required for a sufficient transfer of material will be one day or more, depending upon the diffusivity.

The calculation of diffusion coefficients from the experimental measurements of time and concentration is based on Fick's modified definition:[10]

$$dq = -D\,A\,\frac{\partial c}{\partial x}\,dt \qquad (1)$$

where dq is the amount of material diffusing through a cross section of area A and of thickness ∂x in time dt, and ∂c is the change in concentration over the distance ∂x. Let the concentration of the upper solution be c_u and that of the lower be c_l, the initial concentrations being c_u^0 and c_l^0, respectively. The concentration gradient across the disk at time t, if h is the effective thickness, will therefore be $(c_u^0 - 2c_l + c_l^0)/h$, provided that the volumes of liquid on either side are equal and that there is a linear concentration

---

[10] The minus sign indicates that diffusion takes place in the direction of decreasing concentration.

gradient.   Since q is equal to cV, where V is the volume, equation (1) may be written in the form:

$$\frac{dc}{(c_u^0 - 2c_l^0 + c_l^0)} = k\,D\,dt \qquad (2)$$

in which k is a constant.   Integration of this equation between the limits c_l^0 and c_l gives:

$$K\,Dt = \log\,(c_u^0 - c_l^0) - \log\,(c_u^0 - 2c_l + c_l^0) \qquad (3)$$

in which K, the cell constant, is equal to $2A/2.303\,hV$.

If the initial concentration in the lower cell is zero, equation (3) may be written:

$$K\,Dt = \log\,c_u^0 - \log\,(c_u^0 - 2c_l) \qquad (4)$$

and if the two liquid volumes are not equal, equation (4) has the form:

$$K'\,Dt = \log\,c_u^0 - \log\,[c_u^0 - (1 + V_l/V_u)c_l] \qquad (5)$$

in which V_u and V_l are the upper and lower volumes, respectively.   The cell constant in equation (5) is $A(V_u + V_l)/2.303\,hV_uV_l$.

In the interpretation of results, two fundamental assumptions must be considered.   First, the assumption was made that the concentrations of the solutions change so slowly that a steady state is set up in the diaphragm and a linear concentration gradient exists at all times.   This is not necessarily the case.   Barnes[11] has shown, however, in a rigorous solution of the problem, that this assumption does not lead to an appreciable error in the determination of D, provided that the ratio of the free volume of the membrane to the total volume of liquid is less than 0.1.   Under ordinary experimental conditions this ratio is 0.02 or less.

The second assumption, which is implicit in Fick's law, is that D is a constant for a given material.   Actually, D is a function of concentration and the value of D as determined by equation (4) is a so-called "integral" value over the range of concentrations from one surface of the disk to the other.   Furthermore, the integral diffusion coefficient does not refer strictly to a given concentration range since this range becomes smaller as diffusion proceeds.   In other words, the concentration gradient across the disk changes with time even though the average concentration remains constant.   This factor may be investigated by measuring the diffusion coefficient at various times, under conditions in which the average concentration is held constant.   The true or "differential" diffusion coefficient, which refers to a definite concentration, may be calculated to a high order of approximation from the integral values obtained by equation (4).   Cole

[11] C. Barnes, *Physics*, **5**, 4 (1934).

and Gordon[12] have shown that, provided the condition in the diaphragm is at all times that for a steady state, the following relation holds:

$$D(c_u - c_l) = \int_{c_l}^{c_u} D_d \, dc \tag{6}$$

where D is the measured, and D_d the differential, diffusion coefficient. Under these conditions, if the diffusion coefficient is a linear function of concentration, D can be equal to D_d only at the concentration $(c_u + c_l)/2$. In other words, the diffusion coefficient as calculated by equation (4) is the true differential value for the mean concentration of the two media.   In many cases it has been found that D is unfortunately not a linear function of concentration.   Gordon *et al.*[13] have shown, however, that in such cases this relation is still a good approximation provided that the concentration difference, $c_u - c_l$, is not large.   It is understood, of course, that the volumes on either side of the disk are equal, so that the average concentration in the disk does not change throughout the experiment.

In the derivation of equation (4), account was not taken of the mass flow of solvent, or of more dilute solution, opposite to the direction of the diffusion current.   This reverse flow must take place because of the vacancy left by the material diffusing out.   If we assume that an element of volume dV is occupied by an amount of material dq and that, under linear concentration gradient, c is the average concentration in the disk, then equation (1) may be written:

$$dq/dt = -D \, \partial c/\partial x - c \, dV/dt \tag{7}$$

and since $\qquad\qquad dV/dt = (dV/dq)\,(dq/dt) \tag{8}$

therefore $\qquad\quad dq/dt = -\dfrac{D}{1 + c\,dV/dq}\,(\partial c/\partial x) \tag{9}$

If q is expressed in moles, $dV/dq = \nu$ is the partial molal volume in liters and

$$D_{corr.} = D_{obs.}\,(1 + c\nu) \tag{10}$$

Although the correction factor is small for dilute solutions, it may be of appreciable magnitude when concentrated solutions are involved.

The cell constant of the apparatus, which depends entirely upon its dimensions, should be determined with a material of known diffusivity under conditions reproducible in the cell.   The diffusivity of the material is measured by a free diffusion process.   This procedure is not entirely justifiable since the diffusion coefficient, as previously pointed out, is not a constant but may be a function of concentration, and the conditions in the free diffusion process may not be reproducible in the fritted disk.   The question

[12] A. F. W. Cole and A. R. Gordon, *J. Phys. Chem.*, **40**, 733 (1936).

[13] W. A. James, E. A. Hollingshead, and A. R. Gordon, *J. Chem. Phys.*, **7**, 89 (1939).

of calibration has been discussed extensively by McBain and Dawson,[14] Hartley and Runnicles,[15] Mehl and Schmidt,[16] and Gordon *et al.*[13]   Aqueous 0.1 *N* solution of potassium chloride is generally used for the calibration, but agreement has not been reached as to the absolute value of the diffusivity.   It is suggested[17] that tentatively a value of 1.58 cm.[2] per day be chosen for 0.1 *N* potassium chloride diffusing at 25° C. into water for such time that the final concentration of the original solution is near 0.07 *N*. The analyses of potassium chloride may be conveniently carried out by titration with standard silver nitrate, using dichlorofluorescein as an adsorption indicator.

The temperature variation of diffusion has customarily been expressed by a linear relation of the form:

$$D_2/D_1 = 1 + \alpha(T_2 - T_1) \tag{11}$$

in which α is the temperature coefficient per degree.   This is a fair approximation in some cases, over a limited temperature range, and is useful for the computation of approximate values of D at other temperatures.   Öholm[18] has found that the value of α for strong electrolytes is approximately 0.025 over the temperature range of 5° to 18° C.   Taylor[19] has shown, on the basis of Eyring's[20] theory of absolute reaction rates, that an exponential variation of the coefficient of diffusion with temperature is to be expected. If this is the case, a linear relation should exist between the logarithm of the diffusion coefficient and the reciprocal of the absolute temperature.   Available data to test this relation are very limited but the carefully determined values of Cohen and Bruins[21] on the diffusion of tetrabromomethane in tetrachloroethane show an excellent linear plot in the temperature range of 0° to 55° C.

B.   FREE DIFFUSION METHODS

General.—Absolute measurements of diffusivity in liquids are obtained by the study of free diffusion processes.   It is well to point out, however, that a completely satisfactory laboratory method for obtaining absolute measurements of diffusivity has not yet been developed.   Many experimental methods have been devised, the chief differences being in the

[14] J. W. McBain and C. R. Dawson, *Proc. Roy. Soc. London*, **A148**, 32 (1935).

[15] G. S. Hartley and D. F. Runnicles, *Proc. Roy. Soc. London*, **A168**, 401 (1938).

[16] J. W. Mehl and G. L. A. Schmidt, *Univ. Calif. Pub. Physiol.*, 8, 165 (1937).

[17] A. R. Gordon, *N. Y. Acad. Sci.*, Symposium on "The Diffusion of Electrolytes and Macromolecules in Solution," Oct., 1944.

[18] L. W. Öholm, *Z. physik. Chem.*, **50**, 309 (1905).

[19] H. S. Taylor, *J. Chem. Phys.*, **6**, 331 (1938).

[20] R. H. Ewell and H. Eyring, *J. Chem. Phys.*, **5**, 726 (1937).

[21] E. Cohen and H. R. Bruins, *Z. physik. Chem.*, **103**, 404 (1922).

methods of analysis and of boundary formation. Since free diffusion is a relatively slow process, most methods are time-consuming unless some microtechnique for making the measurements is adopted. In the case of substances of high molecular weight, several weeks may be required for sufficient transfer of material along the diffusion column. Reliable measurements by methods of this type are not to be expected when it is remembered that vibrations and temperature fluctuations cause disturbances in the media. The development of several optical micro- or semi-micromethods of measurement, however, has somewhat overcome the necessity of long-term experiments since a complete series of measurements can be made over a region near the original boundary.

In the method of Fürth and Zuber,[22] which is applicable to colorless materials, changes in concentration are measured under the microscope by observing the progress of the limiting angle of total reflection along a diffusion column. In another method of Fürth,[23] concentrations of colored solutions in the cell are determined with a microscope and adjustable-slit ocular-micrometer, by a comparison of color with reference solutions of known concentration. The optical method developed by Svedberg[24] for the investigation of the spreading boundary in the ultracentrifuge has been adapted by Tiselius and Gross[25] to free diffusion measurements. In this, the diffusion column is photographed with light which is absorbed by the diffusing material but not by the solvent. Concentration changes along the column are then computed from the density gradient of the plate by means of a microphotometer. The method has a particular advantage in that two or more components diffusing together may be measured, provided that their absorption bands lie in different parts of the spectrum.

Several optical refractometric methods, dating back to Wiener,[26] have been devised. Most of these are based on the measurement of refractive-index gradient along the diffusion column. Wiener's method consists of passing light from a uniform source through the diffusion medium in front of which is placed a slit at an angle of 45°, the deviation of the rays produced by the concentration gradient in the cell being recorded on a screen or photographic plate. A distribution curve in terms of refractive-index gradient and distance along the cell is obtained, from which diffusion coefficients may be calculated. A cylindrical lens placed between the plate and the cell transforms the curve to rectangular coordinates.

In the steady-state method of Clack,[27] a thin pencil of light is passed

[22] R. Fürth and R. Zuber, Z. Physik, **91**, 609 (1934).

[23] R. Fürth, Kolloid-Z., **41**, 300 (1927).

[24] T. Svedberg, Kolloid-Z., **36**, 53 (1925).

[25] A. Tiselius and D. Gross, Kolloid-Z., **66**, 11 (1934).

[26] O. Wiener, Ann. Phys., [N. F.] **49**, 105 (1893).

[27] B. W. Clack, Proc. Phys. Soc. London, **36**, 313 (1924).

through the diffusion column at measured positions. The angle of deviation of the ray, brought about by the refractive-index gradient in the column, is measured with an eyepiece. An equation is derived for the calculation of the diffusion coefficient.

A refractometric method has been reported by Littlewood[28] which does not appear to have received the recognition it deserves, since it is unique in that concentrations rather than gradients are measured along the diffusion column. Monochromatic light from a fine wire, incident at a small angle with the surface of the liquid, is refracted downward, emitted through the side wall of the cell, and reflected by a mirror back over the same optical path. The deviation of the ray is a function of the concentration of the solution at the point at which the light leaves the liquid. The path of the light and the position at the cell wall are observed with a traveling telescope and a scale to indicate the angle of the mirror. Concentrations are determined by calibration of the system with solutions of known concentration.

The refractometric-scale method devised by Lamm[29] has received wide popularity and has, to an extent, rendered many other methods obsolete, especially for the investigation of macromolecules. A transparent scale is photographed through the diffusion column, a distorted image of the scale being produced by the refractive-index gradient of the solution near the boundary. Diffusion coefficients are computed from scale line displacements which are measured with a microcomparator.

Conductometric methods have been used to some extent in the special case of the diffusion of electrolytes. These usually depend upon measurements of the conductance between several pairs of electrodes placed along the diffusion column. Recently, a precision method was reported by Harned and French[30] in which the difference in conductance across the top and bottom of the cell is measured at suitable time intervals. The theory of the cell is developed, and the method for the calculation of absolute values of D from the conductance measurements and the depth of the cell is described.

Cells.—The formation of a sharp initial boundary between the two liquids is of primary importance. A type of cell based on the sliding principle of the Tiselius[31] electrophoresis cell and developed by Neurath[32, 33]

[28] T. H. Littlewood, *Proc. Phys. Soc. London*, **34,** 71 (1922).

[29] O. Lamm, *Nova Acta Regiae Soc. Sci. Upsaliensis*, [4] **10,** No. 6 (1937).

[30] H. S. Harned and D. M. French, *N. Y. Acad. Sci.*, Symposium on "The Diffusion of Electrolytes and Macromolecules in Solution," Oct., 1944.

[31] A. Tiselius, *Trans. Faraday Soc.*, **33,** 524 (1937).

[32] H. Neurath, *Science*, **93,** 431 (1941).

[33] H. Neurath, *Chem. Revs.*, **30,** 367 (1942).

for the refractometric-scale method serves admirably for many free diffusion methods. A sketch is shown in figure 2. Neurath[33] has advised that this cell may be obtained from Mr. H. S. Bush, instrument maker of the Department of Chemistry, *Cornell University.* The cell chamber as used by Neurath has the following dimensions: height, 5 cm.; width, 0.5 cm.;

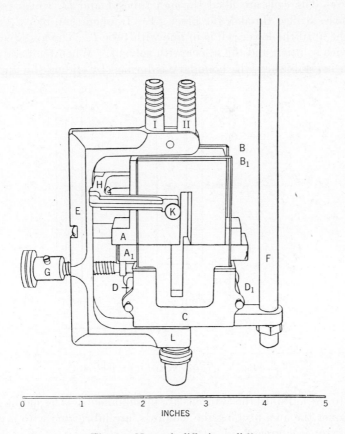

Fig. 2.—Neurath diffusion cell.[32]

and thickness in the direction of the optic axis, 1.7 cm. For the colorimetric method, this thickness should not be over approximately 0.5 cm.

The two parts of the cell proper, A and A_1, may be constructed from stainless steel or other suitable material. Two optically flat glass plates, B and B_1, form the front and back of the cells. The interfaces between the cells and between the glass plates and the cells are highly polished to prevent leakage and to reduce friction. The upper block, A, is fixed firmly to clamp E. The two blocks are pressed together at the sliding surfaces

by a spring and screw at L. The U-shaped clamp, H, which should preferably be attached to rod F,[33] carries screw K, which can be tightened to
exert pressure on the windows. The windows are held in place against cell
A_1 by means of clamp C. The upper part of the apparatus, together with
clamp E, acts as an independent unit which can be moved laterally by
screw G. The cells are filled through tubes I and II, which connect to
small holes drilled through the block, A. In operation, block A is slid to
the right until the lower cell is in line with tube I. The lower cell is then
filled with solution and the upper with solvent. When temperature equilibrium is established, the boundary is formed by sliding the upper block

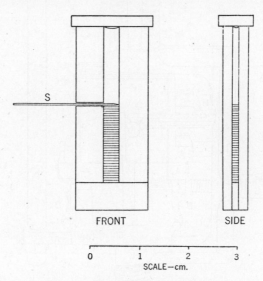

FRONT   SIDE

0   1   2   3
SCALE—cm.

Fig. 3.—Fürth-Nistler diffusion cell.

slowly to the left until the two cells are in alignment. The sliding surfaces,
except over the area forming the windows, are lubricated with a very thin
layer of stopcock grease.

Constructional difficulties limit the usefulness of the Neurath cell, in the
particular form shown in figure 2, if a very thin column of liquid is desired.
In this case, the Fürth microcell in the simplified form devised by Nistler[34]
may be used. A diagram of the cell is shown in figure 3. Two polished
glass plates are cemented to a U-shaped spacer of suitable material such as
glass, metal, or plastic. The spacer has an accurately ground slot at
one side in which the thin draw slide, S, may be fitted, as shown in the
diagram. The slide separates the solution in the lower part from the

[34] A. Nistler, *Kolloidchem. Beihefte*, **28**, 296 (1929).

solvent in the upper part of the cell. The boundary is formed by careful withdrawal of the slide from the liquid compartment. To minimize boundary disturbances the slide should be moved at a slow and uniform rate by means of a mechanical device. The slide is ground to a narrow edge at the end for the purpose of decreasing the turbulence which results from the fall of liquid from the upper part of the cell into the space left by

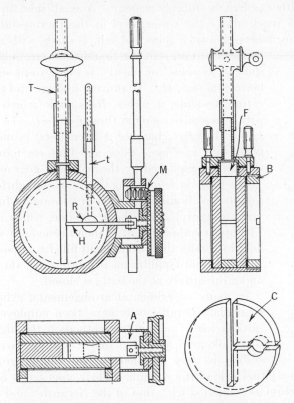

Fig. 4.—Lamm draw-slide diffusion cell.[36]

the slide. A layer of grease in the slot prevents leakage and reduces friction between the sliding surfaces.

Improvements in the Fürth–Nestler draw-slide type of cell have been reported by Lamm[35, 36] in the course of his refractometric investigations. A sketch of the cell in three positions, embodying the latest improvements (Fig. 4), illustrates the mechanical details of construction. The spacer, C, of stainless steel, ebonite, or other suitable material, which is placed be-

[35] O. Lamm, *Nova Acta Regiae Soc. Sci. Upsaliensis*, [4] **10**, No. 6, 20 (1937).
[36] O. Lamm, *Arkiv Kemi, Mineral. Geol.*, **B17**, No. 13 (1943).

tween two circular, optical-glass windows, is shaped to form a cell 6 cm. high and 4 mm. wide. The thickness used by Lamm was 1 cm., but for the Fürth optical method this should be reduced to 5 mm. or less. The windows are held tightly in position against the cell blocks by means of a threaded brass ring and clamp, B. The glass is cushioned against the clamp with rubber gaskets. All surfaces where leakage might occur are covered with vaseline or suitable cement. A small inlet tube, T, is constructed to reach above the water level in the thermostat. The cover construction, where this tube joins the cell, is made with a tight fitting flange, F, to prevent the liquid from creeping. The draw-slide, S, of metal or plastic, is made to fit snugly into the horizontal slot, H. To prevent leakage and to aid in lubricating the slide, a recess, R, is made which can be filled with heavy oil or mercury through tube t. To further insure against leakage, chamber A is enclosed in metal walls and filled with vaseline. Slow and uniform movement of the slide is accomplished by the reducing gear mechanism, M.

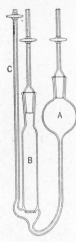

Fig. 5.—
Lamm cylin-
drical diffusion
cell.[38]

The procedure for filling the cell is straightforward. The solution, or liquid, is poured in (through a funnel if necessary) to a level above the draw slide, which is then closed. The upper compartment is then flushed out with the other liquid (usually the solvent) and filled to a point on tube T. After thermal equilibrium is established, the tap, which is under the surface of the bath, is closed.

In many experimental arrangements, cylindrical rather than plane-parallel cells have been employed. They are suitable for refractometric methods if the highest accuracy is not required, provided that a suitably arranged optical system is used and narrow slit diaphragms are placed vertically on either side of the column. Their chief merit lies in the ease of construction as compared with that of the Neurath[32] and Lamm[36] cells. A good discussion of the errors inherent in the use of cylindrical cells has been given by Lamm.[37] This type of cell is not suitable for the optical method of Fürth.[23]

One of the best designs in cylindrical cells is reported by Lamm[38] and is illustrated in figure 5. An important feature in the design is the use of a fritted glass disk at the bottom of the diffusion chamber, B, for leveling the liquid. In practice cell B is about half-filled with the lighter liquid, or solvent, and the stopcock closed. The heavier liquid, or solution, is placed in A and is separated from contact with the liquid in B by an air lock under

[37] O. Lamm, *Arkiv Kemi, Mineral. Geol.*, **B16**, No. 17 (1943).
[38] O. Lamm, *Kolloid-Z.*, **98**, 45 (1942).

the glass disk. After thermal equilibrium is established, the stopcock in tube C is opened for sufficient time to allow the air under the disk to escape. Leveling then begins, and a slight uniform pressure of air is applied to A until the boundary reaches the desired height in tube B. Good boundaries are formed by this method, since turbulent flow is prevented by the fritted disk.

Micro Colorimetric Method.—The method described here, which is based on the principle of color comparison introduced by Fürth,[23] involves a reasonably simple technique. It embodies certain improvements in the way of a different optical system as proposed by Nistler.[34] The method

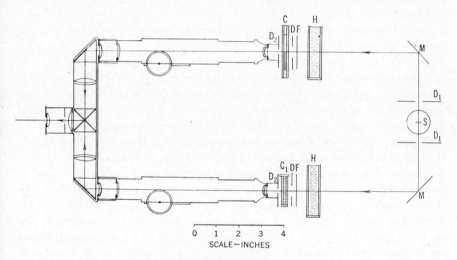

Fig. 6.—Fürth-Nistler diffusion apparatus.

has a special application in the study of dye solutions for which the porous diaphragm method is sometimes unsuitable. The necessary readings may be made in a region closely surrounding the initial boundary, and a complete set of measurements may be obtained in a period of less than an hour. In general, errors introduced by vibrations and temperature fluctuations over this short period of time are negligible.

The experimental method consists essentially in measuring the progress of a given concentration of material along the diffusion column by matching the color with that of a known solution. The concentration of the comparison solution must, of course, be less than that of the original solution in the cell. A schematic diagram of the optical system is shown in figure 6. By means of mirrors, M, and diaphragms, D and D_1, light from a tungsten lamp, S, is split into two parallel beams, one of which passes through the diffusion cell, C, in the region of the boundary and the other through the comparison cell, C_1. The intensity of the light should be adjustable, and balanced in the two beams. If greater intensity is desired, condenser lenses may be placed near the source to focus a slightly converging beam on each cell. In this case it is advisable to use a ribbon filament lamp. Two microscopes having a magnification of about $60\times$ are placed in the beams in a manner such that one is focused on the center of the boundary and the other at a comparable point in the comparison cell. The microscopes are connected by a $1\times$ comparison eyepiece which brings the fields of view of the two microscopes into one ocular. The comparison of color is greatly facilitated by the close proximity of the two fields, which are divided symmetrically along a narrow line. Distances along the column are measured by means of an adjustable-slit ocular-micrometer. If this equipment is not available, a fixed slit may be used in the ocular and the microscope may be mounted on a micrometer slide. An instrument of this type, calibrated to read to 0.01 mm., is supplied by the *Gaertner Scientific Corporation*. With this device, readings may be made over a wider range than with the ocular-micrometer. The use of a slit to narrow the field facilitates the matching of colors. A shield and diaphragm, D_2, is placed over each objective to keep out extraneous light. Heat-absorbing filters, H, such as cells filled with copper chloride solution, are placed in the beams. To improve the color contrast, suitable light filters, F, may be placed in front of the cells. Several cells for comparison solutions should be available in order that measurements can be made at different concentrations during a single experiment. A bank of six or eight cells for the purpose are mounted close together on a rack so that they can be slid conveniently in or out of the field of view of the microscope, in turn. The comparison cells should, of course, be of the same thickness as the diffusion cell.

The procedure is as follows: The comparison cells are filled with solutions at different known dilutions of the solution to be studied. The diffusion cell is then filled and the initial position of the boundary determined by focusing the microscope on the upper level of the liquid in the lower compartment. The interface is then formed in the manner previously described. Starting with the most dilute solution, the comparison cells are brought in turn to a fixed position in front of the microscope and the color compared with that at a measured position in the diffusion column. This procedure is continued until sufficient data are obtained. The progress of fixed concentrations of the solution along the column, in space and time, is thus determined.

The apparent spreading of the boundary, as viewed through the microscope, when the depth of liquid is greater than the depth of focus of the objective, introduces a possible source of error. Fürth and Nistler used cells of only 1.0 mm. thickness. Sheppard and coworkers[39] have obtained satisfactory results, however, with cells up to 5.0 mm. in thickness. Calculations indicate that, in the case of a $4\times$ objective focused on the center of a 4-mm boundary, the apparent spreading will be approximately 0.02 mm. The error thus introduced will be negligible at distances relatively far from the initial boundary where the concentration gradient is small, but a systematic error may be introduced in the region near the boundary. However, on the basis of the Boltzmann assumption (page 294), corrections may be made on readings taken in this region, provided that the initial position of the boundary is determined accurately.

The computation of the diffusion coefficient, D, from measurements of concentration, distance, and time in a one-dimensional free diffusion process, is based fundamentally on Fick's definition:

$$Q = -D\, \partial c/\partial x \tag{12}$$

where Q represents the diffusion current and $\partial c/\partial x$, the concentration gradient. If we substitute this value of Q into the equation of continuity (derived from hydrodynamics):

$$\partial Q/\partial x = -\partial c/\partial t \tag{13}$$

we obtain the relation:

$$\partial c/\partial t = \partial(D\, \partial c/\partial x)/\partial x \tag{14}$$

which is the more common form of the diffusion law. The treatment of this equation depends upon the status of D. If D is a function of concentration and concentration gradient, the equation contains two unknown functions, D and c, of two independent variables, x and t, and consequently cannot be solved without further assumptions. On the assumption that D is constant, which is a close approximation for dilute solutions, equation (14) is readily solved by the use of Fourier's integral.[40] The general solution of the equation so obtained for a diffusion column of infinite length is:

$$c = A + B\, \Psi\left(\frac{x}{\sqrt{4\,Dt}}\right) \tag{15}$$

where $\Psi(x/\sqrt{4\,Dt})$ is the Gauss probability integral and A and B are constants. Under the particular boundary conditions in the experimental method of Fürth described above, the equation has the following form when solved for D:

$$D = \frac{x^2}{4t}\left[\frac{1}{\Psi^*(1 - 2c/c_0)}\right]^2 \tag{16}$$

[39] G. P. Happ, W. Vanselow, and S. E. Sheppard, *unpublished work at Eastman Kodak Company*.

[40] J. W. Williams and L. C. Cady, *Chem. Revs.*, **14**, 171 (1934).

where c_0 is the original concentration of the solution and Ψ^* is the inverse function of the probability integral. When $(1 - 2c/c_0)$ is known from experimental conditions, values of $\Psi^*(1 - 2c/c_0)$ can be obtained directly from the probability integral tables.

If D is a function of c only, it may be determined from equation (14) by introducing the fundamental assumption of Boltzmann,[41] *viz.*, that the migration of the particles follows such a law, that $x/\sqrt{t}$ is a constant for a given concentration. The linearity of the relation x *vs.* $\sqrt{t}$ has in fact been verified experimentally in a number of cases. On this assumption then, $c = f(x/\sqrt{t})$, and if we let $\lambda = x/\sqrt{t}$ equation (14) may be converted to the form:

$$- \frac{\lambda dc}{2d\lambda} = \frac{d}{d\lambda}\left(D\,\frac{dc}{d\lambda}\right) \tag{17}$$

which is again an equation containing the two unknown functions, D and c, but of only one independent variable, λ. Integrating and solving for D, we have:

$$D = - \frac{\lambda cd\lambda}{2dc}\left[1 + \frac{1}{\lambda c}\int_\lambda^\infty cd\lambda\right] \tag{18}$$

The right-hand side of equation (18) may be evaluated by graphical methods from the experimental curves of c *vs.* λ. If the Boltzmann assumption holds, it is necessary and sufficient to assume that $D = f(c)$ only, and equation (18) is, in this case, a rigorous solution of equation (14). Furthermore, the concentration at the initial boundary (where $x = 0$) must remain constant throughout the experiment and an extrapolation of the linear plot x *vs.* $\sqrt{t}$ must pass through the origin. The linearity of x *vs.* $\sqrt{t}$ should therefore be tested in all cases. A typical curve of λ *vs.* c is shown in figure 7 to illustrate the necessary steps in the calculations. For any concentration, c, the slope is determined at the corresponding point, P, and the area $\int_\lambda^\infty cd\lambda$ is determined with a planimeter. Errors introduced by graphical methods may be reduced by using a large-scale diagram. The effect of errors inherent in the graphical integration with a limit of ∞ are largely minimized by the fact that c approaches zero rapidly with increase of λ, and at the lower concentrations where the error is the largest the term in square brackets approaches unity. Eversole and coworkers[42] have written equation (18) in the form:

$$D = \frac{\lambda}{4(-\ln c/c_0)^{1/2}} \cdot \frac{d\lambda}{d(-\ln c/c_0)^{1/2}}\left[1 + \frac{1}{\lambda c}\int_\lambda^\infty cd\lambda\right]$$

[41] L. Boltzmann, *Ann. Physik*, **53**, 959 (1894).

[42] W. G. Eversole, J. D. Peterson, and H. M. Kindsvater, *J. Phys. Chem.*, **45**, 1398 (1941).

in which c_0 is the concentration at the point where $x = 0$. The determination of the slope of the curve λ *vs.* $(-\ln c/c_0)^{1/2}$ at various concentrations is greatly facilitated by the fact that the curve is very nearly linear.

If the Boltzmann assumption does not hold, and D is a function of concentration and concentration gradient, the calculation of D is rather complicated, for practical purposes. In this case D may be obtained from the relation:

$$D = -\frac{Q}{\partial c/\partial x} = \frac{\int_x^\infty (\partial c/\partial t)\,dx}{\partial c/\partial x} \tag{19}$$

by a plot of Q *vs.* $\partial c/\partial x$. Ullmann[43] has used this method of calculation in his investigation of concentrated solutions of ferric saccharate. However, in such cases the interpretation of D, as a coefficient, is obscure. Linearity

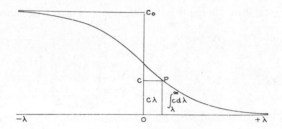

Fig. 7.—Typical plot of c vs. λ.

of x *vs.* $\sqrt{t}$ is to be expected in a normal linear diffusion process, governed only by osmotic pressure. Nonlinearity may be indicative of some other irreversible process accompanying that of diffusion.

Refractometric Scale Method.—Refractometric methods have received extensive popularity in their application to the study of proteins and other macromolecules. Although not as suitable as the fritted-disk method for the study of very dilute solutions, or as suitable as the light-absorption method for the study of mixtures, they have certain attractive advantages. Measurements can be made without interrupting the diffusion process, the absorption of light is not necessary, and the use of colored solutions is not required. In the study of macromolecules greater accuracy is obtainable with these methods, especially that of Lamm,[29] than with other methods. Refractometric methods are based on the phenomenon of the curvature of light in media where concentration gradients exist. The refractive index, rather than the concentration, is measured as a function of the distance along the diffusion column. In the Schlieren methods, the refractive-index

[43] E. Ullmann, *Z. Physik*, **41**, 300 (1927).

gradient is photographed directly in a form of a probability curve. The scale method of Lamm is more tedious, but is capable of greater accuracy.

A sketch of the type of apparatus used in the refractometric-scale method by Lamm[44] and Neurath[45] is shown in figure 8 (not drawn to scale). It should be mounted on a solid base, free from mechanical vibrations. *M* is a uniform light source, such as a mercury arc, mounted in a suitable housing. The light is selected in a region where the solution does not absorb, and is made essentially monochromatic by the use of filters, *G*. A heat filter, *F*, of water or copper sulfate solution, is placed between the lamp and the thermostat. The uniform transparent scale, *S*, ruled on glass, is mounted on an optical bench for ease in the adjustment of its position. Suitable scales, 5 cm. in length and graduated in divisions of 0.02 cm., may be obtained from the *Gaertner Scientific Corporation*.

The diffusion cell, *C* (previously described), is supported in the thermostat with rods of low thermal conductance. To aid in manipulation, the

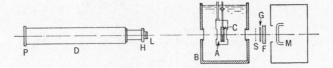

Fig. 8.—Lamm refractometric-scale diffusion apparatus.

cell should be mounted on a vertical sliding device which extends above the level of the water bath. A crosspiece with scale and movable rider is also desirable for adjustment of the ratio of distances to the scale and the camera lens.

The camera, *D*, equipped with slit, and slide holder, *P*, allows for eight or ten exposures on one plate. The plates should be of optical glass and of high speed and contrast, such as Eastman spectroscopic GV. The shutter and diaphragm, *H*, allows for apertures from f:50 to f:100. With very low apertures diffraction effects interfere, while with high apertures there is insufficient definition or resolving power. The camera lens, *L*, of about 100 cm. focal length, is corrected for aberrations. If monochromatic light is used chromatic corrections are, of course, not essential.

B is an insulated water thermostat cushioned on layers of rubber and Celotex as a further precaution against vibrations. Two circular optical glass windows are recessed in the walls perpendicular to the optic axis while a third window on the side allows for observations of the cell. The stirring motor is mounted on a separate support, apart from the thermostat.

44 O. Lamm, *Nova Acta Regiae Soc. Sci. Upsaliensis*, [4] **10**, No. 6 (1937).
45 H. Neurath, *Chem. Revs.*, **30**, 357 (1942).

Turbulence is prevented by placing a hollow metal cylinder around the shaft.

Since temperature control is of the utmost importance for successful measurements, the thermoregulator should have sufficient sensitivity to keep the temperature within about 0.002° C. Lamm[36] has found it more satisfactory to enclose the cell in a metal casing, A, to decrease temperature fluctuations, rather than to use a highly refined temperature-regulating device. An illustration of the casing, containing a draw-slide cell, is given by Lamm.[36] The cell is supported on an ebonite base, while the leads pass through holes in the top. Optical glass windows are provided for passage of the light beam. The casing may be made watertight and so serve as an air chamber, but temperature equilibrium is established more rapidly if it is filled with water. The supporting rods leading from the bath are made of material having low thermal conductance.

In practice, the cell is carefully cleaned, filled with the liquids, and lowered into the bath to a point such that the boundary coincides approximately with the optic axis of the system. After thermal equilibrium is established, the boundary is formed by slow, even motion of the sliding mechanism. Initial time is usually recorded at the beginning of the formation of the boundary, although the choice is somewhat arbitrary. The effective initial time will probably be shortly before this, due to slight disturbances when the boundary is formed. Errors thus introduced will become less the longer the time of diffusion. The camera is focused on the scale and exposures are taken from time to time, depending upon the rate of the diffusion process. For reference purposes it is recommended that two exposures be taken with the cell filled with solvent, one before and one after the experiment. The exposure time should be sufficient (about five seconds) to allow for the equalization of temporary refractive-index gradients in the thermostat liquid. Measurements are discontinued when concentration changes begin to occur at the extreme ends of the column. Scale-line displacement is observed when the light passes through a region of varying refractive index in the cell. The magnitude of the scale-line displacement, and the position of the displaced line with reference to an arbitrarily chosen point, are read with a microcomparator to about 1 μ (micron).

The theory of the curvature of light in a region of varying refractive index was applied by Wiener[26] to the diffusion problem and later reviewed and extended by Lamm.[29] The principle of the method is illustrated by the course of the light paths in figure 9 (not drawn to scale). If a uniform medium (solvent) is contained in the cell, a ray of light from the point, p, is refracted in a linear manner and is imaged on the plate at point p_1. If a gradient in refractive index exists, however, the light is curved in the direction of increasing refractive index and is brought to focus at point p_2. In the development of the theory it is assumed that horizontal layers in the cell are maintained at constant refractive index by gravitational effects. It follows from the theory, to a close approximation, that:

$$p_1 - p_2 = Z = Gb\delta \tag{20}$$

or in a more rigorous treatment that:

$$Z = Gl(\omega_2 - \omega_1) \tag{21}$$

where Z is the scale-line displacement, G is the magnification factor (equal to i/l), b is the optical distance from the scale to the center of the cell, l is the optical distance from the scale to the nearest principle plane of the lens,

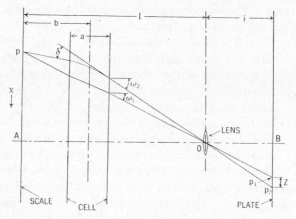

Fig. 9.—Light paths in the refractometric-scale method.

δ is the angle of deviation of the curved pencil of light, and ω_1 and ω_2 are the exit angles of the undeviated and deviated rays. The optical distance is defined as the summation of the geometric distances, each being divided by the refractive index of the corresponding medium traversed by the light. From the theory of light curvature, it is shown that δ is proportional to the refractive-index gradient, dn/dx, at the point where the light traverses the cell, *i. e.*:

$$\delta = a \, dn/dx \tag{22}$$

Combining equation (22) with either (20) or (21) it follows that:

$$Z = Gab \frac{dn}{dx} \tag{23}$$

A means of calculating dn/dx from experimental values of Z is therefore available.

Approximations and assumptions made in the derivation of equation (23) have been discussed by Bridgman and Williams[46] in a review of optical methods. In the derivation it is assumed that the arguments of the angles of inclination of the deviated light pencils with the optic axis are sufficiently small to be substituted for their tangents. Lamm has shown that, for the optical system described, with a diffusion column 6 cm. in height, the maximum error in the substitution will be 0.03%. The assumption is also made that values of n and dn/dx are constant over the portion of the cell traversed by the light ray. This condition is more nearly fulfilled the smaller the angles involved, the smaller the aperture of the lens, and the shorter the distances a and b. The error inherent in the assumption is small under suitably arranged experimental conditions, but may be appreciable when very high concentration gradients are involved. Lamm has pointed out that clear and sharp definition of the image of the scale lines may be used as a convenient criterion for satisfactory experimental conditions and the fulfillment of theoretical requirements.

In order to determine the distance, x, along the diffusion column, coordinate with the positions of the displaced scale lines, z, the values of z must be multiplied by the proportionality factor:

$$F = \frac{l - b}{lG} \tag{24}$$

The experimental results are plotted as z vs. Z or as x vs. dn/dx diagrams, which take the form of probability curves. Further, if the concentration, c, is a linear function of n, curves of x vs. dc/dx may be constructed. For many practical calculations the z–Z diagrams are sufficient and are more convenient to use. The base line is determined by interpolation from several points at the ends of the curve, where changes in concentration have not occurred.

The calculation of the diffusion coefficient, D, is based on Wiener's[26] solution of Fick's law:

$$\frac{\partial n}{\partial x} = \frac{n_1 - n_0}{2 \sqrt{\pi D t}} \cdot e^{-x^2/4Dt} \tag{25}$$

where n_0 and n_1 are the refractive indices of the solvent and solution, respectively. The equation is adequate if n is a linear function of c, if D is a constant, and if the experimental curves have the properties of ideal distribution curves. Fortunately, the assumption of the linearity of n vs. c is justifiable in most cases. If the relation n vs. c is not linear but is known, the concentration function may be determined by suitable integration of the curves. The diffusion coefficient can then be computed from Fick's

---

[46] W. B. Bridgman and J. W. Williams, *Ann. N. Y. Acad. Sci.*, **43**, 195 (1942).

law, in the form given in equation (16). The boundary is located at the point where $c = c_0/2$, or at the position of the maximum ordinate $(dc/dx)_m$.

Several methods for the calculation of D from equation (25) are possible. A typical ideal distribution curve (z–Z diagram) is given in figure 10 to illustrate the meaning of the various symbols involved.

(1) *Maximum ordinate method.* D is related to the point of inflection of the curve by the equation:

$$D = \frac{x_i^2}{2t}\left(\frac{l - b}{lG}\right)^2 \tag{26}$$

The point of inflection is located from the maximum ordinate by the relation: $H_i = H_m/\sqrt{e}$.

(2) *Maximum ordinate–area method.* If x is taken as zero it follows that:

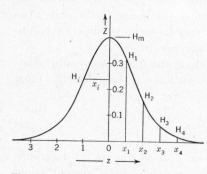

Fig. 10.—Ideal scale-line displacement distribution curve.

$$D = \frac{(n_1 - n_0)^2}{4\,\pi t\,H_m^2}\left(\frac{l - b}{lG}\right)^2 \tag{27}$$

For the computation of D the area, $n_1 - n_0$, under the curve is determined by graphical integration.

(3) *Successive analyses method.* D is related to two points on the curve by the equation:

$$D = \frac{x_2^2 - x_1^2}{4t\,\ln\,(H_1/H_2)}\left(\frac{l - b}{lG}\right)^2 \tag{28}$$

In practice, the curve is divided into a series of chords at points x_1, x_2, etc., with corresponding ordinates H_1, H_2, etc. The whole curve is utilized in the calculation of D by using each pair of successive values of x and H.

(4) *Statistical method.* In this method the experimental curves, x vs. dn/dx, are treated as ideal (Gaussian) distribution curves. According to statistics the ideal curve has the form:

$$S = \frac{N\omega}{\sigma\sqrt{2\pi}} \cdot e^{-\frac{(s-\beta)^2\omega^2}{2\sigma^2}} \tag{29}$$

where S is the frequency, s is the variable and β its arithmetic mean in arbitrary units, ω is the class breadth, $N\omega$ is the total area, in absolute units, and σ is the standard deviation. By comparison of this equation with equation (25), it follows from the linear transformation $x = (s - \beta)\omega$ that:

$$D = \sigma^2/2t \tag{30}$$

According to statistics, σ is defined by $\sigma = \sqrt{\mu_2^0}$, where μ_2^0 is the second moment of the curve about the arithmetic mean, in absolute units. The procedure for determining μ_2^0 is as follows.   The x-axis is divided into evenly spaced units, of unit breadth, numbered outward from an arbitrarily chosen origin near the center.   The ordinate corresponding to a respective number, s_i, on the base line is called S_i.   From statistics the zero moment about the arbitrarily chosen origin in relative units is:

$$\mu_0' = N = \Sigma(S_i) \tag{31}$$

the first moment is:

$$\mu_1' = \beta = \Sigma(s_i S_i)/N \tag{32}$$

and the second moment is:

$$\mu_2' = \Sigma(s_i^2 S_i)/N \tag{33}$$

The second moment about the arithmetic mean in absolute units is:

$$\mu_2^0 = [\mu_2' - (\mu_1')^2]\omega^2 \tag{34}$$

the boundary, or arithmetic mean, being located at the point, $x_0 = \beta\omega$. The value of μ_2^0 can thus be determined, which leads to the computation of D.

It is often advantageous to transform the arbitrary coordinates, s and S, into normal coordinates, as a means of comparing different experimental curves in the same units, or of comparing an experimental curve with the corresponding ideal distribution curve.   This is ordinarily accomplished by the transformations:

$$\xi = \frac{(s - \beta)\omega}{\sigma} \quad \text{and} \quad \psi = \frac{\sigma S}{N\omega} \tag{35}$$

whereby time disappears as a parameter.   The ideal (Gaussian) curve, which may be plotted from mathematical tables, has the form:

$$\psi = \frac{1}{\sqrt{2\pi}} \cdot e^{-\xi^2/2} \tag{36}$$

Deviations from ideal behavior in the experimental curves become apparent by comparison with the corresponding ideal curves.

In the preceding mathematical treatment, only ideal diffusion in a monodisperse system is considered.   However, abnormalities are often encountered, and information may be derived from a study of the shape of the curves.   An excellent discussion of observed abnormalities has been given by Bevilacqua et al.[47]   One type of abnormality is indicated by symmetrical, non-Gaussian curves, the greatest deviation from the ideal curve appear-

---

[47] E. M. Bevilacqua, E. B. Bevilacqua, and M. M. Bender, N. Y. Acad. Sci., Symposium on "The Diffusion of Electrolytes and Macromolecules in Solution," Oct., 1944.

ing at the maximum ordinate.   This type of curve is indicative of a mixture of two or more components, each of which diffuses independently but ideally.   By the ordinary methods of calculation, average values of D are obtained in such cases.   Attempts to resolve a compound diffusion curve of this type into its component curves, by the method of Pearson,[45, 48] are not considered to be successful even for two components, especially if the values of D are nearly alike or the concentration of one component is low.

In the general case it is known that D is not a constant but a variable, dependent upon the concentration.   Deviations from ideal behavior on this account are indicated by assymmetry in the curves.   The maximum ordinate is displaced from the original position of the boundary and moves, with time, to the right or left, depending upon the concentration effect.

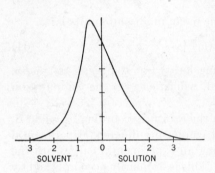

Fig. 11.—Distribution curve for a 1% solution of tobacco mosaic virus protein.[49]

In the diffusion of globular proteins and like molecules the effect is small, but it may be pronounced in the case of elongated particles such as linear polymers.   If mutual entanglement of highly elongated particles retards their motion, an increase in the rate of diffusion with dilution is to be expected. On the other hand, the osmotic-pressure distribution in the system would suggest a higher rate of diffusion in more concentrated solutions.   If D increases with concentration, the position of the maximum ordinate moves toward the solvent, whereas if D increases with dilution the reverse is true.   A typical skew curve, reported by Neurath and Saum[49] for a 1% solution of tobacco mosaic virus protein, is shown in figure 11.   The curve indicates increasing diffusivity toward higher concentrations.

The calculation of D in cases in which concentration effects are in evidence was discussed on page 294.   No solution of the Fick differential equation (14) is available excepting under the further assumption that $c = f(x/\sqrt{t})$.   With refractometric methods, the calculations are not straightforward, since refractive-index gradients rather than concentrations are measured.   However, if n is a linear function of c, or if the relation n $vs.$ c is known experimentally, the concentration function may be determined by suitable integration of the area under the curves.   Then, if the boundary is located (for example, from the relation $\int_0^{c_0} \lambda\, dc = 0$ according to Ger-

[48] K. Pearson, *Trans. Roy. Soc. London*, **A185,** 71 (1894).

[49] H. Neurath and A. M. Saum, *J. Biol. Chem.*, **126,** 438 (1938).

lach^2), D is calculated from the Fick–Boltzmann equation which, when t is constant, has the form:

$$D = -\frac{1}{2t}\frac{dx}{dc}\int_0^c x\,dc \qquad (37)$$

It is advisable to compute D from several curves obtained at different times during the diffusion process.

2. Diffusion in Gels

According to present theories, gels possess a ramifying, more or less coherent, framelike structure that can retain the liquid component and confer rigidity and elasticity upon the system as a whole. The impedance to diffusion in gels is remarkably small as compared with the very high viscosity exhibited on a macro scale. Diffusion evidently takes place in the free liquid contained in the pores and capillary spaces. The permeability of gels appears to depend upon the relative dimensions of the pores and of the diffusing particles. Small particles in dilute gels may diffuse at a rate closely approaching that in the liquid alone, whereas macromolecules may be stopped completely. Friedman and Kraemer[50] have attributed the impedance to diffusion in gels to three causes:

(1) Mechanical blocking, and reduction in the available space by the gel structure.

(2) Resistance to the motion of the particles by the close proximity of the cell walls.

(3) Increase in the viscosity of the liquid in the pores by solution of the gel substance.

The diffusivity may be influenced by a number of factors, such as the age, pH, isoelectric point, and rate and temperature of setting of the gel, and also by the presence of electrolyte. Friedman[51] has shown that even the presence of a nonelectrolyte in the gel may effect the diffusion of another nonelectrolyte. Conditions should therefore be carefully controlled if reproducible results are to be expected. The phenomenon of diffusion offers a means of studying the porosity and structure of gels.

In general, methods for the determination of diffusivity in liquids are not applicable to gel systems. Although convection is absent, other difficulties in boundary formation arise. A satisfactory method has not yet been reported for the formation of a boundary between two solutions in a continuous gel system. Most investigators have taken advantage of the

[50] L. Friedman and E. O. Kraemer, *J. Am. Chem. Soc.*, **52**, 1295 (1930).

[51] L. Friedman, *J. Am. Chem. Soc.*, **52**, 1311 (1930).

liquid–gel interface as a convenient means of obtaining the boundary. This method is not entirely satisfactory, however, since swelling may produce changes in the volume of the gel when it is in contact with the liquid, except in special cases. Kunitz[52] has reported that, in the case of an isoelectric gelatin in dilute buffer solution at the same pH, an equilibrium condition of swelling is established when the gelatin content is about 10%. A further restriction is imposed by the Boltzmann assumption if equation (18) is to be used for the calculation of D, $viz.$, that the concentration of the diffusing material at the boundary remain constant. This necessitates the use of a relatively large volume of solution in order that the drop in concentration in the homogeneous liquid phase be within the desired limits. Since convection is absent in the gel, the duration of the experiment will not affect the accuracy of the measurements appreciably unless such phenomena as cracking or mold formation occur.

Provided that a suitable system is chosen, the diffusivity may be determined by a method of the type reported by Voigtländer[53] A tube of uniform bore and 6 to 8 cm. in length, which is stoppered at one end and ground flat at the other end is used for the diffusion column. The gel is warmed and poured into the tube until a convex meniscus is formed at the top. After sufficient aging has occurred, the excess gel is cut off flush with the end of the tube. The open end of the tube is then immersed in the solution at constant temperature. If the gel does not adhere to glass, the inside of the tube should be covered with a suitable coating. Friedman has used Bakelite varnish in the case of agar gels. The solution should be stirred to maintain homogeneity and should be of sufficient volume that the drop in concentration throughout the experiment is negligible. The vessel should be covered to prevent evaporation of the solvent. Diffusion should not be allowed to proceed to the point that the material reaches the closed end of the tube. After sufficient time has elapsed, the gel is cooled and removed from the tube with a fine steel wire. It is then cut into slices at measured distances from the end and the concentration of material in each slice determined. The author has found that the error introduced in measuring x as the average distance of the two sides of the slice from the boundary, and in assuming a linear concentration gradient across the slice, is ordinarily not large. The slices should be cut as thin as is practicable near the end at which the concentration is the greatest. The method just described is applicable only to gels which have sufficient rigidity to be handled. The slicing is facilitated by the use of a cradle in which the gel is supported. The cradle has narrow vertical slots through which a fine wire may be passed, and is provided with a scale.

[52] M. Kunitz, *J. Gen. Physiol.*, **13**, 565 (1930).
[53] F. Voigtländer, *Z. physik. Chem.*, **3**, 316 (1889).

Eversole and coworkers[54, 55] have recently reported a method suitable for the nvestigation of colored materials, or colorless materials which absorb in the ultraviolet, whereby the diffusing substance is analyzed photometrically.   A diagram of the apparatus is shown in figure 12.

The cell is constructed from two plates of optically polished g'ass fastened to a U-shaped glass or rubber-covered glass spacer   The gel is introduced into the lower part of the cell and allowed to set.   The solution is then put in the upper part.   The concentration of the solution is maintained con-

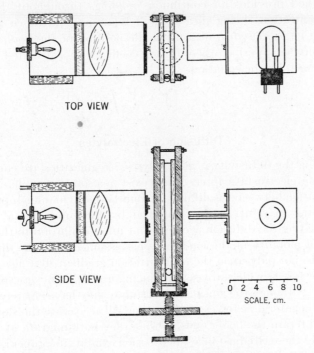

TOP VIEW

SIDE VIEW

0 2 4 6 8 10
SCALE, cm.

Fig. 12.—Eversole diffusion apparatus.[54]

stant by addition of fresh solution, while the excess is drawn off at the top by suction.   A beam of light of constant intensity and about 0.1 mm. in thickness is passed through the cell by the method illustrated in the diagram.   The relative intensity of the light is measured by means o a photoelectric cel and a vacuum-tube amplifier.   Suitable filters may be placed in the beam to increase the relative change in intensity with change in concentration of the colored material.   The photoelectric cell should be prop-

[54] W. G. Eversole and E. W. Doughty, *J. Phys. Chem.*, **41**, 663 (1937).

[55] W. G. Eversole, H. M. Kindsvater, and J. D. Peterson, *J. Phys. Chem.*, **46**, 370 (1942).

erly shielded from extraneous light. The apparatus is calibrated with known solutions so that concentrations may be interpreted in terms of scale readings on the potentiometer. For details in the construction and use of the amplifier, the reader is referred to the original articles. The cell is mounted in a holder which provides for vertical movement by means of a thumbscrew adjustment, and the position of the cell is measured with a cathetometer. The cell is set up in an air thermostat with the thumbscrew projecting through a hole in the bottom.

This method provides for continuous readings throughout the experiment, concentrations being measured in relation to distance and time. Care should be exercised in measuring the position of the boundary. In both the methods described the diffusion coefficient is calculated, as previously explained, by the equation:

$$D = -\frac{\lambda c}{2}\frac{d\lambda}{dc}\left[1 + \frac{1}{\lambda c}\int_{\lambda}^{\infty} c d\lambda\right] \tag{18}$$

3. Diffusion of Electrolytes

In studying the diffusivity of electrolytes, irregularities are encountered because of the electrostatic forces which exist in a solution of charged particles. A relation between the diffusivity and thermodynamic properties of a given material in solution is exemplified by the fundamental Nernst[56] equation relating the diffusion coefficient at infinite dilution to the osmotic pressure and mobility of the ions   Nernst assumed that the diffusion of ions depends, not only upon the concentration gradient, but also upon the electrostatic forces which are set up in maintaining the law of electroneutrality. Although the ions of an electrolyte may have entirely different mobilities, the interionic forces of attraction will accelerate the slower moving ions and retard the faster ones so that they both migrate at the same rate. Under these circumstances, neither ion exhibits its proper rate of free diffusion. The diffusivity of a particular ionic species cannot be determined, therefore, by ordinary methods   Laitinen and Kolthoff[57, 58] have recently reported a method whereby the diffusion coefficient of ions, in the presence of an excess of an indifferent ionized salt, can be determined by measuring electrolytic current–time curves under suitable experimental conditions   A virtually complete state of concentration polarization is set up at the cathode and the transference number of the ion is reduced so that the measured current is due entirely to diffusion.

Mixtures of electrolytes sometimes exhibit very striking diffusion phenom-

[56] W. Nernst, Z. physik. Chem., 2, 613 (1888).

[57] H. A. Laitinen and I. M. Kolthoff, J. Am. Chem. Soc., 61, 3344 (1939).

[58] H. A. Laitinen, Trans. Electrochem. Soc., 82, 289 (1942).

ena. McBain and coworkers[59, 60] have reported that, in certain systems, the diffusion of an ion may be completely stopped or a relatively fast moving ion such as hydrogen may be made to travel faster than its normal rate of free diffusion.   The diffusivity of a particular ionic species will also depend upon whether it is diffusing with, through, or against other ions   McBain and Liu[61] have found that the diffusion of hydrochloric acid in aqueous solution is affected by the presence of the unreactive none'ectrolyte, dextrose.   They attribute the effects to a mutual bombardment by the diffusing particles which causes an acceleration or retardation of their motion, as the case may be.

The diffusivity of charged colloids may be increased to several times the normal rate by the accelerating effect of the counter ions.   Hartley and Robinson[62] have pointed out that the diffusivity may increase with increasing aggregation since the frictional resistance to motion of a complex ion moving in an electric field will be less than that of the constituent single ions.   If additional simple electrolyte is introduced into the system, however, the potential gradient will be reduced, thereby decreasing the diffusivity of the colloidal ions.   The normal diffusivity of the charged colloid will therefore be approached in the presence of a sufficient excess of "swamping" electrolyte.   Under these conditions, the ionic constituents of the colloid need not diffuse at the same rate because the law of electrical neutrality can be satisfied by the other ions present.

III. CALCULATION OF PARTICLE SIZES

A relation between diffusivity and particle size is given by the Stokes–Einstein[63] equation:

$$D = \frac{RT}{N} \frac{1}{6\pi\eta r} \tag{38}$$

in which D = the diffusion coefficient n cm.^{2} per sec., R = the gas constant, 8.31×10^7 ergs per degree per mole, T = absolute temperature, N = Avogadro's constant, 6.02×10^{23}, η = the coefficient of viscosity in poises, and r = the radius of the particle in cm.   This equation is derived on the premise that D is a constant, that osmotic pressure is the impelling force of d ffusion, that the van't Hoff equation, $P = cRT$, is obeyed, and that Stokes' law is applicable to the movement of the particles.   It therefore

---

[59] J. W. McBain and C. R. Dawson, *J. Am. Chem. Soc.*, **56**, 52 (1934).

[60] J. R. Vinograd and J. W. McBain, *J. Am. Chem. Soc.*, **63**, 2008 (1941).

[61] J. W. McBain and T. H. Liu, *J. Am. Chem. Soc.*, **53**, 59 (1931).

[62] G. S. Hartley and C. Robinson, *Proc. Roy. Soc. London*, **A134**, 20 (1931).

[63] A. Einstein, *Ann. Physik*, **17**, 549 (1905).

involves the assumptions that the concentration of particles is low, and that the particles are spherical, electrically neutral, and large compared with those of the solvent.

In the preceding section it was shown that, if the particles are not electrically neutral, correct values of D may be obtained under certain experimental conditions, such as by the addition of so-called "swamping" electrolyte. If the particles are not relatively large, the medium through which they diffuse is not effectively continuous and Stokes' law is not obeyed. Friedman and Carpenter[64] have shown, from a study of aqueous solutions of glucose, that the Stokes–Einstein equation may hold for a substance of molecular weight as low as 180. Eyring,[65] from his theory of liquids and absolute reaction rates, has developed the relation:

$$D = \frac{RT}{N\eta} \frac{\lambda_1}{\lambda_2 \lambda_3} \tag{39}$$

which is applicable to systems in which the molecules are of similar size (self-diffusion in the ideal case) and which supports the view that the diffusivity is a function of the volume and shape of the particle rather than of its mass. In this equation, λ_1 is the distance between two layers of molecules sliding past each other, λ_2 the distance between molecules in the direction of flow, and λ_3 the distance between molecules normal to the direction of flow.

Since equation (38) is based on osmotic theory, it would be expected to hold only for dilute solutions. Friedman and Carpenter[64] have pointed out that the equation is derived on the assumption of free diffusion and that the value of D at infinite dilution should, therefore, be used. They confirm this point in the case of a number of nonelectrolytes. Although equation (38) is applicable only to spherical particles, it may be used in conjunction with other information to obtain values for the molecular weight of unsymmetrical particles. Svedberg[66] has shown that the molecular weight of nonspherical particles may be determined from combined measurements of sedimentation rate and diffusion by the equation:

$$M = \frac{RTs}{D(1 - V\rho)} \tag{40}$$

where s is the sedimentation constant, V the partial specific volume of the solute, and ρ the density of the solvent. In this equation, the assumption is made that the frictional coefficients for sedimentation and diffusion are

---

[64] L. Friedman and P. G. Carpenter, *J. Am. Chem. Soc.*, **61**, 1745 (1939).

[65] H. Eyring, *J. Chem. Phys.*, **4**, 283 (1936).

[66] T. Svedberg, *Z. physik. Chem.*, **127**, 51 (1927).

the same. This is not always the case, however, as several investigators[67, 68] have shown in a study of globular proteins and starch. The coefficient for sedimentation was found to be the lower of the two, probably because the particles migrating in a centrifugal field have a preferred orientation.

Svedberg[69] has also developed the equation:

$$D f/f_0 = \frac{RT}{6\pi N \eta (3MV/4\pi N)^{1/3}} \tag{41}$$

to correct for molecular dissymmetry where f is the experimental molar frictional constant and f_0 is the frictional constant for a spherical molecule of the same mass. Therefore, if the dissymmetry constant, f/f_0, can be determined by any method, the molecular weight of a nonspherical molecule can be calculated. Polson[70] has proposed the empirical equation:

$$\eta_s/\eta_0 - 1 = 4G + 0.098(b/a)^2 \tag{42}$$

for elongated particles, in which η_s/η_0 is the relative viscosity of the solution, G is the fraction of the volume occupied by the solute, and b/a is the ratio of the long axis to the short axis of an ellipsoid, whereby the axial ratio b/a of the molecule may be calculated from measurements of viscosity. A theoretical treatment of the effect of shape by Simha[71] leads to a similar though more complicated relation. Values of b/a obtained in this manner for a number of proteins have been found to agree very well with results obtained by the ultracentrifuge. If the axial ratio is known, the dissymmetry constant may be calculated for prolate or oblate spheroids by the equations of Perrin[72] and Herzog and coworkers.[73] Thus, in certain cases, the molecular weight of nonspherical particles may be obtained from combined viscosity and diffusion measurements.

In the above treatment, the possibility of solvation was not taken into consideration. Svedberg[66] has pointed out that solvation should cancel out in equation (41) from the manner in which it enters into both f and D. Although solvation of the particles must have some effect on the viscosity of a solution, it is probably of very much less importance than the effect of particle shape just discussed.[74, 75] The various empirical equations[76, 77]

[67] L. Friedman and B. R. Ray, *J. Phys. Chem.*, **46**, 1140 (1942).
[68] C. O. Beckmann and Q. Landis, *J. Am. Chem. Soc.*, **61**, 1495 (1939).
[69] T. Svedberg, *Proc. Roy. Soc. London*, **B127**, 1 (1939).
[70] A. Polson, *Kolloid-Z.*, **88**, 51 (1939).
[71] R. Simha, *J. Phys. Chem.*, **44**, 25 (1940).
[72] F. Perrin, *J. phys. radium*, **7**, 1 (1936).
[73] R. O. Herzog, R. Illig, and H. Kudar, *Z. physik. Chem.*, **A167**, 329 (1933).
[74] M. A. Lauffer, *Chem. Revs.*, **31**, 561 (1942).
[75] R. Simha, *J. Applied Phys.*, **13**, 147 (1942).
[76] M. Kunitz, M. L. Anson, and J. H. Northrup, *J. Gen. Physiol.*, **17**, 365 (1934).
[77] G. V. Schulz, *Z. physik. Chem.*, **A158**, 237 (1932).

which have been deduced, relating solution viscosity or osmotic pressure to degree of solvation, on the assumption that the shape effect is negligible, cannot be expected to hold. On the other hand, the treatment of molecular dissymmetry, on the assumption that solvation is negligible, is fairly adequate for ellipsoidal particles. However, the possibility of errors due to solvation, in any calculation of particle size from diffusion coefficients, must be recognized.

General References

Barnes, C., *Physics*, **5,** 4 (1934).

Bourdillon, J., *J. Gen. Physiol.*, **24,** 459 (1941).

Bridgman, W. B., and Williams, J. W., *Ann. N. Y. Acad. Sci.*, **43,** 195 (1942).

Clack, W. B., *Proc. Phys. Soc. London*, **36,** 313 (1924).

Cohen, E., and Bruins, H. R., *Z. physik. Chem.*, **103,** 404 (1922).

Eversole, W. G., Peterson, J. D., and Kindsvater, H. M., *J. Phys. Chem.*, **45,** 1398 (1941).

Eversole, W. G., Kindsvater, H. M., and Peterson, J. D., *ibid.*, **46,** 370 (1942).

Friedman, L., and Carpenter, P. G., *J. Am. Chem. Soc.*, **61,** 1745 (1939).

Friedman, L., and Ray, B. R., *J. Phys. Chem.*, **46,** 1140 (1942).

Fürth, R., *Kolloid-Z.*, **41,** 300 (1927).

Fürth, R., and Zuber, R., *Z. Physik*, **91,** 609 (1934).

Gerlach, B., *Ann. Physik*, **10,** 437 (1931).

Hartley, G. S., and Runnicles, D. F., *Proc. Roy. Soc. London*, **A168,** 401 (1938).

Hollingshead, E. A., and Gordon, A. R., *J. Chem. Phys.*, **9,** 152 (1941), *and earlier papers.*

Lamm, O., *Arkiv Kemi, Mineral. Geol.*, **B16,** No. 17 (1943); **B17,** No. 13 (1943), and earlier papers.

Lamm, O., *Nova Acta Regiae Soc. Sci. Upsaliensis*, [4] **10,** No. 6 (1937).

Lamm, O., and Polson, A., *Biochem. J.*, **30,** 528 (1936).

Lenher, S., and Smith, E. J., *Ind. Eng. Chem., Ind. Ed.*, **27,** 20 (1935).

Linhart, T., *Z. Physik*, **105,** 45 (1937).

Littlewood, T. H., *Proc. Phys. Soc. London*, **34,** 71 (1922).

McBain, J. W., and Dawson, C. R., *Proc. Roy. Soc. London*, **A148,** 32 (1935).

Mehl, J. W., and Schmidt, G. L. A., *Univ. Calif. Pub. Physiol.*, **8,** 165 (1937).

Mouquin, H., and Cathcart, W. H., *J. Am. Chem. Soc.*, **57,** 1791 (1935).

Neurath, H., *Science*, **93,** 431 (1941).

Neurath, H., *Chem. Revs.*, **30,** 357 (1942).

Nistler, A., *Kolloidchem. Beihefte*, **28,** 296 (1929).

Northrup, J. H., and Anson, M. L., *J. Gen. Physiol.*, **12,** 543 (1929).

Svedberg, T., *Proc. Roy. Soc. London*, **B127,** 1 (1939).

Taylor, H. S., *J. Chem. Phys.*, **6,** 331 (1938).

Tiselius, A., and Gross, D., *Kolloid-Z.*, **66,** 11 (1934).

Ullmann, E., *Z. Physik*, **41,** 301 (1927).

Vinograd, J. R., and McBain, J. W., *J. Am. Chem. Soc.*, **63,** 2008 (1941).

Williams, J. W., and Cady, L. C., *Chem. Revs.*, **14,** 171 (1934).

CHAPTER X

CALORIMETRY

JULIAN M. STURTEVANT, *Yale University*

I. INTRODUCTION

1. Scope

The subject of calorimetry is very extensive, and its techniques are usually quite involved. It is therefore not possible to present here a complete discussion of the topic. An attempt has been made to give a broad over-all outline, restricting extensive descriptions to those phases which are of particular importance in organic chemistry. It is even impossible to discuss completely fields of calorimetry in which one may expect that some organic chemists will do experimental work because of the attention to detail necessary in all calorimetric experiments. It is hoped that, in such cases, the discussion will be found to be sufficiently detailed, and the references to the literature sufficiently inclusive, so that a prospective experimenter will not have great difficulty in starting the process of training and equipping himself for calorimetric work.   In some cases, attention has been deliberately focused on the method or apparatus of one worker or school to avoid the confusion which may result from the presentation of several equally reliable procedures.   Particular attention has been paid to the determination of heat capacities because of their importance in the evaluation of free energies; to heats of combustion, for the same reason, and because at present they furnish the most general method for evaluating heats of organic reactions; and to methods for the direct determination of heats of reaction. Because of the author's conviction that the valuable criterion of purity furnished by freezing and fusion curves should be far more widely employed by organic chemists than is at present the case, an effort has been made to describe, in sufficient detail for easy assembly, an apparatus for the observation of such curves.

2.   First Law of Thermodynamics

All chemical and physical processes involve energy changes; calorimetry is concerned with the measurement of these changes.   According to the law of the conservation of energy, or the first law of thermodynamics, the energy of a system is a single-valued function of its state.   Therefore the energy change associated with the change of the system from one state to another is dependent only on the initial and final states, and not on the path followed by the system in going from the initial to the final state.   Thus we may evaluate the energy change associated with the process $A \rightarrow C$ by summing the changes corresponding to the processes $A \rightarrow B$ and $B \rightarrow C$; or, if it is more convenient, those corresponding to the processes $A \rightarrow B'$ and $B' \rightarrow C$.   This statement of the first law of thermodynamics, in its applications to calorimetry, is frequently called the Law of Hess.[1]

It is not possible to define the total absolute energy of a system; we are concerned only with *changes* in energy content.   Thus, when we speak of the energy content of a system in a certain state, we mean the energy change associated with bringing the system to that state from some reference state in which the energy content is arbitrarily set equal to zero.

Since we shall be interested in changes of energy accompanying changes in state, it is at once obvious that the greatest care should be exercised in defining the initial and final states under consideration with sufficient precision to confer on the corresponding energy change a definiteness consistent with the experimental accuracy achieved in measuring it.   All too fre-

---

[1] G. H. Hess, *Ann. Physik*, **50**, 385 (1840); Ostwald's *Klassiker der exakten Wissenschaften*, No. 9, Englemann, Leipzig, 1890.

quently in the past, otherwise precise thermochemical work has been marred by the failure to describe with appropriate detail the states or systems involved.

If, in changing from an initial to a final state, a system performs work against mechanical or other forces, the heat effect accompanying the change is not equal to the total energy change. Since calorimetric measurements are directly concerned only with heat changes, it is essential to have a clear understanding of this point. Suppose the quantity of heat *absorbed* by the system in some process is Q, and the quantity of work performed *by* the system is W. Then the *increase* in energy accompanying the process is:

$$\Delta U \equiv U_2 - U_1 = Q - W \tag{1}$$

where U_1 and U_2 are the energy contents, referred to some arbitrary zero, of the initial and final states, respectively. We shall deal only with processes in which the work terms arise from expansion or contraction of the system under a finite pressure; for a reversible process the term describing the work of expansion or contraction is:

$$W = \int_{V_1}^{V_2} P\,dV \tag{2}$$

where P and V are the pressure and volume of the system, respectively. In the important special case of a reversible process taking place at constant pressure, equation (2) becomes:

$$W = PV_2 - PV_1 = P\Delta V \tag{3}$$

Thus, the heat absorbed by a system during such a process is:

$$Q = \Delta U + P\Delta V = (U_2 + PV_2) - (U_1 + PV_1) \tag{4}$$

It is convenient to represent the property $U + PV$ by H; this quantity is called the *heat content*, or *enthalpy.*

In view of the fact that the change in energy or enthalpy associated with a given process is dependent only on the initial and final states, it is clear that it is permissible to speak of the change of enthalpy (ΔH), for example, when a system changes from an initial state at one pressure to a final state at some other pressure. In other words, changes in the energy content U and the heat content H are not necessarily restricted to constant volume and constant pressure processes. For the important special case in which the initial and final volumes are equal, it is customary to speak of the heat absorbed "at constant volume":

$$Q_v = U_2 - U_1 = \Delta U \tag{5}$$

even though the volume may undergo some changes during the process.

Likewise, if the initial and final pressures are the same, we speak of the heat absorbed "at constant pressure":

$$Q_p = H_2 - H_1 = \Delta H = \Delta U + P \Delta V \tag{6}$$

without in any way implying that the pressure remains constant at all times during the process. For a more complete discussion of the first law, see the standard texts on thermodynamics.[2]

3. Definition of Units

The modern calorimetric method consists essentially in measuring the amount of electrical energy necessary to duplicate (or nullify, in the case of an endothermic process) the thermal effect accompanying a physical or chemical process. Modern calorimetric data are therefore primarily expressed in units of electrical energy. Since potential differences are usually measured in international volts and currents in international amperes, the rational unit of energy is the international joule—the product of international volts by international amperes by seconds.[3] However, chemists are so accustomed to thinking of thermal energies in terms of the energy required to increase the temperature of a mass of water by a given number of degrees that the calorie has been retained as a unit of energy. In order to free this unit from any dependence on past or future determinations of the specific heat of water, it has been redefined[4] in terms of the international joule, 1 calorie being set equal to 4.1833 international joules. This defined calorie is sometimes denoted the 15°-calorie (cal_{15}).[4] One kilocalorie equals 1000 calories. Unless otherwise specified, we use the term joule for the international joule, and calorie for the defined calorie. The temperature at which ice is in equilibrium with air-saturated water under a pressure of 1 atmosphere is taken as 273.16° K., frequently abbreviated 273° K.

II. TEMPERATURE MEASUREMENT AND CONTROL

1. International Temperature Scale

Temperatures in scientific work are expressed in terms of the International Temperature Scale adopted in 1927 by the Seventh General Con-

---

[2] G. N. Lewis and M. Randall, *Thermodynamics and the Free Energy of Chemical Substances*, McGraw-Hill, New York, 1923; L. E. Steiner, *Introduction to Chemical Thermodynamics*, McGraw-Hill, New York, 1941; F. H. MacDougall, *Thermodynamics and Chemistry*, 3rd ed., Wiley, New York, 1939.

[3] The proposed change from international to absolute electrical units has been indefinitely postponed as a result of the war. The relation between international and absolute joules is closely represented by the following (F. D. Rossini, *Chem. Revs.*, 27, 1 (1940), and private communication (1942)): 1 int. joule = 1.00020 ± 0.00005 abs. joule.

[4] F. D. Rossini, *J. Research Natl. Bur. Standards*, 6, 1 (1931); 12, 735 (1934).

ference on Weights and Measures. At the time of its adoption this scale conformed to the thermodynamic scale as closely as possible in view of the experimental knowledge available at that time. However, it is now recognized that the thermodynamic and international scales may differ by as much as 0.05° at some points. The International Scale is defined by several fixed points (each point being given with a number of significant figures consistent with its reproducibility), and by means for interpolating between the fixed points.[5]

Fixed Points.—At the pressure of 1 standard atmosphere, the temperature of equilibrium between liquid and gaseous oxygen = −182.97°, between ice and air-saturated water = 0.000°, between liquid water and its vapor = 100.000°, between liquid sulfur and its vapor = 444.60°, between solid and liquid silver = 960.5°, and between solid and liquid gold = 1063°.

Interpolation.—From the ice point to 660° the temperature, t, is deduced from the resistance, R_t, of a standard platinum resistance thermometer by means of the formula:

$$R_t = R_0 \left(1 + At + Bt^2\right) \tag{7}$$

The constants, R_0, A, and B, are determined by calibration at the ice, steam, and sulfur points. The purity and physical condition of the platinum of the thermometer must be such that $R_{100}/R_0 \geq 1.390$, $R_{444.6}/R_0 \geq 2.645$. A platinum resistance thermometer is also used from −190° to the ice point, with a modified interpolation formula. From 660° to the gold point, the temperature is deduced from the electromotive force of a standard platinum vs. platinum–rhodium thermocouple, one junction of which is at 0°. Above the gold point, temperatures are defined in terms of Wien's radiation formula.

2. Important Types of Thermometers

A. MERCURY-IN-GLASS THERMOMETERS

These thermometers allow the measurement of temperatures with moderate precision in the range of −35° to 360°, or even higher if the mercury is under gas pressure. For measurements of the greatest precision, mercury thermometers have been largely replaced by resistance thermometers or thermocouples.[6] However, short-interval mercury thermometers still find some application in calorimetric work. The familiar Beckmann

---

[5] For a more complete description, see H. T. Wensel, in *Temperature, Its Measurement and Control in Society and Industry*. Reinhold, New York, 1941, p. 3.

[6] For other devices, see various papers in *Temperature, Its Measurement and Control in Science and Industry*.

type can be read, with a lens, to 0.001–0.002°, though considerable care must be exercised to make the accuracy of the readings this good. So-called calorimetric thermometers in which the amount of mercury in the system cannot be changed, as with the Beckmann type, cover a short temperature interval of 10–20°. Barry[7] has described a thermometer for the range of 15–21° which can be read to 0.0001°, and which he considers to have about the limit of precision obtainable with mercury thermometers.

Several precautions must be observed in using mercury thermometers for precise measurements.[8] The correction for exposed stem is considered in the chapter on melting and freezing points (page 32).

Checking Calibration.—The accuracy of the thermometer calibration can be verified by comparison against a platinum resistance thermometer or other reliable instrument. It cannot be safely assumed that the calibration, once made, is permanent. Slow changes in the glass result in changes in the volume of the bulb, so that it is necessary to check the calibration rather frequently at some fixed reference temperature, most conveniently at 0°. Any change in calibration at the reference point can be assumed to hold over the whole range of the instrument, since changes in the scale will be of insignificant magnitude compared with those in the bulb.

Setting Factors for Beckmann Thermometers.—The calibration of the scale of a Beckmann thermometer holds only at one setting of the instrument, since at other settings there are different amounts of mercury in the system. For a thermometer reading correctly at 20°, an observed temperature interval at 50° is almost 1% too small. Tables of these setting factors have been published.[8]

Errors Resulting from Heating.—Temporary changes in bulb volume are likely to result from heating; the bulb may not regain its original volume for several days. With good grades of thermometers this may cause errors of as much as 0.01° for each 10° the bulb is heated above the original temperature. It is thus evident that considerable care must be used in the treatment given a thermometer employed in precise measurements.

Lag Errors.—Sensitive mercury thermometers necessarily have a relatively high lag, and are therefore not suitable for the observation of rapidly changing temperatures. This is one of their chief weaknesses for calorimetric purposes.

B. RESISTANCE THERMOMETRY

In the neighborhood of room temperature, the electrical resistivity of platinum increases by approximately 0.4% per degree. Since platinum is

---

[7] F. Barry, *J. Am. Chem. Soc.*, 42, 1911 (1920).

[8] For a discussion in detail, see J. Busse, in *Temperature, Its Measurement and Control in Science and Industry*. Reinhold, New York, 1941, p. 228.

obtainable in highly reproducible and pure condition, and is relatively unaffected by aging or by gases and fumes over a wide temperature range,
and since electrical resistance can be measured with a high degree of precision, this change of resistivity with temperature furnishes one of the best
means of temperature measurement.[9] As stated above, interpolation in
the International Temperature Scale in the range of $-190°$ to $660°$ is
defined in terms of the platinum resistance thermometer. Many other
metals and alloys have temperature coefficients of resistivity somewhat
larger than that of platinum. While some of these find limited application in temperature indicating devices, they are inferior to platinum for
precise measurements because of their greater susceptibility to external
physical and chemical effects.

Platinum resistance thermometers are wound of annealed wire on mica
supports in such a way that the metal is subjected to as slight a strain as
possible when the thermometer is heated or cooled. For most applications,
the coil is enclosed in a sealed glass or silica tube; when it is desired to minimize the lag of the thermometer, as in calorimetric applications, the coil is
enclosed in a flattened metal case. Thermometers are usually manufactured with a resistance of 25.5 or 2.55 ohms at $0°$, so that the resistance will
change by about 0.1 or 0.01 ohm per degree, respectively. Modern thermometers are provided with four leads, two from each end of the coil, the
use of which is discussed below.

The resistance of a platinum thermometer may be expressed as a power
series in the temperature, a quadratic function being sufficient at temperatures above $0°$. However, since one is usually interested in evaluating the
temperature from the observed resistance, it is more convenient to employ
an equation of the form originally proposed by Callendar:[10]

$$ t = \frac{100(R_t - R_0)}{R_{100} - R_0} + \delta\left(\frac{t}{100} - 1\right)\frac{t}{100} \tag{8} $$

The constants, R_0, $R_{100} - R_0$ (the "fundamental interval"), and δ are determined by calibration at the ice, steam, and sulfur points (page 316);
this calibration is performed by the National Bureau of Standards in
Washington for a reasonable charge. The value of t is calculated from R_t
by successive approximations, the first of which is simply $100\,(R_t - R_0)/$
$(R_{100} - R_0)$. This value of t is used in the relatively small δ term to obtain
the next approximation to t, and the process is repeated until an unchang-

[9] See F. E. Mueller, in *Temperature, Its Measurement and Control in Science and Industry.* Reinhold, New York, 1941, p. 162.

[10] H. L. Callendar, *Trans. Roy. Soc. London*, **178**, 161 (1887); E. H. Griffiths, *ibid.*,
182, 43, 119 (1892); *Phil. Mag.*, **32**, 104 (1891); **47**, 191 (1899).

ing value of t is reached. Experience has shown that δ should be less than 1.51 with a properly constructed and calibrated thermometer.

Measurement of the Resistance of a Thermometer.—Only two methods of measuring the resistance of a thermometer need be mentioned. The first is the potentiometric method, in which the potential drop across the thermometer coil is compared with that across a standard resistor in series with the thermometer. The potential drops need not be measured in absolute terms; the ratio of the two potentials gives directly the ratio of of the two resistances. This method is much employed in low temperature work.

Resistance measurement by means of a Wheatstone bridge is more frequently employed at ordinary temperatures than the potentiometric method. The bridge (Fig. 1) consists of two fixed ratio arms, A and B, of

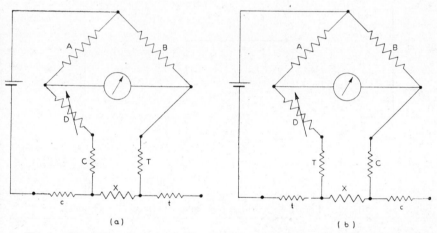

(a)　　　　　　　　　　　　(b)

Fig. 1.—Simple thermometer bridge, illustrating use of four-lead thermometer.

a variable arm, D, and the thermometer, X. With a four-lead thermometer, it is possible to eliminate the resistances of the leads. If $r_A = r_B$ ($r =$ resistance), and the four leads are designated as c, C, T, and t, it is evident that, with the thermometer connected as in figure 1a, at bridge balance:

$$(r_D)_a + r_c = r_X + r_T$$

Correspondingly, with connections as in figure 1b:

$$(r_D)_b + r_T = r_X + r_c$$

Therefore:

$$r_X = \frac{(r_D)_a + (r_D)_b}{2}$$

Thermometer bridges are frequently equipped with a mercury commutator for making this change in connections.

With a 25.5-ohm thermometer, 0.0001 ohm corresponds to 0.001°. The bridge must therefore be constructed and calibrated with great care if precise temperature measurements are to be made. The variable arm usually consists of six decades, the lowest of which is in steps of 0.0001 ohm. The variable resistance of the decade contactors, which is an important source of error in such precise resistance measurements, is ingeniously eliminated in the Mueller-type bridge. The contact resistances in the lower decades are in series with relatively large fixed resistances so that they have only a negligible effect. The decade resistance values result from the shunting of a series of low resistances by the large fixed resistances.

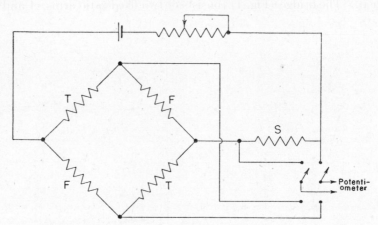

Fig. 2.—Transposed bridge resistance thermometer (Maier).

Too large a current passing through the thermometer will cause fallacious readings as a result of heating of the thermometer coil. With 25.5-ohm thermometers having flattened metal protecting tubes, a current of 5 milliamperes (ma.) is usually employed, while with those enclosed in glass tubes the current should not exceed 2 ma. These currents cause a heating of a few thousandths of a degree in the thermometer. If the measuring current is kept constant, it is usually considered to be safe to assume that the heating is the same at all temperatures and in all media. Since only differences between resistances appear in equation (8), no errors result from this cause if the thermometer is always heated the same fraction of a degree.

It can readily be seen that resistance thermometers may be used for differential temperature measurements by employing two similar thermometers in adjacent arms of a Wheatstone bridge. With two thermometers in opposite arms of the bridge at the same temperature, the advantage is obtained of having twice as large a voltage at the bridge output terminals for a given departure of the temperature of the thermometers from the balance point of the bridge as with a single thermometer. This increased sensitivity, together with the great precision possible in measuring very small output voltages, has been advantageously employed in the "transposed bridge" type of thermometer described by Maier.[11] Two thermometers, T, and two fixed coils, F, with zero temperature coefficient (manganin), wound on the same form, are connected as shown in figure 2. The current through the bridge is adjusted by means of the potetnial drop in the standard resistor, S. The bridge output voltage is measured potentiometrically. This type of thermometer is most satisfactory in the neighborhood of its balance temperature. With a total bridge current of 10 ma., 200-ohm thermometers wound of material having a temperature coefficient of resistivity of 0.3% per degree will have a sensitivity equal to that of 75 copper–constantan thermocouples connected in series.

C. THERMOCOUPLES

If a circuit composed of two different metals (see Fig. 3) contains a current-indicating device, a current is found to flow in the circuit if the

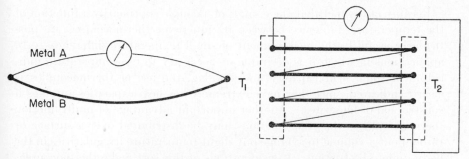

Fig. 3.—Simple thermocouple circuit.   Fig. 4.—Thermocouples connected in series.

two junctions between the metals are maintained at different temperatures $(T_1 \neq T_2)$. The electromotive force (e. m. f.) causing the current flow is a single-valued function of the temperature difference, provided that either T_1 or T_2 is held constant, and the physical or chemical character of the metals is not altered. Such a system is called a *thermocouple*.[12] Several

---

[11] C. G. Maier, *J. Phys. Chem.*, **34**, 2860 (1930).

[12] For a thorough discussion of thermoelectric thermometry, see the articles by W. F. Roeser, R. B. Scott, J. G. Aston, W. P. White, and H. T. Wensel, in *Temperature, Its Measurement and Control in Science and Industry.* Reinhold, New York, 1941.

thermocouples may be connected in series, as in figure 4, to give an e. m. f. which is the sum of the e. m. f.'s of the single couples. Such an arrangement is called a *multijunction thermocouple* or a *thermel*. The thermoelectric power of a thermocouple is of the order of a few to 40 to 50 microvolts (μv.) per degree, depending on the metals and the temperature. In general, the thermoelectric power decreases with the temperature. Table I lists some important data for the four most common types of thermocouple.

TABLE I

CHARACTERISTIC DATA FOR VARIOUS TYPES OF THERMOCOUPLES[a]

Type	Usual temperature range, ° C.	E. m. f. per junction with reference junction at 0° C., mv.			
		$-200°$	$+100°$	$+300°$	$+1000°$
Platinum to platinum–rhodium	0 to 1450	....	0.643	2.315	9.57
Chromel P to alumel	-200 to 1200	-5.75	4.10	12.21	41.31
Iron to constantan	-200 to 750	-8.27	5.40	16.56	58.22
Copper to constantan	-200 to 350	-5.54	4.28	14.86	...

[a] W. F. Roeser, in *Temperature, Its Measurement and Control in Science and Industry.* Reinhold, New York, 1941, p. 180.

Because of the fact that the e. m. f. of a couple is primarily a function of the temperature difference between its junctions, thermocouples are particularly useful in the measurement of small temperature differences. In applications in which it is desirable or necessary to use temperature indicators of small heat capacity and low lag, the use of thermocouples is clearly indicated, since they have extremely low heat capacities and lags if constructed of fine wires. Another important advantage of multijunction thermocouples is that the junctions may be distributed over a surface or throughout a volume to average out slight temperature irregularities in the body under observation. Considerations of this sort make thermocouples extremely valuable in many phases of calorimetry.

Thermocouples can be constructed of such low heat capacity that they can be employed, after being suitably coated with an absorbing film, to indicate the temperature of a body with which they are not in actual contact. This type of "radiation" thermocouple has been used by Lipsett, Johnson, and Maas.[13]

Measurement of Potential.—The potential generated by a thermo-

[13] S. G. Lipsett, F. M. G. Johnson, and O. Maas, *J. Am. Chem. Soc.*, **49**, 925, 1940 (1927); **50**, 1030 (1928). See also H. Keefer, *Physik. Z.*, **29**, 681 (1928), and F. A. Askew, N. S. Jackson, O. Gatty, and J. H. Wolfenden, *J. Chem. Soc.*, **1934**, 1362.

couple is measured with a potentiometer.   The potentiometer principle
is discussed in Volume II, Chapter XXII.

Since the potentials developed by thermocouples are small, potentiometers of relatively high precision are required for calorimetric work.   When
the precision must exceed 5 μv. (0.125° per junction for copper–constantan
couples) a slide wire is generally not used for interpolating between the
steps of the lowest decade.   The interpolation is accomplished by observing galvanometer deflections, or by opposing the small residual e. m. f. by a
small fraction of the potential drop in a resistor carrying current read on a
sufficiently sensitive ammeter (Lindeck method).

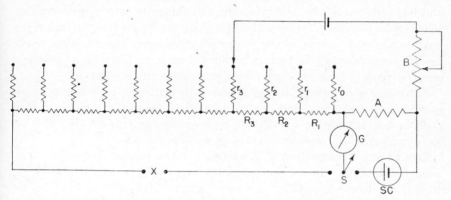

Fig. 5.—Principle of the potentiometer. R_1, R_2, . . ., decade resistors; r_1, r_2, . . .,
compensating resistors; A, accurately known fixed resistor; B, variable resistor; SC,
standard cell; X, source of unknown e. m. f.

With interpolation by galvanometer deflections, a decade arrangement
similar to that shown in figure 5 is employed.   This arrangement keeps the
resistance in the unknown e. m. f.–galvanometer circuit approximately
constant, which is important since a galvanometer is a *current*-measuring
device.   The moving contacts, especially in the lower decades, are frequently put in the battery circuit where stray thermal e. m. f.'s have negligible effect.   The resistors, r_1, r_2, r_3, . . ., serve to keep constant the resistance in the battery circuit.   It is essential to operate with a properly
damped galvanometer.[14]   If the resistance of the potentiometer plus that of
the source of the unknown e. m. f. is not equal to the critical damping re-

---

[14] If a high-sensitivity galvanometer is employed, it is important to support it in such
a way that it is unaffected by mechanical disturbances.   The familiar Julius suspension
will usually be satisfactory.   More elaborate suspensions have been described by M. J.
Brevoort, *U. S. Bur. Mines, Repts. Investigations* **3086**, and by F. T. Gucker, H. B.
Pickard, and R. W. Planck, *J. Am. Chem. Soc.*, **61**, 459 (1939).

sistance of the galvanometer, a suitable series or shunt resistor should be placed in the circuit. It is usually considered best to have the total resistance in series with the galvanometer a little larger than the critical damping value so that the galvanometer is slightly underdamped.

In the measurement of potentials of the order of 1 μv., great care must be exercised to avoid interference from e. m. f.'s arising either from leakage from higher potential circuits or from temperature gradients in nonhomogeneous parts of the circuit (stray thermal e. m. f.'s). White[15] has described methods of shielding for eliminating interference from the first cause, as well as various devices which lessen the troubles due to thermal e. m. f.'s. Provision is usually made for a partial elimination of thermal and leakage e. m. f.'s by observing the galvanometer zero with the circuit as nearly as possible in its operating condition except for the removal of the unknown e. m. f. Thus, in the White potentiometer, which is extensively used in thermometry, the battery and unknown e. m. f. are simultaneously removed from the circuit before the galvanometer zero is observed.

For many applications, it is convenient to employ a recording potentiometer. Several types are now available commercially. Gucker[16] has described an interesting semiautomatic recording potentiometer which he has employed in the observation of very small potentials.

Design and Construction of Thermels.—For temperatures below 300°, copper–constantan (or copper–Advance) thermels are usually employed. If only moderate sensitivity is sought, the number of junctions will be small, and will usually be in part determined by the potentiometric and galvanometric equipment available. In some applications, physical factors limit the number of junctions to a very small number, frequently to one. In such cases, the desired sensitivity of measurement will dictate the choice of the potentiometer and galvanometer. When very high sensitivity, say of the order of microdegrees, is desired, one can use either a relatively small number of junctions[16] with a galvanometer having a very high current sensitivity, such as a Paschen galvanometer, or a higher resistance thermel having as many as 2000 or 3000 junctions[17] with a less sensitive galvanometer. The size of the wires used in constructing the thermel should be carefully considered. A decision here is based on a balance[16, 18] between low electrical resistance and low thermal conduction, with due consideration being given such factors as possible restrictions on the allowable heat capacity of the measuring junctions.

---

[15] W. P. White, in *Temperature, Its Measurement and Control in Science and Industry.* Reinhold, New York, 1941, pp. 265, 279.

[16] F. T. Gucker, H. B. Pickard, and R. W. Planck, *J. Am. Chem. Soc.*, **61**, 459 (1939).

[17] E. Lange and A. L. Robinson, *Chem. Revs.*, 9, 89 (1931).

[18] B. Whipp, *Phil. Mag.*, **18**, 745 (1934).

Thermocouples may take a wide variety of shapes, depending on the particular application. Wherever possible, one should take advantage of the low lag of thermocouple junctions, and of the integrating characteristic of a multijunction thermel, and should distribute the junctions as widely as possible throughout the body the temperature of which is to be measured. The reference junctions will usually be closely bundled together, since in most cases they are located in a region which is free from temperature gradients.

One of the greatest advantages of thermocouples is the ease with which they can be constructed. We shall mention a few of the more important points to be considered in the actual construction. Further details are to be found in papers on this subject,[12, 19] as well as in numerous papers on calorimetry and related subjects. It is obviously important to approach as closely as possible the ideal situation in which the only potential in the thermocouple is that due to the temperature difference to be measured. Since thermal e. m. f.'s are developed when an inhomogeneous metal is exposed to a temperature gradient, the wire used in constructing a thermel should be tested for homogeneity.[19, 20] Furthermore, the thermel should be exposed to as small temperature gradients as possible, and these gradients should be as nearly as possible the same during calibration and subsequent use. Thermels should be constructed so as to avoid subjecting the wires to any strain, particularly after calibration. For work at low or moderate temperatures, the junctions of a thermel may be soft-soldered; at higher temperatures, silver soldering or welding is necessary. In the construction of a multijunction thermel, one should follow, if possible, a systematic procedure in which the insulation resistance of each wire against the rest of the thermel is tested before that wire is incorporated in the thermel.

Calibration of Thermocouples.—In many calorimetric applications, thermels serve as indicators of temperature differences which may be expressed in arbitrary units, and they therefore need not be calibrated. In cases in which calibration is needed, it will frequently be found possible to perform the calibration in the apparatus for which the thermel was designed by measurements on a substance with known thermal properties (such as heat capacity or melting point). If an absolute calibration is necessary, it may be accomplished by determining the e. m. f.'s corresponding to a series of thermometric fixed points (with the reference junctions held at a constant temperature, usually $0°$ C.), or by comparison with a

[19] W. F. Roeser and H. T. Wensel, in *Temperature, Its Measurement and Control in Science and Industry.* Reinhold, New York, 1941, p. 284.
[20] W. P. White, *Phys. Rev.*, **31**, 135 (1910).

calibrated resistance thermometer or gas thermometer. For details, the reader is referred to various articles.[19, 21]

Reference Temperatures.—The most important reference temperature used in thermoelectric thermometry is the melting temperature of ice. White's[22] ice-point apparatus has a Dewar flask contained within a second Dewar, which gives, with good commercial ice, a temperature constant to 0.0001° for at least a day. A good reference temperature at −78.51° is also furnished by solid carbon dioxide.[23]

Whenever possible, a thermocouple should be employed as a differential temperature indicator, since small potentials can be measured with greater precision than large ones, and errors due to inhomogeneity in the thermel wires are lessened if the thermel is not exposed to any large temperature gradients. One of the chief advantages of the twin calorimeter method (page 342) is that the thermel between the two calorimeters is used only for measuring the small temperature difference between them. This important advantage can be secured with a single calorimeter by having the reference temperature close to that of the calorimeter. For this purpose White[24] recommends a so-called cold calorimeter. The reference temperature is furnished by a body of high heat capacity, such as a block of copper in a Dewar flask which is contained in another Dewar. The main thermel goes to the outer cold calorimeter, and an additional thermel from there to the inner calorimeter, the two thermels being connected in series. Each of the calorimeters should be equipped with a heater to hasten the process of bringing them to the desired temperature. The use of metal blocks eliminates the necessity for stirrers.

3. Temperature Control

The problems of temperature control arising in calorimetry generally belong to one of two types, the maintenance of constant temperature, or the maintenance of a constant temperature difference. Corresponding to the

[21] R. B. Scott, in *Temperature, Its Measurement and Control in Science and Industry.* Reinhold, New York, 1941, p. 206. J. G. Aston, *ibid.*, p. 219. W. P. White, H. C. Dickinson, and E. F. Mueller, *Phys. Rev.*, **31**, 159 (1910). E. L. Skau, *Proc. Am. Acad. Arts Sci.*, **67**, 551 (1932); *J. Phys. Chem.*, **37**, 609 (1933). J. S. Burlew and R. P. Smith, *J. Am. Chem. Soc.*, **62**, 701 (1940). E. F. Burton, H. Grayson Smith, and J. O. Wilhelm, *Phenomena at the Temperature of Liquid Helium*, Reinhold, New York, 1940, p. 30.

[22] W. P. White, *J. Am. Chem. Soc.*, **56**, 20 (1934). See also J. L. Thomas, in *Temperature, Its Measurement and Control in Science and Industry*, Reinhold, New York, 1941, p. 159.

[23] R. B. Scott, in *Temperature, Its Measurement and Control in Science and Industry.* Reinhold, New York, 1941, p. 206.

[24] W. P. White, *The Modern Calorimeter.* Chem. Catalog Co., New York, 1928, p. 131.

three types of thermometers mentioned above, thermoregulators may be of liquid-in-glass, resistance thermometer, or thermocouple type. Other types of thermoregulators, such as those using bimetallic elements, find some application, but attention can be restricted to these three types so far as precise temperature control is concerned.

The most convenient means of temperature control is afforded by the familiar mercury regulator in conjunction with an electromagnetic relay.[25] Several points of importance in connection with this type of regulator should be mentioned.

(a) Fouling of the mercury surface in the capillary, with accompanying excessive sticking of the meniscus, results from the sparking which takes

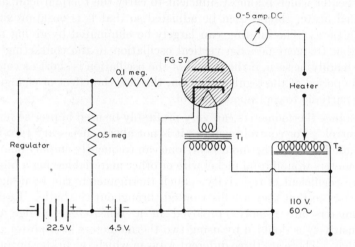

Fig. 6.—Thyratron thermostatic control. T_1, filament transformer, 5 v., 5 amp.; T_2, autotransformer (such as 5-amp. Variac).

place when the relay current is broken. This difficulty is largely eliminated by employing an electronic relay, so that the current at the mercury contact is only of the order of microamperes. Figure 6 shows a very convenient circuit for this purpose, in which the electromagnetic relay is eliminated altogether by the use of a mercury-filled thyratron having sufficient current-carrying capacity to handle directly the controlled part of the heating current. With this arrangement it becomes possible further to diminish sticking of the mercury meniscus by transmitting vibration to the regulator from the stirring motor, since there is no mechanical relay to undergo "chattering." Simple circuits, in which the output of a vacuum tube is

[25] See R. L. Weber, *Temperature Measurement and Control*. Blakiston, Philadelphia, 1941, p. 189.

used to control a mechanical relay, have been described by Redfern[26] and others.

(b) The sensitivity of the regulator is increased by filling it with a liquid, such as toluene, having a higher coefficient of expansion than mercury.   Of course, mercury is used in the part of the regulator at which the circuit is made and broken.   The lag of the regulator is decreased by increasing the ratio of its surface to its volume, and by distributing it as much as possible throughout the body the temperature of which is to be controlled.

(c) A mercury thermoregulator provides only on-off control, so that the bath temperature will necessarily "hunt", i. e. oscillate about an equilibrium point.   To minimize hunting, the bath should be equipped with a steady heater which is almost sufficient to carry the thermal load, and the controlled heater should then be adjusted so that it is on approximately half the time.   The hunting can largely be eliminated by giving a short and rather frequent periodic vertical oscillation to the contacting wire.[27] As can readily be seen, if the period of the oscillation is short as compared with the period of the regulator action, this has the effect of changing the control partially to continuous control.

Resistance thermometers can very profitably be used in precise temperature control.   For control purposes it is not always necessary to use carefully made platinum thermometers; one can frequently employ homemade thermometers wound from nickel wire or other material having a high temperature coefficient of resistivity.   Such thermometers can be designed in many cases so that they are distributed throughout the bath.   Resistance thermometers are usually employed in a Wheatstone bridge circuit. The sensitivity is doubled by using two thermometers in opposite arms of the bridge.   There are three different ways in which the bridge output may be used to control the heater current: (a) The bridge (d. c.) output is indicated by a galvanometer, which controls the heater by means of an on-off photocell relay.[28]   (b) The photocell of the above arrangement is part of a phase-shifting thyratron circuit so that continuous control is obtained,[29] that is, the heater current is a continuous function of the amount of bridge off-balance.   (c) The bridge input is a. c., and the output is suitably amplified and employed in a phase-shifting thyratron circuit.[30]   Any of these

[26] S. Redfern, Ind. Eng. Chem., Anal. Ed., 14, 64 (1942).

[27] M. Gouy, J. Physique, 6, 479 (1897). T. S. Sligh, J. Am. Chem. Soc., 42, 60 (1920).

[28] J. A. Beattie and D. D. Jacobus, J. Phys. Chem., 34, 1254 (1930).

[29] R. M. Zabel and R. R. Hancox, Rev. Sci. Instruments, 5, 28 (1934).   J. A. Beattie, Proc. Am. Acad. Arts Sci., 69, 389 (1934).

[30] M. Benedict, Rev. Sci. Instruments, 8, 252 (1937).   J. M. Sturtevant, ibid., 9, 276 (1938).   D. Bancroft, ibid., 13, 24, 114 (1942), H. S. Roberts, in Temperature, Its Measurement and Control in Science and Industry.   Reinhold, New York, 1941, p. 604.

methods of employing resistance thermometers is capable of giving very close temperature control.

Thermocouples have been employed less frequently in temperature control than the preceding methods. For the maintenance of constant temperature, the e. m. f. generated by a thermel having its reference junctions in an ice bath or other suitable constant-temperature environment is counterbalanced by a source of constant e. m. f. (usually a potentiometer). The balanced condition is maintained by a galvanometer–photocell device which may be of either the on-off or continuous type.

Thermocouples are particularly well adapted to the problem of holding the temperature difference between two bodies equal to zero,[31] since then their differential characteristic is fully utilized. This type of thermocouple control is of great value in adiabatic calorimetry (page 341), when the temperature of the jacket surrounding the calorimeter is to be held equal to that of the calorimeter. Resistance thermometers may also be employed differentially, the two indicating thermometers being placed in adjacent arms of the bridge (page 320).

In designing controlled-temperature installations, there is frequently a tendency to give a great amount of attention to the sensitivity of the control device at the expense of sufficient consideration of other factors, such as heater and control lags, and stirring in liquid baths. The specific requirements depend on the conditions, but it is advisable to make all lags as small as possible. A continuous method of temperature control is to be preferred to an on-off method, since it is then possible to eliminate hunting. It will also frequently be found possible to incorporate in such a control a means for securing some degree of automatic compensation for changes in the temperature of the surroundings.[32] However, for any given installation, there is a definite limit to the sensitivity of a continuous control device beyond which the control will cause hunting.[33] In general, the greater the lags in the installation, the smaller will be the sensitivity of the control at the point at which hunting starts.

It is hoped that sufficient information has been given here for a reasonable choice of the type of control in a particular application. The important subject of temperature control has not been comprehensively treated by any single author, so that it is necessary to search the original literature for detailed information on the subject. The references cited above will

---

[31] J. M. Sturtevant, *Rev. Sci. Instruments*, **9**, 331 (1938); *J. Phys. Chem.*, **45**, 127 (1941).

[32] See, for example, J. M. Sturtevant, *Rev. Sci. Instruments*, **9**, 276 (1938).

[33] L. B. Turner, *Proc. Cambridge Phil. Soc.*, **32**, 663 (1936); *J. Inst. Elec. Engrs. London*, **81**, 399 (1937).

serve as leads. Particular attention should be given to the temperature symposium[34] of the American Institute of Physics.

III. MEASUREMENT OF ELECTRICAL ENERGY

Measurements of electrical energy can be carried out with an exceptional degree of accuracy using readily available instruments. All modern calorimetric measurements are, therefore, in principle if not in fact, referred to measurements of electrical energy, the calorimeter itself serving as an instrument for comparing the chemical or physical energy change in the system under investigation with electrical energy. The energy dissipated in a resistor in an alternating-current circuit cannot be determined with as great accuracy as that in a direct-current circuit, so that, without exception, d.-c. circuits are employed in calorimetry. Aside from this consideration, the use of a. c. would have some advantages; in particular, electrical leakage to the very low voltage d.-c. circuits used in temperature measurement would give less trouble.

The fundamental quantities in measuring electrical energy are potential difference, resistance, and time. If a potential difference, V, measured in international volts, is impressed on a resistance, R, measured in international ohms, for a period of t seconds, the energy dissipated is V^2t/R international joules, or $V^2t/4.1833R$ defined calories. We shall consider first the methods for measuring V^2/R, and then those for measuring time.

1. Measurement of V^2/R

Potential differences are determined by comparison, by means of a potentiometer (page 322), with a standard cell. The resistance of the calorimeter heater may be determined by a Wheatstone bridge such as those used in resistance thermometry (page 319). A more usual procedure is to compare the potential drop across the heater with that across a standard resistor connected in series with it. If the resistance of the standard resistor is R_s and the potential drop across it is V_s, it is evident that the electrical power input is $V^2/R = VV_s/R_s$.

If a good resistance bridge is available, there is no difficulty in preparing a homemade resistance standard reliable to 0.01% or better, provided the resistance is not below about 10 ohms. The resistor is bifilar wound of No. 28 to 34 double silk-covered manganin wire; a cardboard form can be used. After repeated applications of thin layers of glyptal varnish fol-

---

[34] *Temperature, Its Measurement and Control in Science and Industry.* Reinhold, New York, 1941. See also R. L. Weber, *Temperature Measurement and Control*, Blakiston, Philadelphia, 1941.

lowed by baking at 125°, the resistor is mounted in a copper cylinder and hermetically sealed with wax. The resistor should be provided with current-carrying and potential leads. Frequent checks of its resistance should be made until its stability has been demonstrated. The calorimeter heater should be constructed of material having a low temperature coefficient of resistivity. It will usually be found that the resistance of the heater remains sufficiently constant so that it is unnecessary to determine both V and V_s in each experiment, it being sufficient to check occasionally the constancy of their ratio.

Both the standard resistor and the calorimeter heater are equipped with four copper leads, two of which are for measuring the potential drops. The

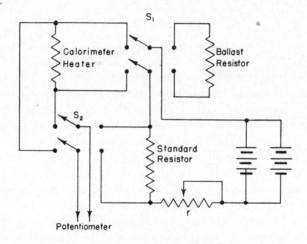

Fig. 7.—Calorimeter heater circuit.

potential leads to the calorimeter heater are attached to the current-carrying leads between the calorimeter and the jacket surrounding it at such a point that the measured potential will include that part of the potential drop in the current leads which supplies energy to the calorimeter. Ordinarily, the proper point of attachment will be approximately halfway between the calorimeter and the jacket. The potential leads can be of relatively fine wire; in deciding on the size of the current leads, consideration must be given to the opposing requirements of minimizing both the energy dissipation in the leads and heat conduction by the leads.

The accurate evaluation of V^2/R is practically impossible unless V is reasonably constant. The most convenient source of constant low voltage is the lead storage cell. A sufficient number of these are used in a series–parallel arrangement in order to obtain the desired voltage with a current drain on each cell not exceeding about 0.1 ampere. The batteries should be discharged into a "dummy" resistor of approximately the same resistance as the calorimeter heater for a period of an hour or more before use, so that they will come to constant voltage.

Figure 7 illustrates a simple circuit for the control of the calorimeter heater current and the measurement of V^2/R. The variable resistor, r, should be of good quality with low temperature coefficient and constant low contact resistance. In particular, the contact resistance should not be affected by such disturbances as mechanical vibrations. These remarks concerning contact resistance apply also to the switch, S_1. If highly accurate timing is not necessary, an ordinary copper knife switch may be employed. Modifications of this switch required for accurate timing are discussed below.

2. Measurement of Time

An ordinary stop watch may be employed for time measurements in many cases. It should be calibrated by comparison over periods of a few hours with an accurate, e. g., an electric clock. It should be established that the calibration of the stop watch is independent of the amount the watch is run down. While a stop watch may be read to 0.2 second, it is very doubtful that the manual closing and opening of the heater switch, S_1 (Fig. 7), can be synchronized with the starting and stopping of the watch with this degree of precision. The psychological error involved can be lessened by mechanical coupling between the switch, S_1, and the watch. Where the frequency of the a. c. power supply is sufficiently defined, electric clocks with a seconds hand can be employed. An electric stop clock or an impulse counter[35] can be conveniently synchronized with the heater switch by replacing the double pole switch shown in figure 7 by a triple pole switch, the third knife of which makes and breaks the clock circuit. With a well-constructed switch, the clock circuit will be synchronized with the heater circuit within 0.05 second or less. If the precision of timing thus obtained is insufficient, improvement will require very considerable elaboration. Several systems for highly reliable short-interval timing have been described.[36]

---

[35] F. T. Gucker, H. B. Pickard, and R. W. Planck, *J. Am. Chem. Soc.*, **61**, 459 (1939).

[36] W. P. White, *Phys. Rev.*, **31**, 686 (1910). D. R. Harper, *Natl. Bur. Standards*, (*U. S.*), *Bull.*, **11**, 259 (1915). E. Lange and E. O. Rounsefell, *Z. physik. Chem.*, **A142**, 351 (1929). E. Lange and J. Monheim, *ibid.*, **A149**, 51 (1930). N. S. Osborne, H. F. Stimson, and E. F. Fiock, *J. Research Natl. Bur. Standards*, **5**, 411 (1930). J. M. Sturtevant, *J. Phys. Chem.*, **45**, 127 (1941).

3.   Measurement of Electrical Energy by Means of a Coulometer

A coulometer[37] measures the product of current by time, by means of the amount of a chemical change produced, such as the plating out of silver from solution or the liberation of iodine from iodide.   Since the development of precise and convenient methods of measuring both resistance and potential, there has been no necessity for using coulometers in the ordinary measurement of electrical energy.   Therefore, these instruments will not be discussed here, although they have one characteristic which may be of importance in some calorimetric applications.   A coulometer measures the integral $\int V/R\ dt$ correctly even for a variable current.   Unfortunately it does not measure directly the energy dissipated in the resistor, which is given by $\int V^2/R\ dt$, unless the current is such a function of time that $(\bar{V})^2 = \bar{V^2}$.

IV.   GENERAL REMARKS ON CALORIMETRY

Heat energy is difficult to control and therefore to measure.   No heat insulator corresponds in perfection to the insulating materials for electrical energy, nor are there conductors of heat energy which do not absorb large quantities of heat.   These and other difficulties have brought about extensive elaboration of calorimetric equipment to meet more exacting requirements of precision, and the development of corrections for the remaining errors.   In this section, some of the more important types of calorimeters and calorimetric methods are briefly characterized.   Detailed discussions are given in later sections.   For a general treatment, particularly of the theory, of calorimetric methods, the reader is referred to White.[38]

1.   Uniformity of Temperature

In general, the temperature of a body can be observed only in a single region, or at best in a few selected regions.   Therefore, not only the calorimeter, but also its surroundings, should be at uniform and measurable temperatures, so that heat losses can be accurately evaluated and corrected for.   Temperature uniformity is obtained in two ways: by thorough stirring in a liquid; and by taking advantage of the high thermal conductivity of metals, particularly copper.   Efficient stirring of a liquid is accomplished in most cases by a propeller, preferably mounted in a tube

---

[37] Ostwald-Luther, *Physikochemische Messungen.* 4th ed., Akadem. Verlagsgesellschaft, Leipzig, 1925, p. 564.   G. A. Hulett, in H. S. Taylor, *Treatise on Physical Chemistry*, 2nd ed., Vol. I, Van Nostrand, New York, 1931, p. 591.   W. A. Roth and H. Troitzsch, *Z. Elektrochem.*, **36**, 242 (1930).

[38] W. P. White, *The Modern Calorimeter.*   Chem. Catalog Co., New York, 1928.

through which the liquid streams.[39]   A reciprocating stirrer, that is, a ring
or series of rings which is moved up and down in the liquid, is inefficient
if there is a relatively large central obstruction, such as a bomb, in the
liquid.   In order to avoid the direct connection between a calorimeter and
its surroundings by a stirrer shaft, or to permit tight sealing of the calorimeter, stirring can be accomplished by rotating the calorimeter,[40] or by a
magnetically operated reciprocating stirrer.[41]   In a long, thin calorimeter
containing a liquid, rapid temperature equalization is obtained even in the
absence of stirring,[42] but this form of calorimeter is unfavorable from the
point of view of thermal leakage to the surroundings because of its large
surface–volume ratio.   It is important that temperature uniformity be
rapidly established after the system has undergone a change.   This requires
that all material beyond the immediate range of the stirring, or other temperature-equalizing mechanism, should have as low a heat capacity and
lag as possible.   In particular, metal parts should be used in the construction of the calorimeter wherever possible, and insulating supports should
be as light as possible.   A strong support for a calorimeter, which is practically free of lag, is furnished by properly spaced loops of dental floss.

2.   Liquid and Aneroid Calorimeters

A quantity of heat is in most cases measured by the temperature rise
which it produces in a suitable calorimeter.   The commonest form of calorimeter is a metal shell filled with a stirred liquid.   Numerous examples
of this type of calorimeter will be found in later sections.   For some purposes, particularly at very high and very low temperatures, an aneroid
calorimeter replaces the liquid-filled calorimeter.   In the aneroid type,
the quantity of heat to be measured raises the temperature of a metal
block, usually constructed of copper because of the high thermal conductivity of this metal.

The lower the "dead" heat capacity of the calorimeter the higher is the
temperature change produced by a given amount of heat.   Thus, in the
determination of heat capacities by observing the temperature change
produced by a known amount of electrical energy, the substance under investigation itself is used as the calorimeter filling; in the case of solids, thin
metal vanes are placed inside the calorimeter to aid in heat distribution

[39] W. P. White, *op. cit.*, p. 65.

[40] S. G. Lipsett, F. M. G. Johnson, and O. Maas, *J. Am. Chem. Soc.*, **49**, 925, 1940
(1927).   K. L. Wolf and H. Frahm, *Z. physik. Chem.*, **A178**, 411 (1937).   J. M. Sturtevant, *J. Phys. Chem.*, **45**, 127 (1941).

[41] B. H. Carroll and J. H. Mathews, *J. Am. Chem. Soc.*, **46**, 30 (1924).   J. H. Awbery
and E. Griffiths, *Proc. Phys. Soc. London*, **52**, 770 (1940).

[42] J. M. Sturtevant, *Physics*, **7**, 232 (1936); *J. Am. Chem. Soc.*, **59**, 1528 (1937).

(page 353). In a bomb calorimeter (page 383), the amount of water surrounding the bomb should be no more than is needed for efficient stirring. In the case of an aneroid calorimeter, the optimum dimensions of the metal block are such as to give sufficiently rapid temperature equalization without undue dead heat capacity.

3. Nonisothermal Calorimeters

In nonisothermal calorimeters, heat quantities are estimated by the temperature changes they produce.

A. CONSTANT-TEMPERATURE ENVIRONMENT

The calorimeter is completely enclosed by a jacket of uniform temperature. The necessary degree of uniformity and accuracy of measurement of the jacket temperature depend on the leakage modulus of the calorimeter and on the desired accuracy in the over-all calorimetric measurement.[43] It is convenient, though not necessary, to have the jacket temperature held constant by automatic regulation (page 326).

Jacket Design.—A constant-temperature environment may be supplied by a jacket containing a stirred liquid, or by a relatively massive metal shield. The former type of jacket is employed in most work at ordinary temperatures, the latter type at low or high temperatures. In both cases, temperature uniformity is more readily obtained when the jacket heater is well distributed throughout the jacket; with aneroid jackets, this is particularly important. Complete distribution of the heating throughout the jacket may be accomplished by Daniels' procedure.[44] The inner and outer (metal) walls of the jacket are insulated from each other. The jacket liquid is an electrolyte of low conductivity. Heating results from an alternating potential applied to the jacket walls. The jacket itself should be reasonably well insulated thermally from its surroundings.

Heat Exchange between Calorimeter and Jacket.—The heat exchange between the calorimeter and its surrounding jacket has several causes. Those which depend chiefly on the temperature difference between the calorimeter and the jacket (the thermal head) are conduction by solid connections between them, convection and conduction by the intervening gas, and radiation. In addition, thermal leakage from the calorimeter may in part be due to evaporation from the calorimeter, a factor which is not solely dependent on the thermal head. Since the thermal leakage is always determined by direct observation, it is convenient to include in the

[43] W. P. White, *op. cit.*,[38] p. 50.

[44] F. Daniels, *J. Am. Chem. Soc.*, **38**, 1473 (1916). J. W. Williams and F. Daniels, *ibid.*, **46**, 903 (1924).

apparent thermal leakage the heat of stirring, which is independent of the thermal head.

Thermal leakage through solid connections, such as supports, electrical connections, etc., should be very small as compared with that due to other causes, provided the connections coming in from outside the jacket are in good thermal contact with the jacket before they go to the calorimeter. Evaporation should be eliminated as completely as possible; whenever possible the calorimeter should be tightly closed. If this is impossible, evaporation is lessened by having the jacket always warmer than the calorimeter.

If the thermal head is smaller than a few degrees, heat exchange due to radiation and gas conduction follows Newton's law. If T is the calorimeter temperature at time t and T_j is the jacket temperature:

$$dT/dt = K(T_j - T) \tag{9}$$

where K is the leakage modulus of the system. Heat exchange due to convection does not follow this law. Since it is very difficult to evaluate the thermal leakage unless equation (9) with a constant value of K is followed during an entire experiment, it is important to keep heat transfer due to convection to a minimum. According to White, this requires that the air gap (at atmospheric pressure) between calorimeter and jacket should not exceed 1 to 1.5 centimeters.

The heat loss during an experiment may be evaluated with lower relative accuracy if it is kept small. There are two general lines of attack in accomplishing this. Either K may be made small, or the thermal head may be kept small. We shall consider here some of the methods of reducing the leakage modulus.

The radiation contribution to the leakage modulus is minimized by having the outside surface of the calorimeter and the inside surface of the jacket highly polished. The conduction contribution[45] is decreased by evacuating the space between the calorimeter and jacket. This is almost universally done in low temperature calorimeters, but seldom at ordinary temperatures, particularly with liquid calorimeters and jackets, because of constructional difficulties. Conduction may also be reduced by using a vacuum-jacketed glass container (Dewar flask) as the calorimeter itself. The chief objection to this type of calorimeter is its relatively high lag, although, in spite of this, it has been employed in very precise work (page 414). The leakage modulus can be decreased by increasing the width of the air gap between the calorimeter and the jacket, provided an increase in convection is prevented by placing in the gap one or more very

---

[45] See D. R. Harper, *Natl. Bur. Standards* (*U. S.*), *Bull.* **11**, 319 (1915), for a discussion of the relative magnitudes of the radiation and conduction contributions.

thin metal convection shields. The heat capacity of these shields must be as small as possible in order to avoid increasing the lag of the calorimeter.

Correction for Heat Exchange.—As pointed out by White,[38] the term "correction" here is somewhat misleading. It is preferable to consider the unknown quantity of heat as measured in two parts, one of which produces a change in the temperature of the calorimeter. The other part flows either from or to the calorimeter, and its magnitude is deduced from the physical laws governing its flow. This point of view emphasizes the fact

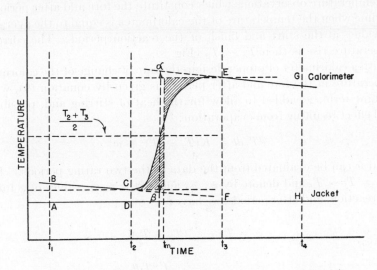

Fig. 8.—Typical time–temperature record for a calorimetric experiment.

that it is possible to carry out precise experiments in a calorimeter which undergoes considerable heat exchange with its surroundings, provided that due care is exercised in controlling and evaluating this heat leakage.

Figure 8 represents the time–temperature curve for a calorimetric experiment on a relatively rapid process (combustion, mixing, electrical calibration, etc.). For a prolonged experiment with a slow process, a curve would be obtained having a relatively much longer period of calorimeter temperature rise. The discussion below does not apply to the latter type of process. As indicated in figure 8, the observations are divided into three sets, those from times t_1 to t_2, and t_3 to t_4, constituting rating periods which may be called the *fore* and *after* periods, and those from t_2 to t_3 constituting the *reaction* period. The temperature changes in the fore and after periods are exaggerated in the diagram. According to equation (9), these changes should be represented by curves; however, K is small enough so that, over the relatively short time intervals involved, these changes can be approximated by straight lines.

Several methods have been devised for evaluating the heat exchange with the surroundings. We shall consider a method which gives results of moderate accuracy in simple cases, and three other methods which can be applied in accurate work.

If the process under observation is very rapid, a fairly accurate value for the corrected temperature rise may be obtained by linear extrapolation of the temperature observations which constitute the fore and after periods to the time when the temperature of the calorimeter is equal to the average of the values at the start and finish of the reaction period. The corrected temperature rise is then $T_\alpha - T_\beta$ (Fig. 8).

With a calorimeter of proper design, the rate of change of the calorimeter temperature in the fore and after periods is given by equation (9), with a constant term, w, added to allow for the heat of stirring and, possibly, a small effect resulting from evaporation:

$$dT/dt = K(T_j - T) + w \qquad (10)$$

K and w can be evaluated from the data of the two rating periods. If we set $\varphi = T_j - T$, and denote by $\tilde{\varphi}_f$, $\tilde{\varphi}_r$, and $\tilde{\varphi}_a$ the *mean* values of φ for the fore, reaction, and after periods, we have:

$$\left.\begin{aligned}
\tilde{\varphi}_f &= T_j - \frac{1}{2}(T_1 + T_2) \\[2ex]
\tilde{\varphi}_r &= T_j - \frac{\int_{t_2}^{t_3} T dt}{t_3 - t_2} \\[2ex]
\tilde{\varphi}_a &= T_j - \frac{1}{2}(T_3 + T_4)
\end{aligned}\right\} \qquad (11)$$

where the integral is evaluated from the plot by counting squares or by means of a planimeter. K and w are evaluated from the equations:[46]

$$R_f \equiv \frac{T_2 - T_1}{t_2 - t_1} = K\tilde{\varphi}_f + w \qquad (12)$$

and

$$R_a \equiv \frac{T_4 - T_3}{t_4 - t_3} = K\tilde{\varphi}_a + w \qquad (13)$$

Here, R_f and R_a are the mean rates of temperature change in the fore and

---

[46] See, however, the interesting discussion by A. King and H. Grover, *J. Applied Phys.*, **12**, 557 (1941).

after periods. The "corrected" temperature increase during the process is then:

$$\Delta T = (T_3 - T_2) - (K\tilde{\varphi}_r + w)(t_3 - t_2) \tag{14}$$

If the term w is sufficiently constant from experiment to experiment and is considered as being known, one of the rating periods can be dropped, so far as the calculations are concerned. In this case we have:

$$K = \frac{R_a - w}{\tilde{\varphi}_a} \tag{15}$$

so that

$$\Delta T = (T_3 - T_2) - \left[(R_a - w) \frac{\tilde{\varphi}_r}{\tilde{\varphi}_a} + w \right] (t_3 - t_2) \tag{16}$$

$$= (T_3 - T_2) - \left[R_a + (R_a - w) \frac{\tilde{\varphi}_r - \tilde{\varphi}_a}{\tilde{\varphi}_a} \right] (t_3 - t_2) \tag{17}$$

Equation (17) is the basis for the method which White[47] calls the "first Geophysical Laboratory method." It is to be noted that, in many cases, $(\tilde{\varphi}_r - \tilde{\varphi}_a)/\tilde{\varphi}_a$ will be a relatively small number, so that w in these cases need be known with only small accuracy.

In some cases, the thermal head cannot be directly measured, for example, if the effective temperature of the environment cannot be determined, as with the older, incompletely jacketed calorimeters. In such cases, some form of the so-called Regnault-Pfaundler method is used. This method is not precise in that the assumption is made that the total heat gain or loss by the calorimeter, aside from that due to the process being studied, follows equation (9). The effect of stirring (and evaporation) is partially taken into account by using the observed calorimeter temperatures to evaluate an *effective* temperature of the surroundings, which differs more or less from the actual temperature of the surroundings because of the stirring effect. If it is assumed that the effective temperature of the environment remains constant, differences in the thermal head are equal to the corresponding differences in calorimeter temperature. Therefore:

$$K = \frac{R_a - R_f}{\tilde{\varphi}_a - \tilde{\varphi}_f} = \frac{R_a - R_f}{\tilde{T}_a - \tilde{T}_f} \tag{18}$$

where $\tilde{T}_a$ and $\tilde{T}_f$ are the mean calorimeter temperatures in the corresponding periods. Since $\tilde{\varphi}_r - \tilde{\varphi}_f = \tilde{T}_r - \tilde{T}_f$, we obtain:

$$\Delta T = (T_3 - T_2) - \left[R_f + \frac{R_a - R_f}{\tilde{T}_a - \tilde{T}_f} (\tilde{T}_r - \tilde{T}_f) \right] (t_3 - t_2) \tag{19}$$

[47] W. P. White, *The Modern Calorimeter.* Chem. Catalog Co., New York, 1928, p. 39

It can be shown that the two rating periods can be interchanged in equation (19), so that:

$$\Delta T = (T_3 - T_2) - \left[R_a + \frac{R_a - R_f}{\tilde{T}_a - \tilde{T}_f}(\tilde{T}_r - \tilde{T}_a)\right](t_3 - t_2) \qquad (20)$$

This equation forms the basis for the "second Geophysical Laboratory method,"[48] which can be applied when K remains reasonably constant (say within $\pm 2\%$) from day to day. In this case, the predetermined value of K is used in equation (20):

$$\Delta T = (T_3 - T_2) - [R_a + K(\tilde{T}_r - \tilde{T}_a)](t_3 - t_2) \qquad (21)$$

This expression gives accurate results in cases where $\tilde{T}_r - \tilde{T}_a$ is small, as frequently happens, since then K is multiplied by a small quantity.

In the method employed by Dickinson,[49] the integral in equation (11) is very readily evaluated. A time, t_m, can be found, such that:

$$(T_i - T_2)(t_m - t_2) + (T_i - T_3)(t_3 - t_m) =$$
$$\int_{t_2}^{t_3}(T_i - T)dt = T_i(t_3 - t_2) - \int_{t_2}^{t_3} Tdt \qquad (22)$$

If we neglect the slight rise of T above T_3 just before t_3 (this rise is greatly exaggerated in figure 8), we readily see from the geometry of the time-temperature curve that t_m is to be taken so that the two shaded areas are equal. Dickinson found that, in combustion experiments, t_m is very nearly the time at which the calorimeter temperature has reached the value $0.60\ (T_3 - T_2) + T_2$. (If the temperature curve were a true exponential curve, the factor here would be 0.63.) Thus, if one can make a fairly accurate estimate of the temperature increase to be expected in an experiment, the heat-exchange correction can be evaluated from a single observation during the reaction period. For limitations in the application of this method, the reader is referred to Dickinson's paper,[49] and to the discussion by White.[50]

In the foregoing discussion, no account has been taken of possible lags in the various temperature measurements. The heat exchange between the calorimeter and the jacket is primarily determined by the temperatures of the outside *surface* of the former and the inside *surface* of the latter. Error will be introduced if the temperature of the surface of a poorly stirred calorimeter, during a period when its temperature is rapidly changing, is inferred from the reading of a thermometer located in its interior. This error is eliminated, except for thermometric lag, which can be made very small in the case of electrical thermometers, if the thermal head is evaluated

---

[48] W. P. White, *op. cit.*, p. 42.

[49] H. C. Dickinson, *Natl. Bur. Standards*, (*U. S.*), *Bull.* **11**, 189 (1915).

[50] W. P. White, *op. cit.*, p. 57.

by thermocouples or resistance thermometers suitably distributed over the surfaces which control the heat exchange. It should be pointed out that lag errors in the evaluation of ΔT are not necessarily confined to those involved in the computation of the heat-leakage correction. White[51] has given a thorough discussion of the various types of lag occurring in calorimetric observations; in particular, he has shown that all *constant* lags introduce negligible errors if the calorimeter is experimentally calibrated.

B. ADIABATIC METHOD

Heat exchange between the calorimeter and its environment is eliminated if the thermal head is zero at all times. This fact is the basis of the adiabatic method originally employed by Person[52] and later independently carried to a high degree of development by Richards[53] and his collaborators.

The maintenance of a zero thermal head is an ideal situation which cannot be realized in actual practice. This simple fact has been often neglected in considerations of the adiabatic method. Actually, the observation of the smooth calorimeter-temperature–time curve, which is needed for the evaluation of the heat-leakage correction in the ordinary method is replaced in the adiabatic method by a manual or automatic adjustment of the jacket temperature. It may happen, particularly in experiments of short duration, that the evaluation of the heat-loss correction can be carried out in the ordinary method with greater accuracy than can be attributed to the "elimination" of the heat loss in the adiabatic procedure. In other words, it is usually not the *size* of the heat-loss term which is important, but the accuracy with which it can be determined.

A very instructive discussion of the relative merits of the ordinary and adiabatic methods has been given by White.[54] We shall mention here four of the advantages of the adiabatic procedure which have led to its very widespread adoption: (1) In the evaluation of the heat-leakage correction in nonadiabatic calorimetry, the assumption is made that the leakage modulus, K, remains constant during an experiment. Errors due to variation in K, and to deviation of the heat exchange from Newton's law, are reduced in the adiabatic method, since the multiplier of K, the thermal head, is small. (2) Maintenance of a small thermal head reduces convection in the air gap. It is thus permissible to use considerably wider air gaps, with correspondingly smaller leakage moduli, in the adiabatic method. This advantage can, however, be realized in the ordinary method, as mentioned above, by employing convection shields. (3)

---

[51] W. P. White, *op. cit.*, p. 86.
[52] See F. T. Gucker, *J. Chem. Education*, **8**, 2398 (1931).
[53] T. W. Richards, *J. Am. Chem. Soc.*, **31**, 1275 (1909).
[54] W. P. White, *op. cit.*,[47] p. 116.

Troubles due to evaporation from an incompletely sealed calorimeter are less serious in the adiabatic method. However, it should again be emphasized that complete elimination of evaporation by tight sealing is always desirable if it can be accomplished. *(4)* The greatest advantage of the adiabatic procedure comes in its application to prolonged[55] calorimetric experiments (see Section IX, pp. 421–431). In such cases, the heat-loss correction in the ordinary method might be as large as, or even larger than, the total quantity of heat to be measured, and it could only be evaluated on the basis of rating periods of such long duration that the relatively simple computational methods outlined above would have to be considerably amplified. On the other hand, in the adiabatic method, the heat-loss term can be held to a small fraction of the total and correction for any deviation from strict adiabaticity can be based on relatively short rating periods. In fact, with constant stirring heat, the deviation from adiabaticity will, in some cases, be sufficiently constant so that it need be determined only occasionally. This is because, as mentioned above, variations in the magnitude of K are of less importance when the thermal head is always small.

In protracted experiments the change of the temperature of the calorimeter is slow enough that the temperature of the jacket can be held equal to that of the calorimeter much more accurately than in experiments on rapid processes. In such cases, it is very advantageous to employ automatic regulation of the jacket temperature. This is conveniently accomplished by a galvanometer–photocell relay (Section III, page 328), the temperature difference between the calorimeter and jacket being indicated by a thermel.

The design of adiabatic calorimeters is similar to that of other calorimeters, with the exception that wider air gaps are usually employed. Examples of adiabatic calorimeters will be found in later sections.

C. TWIN CALORIMETERS

For some purposes, the twin calorimeters first employed by Joule[56] and later by Pfaundler[57] are very valuable. The apparatus consists of two calorimeters as nearly identical in construction as possible, supported within one jacket. The calorimeters can be electrically heated by two heaters (usually of equal resistances) connected in series. If, during an experiment, the temperatures of both calorimeters change at very nearly the same rate, the thermal leakages will be very nearly the same. While this does not

---

[55] See the interesting discussion by F. Barry, *J. Am. Chem. Soc.*, **44**, 899 (1922).

[56] J. P. Joule, *Mem. Proc. Manchester Lit. Phil. Soc.*, **2**, 559 (1845).

[57] L. Pfaundler, *Sitzber. Akad. Wiss. Wien Math.-naturw. Klasse*, **59**, 145 (1869); **100**, 352 (1891).

necessarily mean that the error due to thermal leakage vanishes,[58] it does follow that any small residual error can be accurately evaluated by suitable rating periods. When the adiabatic method is applied to twin calorimeters, virtually complete elimination of the need for any heat leakage correction can be accomplished. Of course, in this case, it is still necessary to make suitable corrections for any differences between the two calorimeters with respect to stirring heats, evaporation effects, etc.

The chief advantage of twin calorimeters is that they permit relative measurements to be made in such a way that the observations of temperature upon which the results are based are essentially differential observations. It thus becomes possible to utilize most advantageously the propperties of thermocouples as indicators of temperature *differences*. For example, in the determination of the heat capacity of a solution, one calorimeter contains pure solvent while the other contains solution. When both calorimeters are heated with precisely the same electrical energy input, through a certain temperature interval, a small temperature difference between the calorimeters will result. This difference can be measured with great precision and, after correction for slight differences in heat losses, stirring heats, etc., leads to a very accurate evaluation of the heat capacity of the solution relative to that of the solvent.

Twin calorimeters have been very successfully applied to measurements of rapid processes, particularly to heats of dilution in the range of low concentrations within which the heat effects are very small. Illustrations of these applications will be found in Section VIII (pages 414–417). Twin calorimeters should be especially valuable in the observation of very slow heat effects.[59] In the case of an exothermic process, the tare calorimeter would be heated sufficiently to maintain its temperature equal to that of the reaction calorimeter, while, in the case of an endothermic process, the solution calorimeter would be heated to hold its temperature equal to that of the tare. At the end of the experiment, the two calorimeters would be heated with their heaters connected in series to determine the difference in the heat capacities of the two calorimetric systems. The successful application of this procedure awaits the development of an accurate method for evaluating the integral, $\int_{t_1}^{t_2} (V^2/R)dt$, where V, the potential impressed on the heater of resistance R, is a function of time t. The advantage of differential temperature measurements characteristic of twin calorimeters is obtained to some extent with a single calorimeter when the temperature

---

[58] See W. P. White, *op. cit.*,[47] p. 126.

[59] To date, only slight application of twin calorimeters to slow processes has been made [A. V. Hill, *J. Physiol.*, **43**, 261 (1911); H. H. Dixon and N. G. Ball, *Sci. Proc. Roy. Dublin Soc.*, **16**, 153 (1920)], and the work so far reported has not employed the compensation heating suggested here.

measurements are made with a thermel the reference junctions of which
are immersed in a "cold calorimeter" such as that described on page 326.

4. Isothermal Calorimeters

In an isothermal calorimeter, a quantity of heat is measured by the
amount of an isothermal phase change which it produces in the calorimeter
material.   The most common and most convenient type of isothermal
calorimeter is the Bunsen[60] ice calorimeter.   The calorimeter usually con-

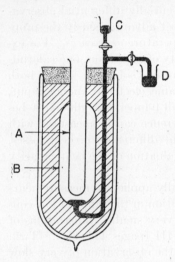

sists of a glass tube, A (see Fig. 9), sealed
into another tube, B, which is filled with
air-free water and mercury.   The bottom of
the outer tube connects by means of a small
glass tube with a mercury reservoir, C, and
a capillary tube leading to a removable
weighed vessel containing mercury.   Tube
B is completely immersed in a mixture of ice
and water in a Dewar flask.   A portion of
the water in B is frozen, after it has been
cooled to $0°$, by temporarily placing a freezing mixture in calorimeter tube A.   An exothermic reaction occurring in A causes some
of the ice in B to melt, giving rise to a contraction in volume and a decrease in the
weight of the mercury in D.   The very slight

Fig. 9.—Ice calorimeter.

heat exchange of the calorimeter with its
surroundings is determined in a rating
period.   The apparatus is calibrated by an electrical heater, or by dropping into it a body of known heat capacity previously brought to a known
temperature.   Because of the isothermal characteristic of the ice calorimeter, it is possible to keep the heat exchange with the surroundings very
low.   The apparatus is therefore particularly useful in the determination
of small and very slow heat effects.   Its chief disadvantage is that it
can be employed only at $0°$.   This disadvantage is partially removed by
employing other substances in place of ice.   Diphenylmethane (m. p.,

---

   [60] R. Bunsen, *Ann. Physik*, **141**, 1 (1870).   For more modern descriptions of ice calorimeters, see Ostwald-Luther, *Physikochemische Messungen*, 4th ed., Akadem. Verlagsgesellschaft, Leipzig, 1925, p. 393; W. A. Patrick and C. E. Greider, *J. Phys. Chem.*, **29**, 1031
(1925); W. Swietoslawski, A. Zmaczyński, I. Zlotowski, J. Salcewicz, and J. Usakiewicz,
Compt. rend., **196**, 1970 (1933), *Roczniki Chem.*, **14**, 250 (1934); W. Hieber and F.
Mühlbauer, *Z. anorg. Chem.*, **186**, 97 (1930); W. Hieber and E. Reindl, *Z. Elektrochem.*,
46, 559 (1940).

24.7°) has been used[61] for this purpose, as have also diphenyl ether[62] and acetic acid.[63]

The vaporization of a liquid or the condensation of a vapor may also be employed for the measurement of heat in an isothermal calorimeter. For example, Simon and Ruhemann[64] have described a calorimeter for determining heat capacities at low temperatures by the method of mixtures (page 372), the heat given up to the calorimeter by a body of slightly higher temperature dropped into it being measured by the increase in vapor pressure of the liquefied gas, such as hydrogen, contained in the calorimeter. Kraus[65] and his collaborators have determined the heat effects of rapid processes in liquid ammonia at its boiling point by measuring the amount of gas evolved by the heat of the reaction. Since isothermal calorimeters are not very frequently employed, no further attention will be given to them here.

5. Importance of Experimental Calibration

In the earlier days of calorimetry, the heat capacity of a calorimeter was frequently estimated from a knowledge of the masses and specific heats of the materials used in its construction. It cannot be too strongly emphasized, however, that calorimetric measurements should be based on electrical calibration wherever this is possible. Even in cases in which the use of an electrical heater for calibration purposes is impossible, as in the case of the rotating calorimeter of Lipsett, Johnson, and Maas,[40] calibration should be accomplished by making observations on a process with a known heat effect. Electrical, or, more generally, experimental, calibration is essential for several reasons. A calorimeter cannot possibly be a perfectly isolated body. The material connections between it and its surroundings have a finite heat capacity, and the only way to make proper allowance for the fraction of this heat capacity which is to be added to that of the calorimeter is through experimental calibration under conditions as nearly as possible like those in the subsequent measurements.

As mentioned above (page 341), White has shown that errors due to constant lags are negligible if experimental calibration is employed. This is

[61] A. N. Shchukarev, I. P. Krivobabko, and L. A. Shchukareva, *Physik. Z. Sowjetunion*, **5**, 722 (1934). M. M. Gordon, *Tsement*, **5**, No. 9–10, 39 (1937).

[62] T. Holmberg, *Soc. Sci. Fennica, Commentationes Phys.-Math.*, **9**, No. 17 (1938).

[63] L. de Visser, *Z. physik. Chem.*, **9**, 767 (1892).

[64] F. Simon and M. Ruhemann, *Z. physik. Chem.*, **129**, 321 (1927). See also C. A. Taylor and W. H. Rinkenbach, *J. Am. Chem. Soc.*, **46**, 1505 (1924).

[65] C. A. Kraus and J. A. Ridderhof, *J. Am. Chem. Soc.*, **56**, 79, (1934). C. A. Kraus and R. F. Prescott, *ibid.*, **56**, 86 (1934). C. A. Kraus and F. C. Schmidt, *ibid.*, **56**, 2297 (1934).

perhaps one of the best reasons for uniformly employing this method of calibration.

6. Calorimeters of Special Types

The variety of designs in calorimetric work is evidence of the fact that it is impossible to state a few simple principles of design which apply to all cases.   We shall mention briefly a few calorimeters of special design.

Chall and Doepke[66] have measured heat effects in liquid ammonia at room temperature.   Calorimeters for use at more or less elevated temperatures have been described by several authors.[67]   Daniels *et al.*[68] devised a calorimeter having quartz windows with which the heats of photochemical processes can be determined.   Rather frequent use[69] has been made of the Favre-Silbermann calorimeter, in which the temperature change is indicated by contraction or expansion of the (unstirred) calorimeter liquid.

V.   HEAT CAPACITIES

The *heat capacity*[70] of a system at temperature T is the limit, as δT approaches zero, of the ratio $\delta Q/\delta T$, where δQ is the amount of heat which must be introduced into the system to increase its temperature from T to $T + \delta T$.   In accordance with the discussion on page 314, we must distinguish the cases in which the system is heated at constant volume and at constant pressure.   Thus, the heat capacity at constant volume is:

$$C_v = (\partial U/\partial T)_v \tag{23}$$

and the heat capacity at constant pressure is:

$$C_p = [\partial(U + PV)/\partial T]_p = (\partial H/\partial T)_p \tag{24}$$

The unit of mass in these expressions is the mole.   If the unit of mass is the

[66] P. Chall and O. Doepke, *Z. Elektrochem.*, **37**, 357 (1931).

[67] See, for example, W. P. White, *op. cit.*,[47] p. 159; L. Navias, *J. Am. Ceramic Soc.*, **6**, 1268 (1923); J. D. Davis, *Ind. Eng. Chem., Ind. Ed.*, **16**, 726 (1924); W. Kangro and R. Grau, *Z. physik. Chem., Bodenstein-Festband*, 85 (1931); L. G. Carpenter and T. F. Harle, *Proc. Phys. Soc. London*, **44**, 383 (1932); O. Kubachewski and A. Walter, *Z. Elektrochem.*, **45**, 630 (1939); L. G. Carpenter and A. R. Bryant, *J. Sci. Instruments*, **16**, 183 (1939).

[68] J. L. Magee, T. W. DeWitt, E. C. Smith, and F. Daniels, *J. Am. Chem. Soc.*, **61**, 3529 (1939).

[69] See H. Schottky, *Physik. Z.*, **10**, 634 (1909).   K. R. Andress and E. Berl, *Z. physik. Chem.*, **122**, 81 (1926).

[70] G. N. Lewis and M. Randall, *Thermodynamics and the Free Energy of Chemical Substances*.   McGraw-Hill, New York, 1923, p. 56.

gram, c_v and c_p are the *specific heats* at constant volume and at constant pressure. For an ideal gas $C_p - C_v = R$, the gas constant; in general:[71]

$$C_p - C_v = -T \frac{(\partial V/\partial T)_p^2}{(\partial V/\partial P)_T} \qquad (25)$$

a quantity which is small in many condensed systems.

1. Importance

The absorption of energy by a substance as its temperature is increased is the result of increasing the populations in the higher energy states available for the molecules. At the relatively low temperatures available to heat-capacity measurements, these higher states are states of higher translational and rotational energy of the molecules, and higher energies of internal motions such as vibrations and rotations of atoms and groups relative to each other. In the case of solids, lattice vibrations and rotations are also of importance. It is thus evident that the study of heat capacities is of the greatest importance in connection with theories of molecular structure and of the various states of aggregation of matter.

Several applications of heat-capacity data may be cited to show their great importance, such as the calculation of the temperature coefficients of heats of reaction, the evaluation of entropies and free energies by means of the third law of thermodynamics, and the establishment of purity by determination of the heat capacity of a solid substance just below its melting point.

A. CHANGE OF HEAT OF REACTION WITH TEMPERATURE

Since the value of ΔH for a reaction is the difference between the sums of the heat contents of the reactants and of the products, it follows from equation (24) that:

$$[\partial(\Delta H)/\partial T]_p = \Delta C_p \qquad (26)$$

where ΔC_p is the sum of the molal heat capacities of the products less that of the reactants. This relation is known as the Kirchhoff, or Person-Kirchhoff,[72] law. Methods of integrating this equation are discussed by Lewis and Randall and others.

The integrated forms of equation (26) enable one to calculate ΔH at any temperature from a measurement of the heat of reaction at a single temperature and a knowledge of the heat capacities of the reactants and products.

B. EVALUATION OF ENTROPIES BY MEANS OF THE THIRD LAW

A restricted statement[73] of the third law of thermodynamics is as follows: The entropy of all "perfect" crystals is zero at the absolute zero, and their heat capaci-

---

[71] G. N. Lewis and M. Randall, *op. cit.*, p. 136.

[72] G. Kirchhoff, *Ann. Physik*, **103**, 177 (1858); G. N. Lewis and M. Randall, *op. cit.*, p. 101. See also F. T. Gucker, *J. Chem. Education*, **8**, 2398 (1931).

[73] J. G. Aston, in H. S. Taylor and S. M. Glasstone, *Treatise on Physical Chemistry*,

(*Footnote continued on page 348.*)

ties approach zero asymptotically near the absolute zero. A "perfect" crystal is one in which a geometrical arrangement of atoms is repeated *without modification* throughout the crystal.

In any infinitesimal process carried out reversibly at constant pressure at temperature T, the entropy change dS is:

$$dS = dH/T \tag{27}$$

It follows from equation (24) that:

$$dS = (C_p/T)dT \tag{28}$$

Integration gives for the entropy of the system at temperature T:

$$S - S_0 = \int_0^T (C_p/T)dT = \int_0^T C_p d \ln T \tag{29}$$

According to the third law, if the system under consideration is composed of a pure substance which forms perfect crystals at $T = 0$, then $S_0 = 0$. If the substance undergoes any phase transitions in the interval $T = 0$ to $T = T$, equation (29) must be modified:

$$S = \int_0^{T_1} C_p d \ln T + (\Delta H_1/T_1) +$$
$$\int_{T_1}^{T_2} C_p \, d \ln T + (\Delta H_2/T_2) + \dots \tag{30}$$

Here, T_1 is the temperature of the first phase transition, ΔH_1 is the isothermal heat of that transition, and so on. In many cases, several phase transitions will be involved, including transitions between different crystalline modifications, melting, and vaporization.[74]

It is obviously impossible to extend measurements of C_p to $T = 0$, so that an extrapolation has to be performed from some low temperature. In the most reliable determinations of entropy, the heat-capacity measurements are extended down to temperatures obtainable by evaporating solid hydrogen under reduced pressure (15° K. or lower). At these low temperatures, the heat capacity is in general very small, and in most cases can be assumed to be proportional to T^3. According to theoretical considerations, it is C_v which should be proportional to T^3 at very low temperatures. However, in the region in which this proportionality holds, the difference between C_v and C_p is usually negligible. With this assumption it readily follows that:

$$\int_0^T C_p d \ln T \approx {}^1\!/_3 (C_p)_T \tag{31}$$

where $(C_p)_T$ is the value of the heat capacity at some low temperature T near 10°

3rd ed., Vol. I, Van Nostrand, New York, 1942, p. 515. See also G. N. Lewis and M. Randall, *op. cit.*, p. 435; R. R. Wenner, *Thermochemical Calculations*, McGraw-Hill, New York, 1941, p. 86; G. S. Parks and H. M. Huffman, *Free Energies of Some Organic Compounds*, Reinhold, New York, 1932, p. 31; E. F. Burton, H. Grayson Smith, and J. O. Wilhelm, *Phenomena at the Temperature of Liquid Helium*, Reinhold, New York, 1940, p. 156.

[74] Methods of determining the heats of phase transitions are considered in Section VII (pages 394–407).

K. The integrals in equation (30) above the lowest temperature at which measurements are made are evaluated graphically.

If the approximation referred to above is not sufficiently accurate, or if the actual measurements do not extend to temperatures as low as 15° K., considerably more elaborate extrapolation procedures must be adopted. These are based on the theoretical treatments of Einstein, Debye, and Born and von Kármán. The reader is referred to the discussions by Aston[75] and Wenner[76] for details concerning these extrapolation methods. Kelley, Parks, and Huffman[77] have described a semiempirical method of extrapolation which has been applied to many organic compounds for which measurements have been extended only down to liquid air temperatures (about 90° K.). This procedure does not lead to very accurate extrapolations, but it is very easy to apply and gives results which are sufficiently accurate for many purposes.

C. FREE ENERGIES

From a practical point of view, one of the most important applications of entropies evaluated from heat-capacity data or by statistical methods is in the calculation of free energies and equilibrium constants. In the words of Rossini:[78] "The ultimate end of chemical thermodynamics may be said to be the evaluation of the free energy of formation, from the appropriate fundamental units of matter, of every substance in all possible states. . . . From the standpoint of the compilation of the ultimate or master table of chemical thermodynamics, the most important thermodynamic properties, in addition to the free energy itself, are the heat content and the entropy; and the successful evolution of the master table is predicted upon the existence of accurate values of the heats of formation and the entropies of formation."

The standard entropy of formation of a substance, ΔS^0, is the entropy increase accompanying the formation of one mole of the substance in its standard state from its elements, taken in their standard states. Entropies of formation usually refer to the standard temperature of 25° C. The entropy increase accompanying a chemical reaction with reactants and products in their standard states is readily obtained as the sum of the absolute entropies, or of the entropies of formation, of the products minus the corresponding sum for the reactants.

For any isothermal process, the important relation:[79]

$$\Delta F = \Delta H - T \Delta S \tag{32}$$

applies. Here, ΔF and ΔH are the increases in free energy and heat content accompanying the reaction. If the process is a reaction in which all of the substances involved are in their standard states, equation (32) becomes:

$$\Delta F^0 = \Delta H^0 - T \Delta S^0 \tag{33}$$

[75] J. G. Aston, loc. cit.,[73] p. 620.

[76] R. R. Wenner, op. cit.,[73] p. 142.

[77] K. K. Kelley, G. S. Parks, and H. M. Huffman, J. Phys. Chem., **33**, 1802 (1929).

[78] F. D. Rossini, Chem. Revs., **18**, 233 (1936).

[79] G. N. Lewis and M. Randall, op. cit.,[70] p. 155.

(The superscript is frequently omitted from the symbol ΔH^0.) This relation is the basis of one of the most important methods of evaluating free energies of formation. Values of ΔH of formation are usually evaluated from calorimetric data, chiefly from heats of combustion (Section VI). The standard free energy change for any reaction can be computed from free energies of formation in exactly the same way as entropies of reaction.

The equilibrium constant, K, for a reversible reaction can be calculated from the standard free energy change for the reaction, and thus also from the changes in heat content and entropy accompanying the reaction with the reactants and products in their standard states, by means of the relation:

$$- \Delta F^0 = RT \ln K \tag{34}$$

The choice of standard states used in these considerations must be clearly specified. In connection with heats of formation (Section VI), the standard state usually employed is that state which is stable at 25° and a pressure of one atmosphere. Thus, for hydrogen the standard state is represented by H_2 (g., 1 atm.). In entropy and free energy calculations, the standard state of a gaseous substance is usually taken as the ideal gas state at unit fugacity. This standard state would more properly be employed also in connection with the heat contents of gases. However, for most gases, this change in standard state corresponds to a difference in heat content which is beyond the limits of present experimental accuracy. The heat content of a gas in the ideal gas state at unit fugacity is the same as the heat content of the real gas at zero pressure.

Empirical and semiempirical rules have been devised which permit the estimation of the entropies and free energies of certain classes of compounds.[80]

D. HEAT CAPACITIES OF SOLIDS JUST BELOW THEIR MELTING POINTS

It will be shown in a later section (page 396) that a critical estimate of the purity of a substance can be based on its behavior during melting. Another criterion of purity which is very closely related to this is obtained from measurements of the heat capacity just below the melting point. It has frequently been observed that the apparent heat capacity of an impure substance shows a rapid increase below the melting point. This phenomenon is called premelting, since it can be attributed to absorption of heat as a result of the melting of a portion of the material. Figure 10 shows a typical heat-capacity curve for such a case. The dotted portion of the lower curve (for the solid state) represents the behavior to be expected for a pure substance. If the heat of fusion is determined by heating the impure substance from T_1 to T_2, it is of course necessary to deduct from the observed heat input the quantities, $\int_{T_1}^{T_m} C_{p(\text{solid})} dT$ and $\int_{T_m}^{T_2} C_{p(\text{liquid})} dT$ (see page 394). In the first integral, the value of $C_{p(\text{solid})}$ employed must be corrected for premelting.

---

[80] See, for example, K. S. Pitzer and D. W. Scott, *J. Am. Chem. Soc.*, **63**, 2419 (1941); G. S. Parks and H. M. Huffman, *op. cit.*;[73] and R. R. Wenner, *op. cit.*,[73] p. 161.

It can be shown[81] on the basis of the laws of dilute solutions, in cases in which no solid solutions are formed, that the observed specific heat of the solid mixture at $T°$ K. is given by:

$$c_{p \text{ (obs.)}} \approx c_p + \frac{n_2 R T_0^2}{(T_0 - T)^2} \tag{35}$$

$$\approx c_p + \frac{\Delta H_f (T_0 - T_m)}{M_1 (T_0 - T)^2} \tag{36}$$

In these equations, n_2 is the number of moles of solute (impurity) per gram of solvent, T_0 is the melting point of the solvent (degrees K.), T_m is the temperature at which the solid solvent is in equilibrium with liquid having the composition of the mixture, ΔH_f is the molar heat of fusion of the solvent, and M_1 is the molecular weight of the solvent. If ΔH_f is measured in calories, R has the value 1.986. These equations are derived on the assumption that equilibrium between solid and liquid phases is maintained during the heat-capacity determination. Experimental[81] results show that it is possible to approach this ideal situation quite closely. In most cases, c_p can be expressed with sufficient accuracy in the form $A + BT$ in the short region below the melting point which is of interest in the present connection. Thus, the mole fraction of impurity can be estimated by fitting the observed specific heats to an equation of the form:

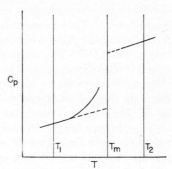

Fig.   10.—Typical   premelting behavior.

$$c_{p \text{ (obs.)}} = A + BT + C/(T_m - T)^2 \tag{37}$$

(since $T_m \approx T_0$). Obviously $n_2 \approx C/R T_m^2$.

It should be noted that equation (36) shows that premelting heat capacities give a much more sensitive criterion of purity than does the lowering of the melting point. Thus, in the case of water, the observed specific heat at $-1°$ C. will exceed the true heat capacity by 80 $(T_0 - T_m)$ calories per degree per gram; an impurity concentration which causes a melting-point lowering of only $0.001°$ will result in an apparent specific heat at this temperature which is approximately 15% larger than the true specific heat.

E.   EMPIRICAL AND THEORETICAL ESTIMATION OF HEAT CAPACITIES

A rough estimate of the molal heat capacity, at constant pressure, of a solid substance at ordinary temperatures may be obtained from Kopp's law.[82] According

[81] H. C. Dickinson and N. S. Osborne, *Natl. Bur. Standards (U. S.), Bull.* **12**, 49 (1915). M. Le Blanc and E. Möbius, *Ber. Verhandl. sächs. Akad. Wiss. Leipzig, Math.-phys. Klasse,* **85**, 75 (1933). E. L. Skau, *J. Am. Chem. Soc.,* **57**, 243 (1935).
[82] H. Kopp, *Ann. Chem., Suppl.,* **3**, 1, 289 (1864).

to this law, the heat capacity of a solid substance can be approximately expressed as the sum of the "heat capacities" of its constituent atoms, if one assigns the following atomic "heat capacities" in calories per degree: C, 1.8; H, 2.3; B, 2.7; Si, 3.8; O, 4.0; F, 5.0; P, 5.4; S, 5.4; and 6.2 for the heavier atoms. The heat capacity of a liquid is generally larger than that of a solid. The constant-pressure heat capacity of a liquid may be roughly approximated by a modification[83] of Kopp's law, using atomic "heat capacities" larger than those given in the preceding paragraph by two calories per degree in each case.

Much attention has been given in recent years to the problem of correlating the molecular structures of gaseous substances with their heat capacities, entropies, and other thermodynamic properties. Statistical mechanical methods have been developed for computing heat capacities and entropies from molecular and spectroscopic data.[84] The agreement between entropies calculated in this way for numerous substances and those obtained from heat-capacity data has given ample verification of the third law. Significant discrepancies found in other cases have been traced to various causes, such as deviation of crystals from the "perfect" crystalline state, or incompleteness in the statistical treatment. For example, it has been found, in the case of ethane and other organic compounds, that it is necessary to modify the statistical treatment to allow for hindering potentials restricting the rotation of groups relative to each other about single bonds. Several semiempirical rules have been developed for estimating the heat capacities of various series of organic compounds.[85, 86] For example, according to Pitzer,[87] the heat capacity of any gaseous normal or branched-chain paraffin above ethane is given, at temperatures up to 450° K., with rather good accuracy by the expression:

$$C_p = 5.65n - 0.62 + t(0.0111n + 0.0158) \tag{38}$$

where n is the number of carbon atoms in the molecule and t is the temperature in degrees centigrade.

2. Determination of Heat Capacities

It is evident from equations (23) and (24) that the *true* heat capacity cannot be determined directly by calorimetric means because this quantity is the slope of the energy or heat content curve. The quantity determined experimentally is a *mean* heat capacity between two temperatures:

$$\tilde{C}_p = \Delta Q/(T_2 - T_1) = (H_2 - H_1)/(T_2 - T_1) \tag{39}$$

in the case of constant pressure. If the curve of C_p *vs.* t is nearly linear between T_1 and T_2, and $T_2 - T_1$ is sufficiently small, the value of $\tilde{C}_p$ can be

[83] R. R. Wenner, *op. cit.*,[73] p. 16.

[84] The literature on this subject is very extensive. Discussions, with references, are given by E. B. Wilson, Jr., *Chem. Revs.*, **27**, 17 (1940); J. G. Aston, *loc. cit.*[73]; R. R. Wenner, *op. cit.*,[73] p. 114.

[85] K. Bennewitz and W. Rossner, *Z. physik. Chem.*, **B39**, 126 (1938).

[86] R. R. Wenner, *op. cit.*,[73] p. 185.

[87] K. S. Pitzer, *J. Am. Chem. Soc.*, **63**, 2413 (1941).

identified with C_p at $(T_1 + T_2)/2$. This approximation can be safely made in most cases if $T_2 - T_1$ does not exceed $5°$. Due allowance must be made for any change in the distribution of the material between the phases present. Thus, in determining the heat capacity of a liquid, some of the energy introduced is used in vaporizing a small fraction of the liquid.

Certain of the procedures for determining heat capacities will be considered here in some detail, particularly with regard to the calorimetric apparatus employed. Attention will be limited to methods and apparatus which may be of interest or of practical value to organic chemists. A very inclusive review on heat capacities will be found in the monograph by Eucken.[88] However, it should be borne in mind that many important experimental and theoretical advances have been made in the last decade.

The experimental procedures discussed on pages 353–374 are classified according to whether they apply to measurements at low (10° K. to room temperature), moderate, or high temperatures.

A. DETERMINATION OF HEAT CAPACITIES AT LOW TEMPERATURES

Most of the work at low temperatures has been carried out by the Nernst[89] method. The material under investigation is contained in a metal calorimeter which is equipped with a heater and a thermometric device (either resistance thermometer or thermocouple). The calorimeter is supported inside a jacket of large heat capacity and accurately measureable temperature. This jacket is contained within another vessel (frequently a Dewar flask) which is cooled by liquid air or liquid hydrogen. Provision is made for evacuating the space between the jacket and the calorimeter to a very low pressure to improve the isolation of the calorimeter. In the Nernst type of apparatus, the jacket is held at a constant temperature during a heat-capacity determination, and correction is made for the small heat leakage from the calorimeter. Recently, several adiabatic calorimeters have been described in which the jacket–calorimeter temperature difference is kept so small that thermal leakage is negligible.

Considerable elaboration and refinement of low-temperature calorimeters have taken place in recent years, particularly in this country.[90] The apparatus de-

---

[88] A. Eucken, *Energie- und Wärmeinhalt*. Vol. VIII, Part 1, of Wien-Harms, *Handbuch der Experimentalphysik*, Akadem. Verlagsgesellschaft, Leipzig, 1929.

[89] A. Eucken, *Physik. Z.*, **10**, 586 (1910). W. Nernst, *Sitzber. preuss. Akad. Wiss. Physik.-math. Klasse*, **1910**, 262; *Ann. Physik*, **36** 395 (1911).

[90] (A) G. E. Gibson and W. F. Giauque, *J. Am. Chem. Soc.*, **45**, 93 (1923); W. F. Giauque and R. Wiebe, *ibid.*, **50**, 101 (1928); W. F. Giauque and H. L. Johnston, *ibid.*, **51**, 2300 (1929); W. F. Giauque and C. J. Egan, *J. Chem. Phys.*, **5**, 45 (1937). (B) F. Lange, *Z. physik. Chem.*, **110**, 343 (1924). (C) G. S. Parks, *J. Am. Chem. Soc.*, **47**, 338 (1925). (D) R. W. Millar, *ibid.*, **50**, 1875 (1928). (E) W. M. Latimer and

(Footnote continued on page 355.)

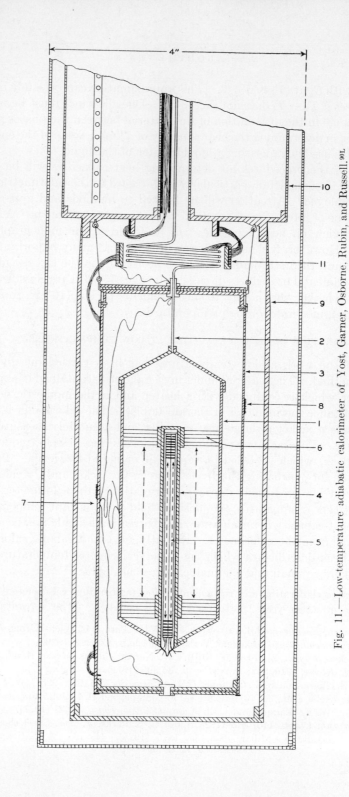

Fig. 11.—Low-temperature adiabatic calorimeter of Yost, Garner, Osborne, Rubin, and Russell.[90L]

scribed by Yost *et al.*[90L] illustrates the equipment which is used in work from 15° K. to room temperature. Their calorimeter is of the adiabatic type first employed by Lange,[90B] and later further developed by Southard and Brickwedde.[90G] Aston and Eidinoff[90H] have also published a description of an adiabatic apparatus which is somewhat different from that of Yost *et al.*

Figure 11 shows in detail the lower part of the calorimetric assembly of Yost *et al.* The whole assembly is contained within a Dewar flask which serves as a liquid-air container. The gold-plated copper calorimeter, *1*, is suspended by filling tube *2* within an electrically heated radiation shield, *3*. The calorimeter is equipped with a well, *4*, which contains a platinum-encased coil of platinum wire, *5*, which serves both as heater and as thermometer. Perforated disks, *6*, extending from the re-entrant well to the wall of the calorimeter serve to decrease the time necessary to attain thermal equilibrium after a heating period. The temperature difference between the shield and the calorimeter is indicated by thermocouples, *7*, and is held close to zero by means of shield heaters *8*. The shield is supported within an outer copper shield, *9*, beneath liquid hydrogen container *10*. Filling tube *12* is coiled within a heated copper ring, *11*, and the electrical leads are coiled outside the ring, to prevent cold spots by conduction from the hydrogen container. Temperatures down to about 12° K. are obtained by evacuating the hydrogen container with a high-capacity pump. During the cooling process, the vacuum in spaces *B* is broken with 1–2 cm. pressure of helium while maintaining a high vacuum in space *A*. After the cooling is completed, spaces *B* are again evacuated. This calorimeter is designed for measurements on condensed gases. In the case of measurements on a substance which is liquid or solid at ordinary temperatures, the substance is sealed in the calorimeter, usually with helium gas to improve thermal equilibration, and there is no need for a filling tube.

One of the most important and difficult phases of low-temperature calorimetry is the establishment of a temperature scale. In the range below 85° K., the lower limit of the present International Temperature Scale (page 315), temperature measurements are made in terms of the helium-gas thermometer. Discussions of the problem of low-temperature thermometry will be found in the papers already cited[90] as well as in other publications.[91]

B. S. Greensfelder, *ibid.*, **50**, 2202 (1928); K. S. Pitzer and L. V. Coulter, *ibid.*, **60**, 1310 (1938). (F) D. H. Andrews, *J. Franklin Inst.*, **206**, 285 (1928). (G) J. C. Southard and F. G. Brickwedde, *J. Am. Chem. Soc.*, **55**, 4378 (1933). (H) J. G. Aston and G. H. Messerly, *ibid.*, **58**, 2354 (1936); J. G. Aston and M. L. Eidinoff, *ibid.*, **61**, 1533 (1939). (I) E. G. Haas and G. Stegeman, *ibid.*, **58**, 879 (1936). (J) J. E. Ahlberg, E. R. Blanchard, and W. O. Lundberg, *J. Chem. Phys.*, **5**, 539 (1937) (down to 2° K.). (K) R. W. Blue and J. F. G. Hicks, *J. Am. Chem. Soc.*, **59**, 1962 (1937). (L) D. M. Yost, C. S. Garner, D. W. Osborne, T. R. Rubin, and H. Russell, *ibid.*, **63**, 3488 (1941). (M) K. Clusius and L. Popp, *Z. physik. Chem.*, **B46**, 63 (1940) (requires only 3 ml. of material). (N) R. A. Ruehrwein and H. M. Huffman, *J. Am. Chem. Soc.*, **65**, 1620 (1943).

[91] J. C. Southard and R. T. Milner, *J. Am. Chem. Soc.*, **56**, 4384 (1933). H. J. Hoge

(*Footnote continued on page 356.*)

Entropies which are sufficiently accurate for many purposes, including the evaluation of the free energies of many organic compounds at room temperature, may be computed from heat-capacity measurements extending down only to liquid-air temperatures (90° K.). Apparatus for such measurements which is somewhat simpler than that described above, has been employed by Parks,[90c] Haas and Stegeman,[90r] and others.

Andrews and coworkers[92] have made considerable use of the "calibrated heat conductivity calorimeter" for determining heat capacities. The apparatus described by Stull is particularly interesting because moderately accurate results (1–2%) are obtained with small amounts (5 ml.) of material. The calorimeter is heated by conduction and radiation from a surrounding jacket by means of a constant thermal head. The rate of temperature rise of the calorimeter under these conditions is compared with the rate of rise obtained under the same conditions when the calorimeter contains a standard substance of known heat capacity.

The method of mixtures has been employed at low temperatures for solids, liquids, and gases. The sample may be cooled to a definite temperature and then introduced into a calorimeter at ordinary temperature, or the calorimeter itself may be at a low temperature,[93] as in the case of the hydrogen vaporization calorimeter. Further discussion of the method of mixtures will be found on page 372.

Further discussion of the method of mixtures will be found on page 372.

B. DETERMINATION OF HEAT CAPACITIES AT MODERATE TEMPERATURES

Determination of the heat capacities of gases, liquids, and solids will be considered separately, and attention will be confined to several representative reliable methods. Complete discussions are given in the monographs by Eucken[88] and Partington and Shilling.[94] The classification of experimental methods according to temperature is quite arbitrary, and most of the methods considered in these paragraphs can be extended to low or high temperatures by suitable modifications in design and procedure.

Gases and Vapors.—*Heat Capacity at Constant Pressure.*—The con-

and F. G. Brickwedde, *J. Research Natl. Bur. Standards*, 22, 351 (1939). E. F. Burton, H. Grayson Smith, and J. O. Wilhelm, *op. cit.*,[73] Chapter 3. Articles by H. T. Wensel, F. G. Keyes, J. R. Roebuck and T. A. Murrell, H. J. Hoge, R. B. Scott, and J. G. Aston, in *Temperature, Its Measurement and Control in Science and Industry*, Reinhold, New York, 1941.

[92] D. H. Andrews, *J. Am. Chem. Soc.*, 48, 1287 (1926). E. Haworth and D. H. Andrews, *ibid.*, 50, 2998 (1928). R. H. Smith and D. H. Andrews, *ibid.*, 53, 3644 (1931). D. R. Stull, *ibid.*, 59, 2726 (1937). W. T. Ziegler and C. E. Messer, *ibid.*, 63, 2694 (1941).

[93] F. Simon and M. Ruhemann, *Z. physik. Chem.*, 129, 321 (1927).

[94] J. R. Partington and W. G. Shilling, *The Specific Heats of Gases*. Van Nostrand, New York, 1924.

tinuous-flow method used by Callendar and Barnes[95] for liquids has been extensively employed in the determination of the heat capacities, at constant pressure, of gases and vapors. Its adaptation to this purpose was first undertaken by Scheel and Heuse.[96] The method is very simple in principle, though accurate results can be obtained only if great care with regard to experimental details is taken. Gas or vapor is passed at a known constant rate over an electrical heater, and the temperature of the gas stream is measured just before and just after passing over the heater, after a steady state has been reached. If the rate of flow of the gas is F moles per second, the power input to the heater is W watts, and the (corrected) temperature rise is ΔT, the mean heat capacity of the substance is:

$$\tilde{C}_p = W/(4.1833\,\Delta T\,F) \tag{40}$$

in calories per mole. Since the value of ΔT is usually small, the heat capacity obtained can in most cases be identified with the true heat capacity at the mean temperature of the experiment. The heat capacity of the calorimeter does not appear in this expression because measurements are made only after a steady state has been reached. If the heat capacity of the calorimeter is unduly large, excessive lengths of time are required for the establishment of the steady state.

It is impossible, in this method, to work under strictly adiabatic conditions because the calorimeter itself is not at a uniform temperature. Consideration must be given to minimizing both the heat exchange of the calorimeter with its surroundings and the heat exchange between the various parts of the calorimeter resulting from causes other than the flow of the gas. It is not feasible to eliminate completely these sources of error. The relative effect of heat leakage from the calorimeter and of heat exchange between the heater and the thermometers resulting from conduction by the material of the calorimeter and from radiation should decrease with increasing rate of flow. The procedure is therefore usually followed of measuring the apparent heat capacity with different rates of flow and extrapolating to infinite rate of flow. The apparent heat capacity in most cases varies linearly with $1/F^n$, where the power, n, depends on the type of apparatus,[97] so that the extrapolation is easily carried out. In general, the sources of internal heat exchange are minimized by providing poorly conducting material for the gas path between the first thermometer and the heater, and by interposing suitable radiation shields between the thermometers and the heater. The heater should have sufficient surface in good thermal contact with the gas so that its temperature does not exceed that of the gas by

[95] H. L. Callendar, *Trans., Roy. Soc. London*, **A199**, 55 (1902).

[96] K. Scheel and W. Heuse, *Ann. Physik*, **37**, 79 (1912); **40**, 473 (1913); **59**, 86 (1919).

[97] J. B. Montgomery and T. De Vries, *J. Am. Chem. Soc.*, **64**, 2372 (1942).

more than a few degrees.   If the elimination of errors due to heat exchange
has been satisfactorily accomplished, experiments in which the rate is varied
and ΔT is held constant should give values for the apparent heat capacity
falling on the same straight line when plotted against $1/F^n$ as that given
by holding W constant and allowing ΔT to vary.

Satisfactory values for ΔT can be obtained only if the rate of flow is constant.   This is readily accomplished
in the case of substances which are
easily condensed, for then the liquid
can be boiled under constant pressure
by a constant input of electrical energy,
the boiler being under adiabatic conditions.   Arrangements for this purpose have been described by Bennewitz
and Rossner,[98] Pitzer,[99] Montgomery
and De Vries,[97] and others.   The accurate control of the flow of gases is
a more difficult problem, as evidenced
by the complicated apparatus used for
this purpose by Osborne, Stimson, and
Sligh.[100]   Scheel and Heuse[96] designed
an ingenious mercury recirculating
pump for use with rare gases.

If the design of the calorimeter is
such that there is an appreciable resistance to the flow of the gas between the
two thermometers, there will be a
pressure drop in this region which
will become larger at higher rates of
flow.   The corresponding drop in temperature is to be applied as a correction to ΔT.   If the expansion is considered as taking place adiabatically,
the temperature drop is given by:

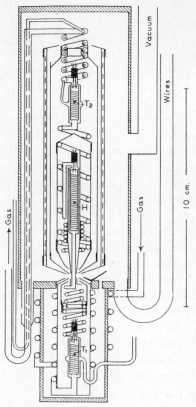

Fig. 12.—Flow calorimeter of Osborne, Stimn, and Sligh.   [98]

$$(\Delta T)_\mu = (\partial T/\partial P)_H \Delta P = \mu \Delta P \qquad (41)$$

where μ, the Joule-Thompson coefficient of the gas is taken as constant in
the small temperature and pressure intervals involved.   The assumption is

[98] K. Bennewitz and W. Rossner, *Z. physik. Chem.*, **B39**, 126 (1938).

[99] K. S. Pitzer, *J. Am. Chem. Soc.*, **63**, 2413 (1941).

[100] N. S. Osborne, H. F. Stimson, and T. S. Sligh, *Natl. Bur. Standards Sci. Papers*,
20, 119 (1924–1926).

usually made that the magnitude of this correction is negligible, though Osborne, Stimson, and Sligh[100] included provision in their apparatus for the direct measurement of the pressure drop, in order to be able to apply the correction precisely.

The calorimeter employed by Osborne, Stimson, and Sligh is shown in cross section in figure 12. Heavy lines represent copper and thin lines German silver. For a complete discussion and description of the design, reference may be made to the original article. The outstanding feature of this instrument is the reduction of the heat leakage to 0.1 to 0.2% of the total temperature change, which is accomplished by the complex system of two essentially independent thermal shields; one for the

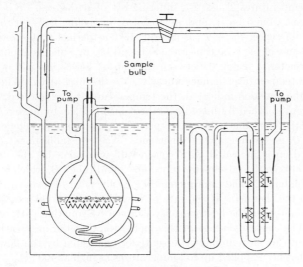

Fig. 13.—Flow calorimeter of Pitzer.

lower temperature region of the first thermometer, T_1, and the other for the region of the heater, H, and the second thermometer, T_2, where the temperature is higher. Measurements made with this calorimeter on ammonia from $-30°$ to $150°$ C., and from 0.5 to 20 atm., gave results accurate to 0.1 or 0.2%.

In recent publications[97–99, 101] considerably simpler apparatus has been described with which results of lower accuracy are obtained. The apparatus used by Pitzer[99] is represented in figure 13. Vapor is generated at a constant rate in an "adiabatic" boiler and is then brought to the temperature of the thermostatically controlled bath at the right of the diagram. After passage over the platinum resistance thermometer, T_1, the vapor is heated by the platinum heater, H, and is then passed over thermometers T_2 and T_3. The tubes containing the thermometers and heater are wrapped in aluminum foil to reduce radiation, and are enclosed in an evacuated bulb. Pitzer found that the same heat capacity was obtained on extrapo-

[101] T. De Vries and B. T. Collins, *J. Am. Chem. Soc.*, **63**, 1343 (1941).

lation to infinite rate of flow regardless of whether the temperature increase caused by the heater was measured by T_2 or by T_3. After a steady state is reached, the rate of flow is determined by weighing a sample collected at the three-way stopcock during a measured time interval. It is to be noted that measurement of the heat input into the boiler, together with the weight of sample collected in a measured interval, gives the information necessary to evaluate the heat of vaporization of the liquid. During the establishment of the steady state, the vapor is condensed and returned to the vaporizer.

A modification of the Scheel and Heuse method has been developed recently by Bennewitz and Schulze,[102] and has been employed by Dailey and Felsing.[103] The apparatus is shown diagrammatically in figure 14. Two metal blocks, A and B, are held at temperatures $T_A < T_B$, differing by a few degrees. B is heated by a heating element wound on it, and A is cooled by cooling coils on rods N. The temperature difference, $T_B - T_A$ is measured by a thermel (not shown). Fitting snugly into each block is a thin-walled glass tube, E, which is about three millimeters in diameter in region C between the blocks. If no gas is flowing through the tube, the temperature changes linearly with distance at C. When, however, gas flows in the direction indicated, the temperature at C is lowered. The linear gradient is re-established by introducing heat into the gas by means of heater H, made of a loop of very fine wire held in place by the leads, L, at one end and by a quartz fiber, Q, and spring at the other end. The re-establishment of the linear temperature drop is indicated with considerable precision by the multijunction thermel, T, between the calorimeter tube and "blind tube" D, which is constructed of the same material. The calorimeter tube is silvered to prevent radiation from the heater to the thermel. If the rate of flow through the calorimeter tube is F moles per second, then the heat capacity is given by equation (41), where $\Delta T = T_B - T_A$. The chief advantage of this method is that the heat exchange of the calorimeter with its surroundings is essentially unaffected by the flow of the gas. The method has been applied up to temperatures as high as 400° C.

The determination of C_p of a gas can be accomplished by a modification of the method of mixtures. The gas, flowing at a constant rate, is warmed or cooled by passage through a heat exchanger held at constant temperature and is then led through a calorimeter. The calorimeter temperature is usually considerably different from that to which the gas is initially brought, so that a mean heat capacity is obtained. This method has been applied by several investigators.[104] Particular reference should be made to the work of Holborn and Henning,[105] who have determined the mean heat capacities of gases up to 1400° C., and of McCollum.[106] The latter investigator cooled the gas to a temperature slightly below that of the calorim-

[102] K. Bennewitz and O. Schulze, *Z. physik. Chem.*, **A186**, 299 (1940).

[103] B. P. Dailey and W. A. Felsing, *J. Am. Chem. Soc.*, **65**, 42, 44 (1943).

[104] See A. Eucken, *op. cit.*,[88] p. 391 *et seq.*

[105] L. Holborn and F. Henning, *Ann. Physik*, **18**, 739 (1905); **23**, 809 (1907).

[106] E. D. McCollum, *J. Am. Chem. Soc.*, **49**, 28 (1927).

eter, and held the calorimeter at a constant temperature by means of electrical heating.

The most troublesome source of error in the method of mixtures as ap-

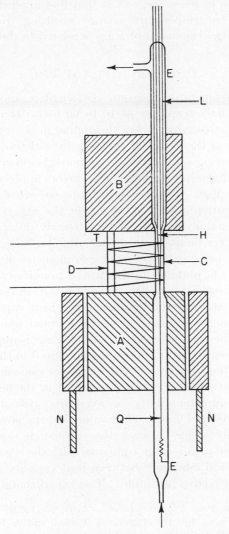

Fig. 14.—Flow calorimeter of Bennewitz and Schulze.

plied to gases is the conduction of heat from (or to) the calorimeter along the tube connecting the precooler (or perheater) with the calorimeter. The assumption frequently made, that this heat exchange can be evaluated from observations made when the gas is not flowing through the calorimeter, is incorrect.[104]

A method for the determination of C_p of gases which has received considerable attention in recent years[107] is that first applied by Lummer and Pringsheim.[108] The temperature change resulting from an isentropic (reversible adiabatic) expansion of a gas is related to the heat capacity by the expression:

$$C_p = T(\partial V/\partial T)_p/(\partial T/\partial P)_s \qquad (42)$$

In observing the temperature–pressure coefficient, a sample of the gas contained in a large flask (capacity of 10 to 60 liters) is allowed to expand suddenly to a pressure slightly below the orginal pressure; the temperature change, measured at the center of the flask by a thermometer having the lowest possible heat capacity and time lag, must be observed within a very short interval of time after the expansion, before appreciable heat loss to the walls can take place. The expansion must be carried out in such a way that convection currents are not set up in the gas. The temperature-measuring device usually consists of an extremely thin platinum wire employed as a resistance thermometer in one arm of a Wheatstone bridge, the bridge off-balance being indicated by a galvanometer of very short period. The mean value of C_p obtained in this way is practically equal to the true heat capacity at the mean temperature and pressure of the experiment.

Heat Capacity at Constant Volume.—The heat capacity of a gas at *constant volume* can be evaluated from its thermal conductivity at very low pressures. The thermal conductivity of a gas is approximately independent of its pressure until the pressure is reduced to the region at which the mean free path of the gas molecules is of the same order of magnitude as the distance between the surfaces involved in the heat exchange. In this region, thermal conductivity becomes proportional to the pressure. If the pressure is reduced to such a low value that the possibility of molecular collisions in the space between the surfaces is essentially excluded (*i. e.*, the mean free path is large compared with the separation of the surfaces), the theoretical relation[109] between heat capacity and thermal conductivity becomes relatively simple. The experimental procedure,[110, 111]

[107] J. R. Partington, *Proc. Roy. Soc. London*, **A100**, 27 (1922). A. Eucken and K. v. Lüde, *Z. physik. Chem.*, **B5**, 413 (1929). A. Eucken and A. Parts, *ibid.*, **B20**, 184 (1933). B. H. Sage, D. C. Webster, and W. N. Lacey, *Ind. Eng. Chem., Ind. Ed.*, **29**, 1309 (1937). G. B. Kistiakowsky and W. W. Rice, *J. Chem. Phys.*, **7**, 281 (1939).

[108] O. Lummer and E. Pringsheim, *Ann. Physik*, **64**, 555 (1898).

[109] M. Knudsen, *Ann. Physik*, **34**, 593 (1911).

[110] A. Eucken and K. Weigert, *Z. physik. Chem.*, **B23**, 265 (1933).

[111] G. B. Kistiakowsky and F. Nazmi, *J. Chem. Phys.*, **6**, 18 (1938). G. B. Kistiakowsky, J. R. Lacher, and F. Stitt, *ibid.*, **7**, 289 (1939).

consists essentially of measuring, by means of its resistance, the temperature of an electrically heated platinum wire which is supported in a cylindrical space of small radius. The temperature of the cylindrical wall is also observed. Measurements are made with the space between the wire and the wall evacuated, and then filled with gas at very low pressure, the former measurement allowing correction for radiation to be made. One of the chief difficulties with this method is that a gas molecule does not acquire the temperature of the wire or the wall after a single collision with either, so that the conduction of heat is not as large as it would be in the ideal case. An empirical evaluation of the "accommodation coefficient," which allows for this deviation from ideality, depends on measurements made under conditions such that the results can be compared with C_v values determined by other methods. This method is of importance in that it is the only procedure by which one can obtain heat-capacity data directly at very low pressures where the gas behaves very nearly in accordance with the perfect gas law.

The heat capacity at constant volume and the ratio, C_p/C_v (= γ), of many gases have been evaluated from measurements of the velocity of sound.[94] Cornish and Eastman[112] have discussed this method and have described an apparatus which they employed with hydrogen from 80° to 370° K.

Reduction of the Heat Capacity to the Ideal Gas State.—In comparing the observed heat capacities of gases with predictions based on theoretical treatments,[113] one is usually interested in the heat capacity of the gas corrected to the ideal gas state at a fugacity of one atmosphere. Since the heat capacity of an ideal gas is independent of pressure, the desired standard heat capacity, C_v^0 or C_p^0, is the heat capacity of the real gas at zero pressure (infinite dilution). We shall indicate briefly two methods employed in the reduction of C_p to C_p^0. It should be noted that:[114]

$$C_p^0 - C_v^0 = R \tag{43}$$

If the value of $(\partial C_p/\partial P)_T$ as a function of pressure is known, C_p^0 can be calculated by means of the relation:

$$C_p^0 = C_p - \int_0^P (\partial C_p/\partial P)_T dP \tag{44}$$

[112] R. E. Cornish and E. D. Eastman, *J. Am. Chem. Soc.*, **50**, 627 (1928).

[113] See, for example, K. Bennewitz and W. Rossner, *loc. cit.*;[98] K. Pitzer, *loc. cit.*;[99] P. Fugassi and C. E. Rudy, *Ind. Eng. Chem., Ind. Ed.*, **30**, 1029 (1938); C. J. Dobratz, *ibid.*, **33**, 759 (1941); G. B. Kistiakowsky and W. W. Rice, *J. Chem. Phys.*, **7**, 281 (1939); G. B. Kistiakowsky and F. Nazmi, *ibid.*, **6**, 18 (1938); G. B. Kistiakowsky, J. R. Lacher, and F. Stitt, *ibid.*, **7**, 289 (1939); B. P. Dailey and W. A. Felsing, *loc. cit.*[103]

[114] G. N. Lewis and M. Randall, *Thermodynamics and The Free Energy of Chemical Substances.* McGraw-Hill, New York, 1923, p. 65.

$(\partial C_p/\partial P)_T$ can be evaluated from data on the Joule-Thompson coefficient of a gas:[114]

$$(\partial C_p/\partial P)_T = -\mu(\partial C_p/\partial T)_p - C_p(\partial\mu/\partial T)_p \tag{45}$$

Sage, Webster, and Lacey[107] have employed this relation, the integral:

$$\int_0^P [\mu(\partial C_p/\partial T)_p + C_p(\partial\mu/\partial T)_p]dp \tag{46}$$

being estimated by graphical integration.

The value of $C_p^0 - C_p$ can be evaluated from various empirical equations of state. Frequent application has been made of the Berthelot equation for this purpose. It can be shown that this equation leads to the results:

$$C_p^0 - C_p = -\frac{81RPT_c^3}{32P_cT^3} \tag{47}$$

and

$$C_v^0 - C_v = -\frac{27RPT_c^3}{32P_cT^3} \tag{48}$$

where P_c and T_c are the critical pressure and temperature of the gas, respectively. One should, of course, be certain that the equation of state employed applies with sufficient accuracy, since serious errors may be introduced if this is not the case.[115]

Liquids.—The application of heat-capacity data of pure liquids to the evaluation of entropies is discussed above (page 347). The heat capacities of liquid mixtures and of solutions, both of nonelectrolytes and electrolytes, are of great significance in connection with the physics and thermodynamics of such systems. For example, the heat capacities of very dilute aqueous solutions of electrolytes have been frequently studied in connection with the Debye-Hückel theory of such solutions.

Direct Method.—The Nernst type of calorimeter is frequently employed up to temperatures in the neighborhood of room temperature for the determination of the heat capacities of liquids.[116] Somewhat less accurate results can be obtained with considerably simpler apparatus; with more elaborate calorimeters specifically designed for use with liquids at ordinary temperatures, values of C_p accurate to 0.01% or better have been obtained.

---

[115] N. S. Osborne, H. F. Stimson, T. S. Sligh, and C. S. Cragoe, *Refrig. Eng.*, **10**, 145 (1923).

[116] See particularly M. Le Blanc and E. Möbius, *Ber. Verhandl. sächs. Akad. Wiss. Leipzig, Math.-phys. Klasse*, **85**, 75 (1933). These authors describe a vacuum calorimeter of the Nernst type with which results accurate to $\pm0.1\%$ are obtained with a temperature rise of only 0,1°,

It has been frequently demonstrated[117] that values of C_p of liquid systems accurate to about 1% may be obtained with the simple apparatus represented diagrammatically in figure 15. A silvered Dewar flask serves as the calorimeter. It is closed by a rubber stopper and submerged in a water bath which may be kept either at constant temperature or at the same temperature as the calorimeter. The calorimeter heater is a coil of constantan or manganin wire enclosed in a glass tube. It is supplied with both potential and current leads. The liquid in the calorimeter is stirred at a constant

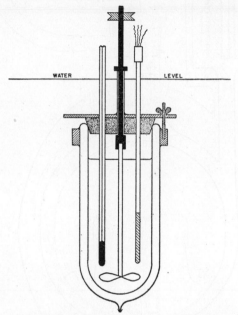

WATER   LEVEL

Fig. 15.—Simple calorimeter for determining heat capacities of liquids.

rate by a propeller stirrer. Heat leakage along the stirrer shaft is reduced by a section of poorly conducting material such as Bakelite or Lucite. The temperature of the liquid in the calorimeter is measured by a Beckmann thermometer, or, better, by a resistance thermometer or a thermel.

Heat capacities can be determined on relatively small samples of liquids in an unstirred adiabatic calorimeter[118] provided a metal calorimeter having a large ratio of length to diameter is used, with its heater wound on its outside surface.

[117] See, for example, F. R. Bichowsky, *J. Am. Chem. Soc.*, **45**, 2225 (1923); B. C. Hendricks, J. H. Dorsey, R. LeRoy, and A. G. Moseley, *J. Phys. Chem.*, **34**, 418 (1930).
[118] J. M. Sturtevant, *J. Am. Chem. Soc.*, **59**, 1528 (1937); *Physics*, **7**, 232 (1936).

The development of the single adiabatic calorimeter for determining the heat capacities, as well as other thermal properties, of liquids has been carried to a very advanced state by Osborne, Stimson, and Ginnings[119] in their work on water be-

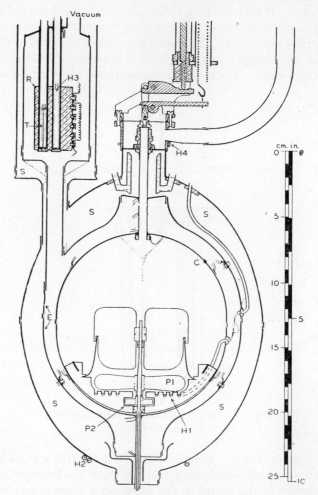

Fig. 16.—Highly developed adiabatic calorimeter
(Osborne, Stimson, and Sligh).

tween 0° and 100°. Their results will undoubtedly remain unchallenged in accuracy for some time to come. Figure 16 is a scale drawing of their apparatus.

119 N. S. Osborne, H. F. Stimson, and D. C. Ginnings, *J. Research Natl. Bur. Standards*, **23**, 197 (1939). For earlier work see N. S. Osborne, H. F. Stimson, and E. F. Fiock, *ibid.*, **5**, 411 (1930), and N. S. Osborne, H. F. Stimson, and D. C. Ginnings, *ibid.*, **18**, 389 (1937).

Spherical calorimeter C (for heat-capacity determinations the tube at the top of the calorimeter is closed off to prevent condensation of material in it) is supported within evacuated envelop E, the latter being surrounded by a saturated steam bath maintained at the temperature of the calorimeter by heater $H2$. The steam bath is contained in a metal guard (not shown) the temperature of which can be controlled. The temperature of the calorimeter is determined by several thermoelements attached to its surface, the reference junctions being at the temperature of metal reference block R. The temperature of this block is determined by a platinum resistance thermometer, T. The contents of the calorimeter are vigorously stirred by propellers $P1$ and $P2$, driven from below the calorimeter. The calorimeter heater is immediately below the stirrers.

Determinations of heat capacities are usually relative measurements in that the heat capacity of the calorimeter is determined with the calorimeter containing water or some other reference substance. The measurements of Osborne et al. are absolute measurements because the heat capacity of the calorimeter was calculated from a comparison of the data obtained with small amounts of water in the calorimeter with those obtained with large amounts.

The specific heat of air-free liquid water in the range 0° to 100° C. at a pressure of one atmosphere was found by Osborne et al. to be expressed by the empirical equation:

$$c_p = 4.1690 + 3.64 \times 10^{-14} (t + 100)^{5.26} + 0.0467 \times 10^{-0.036t} \quad (49)$$

where c_p is expressed in international joules per degree C. per gram, and t is expressed in degrees C. It should be noted that the presence of dissolved air causes differences in the heat capacity of water which become appreciable in accurate work.

The twin adiabatic procedure (page 342) is ideally suited to the precise determination[120] of the heat capacities of solutions, particularly those of dilute solutions, relative to the heat capacity of the pure solvent. In such measurements, pure solvent is contained in the tare calorimeter and solution in the working calorimeter. The calorimeters are heated with their heaters in series, and the heat capacity of the solution is evaluated from the known resistance ratio of the heaters and the small difference in the temperatures of the calorimeters at the end of the heating period.

Gucker, Ayres, and Rubin[120D] have refined this method by using variable heaters, so that the ratio of resistances of the heaters required to increase the temperatures of the two calorimeters by exactly the same amount can be determined with high

[120] (A) T. W. Richards and F. T. Gucker, *J. Am. Chem. Soc.*, **47**, 1876 (1925); F. T. Gucker, *ibid.*, **50**, 1005 (1928). (B) M. Randall and W. D. Ramage, *ibid.*, **49**, 93 (1927); M. Randall and F. D. Rossini, *ibid.*, **51**, 323 (1929); M. Randall and M. D. Taylor, *J. Phys. Chem.*, **45**, 959 (1941). (C) F. T. Gucker and K. H. Schminke, *J. Am. Chem. Soc.*, **54**, 1358 (1932); **55**, 1013 (1933). (D) F. T. Gucker, F. D. Ayres, and T. R. Rubin, *ibid.*, **58**, 2118 (1936). (E) C. B. Hess and B. E. Gramkee, *J. Phys. Chem.*, **44**, 483 (1940); C. B. Hess, *ibid.*, **45**, 755 (1941).

precision. Figure 17 shows the calorimetric assembly employed. The calorimeters, C, spun from a gold–platinum alloy, are supported within submarine J by dental floss (not shown), the submarine being contained in an adiabatic water jacket. The calorimeter leads carry wells for the main thermel, M (20 junctions, copper–constantan), the adiabatic control thermels, A (5 junctions), and the heaters (not shown). Each calorimeter is equipped with a propeller stirrer the shafts of which are led out of the calorimeters in such a way that evaporation is negligible. The chief innovation in this apparatus is the design of the calorimeter heaters. These

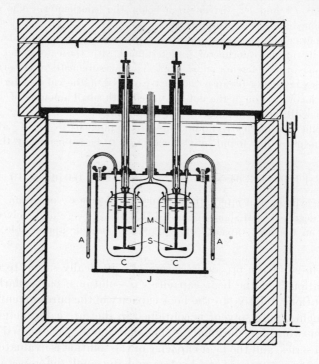

Fig. 17.—Adiabatic twin calorimeter (Gucker, Ayres, and Rubin).

are constructed in the sections indicated in figure 18, so that it is possible to obtain ratios between the resistances of the heaters varying from 0.9800 to 1.3700 in steps of 0.0003 to 0.0004. The resistance ratios are determined by the Wheatstone bridge shown in figure 18. Since it is not feasible to employ potential leads for each individual heater unit, particular precautions are necessary to insure the constancy of lead resistances and to make appropriate corrections for that fraction of the energy dissipated in the leads which is effective in heating the calorimeters. Measurements are made, for each pair of liquids in the calorimeters, of the deflections of the main thermel galvanometer resulting when the calorimeters are heated through a temperature interval of one degree for two or three different values of the ratio of the heater resistances. It is found that these deflections vary linearly with the resistance ratios, so that the value of the ratio for which no temperature difference would result can be readily obtained by interpolation. If x_0 is the value of the resistance ratio at the balance point with the calorimeters containing w_0 grams of pure solvent, and x is the corresponding ratio when the working calorimeter contains w_s grams of solution while the tare contains w_0 grams of solvent, then the specific heat of the solution, c_s, is obtained from the expression:

$$c_s w_s = [c_0 w_0 x_0 + c_1(x_0 - x)]/x \tag{50}$$

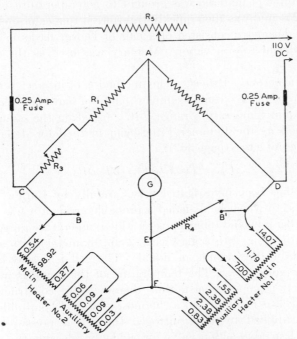

Fig. 18.—Diagram of heaters and resistance bridges employed with the calorimeter illustrated in Fig. 17.

where c_0 is the specific heat of the solvent and c_1 is the heat capacity of the working calorimeter. c_1 need not be known with great accuracy; it is evaluated from a pair of experiments in which some of the pure solvent in the working calorimeter is displaced by a copper vessel which in one case is filled with air and in the other with solvent. No account need be taken of heat losses to the jacket if the two calorimeters are reasonably similar in construction. In the case of aqueous solutions, measurements made at $t°$ C. are obtained in terms of cal_t. Gucker and coworkers have obtained with this apparatus results accurate to $\pm 0.01\%$.

Heat capacities of liquids at temperatures considerably above their boiling points can be determined in calorimeters of sufficiently massive construction to withstand the pressures encountered. Osborne[121] obtained precise results for liquid ammonia at temperatures up to 50° C. in an un-stirred adiabatic calorimeter equipped with internal heat distributing vanes. Several calorimeters have been described which permit stirring of their contents at relatively high pressures.[122]

Method of Mixtures.—The method of mixtures has been employed only rarely in determining heat capacities of liquids at ordinary temperatures. An example is furnished by the work of Nelson and Newton[123] on glucose glass. A sample of material was brought to a temperature in the neighborhood of 25° and was then quickly transferred to a calorimeter at about 60°. The calorimeter consisted of a pair of Dewar flasks in a container jacketed with chloroform vapor. Mercury was used as the calorimetric liquid.

"Piezothermometric" Method.—This method is of interest because measurements can be made on small samples (5 ml.) of material over practically the entire liquid temperature range. It is based on the same thermodynamic relation as the Lummer-Pringsheim method for determining the heat capacities of gases (page 362):

$$C_p = T(\partial V/\partial T)_p/(\partial T/\partial P)_s \qquad (51)$$

The method has been investigated very carefully by Burlew,[124] who obtained results, to which he assigned a probable error of a few tenths of a per cent, for benzene and toluene over a wide temperature range. In Burlew's apparatus (Fig. 19), a glass cell (2-cm. diameter) with a gooseneck opening contains the sample of liquid. The cell is sealed by mercury placed in the gooseneck. The temperature of the liquid is measured by a single-junction copper–constantan thermocouple constructed of fine wires. The cell is contained in a thermostated steel bomb filled with oil. Pressure is supplied by tank nitrogen through a pressure•distributor equipped with a rapid-action valve for suddenly releasing the pressure on the bomb. Pressures are measured by a free piston gauge. The liquid is subjected to a pressure of 10–20 atmospheres, and after establishment of thermal equilibrium, the pressure is released. Burlew found that, with pressure decreases of 10–20 atmospheres, benzene and toluene showed temperature drops of about 0.4°. Measurements were made over a series

[121] N. S. Osborne, *Natl. Bur. Standards (U. S.), Bull.* **14,** 133 (1918). N. S. Osborne and M. S. van Dusen, *ibid.,* **14,** 397 (1918).

[122] N. S. Osborne, H. F. Stimson, and E. F. Fiock, *J. Research Natl. Bur. Standards,* **5,** 411 (1930). N. S. Osborne, H. F. Stimson, and D. C. Ginnings, *ibid.,* **18,** 389 (1937). B. H. Carroll and J. H. Mathews, *J. Am. Chem. Soc.,* **46,** 30 (1924). J. H. Awbery and E. Griffiths, *Proc. Phys. Soc. London,* **52,** 770 (1940).

[123] E. W. Nelson and R. F. Newton, *J. Am. Chem. Soc.,* **63,** 2178 (1941).

[124] J. S. Burlew, *J. Am. Chem. Soc.,* **62,** 681, 690, 696 (1940).

of pressures to determine the small pressure variation of $(\partial T/\partial P)_s$ so that the results could be corrected to one atmosphere.

Burlew includes in his third paper[124] a consideration of all previous values for the heat capacities of benzene and toluene. It is very instructive to note the discordance of these data, particularly some of the older data. This illustrates the great need for the redetermination of many of the thermal quantities already reported in the literature.

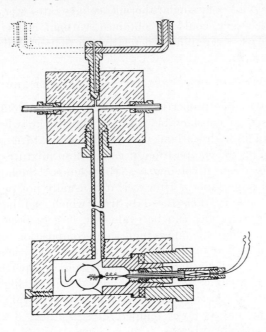

Fig. 19.—Piezothermometric cell for determining $(\partial T/\partial P)_s$ (Burlew).

Solids.—*Direct Method.*—As in the case of liquids, the Nernst type of calorimeter can be applied to the determination of the heat capacities of solids at ordinary temperatures. In the case of a compact solid having a high thermal conductivity, such as a metal, it is possible to dispense with the calorimeter shell and temperature-equalizing vanes usually employed. Accurate measurements of the specific heat of copper have been made by Harper[125] in which 50 meters of rather heavy copper wire coiled in a helix served as calorimeter, heater, and resistance thermometer.

Method of Mixtures.—The work of Andrews, Lynn, and Johnston[126] on

---

[125] D. R. Harper, *Natl. Bur. Standards* (*U. S.*), *Bull.* **11**, 259 (1914).

[126] D. H. Andrews, G. Lynn, and J. Johnston, *J. Am. Chem. Soc.*, **48**, 1274 (1926).

various organic substances may be cited as an example of the application of this method at moderate temperatures. The sample, contained in a glass container, was heated to the desired temperature, and then rapidly dropped into a calorimeter at about 25°. The calorimeter consisted of a Dewar flask filled with kerosene which was stirred by a reciprocating stirrer. The temperature of the calorimeter was measured relative to that of a similar Dewar flask by means of a thermel. It was found that, if a pair of Dewar flasks having very similar thermal leakage rates was selected, results of moderate accuracy could be obtained without jacketing the flasks. The heat capacities were obtained relative to that of a silver rod used as reference material.

C. DETERMINATION OF HEAT CAPACITIES AT ELEVATED TEMPERATURES

The thermodynamic properties of some organic compounds at elevated temperatures are of considerable interest; thus, a knowledge of the free energies of paraffin hydrocarbons up to high temperatures will permit predictions regarding the composition of equilibrium mixtures resulting from isomerization reactions involving these compounds. Such reactions are of great technical importance. However, it is usually not possible to determine by direct observations the data from which such high-temperature thermodynamic properties can be evaluated, largely because of the fact that nearly all organic substances undergo decomposition (or at least isomerization) when heated to elevated temperatures. Considerable progress has been made in calculating the thermodynamic properties of relatively simple molecules, such as the paraffin hydrocarbons, at high temperatures from molecular and spectroscopic data combined with values for the thermodynamic functions at lower temperatures (see page 352 for references to the literature on this subject).

Because of the fact that direct high-temperature heat-capacity measurements can very seldom be made on organic compounds, we shall not give much attention to such measurements except for a consideration of the method of mixtures as applied to solids and liquids. Several of the procedures for determining heat capacities which have been previously mentioned can be employed at elevated temperatures. Thus, Holborn and Henning[105] employed the method of mixtures for gases up to temperatures as high as 1400° C., and Dailey and Felsing[103] used the procedure of Bennewitz and Schulze[102] for some paraffin hydrocarbons up to 400° C.

The Method of Mixtures for Solids and Liquids.—If T_1 is the temperature to which the sample is initially heated, and T_0 and T_0' are the initial and final temperatures of the calorimetric system having an energy equivalent E, it is readily seen that the *mean* heat capacity of the sample, in the temperature interval T_0' to T_1, is given by:

$$\tilde{C}_s = E \frac{T_0' - T_0}{T_1 - T_0'} - \tilde{C}_c \tag{52}$$

where $\tilde{C}_c$ is the mean heat capacity of the container in the same temperature interval. If the pressure on the sample is the same at both the initial and final temperatures:

$$H_{T_1} - H_{T_0'} = \tilde{C}_s (T_1 - T_0')(M/m_s) \tag{53}$$

where m_s is the weight of the sample and M is the molecular weight of the substance. The heat function may then be differentiated either graphically or analytically to give the true heat capacity:

$$\left[\frac{\partial (H_{T_1} - H_{T_0'})}{\partial T} \right]_P = C_p \tag{54}$$

The furnace for preheating the sample must obviously contain a region of sufficiently uniform temperature. This can be accomplished by using a furnace with a large ratio of length to bore. In some cases, the sample is preheated in a vessel surrounded by a vapor or liquid bath of known temperature. It cannot be assumed that the heat loss during the fall from the preheater into the calorimeter is negligible. If the apparent heat capacity of the empty sample container is evaluated by observations made under the same conditions as those existing during the determination of the heat capacity of the sample, it may be assumed that the heat losses during the drop cancel out, provided the sample container itself has a sufficiently large heat capacity. From this point of view, it is advantageous for the container to be constructed of material having not too high a thermal conductivity. Heat loss during the drop can be materially reduced[127] by evacuating the furnace, calorimeter, and connecting tube to a pressure of about one millimeter; at this pressure, the static thermal conductivity of a gas is approximately the same as at atmospheric pressure, so the attainment of thermal equilibrium in the furnace and calorimeter is not slowed down, while at the same time the sample during its fall will lose much less heat to the surrounding gas.

For the receiving calorimeter, one can employ any sufficiently precise apparatus of convenient design, such as those described elsewhere in this chapter. The only modification of ordinary design which is needed is the provision either of openings in the calorimeter and jacket covers which are large enough for the sample to fall through, or of means for temporarily removing these covers. Receiving calorimeters are of two types, either a stirred liquid[128] or an aneroid (metal block) calorimeter. With a liquid

[127] K. Bornemann and O. Hengstenberg, *Metall u. Erz*, **17**, 319, 339 (1920).

[128] See, for example, M. A. Mosesman and K. S. Pitzer, *J. Am. Chem. Soc.*, **63**, 2348 (1941).

receiver, precautions must be taken to avoid splashing of the liquid (the amount of liquid in the calorimeter, or the energy equivalent of the calorimeter, should in any case be determined after, rather than before, the drop) when the sample drops into it.   This difficulty, as well as errors caused by possible vaporization of the calorimeter liquid by a hot sample, is avoided by the use of an aneroid receiver.   It is evidently advantageous to have the "dead" heat capacity of the calorimeter as small as is consistent with good design so far as other factors, such as temperature equalization and heat loss to the calorimeter surroundings, are concerned.   In the case of an aneroid calorimeter, the consideration of temperature equalization is particularly important.

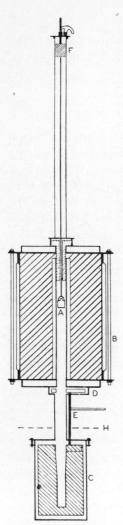

An apparatus (Fig. 20) described by Southard[129] illustrates several of the points mentioned above.   The copper block calorimeter, C, is enclosed in a brass case immersed to level H in a thermostat at 25°.   The receiving well is closed by a circular copper gate except at the instant of the drop, the gate being manipulated by eccentric shaft E. The sample, contained in a platinum–rhodium capsule, A, is heated in furnace B, which is surrounded by a water-cooled jacket.   The capsule is suspended in the furnace by a fine platinum–rhodium wire, so that it is easily replaced in the furnace for another determination without dismounting the apparatus in any way.   The temperature of the sample is determined by a noble-metal thermocouple situated just above it in the furnace tube.   A notable feature of Southard's design is the water-cooled gate, D, mounted on shaft E, which prevents heat leakage to the calorimeter even when the furnace is at 1500°.

White[130] has described in detail a receiving aneroid which incorporates several interesting features of design, including an automatic arrangement for closing the receiving well as soon as the sample has fallen into it.

VI.   HEATS OF COMBUSTION

The determination of heats of combustion, particularly of organic compounds, has long occupied an important place in thermochemistry.   Interest in the heats of combustion of substances used as

Fig. 20.—Calorimeter for determination of heat capacities by the method of mixtures (Southard).

[129] J. C. Southard, *J. Am. Chem. Soc.*, **63**, 3142 (1941).

[130] W. P. White, *The Modern Calorimeter*. Chem. Catalog Co., New York, 1928, p. 165.

fuels is of obvious origin; of much greater scientific interest are the applications of combustion data to the evaluation of other quantities such as .
heats and free energies of formation, and heats of reaction. It is important
to note that, with respect to the experimental accuracy required, there is
an essential difference between these two types of application of combustion data. In the comparison of the calorific value of fuels, data having
an accuracy of the order of 1% will usually suffice, while the calculation
of important thermodynamic quantities from heats of combustion requires
data of the highest quality. Since apparatus for the determination of
heats of combustion of a relatively low order of precision may be readily
purchased and is easily used, attention in this section will be concentrated
on modern methods by which data having an accuracy of a few hundredths
of a per cent may be obtained. We shall first discuss some of the more
important applications of heats of combustion, and then describe in some
detail the experimental procedures employed in their determination.

1. Applications

Modern heats of combustion refer, in most cases, to a reaction taking
place isothermally, with all the substances involved being in their standard states. The standard state of each substance is taken as the form
which is stable at 25° under a pressure of one atmosphere. (In most of the
older work on heats of combustion the standard temperature was 18°.)
Since the halogens and sulfur become aqueous halogen acid or aqueous
sulfuric acid, respectively, in the combustion process, it is customary to
report heats of combustion of substances containing these elements with
the halogen or sulfur in the products in the form of the corresponding
aqueous acid. Of course, in each case the concentration of the acid
should be clearly specified.

A. HEATS OF FORMATION

The results of combustion calorimetry are conveniently summarized in
the form of heats of formation. The standard heat of formation of a substance may be defined as the heat content of one mole of the substance less
the sum of the heat contents of the appropriate amounts of the elements
from which the substance is formed, the substance and the elements being
in their standard states. It is customary to take the following standard
states for the elements: graphite; gaseous hydrogen, oxygen, nitrogen,
and halogen at one atmopshere; and rhombic sulfur. The calculation of
a heat of formation requires a knowledge of the heats of formation of the
products of the combustion of the substance, namely, carbon dioxide,

water, and aqueous sulfuric and halogen acid.   Thus in the case of the substance $C_aH_bO_c$, it readily follows from Hess's law that

$$aC_{graphite} + b/2\ H_{2(g.,\ 1\ atm.)} + c/2\ O_{2(g.,\ 1\ atm.)} = C_aH_bO_{c(s.,\ l.,\ or\ g.,\ 1\ atm.)}$$

$$\Delta H_f = -\Delta H_c + a\,\Delta H_{f(CO_2)} + b/2\,\Delta H_{f(H_2O)} \tag{55}$$

where ΔH_c is the standard heat of combustion of the substance, and ΔH_f, $\Delta H_{f(CO_2)}$, and $\Delta H_{f(H_2O)}$ are, respectively, the standard heats of formation of the substance, of carbon dioxide, and of water.

Very careful work, largely at the National Bureau of Standards, has furnished reliable data for the heats of formation[131] of water and carbon dioxide at 25°.   (The heat content of a solid or a liquid is practically independent of pressure at ordinary pressures.   For this reason it is permissible to omit the specification of pressures after the formulas of liquids and solids.):

$$H_{2(g.,\ 1\ atm.)} + {}^1/_2\ O_{2(g.,\ 1\ atm.)} = H_2O_{(l.)}$$

$$\Delta H_{f(H_2O)} = -285,795 \pm 40\ int.\ j.\ per\ mole =$$

$$-68,318.1 \pm 9.6\ cal.\ per\ mole \tag{56}$$

$$C_{graphite} + O_{2(g.,\ 1\ atm.)} = CO_{2(g.,\ 1\ atm.)}$$

$$\Delta H_{f(CO_2)} = -393,355 \pm 46\ int.\ j.\ per\ mole =$$

$$-94,029.8 \pm 11.0\ cal.\ per\ mole \tag{57}$$

As an example of the corresponding values needed when other elements are present, we may cite the case of sulfur.[132]   The combustion data given by Moore, Renquist, and Parks refer to the reaction forming $H_2SO_4 \cdot 1.7\ H_2O$, so that the heat of formation needed is:

$$S_{rhombic} + 2.7\ H_2O_{(l.)} + {}^3/_2\ O_{2(g.,\ 1\ atm.)} = H_2SO_4 \cdot 1.7\ H_2O_{(l.)}$$

$$\Delta H_{f(H_2SO_4)} = -135,010\ cal.\ per\ mole \tag{58}$$

B.   COMPILATIONS OF HEATS OF COMBUSTION AND FORMATION

The heats of formation of many organic compounds containing one or two carbon atoms are given by Bichowsky and Rossini[133] in their important thermochemical tables.   Kharasch[134] made a rather complete critical compilation of the heats of combustion of organic compounds, which was also

[131] F. D. Rossini, *Chem. Revs.*, **27**, 1 (1940).

[132] G. E. Moore, M. L. Renquist, and G. S. Parks, *J. Am. Chem. Soc.*, **62**, 1505 (1940).

[133] F. R. Bichowsky and F. D. Rossini, *The Thermochemistry of Chemical Substances.* Reinhold, New York, 1936.

[134] M. S. Kharasch, *J. Research Natl. Bur. Standards*, **2**, 359 (1929).

published in *International Critical Tables*.[135]   Additional tabulations have been made[136] which cover the literature through 1935.

C. FREE ENERGIES

The standard free energy of formation is the free energy increase accompanying the formation of a substance in its standard state from its elements in their standard states.   This quantity is frequently spoken of simply as the free energy of the substance.   The important role played by heats of formation in the evaluation of free energies of formation has already been indicated in Section V (page 349) in connection with the use of the fundamental relation:[79]

$$\Delta F_f^0 = \Delta H_f - T \Delta S_f^0 \tag{59}$$

for this purpose.   The standard entropy of formation, ΔS_f^0, is the entropy of the substance less the sum of the entropies of its elements, the individual entropies being evaluated either from heat-capacity measurements extending to low temperatures, or from molecular data.   This application of heats of formation illustrates most clearly the great need for attaining the highest possible precision in the determination of the heats of combustion from which they are derived.   According to Rossini,[137] "... in most cases the relative magnitudes and absolute accuracies of the values of ΔS_f^0 and ΔH_f are such that the resulting uncertainty in ΔF_f^0 is practically equal to the error in ΔH_f."   A large fraction of the combustion data appearing in the literature before 1930 is of insufficient accuracy to be of much value in the calculation of thermodynamic quantities.   For example, in the case of the isomerization of cyclohexane to methylcyclopentane, the equilibrium measurements of Glasebrook and Lovell[138] gave a value for the entropy change in fairly good agreement with the value derived from heat-capacity data.   However, the changes in heat content and free energy differed even with respect to sign from the values deduced by Parks and Huffman[139] from older combustion heats.   A redetermination[140] of these heats with modern precision has eliminated the discrepancies.

[135] *International Critical Tables*.   Vol. V, McGraw-Hill, New York, 1929, p. 162.

[136] *Tables Annuelles de Constantes et Données Numeriques*.   Vol. VII, p. 150 (1925–1926);   Vol. VIII, p. 177 (1927–1928);   Vol. IX, p. 122 (1929);   Vol. X, p. 119 (1930); Vol. XI, Section 12 (1931–1934).   Landolt-Börnstein, *Physikalisch-Chemische Tabellen*, 5th ed., Vol. II, p. 1586;   supp. Vol. I, p. 866;   supp. Vol. IIb, p. 1633;   supp. Vol. IIIc, p. 2893 (up to March, 1936).

[137] F. D. Rossini, *Chem. Revs.*, **18**, 233 (1936).

[138] A. L. Glasebrook and W. G. Lovell, *J. Am. Chem. Soc.*, **61**, 1717 (1939).

[139] G. S. Parks and H. M. Huffman, *The Free Energies of Some Organic Compounds*. Reinhold, New York, 1932, p. 90.

[140] G. E. Moore and G. S. Parks, *J. Am. Chem. Soc.*, **61**, 2561 (1939).

Free energies may be added and subtracted just as may ΔH values. Thus, if the free energies of formation of all the substances except one involved in a reaction are known, the free energy of that one can be evaluated from a knowledge of the free energy change accompanying the reaction, with all the substances in their standard states. This standard free energy for the reaction is given by the expression:

$$\Delta F^0 = -RT \ln K \tag{60}$$

where K is the equilibrium constant (page 350). In cases in which it is difficult to obtain a sufficiently precise equilibrium constant at a single temperature, considerable improvement may be obtained by correlation of equilibrium constants determined over a range of temperature with appropriate thermal data.[141] The heat-capacity change accompanying the reaction may be expressed by the empirical equation:

$$C_p = a + bT + cT^2 \tag{61}$$

which on integration gives:

$$\Delta H = \Delta H_0 + aT + \frac{1}{2}bT^2 + \frac{1}{3}cT^3 \tag{62}$$

Substituting this equation in:

$$\frac{d(\Delta F/T)}{dT} = -\Delta H/T^2 \tag{63}$$

and integrating, we obtain:

$$\Delta F^0/T = -R \ln K = (\Delta H_0/T) - a \ln T - \frac{1}{2}bT - \frac{1}{6}cT^2 + I \tag{64}$$

where ΔH_0 and I are integration constants. If the function:

$$\Sigma \equiv -R \ln K + a \ln T + \frac{1}{2}bT + \frac{1}{6}cT^2 \tag{65}$$

is plotted against $1/T$, a straight line should be obtained having the slope, ΔH_0, and intercept I. In general, the precision of drawing the Σ plot is considerably increased if a reliable value of ΔH at some temperature within the range under consideration is available, for then the slope of the plot can be determined by equation (62). Such a value of ΔH can be obtained from combustion data.

Sufficient data on the free energies of formation of some of the simpler types of organic compounds have been obtained so that it is possible to make some empirical generalizations. Results of this sort will be found in the monograph by Parks and Huffman.[139] More recent efforts in this direction have been made by several authors. Thus, Parks[142] finds that the free energies at 25° of the liquid normal paraffins having more than five carbon atoms are well represented by the expression:

$$\Delta F_f^0 = -8912 + 1243n, \text{ cal. per mole} \tag{66}$$

where n is the number of carbon atoms in the molecule. Bruins and Czarnecki[143]

[141] G. S. Parks and H. M. Huffman, op. cit., p. 57.

[142] G. S. Parks, Chem. Revs., **27**, 75 (1940).

[143] P. F. Bruins and J. D. Czarnecki, Ind. Eng. Chem., Ind. Ed., **33**, 201 (1941).

have succeeded in expressing with moderate accuracy the free energies of some types of organic compounds in terms of bond free energies, the free energy for each bond being expressed as a function of temperature. Extensive correlations[144] of this type are to be expected when a wide range of accurately determined free energies becomes available.

D.   HEATS OF REACTION

The most general method for evaluating the heats of organic reactions is by means of combustion heats. This method, however, leads to rather inaccurate results in most cases. The sum of the heats of combustion of the reactants is usually a large number which differs only by a small amount from the corresponding sum for the products, so the difference between these two sums, the heat of the reaction, may be very seriously in error. Furthermore, heats of reaction calculated in this way refer only to reactions with all the substances in their combustion standard states. Additional data, such as heats of solution, vaporization, etc., are necessary to convert such heats of reaction to conditions which may be of more practical interest.

Because of these limitations, attention has been given in recent years to the problem of the direct determination of the heats of reactions which are not complete in a very short interval of time. Sufficient progress has been made to indicate that rather general methods for such determinations can be worked out. This type of calorimetric work is discussed in Section IX (pages 423–431). There are many processes, investigation of which will remain beyond the scope of these direct methods because of limitations imposed by side reactions or calorimetric difficulties. In such cases, the use of combustion heats will continue to be of importance.

As an example of the inaccuracy of the calculation of heats of reaction from heats of combustion, and the value of direct determination of this quantity, we cite a rather extreme case. Huffman and Fox[145] have determined the heats of combustion of α-D-glucose and β-D-glucose:

$$C_6H_{12}O_{6(\alpha)(s.)} + 6\ O_{2(g., 1\ atm.)} = 6\ CO_{2(g., 1\ atm.)} + 6\ H_2O_{(l.)}$$
$$-\Delta H_{(298° K.)} = 669.58\ \text{kcal. per mole} \tag{67}$$

$$C_6H_{12}O_{6(\beta)(s.)} + 6\ O_{2(g., 1\ atm.)} = 6\ CO_{2(g., 1\ atm.)} + 6\ H_2O_{(l.)}$$
$$-\Delta H_{(298° K.)} = 671.08\ \text{kcal. per mole} \tag{68}$$

From these data we can calculate the heat of the process:

$$C_6H_{12}O_{6(\alpha)(s.)} = C_6H_{12}O_{6(\beta)(s.)}$$
$$\Delta H_{(298° K.)} = 1.50\ \text{kcal. per mole} \tag{69}$$

[144] See, for example, C. L. Thomas, G. Egloff, and J. C. Morrell, *Ind. Eng. Chem., Ind. Ed.*, **29**, 1260 (1937); C. M. Thacker, H. O. Folkins, and E. L. Miller, *ibid.*, **33**, 584 (1941); K. S. Pitzer and D. W. Scott, *J. Am. Chem. Soc.*, **63**, 2419 (1941).

[145] H. M. Huffman and S. W. Fox, *J. Am. Chem. Soc.*, **60**, 1400 (1938).

Direct calorimetric measurements[146] of the heats of mutarotation in solution and the heats of solution of the two forms of D-glucose lead to the value $\Delta H_{(298° K.)} = 1.165$ kcal. per mole. The difference here, amounting to about 30% of the heat of reaction, is only 0.05% of either heat of combustion.

Prosen and Rossini[147] have recently developed a method for the evaluation of heats of isomerization from combustion experiments which considerably reduces the inaccuracies inherent in the usual procedure. In principle, the method consists in determining the ratio of the masses of two isomers (in the work cited, involving the hexanes, the masses of carbon dioxide formed in the combustions were actually employed) the combustion of which produces equal temperature rises in the calorimetric system. Since all the experiments are carried out under nearly identical conditions, calorimetric uncertainties are minimized. It may be noted that the reactions studied by Prosen and Rossini, namely, the isomerization of hydrocarbons, cannot possibly be investigated by the direct calorimetric method.

E. BOND ENERGIES

Various attempts[148] have been made to discover additive relations between heats of combustion, or values derived from them, and molecular structure. The consideration of bond energies affords a fruitful, if not

TABLE II

BOND ENERGIES[a]

Bond	Energy, kcal./mole	Bond	Energy, kcal./mole		Bond	Energy, kcal./mole	
H—H	103.4	O—H	110.2		C=N	94	
C—C	58.6	S—H	87.5		C≡N	144	(HCN)
N—N	20.0	H—F	147.5		C≡N	150	(cyanides)
O—O	34.9	H—Cl	102.7		C—S	54.5	
S—S	63.8	H—Br	87.3		C=S	103	
F—F	63.5	H—I	71.4		C=C	100	
Cl—Cl	57.8	C—O	70.0		C≡C	123	
Br—Br	46.1	C=O	142	(formaldehyde)	C—F	107.0	
I—I	36.2	C=O	149	(aldehydes)	C—Cl	66.5	
C—H	87.3	C=O	152	(ketones)	C—Br	54.0	
N—H	83.7	C—N	48.6		C—I	45.5	

[a] L. Pauling, *Nature of the Chemical Bond and the Structure of Molecules and Crystals.* Cornell Univ. Press, Ithaca, 1940.

very quantitative, basis for correlating such data. The total heat of dissociation of a polyatomic substance into atoms, a value which can be cal-

[146] J. M. Sturtevant, *J. Phys. Chem.*, **45**, 127 (1941).

[147] E. J. R. Prosen and F. D. Rossini, *J. Research Natl. Bur. Standards*, **27**, 289 (1941).

[148] (A) K. Fajans, *Ber.*, **53**, 643 (1920); **55**, 2826 (1922); *Z. physik. Chem.*, **99**, 395 (1921). (B) M. S. Kharasch, *J. Research Natl. Bur. Standards*, **2**, 359 (1929). (C) N. V. Sidgwick, *Some Physical Properties of the Covalent Link in Chemistry*, Cornell Univ. Press, Ithaca, 1933. (D) L. Pauling, *Nature of the Chemical Bond and the Structure of Molecules and Crystals*, Cornell Univ. Press, Ithaca, 1940.

culated from combustion data, is equal to the sum of the energies of the bonds in the substance. It is not, however, possible to deduce individual bond energies from these sums, as it is in the case of diatomic molecules; only mean values can be obtained. Table II gives a selection of the bond energy values published by Pauling. These values are so chosen that their sums represent, with an accuracy of about ± 2 kcal. per mole, the $-\Delta H$ values for the formation of gaseous substances from gaseous atoms at 1 atm. and 18°; most of the thermochemical data used in deducing these bond energies were taken from Bichowksy and Rossini.[133] The values used for the heats of formation $(-\Delta H)$ of the elements in their usual standard states from monoatomic gases are given in table III. The method of computing the bond energies of table II can be illustrated as follows. For methane we have:

$$C_{diamond} + 2 H_{2(g.)} = CH_{4(g.)}$$
$$\Delta H_{291} = -18.24 \text{ kcal. per mole} \tag{70}$$

Also:

$$C_{diamond} = C_{monatomic\ gas}$$
$$\Delta H_{291} = 124.3 \text{ kcal. per mole} \tag{71}$$

and:

$$H_{2(g.)} = 2H_{(g.)}; \quad \Delta H_{291} = 103.4 \text{ kcal. per mole} \tag{72}$$

Therefore:

$$C_{(g.)} + 4 H_{(g.)} = CH_{4(g.)}; \Delta H_{291} = -349.3 \text{ kcal. per mole} \tag{73}$$

In spite of the fact that it is certain that the energy necessary to dissociate each successive hydrogen atom from methane is not equal to one quarter of this value, it is nevertheless convenient to define the average energy required, 87.3 kcal. per mole, as the energy of the C—H bond in methane. Similary, we find for ethane:

$$2 C_{(g.)} + 6 H_{(g.)} = C_2H_{6(g.)}$$
$$\Delta H_{291} = -579.8 \text{ kcal. per mole} \tag{74}$$

If the assumption is made that the C—H bonds in ethane have the same average energy as those in methane, we obtain for the energy of the C—C bond the value $579.8 - 6(87.3) = 56.0$ kcal. per mole. This value differs from that given in table II because it is found that better agreement with experiment is obtained for the higher paraffin hydrocarbons if the latter value is employed.

In some tabulations of bond energies, the reference state of the carbon atom is taken as the [5]S state instead of the normal [3]P state used in Pauling's tabulation. It should also be noted that the above bond energies calculated for 18° include the vibrational, rotational, and translational energies of the molecules.   It would be preferable to correct the thermochemical data to 0° K., but in most cases the heat-capacity data necessary for this correction are not available.

There is abundant evidence that bond energies defined in the manner described above are not strictly additive.   This has already been illustrated by the fact that the value for the C—C bond deduced from the heats of formation of methane and ethane is not suitable for the higher paraffin hydrocarbons.   Rossini[149] has summarized the most reliable data on the heats of combustion of the normal paraffin hydrocarbons and the normal primary alcohols and has found that, contrary to

TABLE III

HEATS OF FORMATION OF ELEMENTS IN THEIR STANDARD STATES FROM MONATOMIC GASES

Element	Heat of formation, kcal./mole	Element	Heat of formation, kcal./mole
H_2	103.4	F_2	63.6
C	124.3^a	Cl_2	57.8
N_2	170.2	Br_2	53.8
O_2	118.2	I_2	51.2
S	66.3		

^{a} This is the heat of sublimation of diamond.   When the usual standard state of carbon is employed, the heat of sublimation of graphite, 124.1 kcal. per mole, is to be employed.   See E. C. Baughan, Nature, 147, 542 (1941).

the prediction based on the assumption of the additivity of bond energies, the introduction of a CH_2 group does not cause a constant increment in the heat of combustion until the number of carbon atoms exceeds five.   He interprets this as indicating that the influence of an atom, so far as energy is concerned, extends to the atom second removed from it.   With five or more carbon atoms present, extending either of the above series merely consists in introducing additional CH_2 groups in the middle of the molecule under effectively constant conditions.

Further evidence[147, 150] of the nonadditivity of bond energies is afforded by the heats of isomerization of paraffin hydrocarbons determined by Rossini and coworkers.   Thus, for the isomerization of n-heptane to 2,2-dimethylpentane at one atmosphere, Prosen and Rossini have found:

$$n\text{-heptane }_{(g., 1 \text{ atm.})} = 2,2\text{-dime hylpentane }_{(g., 1 \text{ atm.})}$$
$$\Delta H_{298.16} = -4.45 \text{ kcal. per mole} \tag{75}$$

[149] F. D. Rossini, J. Research Natl. Bur. Standards, 13, 21, 189 (1934).

[150] F. D. Rossini, J. Research Natl. Bur. Standards, 15, 357 (1935); J. W. Knowlton and F. D. Rossini, ibid., 22, 415 (1939); E. J. R. Prosen and F. D. Rossini, ibid., 27, 519 (1941).   See also C. M. Anderson and E. C. Gilbert, J. Am. Chem. Soc., 64, 2369 (1942).

The simple summation of bond energies is, of course, unable to account for this relatively large difference in heats of formation. Attempts[151] have been made to modify the postulate of simple additivity in such a way that difficulties of this sort are eliminated.

Despite the approximate nature of heats of formation calculated from bond energies, they are of considerable interest in connection with problems of molecular structure. A molecule whose structure cannot be represented satisfactorily by a single classical valence bond formula can, in one type of approximation method, be more accurately considered as a resonance hybrid of several such structures. In such a case, the difference between the observed heat of formation and that calculated for one of the contributing structures with the help of the table of bond energies gives an empirical value for the resonance energy relative to the structure considered. For example, the heat of combustion of benzene leads to the value $-\Delta H_f = 1039$ kcal. per mole; one would predict for a single Kekulé structure the value $-\Delta H_f = 6(C\text{—}H) + 3(C\text{—}C) + 3(C\text{=}C) = 1000$ kcal. per mole. The difference, 39 kcal. per mole, is the resonance energy of benzene relative to the Kekulé structure. The reader is referred to Pauling's book[148D] for further discussion and illustration of the importance of heats of combustion in connection with resonance.

Wrinch and Harker[152] have suggested that the concept of *constant* bond energies should be dropped, and be replaced by the assumption that, for the bonds formed between each pair of atoms, there is a one-to-one relation between bond energy and bond length. Thus, they point out that the energies of $C\text{—}N$, $C\text{=}N$, and $C\text{≡}N$ bonds fall on a smooth curve when plotted against bond length. They suggest that, on this basis, the heat of formation of a molecule will be directly deducible from its geometry without any consideration of bond character or resonance.

2. Bomb Calorimetry

A. DESCRIPTION OF APPARATUS

The heats of combustion of solids and liquids are usually determined by combustion in a bomb in an excess of oxygen. The bomb is immersed in a calorimeter containing a suitable liquid, usually water. The calorimeter is surrounded by a jacket; in the ordinary method the temperature of the jacket is held constant, while in the adiabatic method the temperature of the jacket is maintained equal to that of the calorimeter. Combustion

[151] See, for example, V. Dietz, *J. Chem. Phys.*, **3**, 58, 436 (1935); R. Serber, *ibid.*, **3**, 81 (1935); E. Mack, *J. Phys. Chem.*, **41**, 221 (1937).

[152] D. Wrinch and D. Harker, *J. Chem. Phys.*, **8**, 502 (1940). See also R. F. Barrow, *Trans. Faraday Soc.*, **36**, 1053 (1940).

experiments are almost without exception of relatively short duration, so that there is little to be gained from the added complications of the adiabatic method (page 341). Bomb calorimeters are, fundamentally, devices for comparing the heats of combustion processes with known amounts of electrical energy. However, since very careful measurements[153] of the heat of combustion of benzoic acid have been made, it is possible, without serious loss of accuracy, to use the combustion calorimeter to compare the heat of combustion of the substance under investigation with that of benzoic acid, thus eliminating the need for a calorimeter heater (a crude heater will still be desirable to facilitate the adjustment of the temperature of the calorimeter) and the accessory apparatus for the measurement of electrical energy. In order for the comparison between combustion heat and electrical energy, or between two different combustion heats, to be made as accurately as possible, it is important that the time–temperature curves for the two processes be as nearly alike as possible. In this way inaccuracies in the calorimetric observations, particularly those resulting from heat leakage to the surroundings, will be minimized. Combustion apparatus with which a high degree of precision may be obtained has been described by several experimenters in this field. It will be sufficient to restrict our attention to the apparatus described in several publications from the National Bureau of Standards, since, in its later forms, it is at least equal in precision to any other bomb calorimeter.

Figure 21 represents diagrammatically the bomb itself.[154] The bomb, A, is constructed of Illium, a corrosion-resistant alloy, and has an internal volume of 385 milliliters. The head, B, also of Illium, is pressed against the bomb by 16 setscrews, a tight seal being insured by gold gasket C. Connections D, with standard tapers, can be inserted for flushing and filling the bomb with oxygen and for analyzing the gaseous products of combustion. The material to be burned is placed in platinum cup E, and is ignited by fusing a small coil of fine iron wire, F, supported from two platinum lead wires, G. Solid substances which have sufficiently low vapor pressures can be weighed directly into the cup, usually in the form of pellets. Liquid substances are contained in thin-walled glass ampoules with flattened sides, the ampoules being almost completely filled so that they will withstand the oxygen pressure. With some substances complete combustion is facilitated by the addition of some easily burned substance such as paraffin oil. When this procedure is employed, it is of course necessary to deduct the heat of combustion of the auxiliary substance from the ob-

[153] R. S. Jessup, *J. Research Natl. Bur. Standards*, **29**, 247 (1942).

[154] E. J. R. Prosen and F. D. Rossini, *J. Research Natl. Bur. Standards*, **27**, 289 (1941). Similar apparatus has been described by H. M. Huffman and E. L. Ellis, *J. Am. Chem. Soc.*, **57**, 41 (1935), J. W. Richardson and G. S. Parks, *ibid.*, **61**, 3543 (1939), and others.

served value. It should be noted that the assumption that the over-all heat of combustion is additive is not in general true[155] because of the heat of mixing. Any error from this source, however, will usually be very small. It is standard practice to place one milliliter of water in the bomb to insure saturation of the oxygen, and to use an initial oxygen pressure of 30 atmospheres.

The bomb is submerged in a calorimeter containing approximately 3 liters of water. It is essential that the calorimeter liquid be very thoroughly stirred, but with as small a heat of stirring as possible. The design

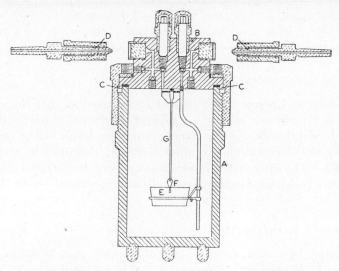

Fig. 21.—Bomb for combustion calorimetry (Prosen and Rossini). (For the functions of parts not mentioned in the text, see the original paper.)

described in detail by Dickinson[156] is very satisfactory. Particular care should be taken that the calorimeter cover is in good thermal contact with the calorimeter liquid, and is sufficiently tight to prevent evaporation. Evaporation may also be lessened by a thin film of oil on the surface of the calorimeter liquid. For electrical calibration, the calorimeter is equipped with a heating coil fitting snugly around the body of the bomb. The coil is supplied with a pair of potential leads joined to the main leads midway between the calorimeter and the jacket. The temperature of the calorimeter liquid is measured with a platinum resistance thermometer (page 317).

155 E. W. Washburn, *J. Research Natl. Bur. Standards*, **10**, 525 (1933).
156 H. C. Dickinson, *Natl. Bur. Standards (U. S.)*, *Bull.* **11**, 189 (1915).

A constant-temperature water jacket surrounds the calorimeter on all sides with an air gap of approximately one centimeter. Dickinson[156] has described a jacket with a removable cover through which the jacket liquid also circulates. The water in the jacket is thoroughly stirred, and its temperature is held constant to within a few thousandths of a degree by a thermostat (see page 326). Rossini recommends that the jacket temperature be a little higher than the final temperature of the bomb as a further protection against evaporation from the calorimeter.

Bomb calorimeters have been described[157] which are much smaller than the bomb illustrated above. These microbombs require only about 0.01 gram of substance, as compared with about 1 gram required by bombs of ordinary size. However, the lower precision obtainable with such apparatus is probably insufficient for modern requirements.

B.   ELECTRICAL CALIBRATION

The heater and power supply should be designed so that the electrical calibration experiments involve a temperature change of nearly the same magnitude and duration as the combustion experiments. The method of measuring the electrical energy input has been described in Section III (page 330). The calorimetric procedure employed in electrical calibration experiments is similar to that in combustion experiments to be described below.

C.   BENZOIC ACID CALIBRATION

Calibration by means of combustion of standard sample benzoic acid[158] is sufficiently accurate for most purposes. The accepted value for the heat of combustion of benzoic acid is that of Jessup.[153] The procedure is precisely the same as that described below, except that it is unnecessary to apply the complete Washburn corrections.

D.   COMBUSTION PROCEDURE

The procedure described in detail by Prosen and Rossini[159] is typical of those employed by other investigators. After the calorimeter and jacket have been brought to the desired temperatures, observations of the calorimeter temperature (actually the resistance of a resistance thermometer) are made every two minutes during a "fore" period of 20 minutes. The charge is then ignited and the calorimeter temperature is observed more

[157] M. Padoa and B. Foresti, *Gazz. chim. ital.*, **53**, 493 (1923); *Ber.*, **58**, 1339 (1925). W. A. Roth, *Chem. Fabrik*, 1936, 10–12.

[158] Obtainable from the *National Bureau of Standards*, Washington, D. C.

[159] E. J. R. Prosen and F. D. Rossini, *J. Research Natl. Bur. Standards*, **27**, 289 (1941).

frequently, particularly while the temperature is rising rapidly, for 15–20 minutes during the "reaction" period. Finally, the temperature is followed for an additional 20 minutes, the "after" period, with readings every 2 minutes. The temperature–time curve is practically a straight line during the fore and after periods.

3. Corrections to Combustion Data

The corrections for *thermal leakage and stirring* can be evaluated in various more or less equivalent ways (see Section IV). *The ignition correction* for the temperature rise resulting from the burning of the fuse wire is determined by blank experiments. Small amounts of *nitric acid* are formed by oxidation of the nitrogen impurity in the oxygen. The nitric acid is determined by titration at the end of the combustion, and the correction calculated, taking 13,800 calories per mole for the heat evolved in the formation of dilute aqueous nitric acid from nitrogen, oxygen, and water. This correction is expressed as a temperature change by using an approximate value for the heat capacity (energy equivalent) of the calorimeter.

In the *correction to the isothermal process*, we denote by $\Delta T_{corr.}$ the temperature rise which has been corrected as outlined in the preceding paragraph. In individual cases, other corrections may be necessary; analysis of the products of combustion may, for example, indicate the need for additional corrections. As actually carried out, the combustion process takes place over a range of temperature. The quantity in which we are interested, however, is the heat effect which would be observed if the process were to take place isothermally. The heat absorbed in the actual bomb process is conveniently calculated for the *initial* temperature of the combustion, since one can more easily evaluate the heat capacity of the products than of the reactants. As pointed out by Richards,[160] if the heat capacity of the final system in a calorimetric experiment is employed in calculating the heat of the process from the observed temperature rise, the value obtained refers to the initial temperature of the experiment. If the energy equivalent, or heat capacity of the calorimetric system with the bomb filled precisely as for a combustion experiment, except for the omission of the sample for combustion and the fuse wire, is denoted by E, then the heat absorbed, per mole of substance, in the bomb process occurring isothermally at the initial temperature is:

$$-\Delta U_B = \Delta T_{corr.} (E + C) \cdot M/m \qquad (76)$$

where M is the molecular weight of the substance, and m is the mass of the sample in grams, *corrected to vacuum*. In this expression, C is a heat ca-

---

[160] T. W. Richards, *J. Am. Chem. Soc.*, 25, 209 (1903).

pacity term which, according to Washburn,[155] can be expressed in the following form, which holds with sufficient accuracy for any substance of the formula $C_aH_bO_c$ in the region of room temperatures:

$$C = 0.158m_{Fe} + \frac{m}{M}\left[(1.77_1 + 0.0112P)a + 7.74b + 2.5c\right] -$$

$$34n_{HNO_3}, \text{ cal. per degree C.} \quad (77)$$

In this equation, m_{Fe} is the mass of iron wire burned to Fe_2O_3, P is the final pressure in the bomb in atmospheres, and n_{HNO_3} is the number of moles of HNO_3 formed. If the substance contains other elements, suitable terms must be added in evaluating C.

The energy equivalent, E, cannot be assumed to be independent of temperature; it is therefore to be determined over the same temperature interval as that resulting from the combustions. If benzoic acid is used for calibration, the known value of ΔU_B for benzoic acid[153] and the calculated value of C are employed in equation (76) to evaluate E.

4. Reduction to Standard Conditions. The Washburn Corrections

Following Washburn's[155] recommendation, the Permanent Committee on Thermochemistry of the International Union of Chemistry in 1934 recommended using carefully standardized experimental conditions. Thus, the initial oxygen pressure should be 30 atmospheres, three milliliters of water per liter of bomb volume should be added, and, in the case of benzoic acid, three grams per liter of bomb volume should be burned. With other substances, the sample size should be sufficient to give about the same temperature rise as given by this amount of benzoic acid.

Washburn pointed out that the actual bomb process had not been completely defined by previous workers, and that the precision obtainable by modern calorimetric methods is such as to make this lack of definition significant. Furthermore, the initial and final states in an actual combustion process, even when completely defined, are thermodynamically uninteresting or trivial, and suitable corrections should be employed to refer the calorimetric data to a convenient set of standard states. Washburn has given in complete form the methods of computation of the necessary corrections. It will be sufficient for our purposes to indicate briefly the nature of the more important corrections, and to refer the reader to Washburn's paper for further details. *It cannot be too strongly emphasized that one should always apply the Washburn corrections to combustion data.* The value of much of the combustion data published since 1933, particularly in other countries, is impaired by the failure of the authors to apply any but the more obvious corrections to their work.

We have indicated above how the heat, ΔU_B, of the actual bomb process is calculated. A quantity of more utility and interest is the heat, ΔU_R, absorbed when one mole of substance in its standard state, at the standard temperature T_s, reacts with an equivalent amount of oxygen gas under a pressure of one atmosphere to form pure carbon dioxide gas and pure liquid water, both under a pressure of one atmosphere, the reaction taking place without the production of any external work. It is of no significance that this process is not experimentally realizable. This definition of ΔU_R applies in the case of a compound containing only carbon, hydrogen, and oxygen. If other elements are present, the final state of the combustion products derived therefrom must, of course, be specified. Thus, for a substance containing only carbon, hydrogen, and oxygen the process to which ΔU_R refers can be written:

$$C_aH_bO_{c(\text{s. or l.; 1 atm.})} + (a + b/2 - c/2)\, O_{2(\text{g., 1 atm.})} =$$
$$a\, CO_{2(\text{g., 1 atm.})} + b/2\, H_2O_{(\text{l., 1 atm.})} \quad (78)$$

It is not necessary to include the case of a substance which is stable as a gas at T_s, since the heats of combustion of such compounds are more conveniently determined by means of the flame calorimeter (page 391). If a mixture of substances[155] is burned, $C_aH_bO_c$ represents the empirical composition of the mixture. The quantity ΔU_R in many cases differs only slightly from ΔU_B, but in other cases the difference amounts to as much as several tenths of a per cent.

For purposes of computation the hypothetical process corresponding to ΔU_R may be broken up into any convenient set of steps, one of which must be the actual bomb process. Washburn[155, 161] finds the following set of steps involve ΔU values which may be calculated with sufficient accuracy:

"*Step 1.* n_{O_2} moles of oxygen at T_s and 1 atm. are compressed into the bomb which contains n moles of the substance to be burned and n_W g. of liquid water. The initial pressure of the oxygen in the bomb is p_1 atm. at T_s. . . .

"*Step 2.* The combustion is carried out in the usual way, and the quantity. $-\Delta U_B$, is calculated for T_s. The final pressure in the bomb is $(p_2 + p_W)$ atm. at T_s, p_W being the partial pressure of the water vapor in the final system. . . .

"*Step 3.* The aqueous solution of carbon dioxide and oxygen is separated from the gas phase and is confined under the pressure $(p_2 + p_W)$ atm. . . .

"*Step 4.* With the aid of a membrane permeable only to carbon dioxide, the dissolved carbon dioxide is allowed to escape from its aqueous solution into a space at zero pressure, after which it is compressed to 1 atm. . . .

"*Step 5.* The pressure on the water is now reduced to 1 atm. and the

---

[161] The notation used by Washburn has been somewhat modified.

dissolved oxygen is removed as a gas at 1 atm. At the same time the water vapor present in the bomb at the completion of the combustion is removed in the form of pure liquid water under a pressure of 1 atm. . . .

"*Step 6.*   The gas phase (oxygen and carbon dioxide) in the bomb is now expanded to zero pressure. . . .

"*Step 7.*   The oxygen and carbon dioxide are demixed at zero pressure. . .

"*Step 8.*   The oxygen and carbon dioxide are each compressed to 1 atm. . . ."

Denoting by ΔU_1, ΔU_2, . . . ΔU_8 the increases in energy accompanying each of these steps, and noting that:

$$\Delta U_2 = n \Delta U_b \tag{79}$$

$$\Delta U_3 = \Delta U_7 = 0 \tag{80}$$

we have:

$$n \Delta U_R = n \Delta U_B + \Delta U_1 + \Delta U_2 + \Delta U_4 + \Delta U_5 + \Delta U_6 + \Delta U_8$$
$$= n \Delta U_B + \Delta U_{\text{corr.}} \tag{81}$$

or·

$$\Delta U_R = \Delta U_B [1 + (\Delta U_{\text{corr.}}/n \Delta U_B)] \tag{82}$$

Some of the energy terms involved in $\Delta U_{\text{corr.}}$ are of negligible magnitude; the remainder can be evaluated by the methods given in detail by Washburn.

It is not always convenient to have the initial temperature of a combustion experiment coincide with the standard temperature, T_s. The value of ΔU_R can be corrected to the standard temperature by means of the relation:

$$d(\Delta U_R)/dT = \Delta C_v \tag{83}$$

where ΔC_v is the difference between the sum of the molal heat capacities, at constant volume, of the products and that of the reactants (for the substance to be burned and the water present, the heat capacities at constant pressure can be used). This correction is always small for combustion reactions, amounting, in the case of benzoic acid, to only -0.22 calorie per gram per degree C.; it can be calculated with sufficient accuracy over any temperature interval in the region of room temperature by means of the expression:

$$\Delta U'_R - \Delta U_R = \cdot (T' - T) (1.78a + 7.74b + 2.492c - C_p) \tag{84}$$

for the substance $C_a H_b O_c$. Here C_p is the heat capacity per mole of the substance to be burned, and the remaining terms in the second parentheses express the total heat capacity of the products. The unit of energy is the calorie. The temperature coefficient of ΔU_B differs from that of ΔU_R by only a negligible amount.

5. Calculation of ΔH_c

For most thermodynamic calculations, the quantity of greatest interest to be derived from combustion experiments is the difference in heat content between the products and reactants. This quantity, which is denoted by ΔH_c if all the substances are in their standard states, is obtained from ΔU_R by means of the equation (see page 314):

$$\Delta H_c = \Delta U_R + \Delta(PV) \tag{85}$$

Since oxygen and carbon dioxide under a pressure of one atmosphere behave approximately as perfect gases, this expression can, with sufficient accuracy be written:

$$\Delta H_c = \Delta U_R + \Delta nRT \tag{86}$$

where Δn is the difference between the number of moles of carbon dioxide formed and oxygen consumed when one mole of substance is burned (if nitrogen is present, allowance has to be made for the fact that this element also appears in the gaseous state in the products of the combustion). In equation (86), the volume changes in condensed phases are neglected. At $298.16°$ K., RT has the value of 592.3 calories per mole.

6. Flame Calorimetry

The heats of combustion of substances which are gaseous or have high vapor pressures at room temperature are most conveniently determined in a flame calorimeter. The substance is burned in oxygen (usually present in excess) at constant pressure. Rossini[162] has described a flame calorimeter with which highly precise results have been obtained. Figure 22 illustrates the reaction vessel employed.[163] Combustion takes place at the silica burner tube, F, a spark being used to initiate the reaction. The platinum spark leads are broken by a two-millimeter gap at the top of the inlet tubes, B and C, so that conduction of heat from the reaction vessel by the leads will be the same during combustions, when the vessel is hot as during calibration experiments. Most of the water formed collects in the condensing chamber, H; the carbon dioxide, some water vapor, and excess oxygen go out through cooling coil E to tubes for the absorption of the water and carbon dioxide. The reaction vessel is immersed in a calorimeter containing water and surrounded by a constant-temperature

---

[162] F. D. Rossini, *J. Research Natl. Bur. Standards,* **6**, 1 (1931); **7**, 329 (1931); **8**, 119 (1932). See also C. B. Miles and H. Hunt, *J. Phys. Chem.,* **45**, 1346 (1941).

[163] A different type of reaction vessel is described by Rossini, [*J. Research Natl. Bureau Standards,* **12**, 735 (1934)] which was found to be preferable in the combustion of hydrocarbons.

jacket, the calorimeter and jacket being of a design similar to that used with a bomb calorimeter.

The temperature observations are made as with the bomb calorimeter. At the start of the reaction period, the gases for reaction, which have been previously led to waste, are carried into the reaction vessel, and the spark circuit is closed for a fixed length of time. After a sufficient amount of combustion has taken place, the gases are again led to waste, provision being made for sweeping out the combustible gas remaining in the inlet tube, and the reaction period is terminated after the calorimeter temperature has resumed a course linear with respect to time. The temperature readings are corrected for stirring and heat leakage as described previously. The apparatus is readily adapted to the combustion of liquids having sufficiently high vapor pressures. An inert carrier gas such as helium or air is saturated with the substance at a temperature somewhat below that of the calorimeter.

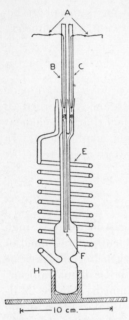

Fig. 22.—Reaction vessel for flame calorimetry (Rossini).

Three rather important corrections must be made which did not arise in bomb calorimetry. A small fraction of the observed heat evolution is due to the ignition spark; the appropriate correction is determined by blank experiments. A "gas" correction becomes necessary if the entering gases are not at the same temperature as the calorimeter. This correction can be calculated from the heat capacities of the gases, the volumes being measured by flowmeters. A "vaporization" correction is calculated to allow for the fact that some of the water from the combustion leaves the reaction vessel in the form of vapor. The amount of water vaporized is determined by absorption in Dehydrite and phosphorus pentoxide.

The amount of reaction taking place is best determined by weighing the carbon dioxide formed, after absorption, e. g., in Ascarite (sodium hydroxide on asbestos). It is, of course, necessary to establish that the combustion is complete under the conditions of the experiment. An indication of this can be obtained from a careful comparison of the weights of carbon dioxide and water formed in the reaction, and from a test for carbon monoxide in the gases which are not absorbed in the Dehydrite and Ascarite.

Determination of the energy equivalent of the calorimeter is accomplished by electrical calibration, or by the combustion of some substance such as hydrogen. The Permanent Committee on Thermochemistry recommends the reaction of the combustion of hydrogen in oxygen for the calibration of constant-pressure flame calorimeters, using the values obtained at the National Bureau of Standards.[162]

The appropriate energy equivalent to be used in each combustion experiment includes the heat capacity of half of the *liquid* water formed in the reaction. The energy equivalent is determined at the same mean temperature as the heat of combustion. It is not possible to correct the result of a combustion experiment to give the heat of the isothermal process by a method analogous to that used in bomb calorimetry, because the products of the reaction leave the calorimeter at a steadily increasing temperature. However, the result obtained can with high accuracy be identified with the heat of the isothermal process occurring at the mean temperature of the experiment. Combustion experiments with the flame calorimeter give directly the heat of the reaction at a constant total pressure, in most cases one atmosphere. If a carrier gas is employed, it can be assumed that the heat of separating the carrier gas and the vapor of the substance burned is negligible.

7. Estimation of Errors

In the assignment of uncertainties to combustion data, the procedure recommended by Rossini and Deming[164] should be followed. This procedure applies when the fluctuations of the individual observations of a measured quantity are purely random in nature. An estimate of the standard deviation, s, to be assigned to the determination of such a quantity is made by means of the formula:

$$s = \sqrt{\Sigma v_i^2 / n(n-1)} \tag{87}$$

where v_i is the deviation of the ith observation from the mean of the set of n observations. It is recommended that eight to twelve observations be made. In the evaluation of a heat of combustion, essentially independent sets of observations will be concerned with the determination of the energy equivalent of the calorimeter, and with the determination (in degrees temperature rise per mole or other arbitrary units, such as ohms per gram carbon dioxide) of the heat of combustion of the substance under investigation. Separate standard deviations are estimated for each of these sets. If the energy equivalent is determined by means of benzoic acid, there must also be included the standard deviation for the set of observations leading to the "accepted" value for the heat of combustion of this substance. If we denote by $\bar{x}, \bar{y}, \bar{z} \ldots$, the mean values obtained for the energy equivalent of the calorimeter, the "accepted" heat of combustion of the standardizing substance, the heat of combustion of the substance under investigation, etc., and by $s_x, s_y, s_z \ldots$,

---

[164] F. D. Rossini and W. E. Deming, *J. Wash. Acad. Sci.*, **29**, 416 (1939).

the corresponding standard deviations, the standard deviation to be assigned to the final heat of combustion, ΔH_c (in joules or calories per mole), is

$$s_c = \Delta H_c \sqrt{(s_x/\bar{x})^2 + (s_y/\bar{y})^2 + (s_z/\bar{z})^2 + \ldots} \qquad (88)$$

This equation follows from the law of combination of errors, since the quantities $\bar{x}, \bar{y}, \bar{z} \ldots$, all enter to their first powers only in the calculation of ΔH_c. The over-all precision uncertainty interval in ΔH_c is then set equal to $2s_c$, that is, ΔH_c is reported as $\Delta H_c \pm s_c$.

It should be clearly realized that an uncertainty interval evaluated in this way is merely a standardized method for expressing the *precision* of the final result. Constant systematic errors may make the *accuracy* of the result far inferior to its precision. It is the responsibility of the individual experimenter to exert every possible effort to reduce systematic errors to the point at which they cannot affect the final result by amounts exceeding a fraction of the estimated uncertainty interval. If it is known that, for some reason, a quantity can be measured with a precision higher than the accuracy that can be attained, the estimated uncertainty interval should be broadened appropriately by inclusion, or modification, of a corresponding term in equation (88). Furthermore, it is advisable to add to the value of s_c an arbitrary allowance for a 10% uncertainty in the Washburn corrections. An uncertainty interval which includes all known nonrandom sources of error in addition to the individual standard deviations is termed an *accuracy* uncertainty interval. It has been assumed in the above discussion that the accuracy of calibration of the temperature, electrical, and other measuring devices employed is consistent with the precision obtainable in their use.

In view of the fact that the modern technique of determining combustion heats can lead to results having an accuracy, so far as the calorimetric measurements are concerned, of a few hundredths of a per cent, it is obvious that the greatest care must be exercised in establishing the purity of the substances investigated. In connection with liquid compounds, for example, the solubility of air in the material may be high enough to introduce significant errors in weighing. Criteria of purity based on the thermal behavior of a substance in the neighborhood of its melting point are discussed in Sections V and VII (pages 350 and 396).

VII. HEATS OF FUSION, TRANSITION, AND VAPORIZATION

1. Heats of Fusion

The most accurate data on heats of fusion have been determined in the Nernst type of calorimeter, described on page 353, which is employed in determining heat capacities. The heat necessary to raise the temperature of a known mass of substance from slightly below its melting point to slightly above is measured; this information, together with a knowledge of the heat capacities of the substance in the solid and liquid states, is sufficient to determine the heat absorbed in the melting process, provided the sample under investigation is pure. It is evident that the heat absorbed per mole at constant pressure in going from temperature T_1 to temperature T_2 is:

$$\Delta Q = \int_{T_1}^{T_m} C_p \text{ (solid) } dT + \Delta H_f + \int_{T_m}^{T_2} C_p \text{ (liquid) } dT \qquad (89)$$

where ΔH_f is the heat of fusion per mole. During the actual melting of the sample, the temperature will remain practically constant at the melting temperature, T_m, of the substance.

In the method of mixtures (page 372), observations of the heat evolved when the material is cooled to the temperature of the calorimeter are made, with initial temperatures above and below the melting point. The calculation of the heat of fusion from such data is carried out by means of equation (89), where the integrals are evaluated using true heat capacities.

It is necessary to be certain that the crystalline modification of the material used in these measurements is the modification which exists in equilibrium with the liquid substance at the melting point. If the liquid is rapidly cooled to a temperature below its melting point, a metastable form may be obtained which may change to the stable form only very slowly. In the case of certain organic compounds, glasses are obtained rather than crystalline solids, and transition to the crystalline state may be extremely slow. It is obvious that the method of mixtures cannot be applied in such cases. In the ordinary calorimetric method, indication of these abnormalities, in the case of pure substances, is obtainable from the behavior of the temperature of the sample during melting; if equilibrium between solid and liquid forms is not established, there will be no period of approximately constant temperature during melting. Equation (89) will lead to erroneous results with substances which are not pure, since in such cases the melting process is not strictly isothermal. In particular, the phenomenon of "premelting" (page 350) may be of considerable importance even with relatively pure substances. The first integral in equation (89) will be too large if observed heat capacities are utilized without regard for premelting. In many cases, the observed heat capacities below the melting point can be corrected for premelting as outlined on page 350.

Heats of fusion or freezing may also be determined in a calibrated heat-conductivity calorimeter (page 356). It is possible[165] to obtain an estimate of the heat of fusion in this type of calorimeter without any direct knowledge of the heat capacities of the substance in the liquid and solid states. Heats of fusion can be deduced from measurements of solubility[166]

---

[165] See, for example, L. E. Steiner and J. Johnston, *J. Phys. Chem.*, **32**, 912 (1928).
[166] G. N. Lewis and M. Randall, *Thermodynamics and the Free Energy of Chemical Substances*. McGraw-Hill, New York, 1923, p. 229.

and of freezing point lowering.[167]   In an ideal solution, or in a sufficiently dilute solution, van't Hoff's law of the lowering of the freezing point holds·

$$\frac{dT}{dN_2} = \frac{RT^2}{\Delta H_f}\left(\frac{k}{k'} - 1\right) \tag{90}$$

In this expression k/k' is the distribution coefficient of the solute between solid and liquid phases, N_2 is the mole fraction of the solute, and T is the melting temperature.   If ΔH_f, the molal heat of fusion of the solvent, is measured in calories, R has the value 1.986.   In cases in which solid solutions are not formed, $k/k' = 0$; in such cases, integration of equation (90) (ΔH_f can be considered to be constant over a short range of temperature) gives:

$$T_0 - T = \frac{RN_2 T_0^2}{\Delta H_f} \tag{91}$$

where T_0 is the melting point of the pure solvent, and T is the temperature at which the liquid mixture is in equilibrium with pure crystalline solvent. Since, in dilute solutions:

$$N_2 \approx \frac{n_2 M_1}{w_1} = \frac{m_2}{1000} M_1 \tag{92}$$

where w_1 is the weight of solvent present, M_1 is the molecular weight of the solvent, n_2 is the number of moles of solute, and m_2 is the molality of the solute (moles per 1000 grams solvent), we have:

$$\Delta H_f \approx \frac{m_2 M_1 R T_0^2}{1000(T_0 - T)} \tag{93}$$

This equation cannot be applied to the determination of ΔH_f unless the molecular weight of the solute *in the solution* is known; it is thus necessary that the simple solute molecules do not undergo association or dissociation under the conditions of the experiment.

2.   Time–Temperature Curves

The behavior of a substance on being gradually cooled or heated through its transition between the liquid and solid states gives valuable information concerning its purity.   It is probable that this behavior serves as one of the most critical and most widely applicable criteria of purity[168]; because of

---

[167] G. N. Lewis and M. Randall, *op. cit.*, p. 237.   A. Eucken, *Energie- und Wärmeinhalt*, Vol. VIII, Part 1, of Wien-Harms, *Handbuch der Experimentalphysik*, Akadem. Verlagsgesellschaft, Leipzig, 1929, p. 590.   F. W. Schwab and E. Wichers, in *Temperature, Its Measurement and Control in Science and Industry*, Reinhold, New York, 1941, p. 256.

[168] See the discussions by W. P. White, *J. Phys. Chem.*, **24**, 393 (1920);   E. W. Washburn, *Ind. Eng. Chem., Ind. Ed.*, **22**, 985 (1930);   and E. L. Skau, *Proc. Am. Acad. Arts Sci.*, **67**, 551 (1932).

its close connection with heats of fusion, and its relative ease of application, it will be discussed at some length here.

Suppose a sample of material is cooled from slightly above its melting point by heat interchange with a surrounding shield the temperature of which is reduced at a uniform rate. If the substance is *very* pure, and thermal equilibrium is maintained during freezing, a time–temperature curve such as *hcdef* in figure 23 will be obtained. The shield temperature is represented by the heavy straight line. The initial cooling below the freezing temperature (undercooling) may be controlled to some extent by inoculation with a crystal of the substance. If the rate of heat interchange between the shield and sample is known, the heat of fusion can be estimated from the time–temperature curve. This is most conveniently done

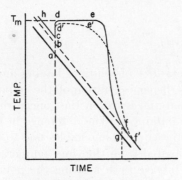

Fig. 23.—Cooling curves for a pure (unbroken curve) and an impure substance.

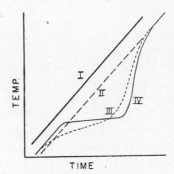

Fig. 24.—Heating curves for a pure (unbroken curve) and an impure substance.

by graphical evaluation of the area *bcdefb;* an error (usually small) is inherent in this procedure as a result of the fact that the rise in temperature *cd* is accomplished by heating the liquid substance, whereas the integration is based on the assumption that all the temperature change takes place with the substance in the solid state. If the heat interchange between shield and sample follows Newton's law, then the heat absorbed by the sample, Δq, is:

$$-\Delta q = k \int_a^g (T - T_s)dt \qquad (94)$$

where t is the time, T and T_s are the temperatures of the sample and shield, respectively, and k is the Newton's law constant for the system. This integral is obviously equal to the area *bcdefb* plus the area *abfga;* the latter area is the heat evolved in cooling the solid and the sample container to the temperature at point *f.*

If an impure substance is cooled, a curve similar to *hcd'e'f'* will be obtained. The temperature during freezing will not remain as constant as before; in most cases, the first material to crystallize will be pure "solvent," the remaining liquid becoming more concentrated in the impurity as freezing progresses. Therefore, the freezing point of the remaining liquid will be lower by increasing amounts. It is evident, however, that the area $bcd'e'f'b$ will be approximately equal to the area $bcdefb$, if the same amount of material is used and if the impurity is not present in a large amount. Experience has shown[169] that the presence of relatively small amounts of impurities produces a marked change in the form of the freezing curve, the greatest differences per unit amount of impurity being found in the nearly pure substance.

Equation (90) (for the case of no solid solutions) on integration between N_2' and N_2'' gives:

$$T' - T'' = \frac{RM_1T'^2}{1000\,\Delta H_f}\,(m_2'' - m_2') \qquad (95)$$

where T' and T'' are the freezing temperatures of solutions having molalities m_2' and m_2'', respectively. If m_2' is the concentration of the impurity in the original sample, after half the material is frozen the concentration will be $2m_2'$, provided equilibrium is maintained. The difference in temperature between these two points on the curve then enables one to estimate m_2'. If necessary, ΔH_f can be estimated from the time–temperature curve as described above. The usual procedure in locating the point at which half the material is frozen is to assume that the rate of freezing is proportional to the time.[170] It is evident that some error will be introduced here as a result of the falling temperature of the shield, though this will to some extent be compensated by a decrease in heat loss from the sample resulting from accumulation of solid material at the walls of the sample container. However, unless considerable precision is sought, it is probable that a sufficiently good estimate can be made in this way. The point of half-solidification is then halfway between the start of freezing and the point e where the time–temperature curve starts to dip down. With a rather impure sample, considerable difficulty will, of course, be experienced in locating this point.

Information as to the order of magnitude of impurity concentration can be obtained by comparing the original curve with the curve obtained after the addition of a small amount of some substance which does not form a solid solution with the substance under test; if the identity of the impurity is known, the added substance should be the same. In making this

---

[169] See, for example, the excellent curves given by Schwab and Wichers, *loc. cit.*[167]

[170] The error in this procedure is discussed by Schwab and Wichers, *loc. cit.*[167]

comparison, it should be remembered that the first small amounts of impurity have the largest effect on the form of the curve.

Heating curves may also be employed as a criterion of purity. An ideal heating curve (*IV*) is shown in figure 24 (page 397), together with a curve obtained with an impure compound (*III*). The heavy line (*I*) represents the temperature of the shield, and the dashed line (*II*) is the extrapolation of the portion of the curves corresponding to complete liquefaction. As in the case of cooling curves, an estimate of the heat of fusion can be made by graphical integration. If the process of fusion is observed in a calorimeter in such a way that the sample may be held in a condition of partial fusion long enough for equilibrium to be established, a definite estimate of impurity concentration can be made from the change of sample temperature with proportion melted,[171] which in this case is estimated from the amount of electrical heat input since the start of fusion.

Skau[168] has described, for the observation of freezing and melting curves, an apparatus which is very readily constructed. A small sample (approximately 0.5 gram) of material is contained in a sealed ampoule (Fig. 25) constructed of very thin glass[172] and containing a well into which is inserted a copper–constantan thermocouple (one junction will suffice if potential measurements are made to the nearest microvolt). The

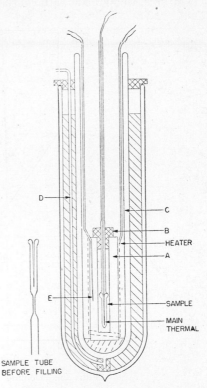

Fig. 25.— Skau's apparatus for time–temperature curves.

well is filled with vaseline or other suitable substance, depending on the temperature at which measurements are to be made. The sample tube is fastened by thread or thin wire to a piece of thin-walled glass tubing, which supports the sample in shield *A* by means of loosely fitting plastic stopper *B*, the latter being equipped with a long handle so that the sample may be easily removed from the shield. The shield is a cylinder of copper electri-

---

[171] See, for example, G. H. Messerly and J. G. Aston, *J. Am. Chem. Soc.*, **62**, 886 (1940).

[172] Wafer weight tubing, No. 50105, obtainable from *Kimble Glass Co.*, Vineland, N. J.

cally heated by a winding on its outside surface, and is supported by a cork at its bottom in a Dewar flask, C. The Dewar is connected by tube D to a vacuum line so that the rate of heat transfer between the shield and the outside bath may be partially controlled by the pressure in the Dewar. This flask is immersed in a suitable bath of moderately constant temperature. The arrangement shown in figure 25 is suitable for work at low temperatures, the outside bath consisting of liquid air contained in a second

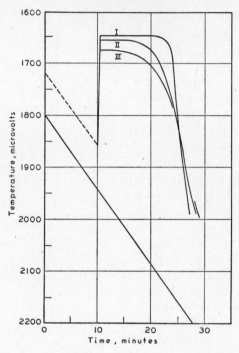

Fig. 26.—Cooling curves obtained with Skau's apparatus.

Dewar flask. Other convenient baths are supplied by solid carbon dioxide-trichloroethylene mixtures, ice and water, or a roughly thermostated liquid bath for higher temperatures. It is convenient to be able to observe the sample while it is in place in the apparatus. To this end, a slot is milled in the shield and the Dewar flasks are left unsilvered for a narrow strip on each side.

The temperatures of the sample and the shield are measured by thermocouples, an ice bath (see page 326) serving as the reference temperature. The shield junctions, E, should be located near the sample as indicated in the diagram, in good thermal contact with the shield. The thermocouples can be calibrated in the same apparatus by observing the heating or cooling curves for pure reference substances. For work at relatively low temperatures, the compounds listed by Skau[173] may be used. Samples of some of these compounds, as well as samples of naphthalene, benzoic acid, tin, and other substances suitable for calibration at higher temperatures, may be obtained from the *National Bureau of Standards*, Washington, D. C.

Typical freezing curves[168] obtained with this apparatus are shown in figure 26. The heavy curve represents the temperature of the shield. The

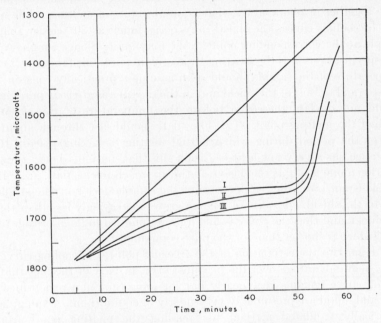

Fig. 27.—Heating curves obtained with Skau's apparatus.

dependence of the shape of the cooling curve on purity is clearly shown. Curve *I* was obtained with pure chlorobenzene, curve *II* with chlorobenzene containing 0.5 mole per cent of *m*-dichlorobenzene, and curve *III* with a partially purified sample of chlorobenzene. It can be seen that the shape of the cooling curve furnishes a more sensitive test of purity than does the actual value of the freezing point. The impurity in the material corresponding to curve *II* lowered the freezing point only 0.23°, but was sufficient to cause a very marked change in the shape of the curve.

Skau[168] concluded that heating curves obtained with this apparatus have

173 E. L. Skau, *J. Phys. Chem.*, **37**, 609 (1933).

several advantages over cooling curves in making qualitative observations regarding purity. Heating curves obtained with the same three samples as used for the curves of figure 26 are shown in figure 27. The fusion curves are more conveniently observed because there is no need to remove the sample for inducing crystallization, as in the case of the freezing curves. Heating curves can be observed with any substance which can be made to crystallize in the temperature range available, regardless of the degree of undercooling necessary or the rate of crystallization. Heating curves seem to be more sensitive to very small amounts of impurity because the impurities exert their greatest effect at a time when the shield and sample are close together in temperature, that is, at the start of melting, while in the case of cooling curves the shield may be as much as 20° colder than the sample at the corresponding point. We may quote Skau's summary[168] of the specifications for the heating curve of a pure substance: "(1) The temperature of the sample should soon assume a practically constant rate of rise equal to that of the shield and in the case of an *extremely* pure sample should not deviate therefrom before the temperature of the *shield* has reached the melting point. (2) The 'flat' should last through about one half of the period during which actual melting is taking place. If the substance has a very low heat of fusion this 'flat' may be short; thus this criterion alone is not as conclusive as the approach to the 'flat'. . . . If the sample is not pure, the temperature of the sample does not rise parallel to that of the shield. Its rate of change grows increasingly less than that of the shield, and thus the curve is much more rounded in its approach to the 'flat,' which is shorter than for the pure compound."

In regard to the estimation of the freezing point, the cooling curve has some small advantage over the heating curve, in view of the fact that the cooling curve remains very nearly flat for some time in a region in which solid and liquid are presumably very nearly in equilibrium. Skau gives an empirically validated method for reading the melting point from a heating curve; this is taken as the "temperature of the sample two minutes before the beginning of the change in direction of the curve at the end of the 'flat.'"

It is very strongly urged that organic chemists become familiar with the technique described in this section in order that they can establish quickly and quite surely the purity of their more important preparations.

3. Heats of Transition

Heats of transition between different solid phases are in general determined by methods similar to those employed in the determination of heats of fusion. It should be noted, however, that, whereas the general pattern of behavior of all pure substances at their melting points is relatively constant, a wide variety of patterns is observed in the case of transitions.   For example, the heat capacity of solid ethylene dichloride[174] rises to a rather sharp maximum at 177° K., but no sharp isothermal transition takes place, while the heat capacity of solid ethylene dibromide rises rapidly below 249.5° K., at which temperature there is a sharp transition to a form having a much lower heat capacity.   Interesting transitions are observed in substituted ammonium salts[175] similar to those first observed by Simon[176] in the case of the unsubstituted ammonium salts.   Discussion of the various types of transitions, and their theoretical interpretation, will be found in the papers presented at a symposium[177] of the New York Academy of Sciences on this subject.

4. Heats of Vaporization

Heats of vaporization[178] are usually evaluated either by direct calorimetric observation of the amount of heat necessary to vaporize a known amount of material, or by calculation from the change of vapor pressure with temperature.   These two methods are discussed briefly below.   Generally, less satisfactory results can be obtained from measurement of the heat evolved on condensing a known amount of vapor,[179] and by various modifications of the method of mixtures.

A.   CALORIMETRIC DETERMINATION

Heats of vaporization may be determined in calorimeters similar to those used for determining heat capacities (page 352), the only important addition to the apparatus resulting from the necessity of measuring the amount of material vaporized.   Various means for collecting and measuring the amount of material vaporized have been described.   With low-boiling substances, the vaporized material can be collected in the gas state and its volume measured,[180] or it can be absorbed chemically.[181] The vapor may be condensed at a low temperature,[182] or at a regulated

---

[174] K. S. Pitzer, *J. Am. Chem. Soc.*, **62**, 331 (1940).

[175] J. C. Southard, R. T. Milner, and S. B. Hendricks, *J. Chem. Phys.*, **1**, 95 (1933).

[176] F. Simon, *Ann. Physik*, **68**, 241 (1922).

[177] Conference on "Physics of the Solid State," N. Y. Acad. Sci., Feb. 27 and 28, 1942.

[178] See A. Eucken, *Energie- und Wärmeinhalt*. Vol VIII, Part 1, of Wien-Harms, *Handbuch der Experimentalphysik*, Akadem. Verlagsgesellschaft, Leipzig, 1929, p. 527.

[179] A. Eucken, *op. cit.*, p. 543. See also A. S. Coolidge, *J. Am. Chem. Soc.*, **52**, 1874 (1930).

[180] W. F. Giauque and H. L. Johnston, *J. Am. Chem. Soc.*, **51**, 2300 (1929). R. M. Kennedy, M. Sagenkahn, and J. G. Aston, *ibid.*, **63**, 2267 (1941).

[181] W. F. Giauque and R. Wiebe, *J. Am. Chem. Soc.*, **50**, 101, 2193 (1928).

[182] D. M. Yost, D. W. Osborne, and C. S. Garner, *J. Am. Chem. Soc.*, **63**, 3492 (1941). F. G. Keyes and J. A. Beattie, *ibid.*, **46**, 1753 (1924). J. F. Lemons and W. A. Felsing, *ibid.*, **65**, 46 (1943).

temperature very slightly below that of the calorimeter.[183]   In some cases, the amount of material vaporized may be determined by adsorption on a suitable adsorbent.[184]   Electrical energy is introduced at a rate sufficient to maintain the calorimeter at approximately constant temperature during the evaporation.

It is necessary for the evaporation to be carried out in such a way that equilibrium is maintained during the process.   If too rapid evaporation takes place, the surface of the liquid will be cooled, the effective temperature of evaporation will be below that indicated by thermometric observation of the calorimeter, and the vapors leaving the calorimeter will be too cold.   If there is an appreciable pressure drop between the calorimeter and the receiver, there will be a corresponding Joule-Thompson cooling.   If part or all of the pressure drop occurs within the calorimetric system, the appropriate correction must be made.[185]

Another source of error, which is of increased importance in experiments at lower pressures, is entrainment of liquid in the vapor leaving the calorimeter.   At low pressures, high vapor velocities are needed to achieve a sufficiently rapid evaporation, so that proper precautions against entrainment become more difficult.   The error due to lack of maintenance of equilibrium will also tend to increase at low vapor pressures.   Errors from these causes are decreased by leading the vapor through a spiral tube[186] before allowing it to leave the calorimeter, or by placing baffles[187] in the top of the calorimeter.

Coon and Daniels[184] employed an inert carrier gas to transport the vaporized material to the collecting apparatus.   When this procedure is followed, careful consideration must be given to the possibility that the carrier gas is introduced at so rapid a rate that equilibrium is not maintained.

Several more or less obvious corrections must be applied to the results of a vaporization experiment.   Allowance must be made for dead spaces in the system which introduce errors in the measurement of the amount of material vaporized.   Account also must be taken of the fact that the volume originally occupied by liquid is occupied by vapor at the end of the experiment.   If any change in temperature takes place during the experiment, the appropriate heat capacity correction ($\int C_p dT$) must be applied.

---

[183] J. G. Aston and G. H. Messerly, *J. Am. Chem. Soc.*, **58**, 2354 (1936).   J. G. Aston, M. L. Eidinoff, and W. S. Forster, *ibid.*, **61**, 1539 (1939).

[184] E. D. Coon and F. Daniels, *J. Phys. Chem.*, **37**, 1 (1933).

[185] See, for example, F. G. Keyes and J. A. Beattie, *J. Am. Chem. Soc.*, **46**, 1753 (1924).

[186] F. G. Keyes and J. A. Beattie, *loc. cit.*   J. A. Sutcliffe, F. C. Lay, and W. L. Prichard, *Proc. Roy. Soc. London*, **A115**, 88 (1927).

[187] F. Henning, *Ann. Physik*, **21**, 849 (1906).   N. S. Osborne, *Natl. Bur. Standards (U. S.)*, *Bull.* **14**, 133 (1918).   N. S. Osborne and M. S. Van Dusen, *ibid.*, **14**, 397 (1918).

Very careful measurements of the heats of vaporization of water over a large temperature range[188] and on other liquids[187, 189] show clearly the precautions which must be taken in order to obtain highly precise data. A relatively simple apparatus described by Mathews and Fehlandt[190] yields data on the heats of vaporization, at their boiling points, of liquids boiling at moderate temperatures. This apparatus is a modification of that described by Brown[191] and Smith.[192] The amount of material vaporized from the inner tube (Fig. 28) by means of a known input of electrical energy is determined directly by weighing. The vaporizer tube is hung from a balance by a thin platinum wire, contact with the external source of current being made by means of two platinum wires dipping into mercury-filled tubes. Condensation of material on the supporting platinum wire where it emerges from the apparatus is prevented by a small auxiliary heater and a slow stream of dry air led in through a side arm. After regular ebullition with a current of one ampere has been established, the time required for the vaporizer to lose a definite weight is measured. The evaporation is made very nearly isothermal and adiabatic by jacketing the vaporizer tube with the vapor of the substance under examination produced in the small boiler at the

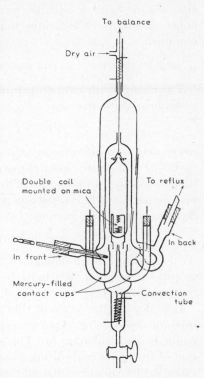

Fig. 28.—Apparatus for determination of heats of vaporization (Mathews and Fehlandt).

bottom of the apparatus. Any deviation from adiabaticity is determined by observations of the rate of loss of material from the vaporizer before

[188] N. S. Osborne, *J. Research Natl. Bur. Standards*, **4**, 609 (1930). N. S. Osborne, H. F. Stimson, and E. F. Fiock, *ibid.*, **5**, 411 (1930). N. S. Osborne, H. F. Stimson, and D. C. Ginnings, *ibid.*, **23**, 197 (1939).

[189] E. F. Fiock, D. C. Ginnings, and W. B. Holton, *J. Research Natl. Bur. Standards*, **6**, 881 (1931). See also B. H. Sage, H. D. Evans, and W. N. Lacey, *Ind. Eng. Chem.*, *Ind. Ed.*, **31**, 763 (1939).

[190] J. H. Mathews, *J. Am. Chem. Soc.*, **48**, 562 (1926); J. H. Mathews and P. R. Fehlandt, *ibid.*, **53**, 3212 (1931).

[191] J. C. Brown, *J. Chem. Soc.*, **1903**, 987.

[192] A. C. Smith, *Proc. Roy. Soc. Edinburgh*, **24**, 450 (1903).

and after introducing electrical energy. Measurements can be made on as little as 30 milliliters of material. Mathews and Fehlandt have determined the heats of vaporization of numerous organic compounds boiling in the range of 35° to 215°. Comparison of Mathews' results for methanol, ethanol, and benzene with the very accurate ones reported by Fiock, Ginnings, and Holton[189] indicates that an accuracy of about ±0.3% can be obtained.

B. EVALUATION FROM VAPOR PRESSURES

The change with temperature of the vapor pressure, P, is related to the molar heat of vaporization $\Delta H_{vap.}$ by the Clapeyron expression:[193]

$$dP/dT = \Delta H_{vap.}/T \Delta V \qquad (96)$$

where ΔV is the increase in volume when one mole of substance is vaporized. At sufficiently low temperatures (low vapor pressures), the vapor may be assumed to obey the perfect gas law, and the volume of the liquid may be neglected in comparison with that of the vapor. Under these conditions equation (96) becomes:

$$- d \ln P/d(1/T) = \Delta H_{vap.}/R \qquad (97)$$

At temperatures high enough so the vapor pressure exceeds $1/10$ to $1/4$ atmosphere, equation (96) must be applied in conjunction with state data from which ΔV may be evaluated.

It is beyond the scope of this article to consider in detail the methods used for determining vapor pressures. Suffice it to state that two general methods are available: (a) The static method consists of direct observation of the pressure resulting from equilibration of liquid and vapor; as an example of a very careful application of this method we may cite the work of Osborne, Stimson, Fiock, and Ginnings.[194] (b) In the dynamic method, the vapor pressure is deduced from the amount of material removed by a known volume of an inert carrier gas at known temperature and total pressure.

5. Trouton's and Hildebrand's Rules

A rough approximation to the molar heat of vaporization of *nonpolar* liquids may be obtained from Trouton's rule,[195] which states that, for such compounds, the entropy of vaporization at the normal boiling point on the absolute scale ($\Delta H_{vap.}/T_B$) is approximately 21 calories per mole per degree C. The actual Trouton's "con-

[193] G. N. Lewis and M. Randall, *Thermodynamics and the Free Energy of Chemical Substances.* McGraw-Hill, New York, 1923, p. 134. A. Eucken, *op. cit.,*[178] p. 555.

[194] N. S. Osborne, H. F. Stimson, E. F. Fiock, and D. C. Ginnings, *J. Research Natl. Bur. Standards*, **10**, 155 (1933).

[195] R. Pictet, *Ann. chim. phys.*, **9**, 180 (1876). F. Trouton, *Phil. Mag.*, **18**, 54 (1884).

stants" show a definite trend toward higher values for liquids of higher boiling point. Hildebrand[196] has shown that, if the comparison is made at temperatures at which the vapor concentrations are equal (he arbitrarily chose the value of 0.005 mole per liter), this trend is largely eliminated. At this vapor concentration the entropy of vaporization is approximately 27 calories per mole per degree C. Polar substances such as ammonia and water have larger values, about 32 or 33.

6. Heats of Adsorption

Limitations of space preclude any discussion of heats of adsorption.[197] This subject has been of considerable importance in connection with the study of surface catalysis.

VIII. HEATS OF SOLUTION, DILUTION, AND MIXING

There is no fundamental distinction to be drawn between heats of solution, dilution, and mixing. According to common usage, one speaks of the heat effect accompanying the solution of a solid or a gas in a liquid as a heat of solution, while that accompanying the solution of one pure liquid in another is called a heat of mixing. A heat of dilution refers to the mixing of a solution with the corresponding pure solvent, or to the mixing of two solutions containing the same components in different concentrations. A heat of solution, dilution, or mixing is said to be positive if heat is absorbed in the process.

1. Applications

A. HEATS OF SOLUTION

The heat of a reaction can be evaluated from the heats of combustion of the reactants and products, by the application of Hess's law (page 313). It can likewise be evaluated from the heats of solution of the reactants and of the products in some solvent in which the reactants give precisely the same solution as the products. Where it can be applied, this procedure is likely to be more satisfactory than that based on heats of combustion since the heat of reaction is obtained as the difference between relatively small heats of solution. Because of a change of the solvent by each individual solute, the heat effect accompanying simultaneous solution of several reactants is not always the sum of the various individual heats of solution, though in most cases of dilute solutions additivity will be very nearly fulfilled. The same restriction applies also, of course, if more than one product is formed. The method under consideration is of particular value

---

[196] J. H. Hildebrand, *J. Am. Chem. Soc.*, **37**, 970 (1915).

[197] See, for example, R. A. Beebe and H. S. Taylor, *J. Am. Chem. Soc.*, **46**, 43 (1924); W. E. Garner and F. J. Veal, *J. Chem. Soc.*, **1935**, 1436.

when direct measurements of the desired heat effect are ruled out by calorimetric limitations. It has been applied to several inorganic problems.[198] Hieber and his collaborators[199] have used it to evaluate the heats of formation from their components of numerous metal complexes with amines; and Campbell and Campbell[200] estimated the heats of formation of various organic molecular compounds.

Heats of solution are of further importance in converting the heat of a reaction in solution, where the heat may be more conveniently measured, to the heat which would be observed if the reaction took place in the absence of solvent. Thus Sturtevant[201] measured the heat of mutarotation of α- and β-D-glucose in aqueous solution, and employed the heats of solution of the two isomers to evaluate the heat of isomerization of solid α-glucose to solid β-glucose. Williams[202] determined the heats of hydrogenation of some substances in acetic acid and evaluated the hydrogenation heats of the undissolved compounds by means of the appropriate heats of solution.

Occasionally, heats of solution have been used to evaluate the relative heat contents of substances in solution, though heats of dilution are usually to be preferred for this purpose.

B. HEATS OF DILUTION

Heats of dilution are chiefly of importance in the evaluation of certain thermodynamic quantities relating to solutions.[203] If the total heat content of a solution containing n_1 moles of solvent and n_2 moles of solute is represented by H, then the *partial molal heat contents* of the solvent and solute are defined as $\bar{H}_1 = \partial H/\partial n_1$ and $\bar{H}_2 = \partial H/\partial n_2$. Since it is impossible to state the absolute value of heat contents, it is necessary to consider heat contents relative to a specified reference state. Thus, the partial molal heat contents of the solvent and solute at infinite dilution are represented by $\bar{H}_1^0$ and $\bar{H}_2^0$ and *relative* partial molal heat contents are defined: $\bar{L}_1 = \bar{H}_1 - \bar{H}_1^0$ and $\bar{L}_2 = \bar{H}_2 - \bar{H}_2^0$. The relative heat content of the solution is given by

$$L = n_1\bar{L}_1 + n_2\bar{L}_2 \tag{98}$$

Evidently, at infinite dilution $\bar{L}_1^0 = \bar{L}_2^0 = L^0 = 0$. It is convenient to define the *apparent* relative molal heat content of the solute by the equation:

$$\Phi L_2 \equiv \Phi H_2 - \Phi H_2^0 \equiv (L - n_1\bar{L}_1^0)/n_2 = L/n_2 \tag{99}$$

[198] M. M. Popov, A. Bundel, and W. Choller, *Z. physik. Chem.*, **A147**, 302 (1930). J. C. Southard, *Ind. Eng. Chem.*, *Ind. Ed.*, **32**, 442 (1940). S. G. Lipsett, F. M. G. Johnson, and O. Maas, *J. Am. Chem. Soc.*, **50**, 1030 (1928).

[199] W. Hieber, *et al.*, *Z. anorg. Chem.*, **186**, 97 (1930); *Z. Elektrochem.*, **40**, 256 (1934); **44**, 881 (1938); **46**, 556 (1940).

[200] A. N. Campbell and A. J. R. Campbell, *J. Am. Chem. Soc.*, **62**, 291 (1940).

[201] J. M. Sturtevant, *J. Phys. Chem.*, **45**, 127 (1941).

[202] R. B. Williams, *J. Am. Chem. Soc.*, **64**, 1395 (1942).

[203] G. N. Lewis and M. Randall, *op. cit.*,[193] p. 87.

In the case of aqueous solutions, concentrations are usually expressed in molalities (moles of solute per 1000 grams water), represented by m. If L is the relative heat content of an amount of solution containing 1000 grams (55.51 moles) of water, then:

$$L = 55.51\bar{L}_1 + m\bar{L}_2 \tag{100}$$

and

$$\Phi L_2 = L/m \tag{101}$$

Suppose a solution of molality m_1 is diluted with solvent to molality m_2. If ΔH is the heat absorbed in this process per mole of solute:

$$\Delta H = (\Phi H_2)_{m_2} - (\Phi H_2)_{m_1} \tag{102}$$

Successive dilutions can be carried out with decreasing va ues of m_2, and finally an extrapolation to $m_2 = 0$ performed to give

$$\Delta H_{m_2=0} = \Phi H_2^0 - (\Phi H_2)_{m_1} = -(\Phi L_2)_{m_1} \tag{103}$$

If a theoretical relation for the slope of the ΔH curve at $m_2 = 0$ is available, such as that provided by the Debye-Hückel limiting slope for strong electrolytes of sufficiently simple valence type, this extrapolation can frequently be performed with considerable precision. The dilutions to intermediate concentrations can then be employed to establish the variation of ΦL_2 with concentration up to m_1. The relative partial molal heat contents can be evaluated by graphical or analytical differentiation:

$$\bar{L}_2 = \frac{\partial L}{\partial m} = \Phi L_2 + m\frac{\partial \Phi L_2}{\partial m} \tag{104}$$

$$\bar{L}_1 = m(\Phi L_2 - \bar{L}_2)/55.51 \tag{105}$$

Similar expressions for $\bar{L}_1$ and $\bar{L}_2$ in other concentration units are readily obtained.

The method outlined here for evaluating the relative heat contents is based on so-called "long chord" dilutions—dilution of a small amount of solution with a relatively large amount of water. Young and his collaborators[204] have shown that the partial heat contents, in particular, can be more accurately evaluated by means of "short chord" dilutions, in which the concentration of the solute is changed only slightly, and have found that application of their method of calculation to much of the dilution data of Lange and Robinson[205] and their coworkers results in very much improved agreement of the observed limiting slopes with those predicted on the basis of the Debye-Hückel theory, as compared with limiting slopes evaluated from the dilution data by the method outlined above. Indeed, the conformance of heats of dilution to the requirements of the theory has constituted one of the most striking confirmations of the essential validity of the theory.

[204] T. F. Young and O. G. Vogel, *J. Am. Chem. Soc.*, **54**, 3030 (1932). T. F. Young and W. L. Groenier, *ibid.*, **58**, 187 (1936). T. F. Young and P. Seligman, *ibid.*, **60**, 2379 (1938).

[205] E. Lange and A. L. Robinson, *Chem. Revs.*, **9**, 89 (1931).

It should be noted that, in dilution experiments extending to very low concentrations, complications may arise because of heat effects resulting from the disturbance of the dissociation equilibrium of the solvent.[206]

The *apparent molal heat capacity* of the solute is defined as $\Phi C_{p_2} = (C_p - 55.51\,\bar{C}_1^0)/m$. *Partial molal heat capacities* can be evaluated from ΦC_{p_2} in just the same way as the corresponding heat contents:

$$\bar{C}_{p_2} = \frac{\partial C_p}{\partial m} = \Phi C_{p_2} + m\,\frac{\partial \Phi C_{p_2}}{\partial m} \tag{106}$$

$$\bar{C}_{p_1} - \bar{C}_{p_1}^0 = m(\Phi C_{p_2} - \bar{C}_{p_2})/55.51 \tag{107}$$

It can be shown that:

$$\Phi C_{p_2} = \frac{\partial}{\partial T}\,(\Phi L_2) \tag{108}$$

and

$$\frac{\partial}{\partial m}\,(\Phi C_{p_2}) = \frac{\partial}{\partial T}\left[\frac{\partial}{\partial m}\,(\Phi L_2)\right] \tag{109}$$

These equations allow the evaluation of apparent and partial molal heat capacities from heats of dilution determined at two temperatures. The heat capacities determined in this way will usually be very precise.

C. HEATS OF MIXING

The heat of mixing two liquids is of considerable interest in connection with theories of liquid mixtures. Thus Vold[207] found from measurements on several systems that the molal change in heat content on mixing two normal liquids to give a solution in which the mole fractions are N_1 and N_2 is rather well represented by an equation based on the theory of mixtures developed by Hildebrand and Wood:[208]

$$\Delta H = \frac{N_1 V_1 N_2 V_2}{N_1 V_1 + N_2 V_2}\left[\left(\frac{E_1^0}{V_1}\right)^{1/2} - \left(\frac{E_2^0}{V_2}\right)^{1/2}\right]^2 = \frac{N_1 V_1 N_2 V_2}{N_1 V_1 + N_2 V_2}\,D_{12} \tag{110}$$

In this equation, V_1 and V_2 are the molal volumes of the pure liquids, and E_1^0 and E_2^0 their energies of vaporization to zero pressure, respectively. In the derivation of equation (110), it was assumed that the volumes are additive on mixing at constant pressure, that the interaction between a pair of unlike molecules can be approximated by the geometrical mean of the interactions between pairs of like molecules, and that the different molecular species are randomly mixed in the solution. Examples will be mentioned below of systems in which these assumptions are not valid. However, in systems composed of molecules deviating not too much from

[206] See, for example, E. Doehlemann and E. Lange, *Z. physik. Chem.*, **A170**, 391 (1934); J. M. Sturtevant, *J. Am. Chem. Soc.*, **62**, 3519 (1940).

[207] R. D. Vold, *J. Am. Chem. Soc.*, **59**, 1515 (1937).

[208] J. H. Hildebrand and S. E. Wood, *J. Chem. Phys.*, **1**, 817 (1933). See also G. Scatchard, *Trans. Faraday Soc.*, **33**, 160 (1937); G. Scatchard, S. E. Wood, and J. M. Mochel, *J. Am. Chem. Soc.*, **61**, 3206 (1939); **62**, 712 (1940); *J. Phys. Chem.*, **43**, 119 (1939).

spherical symmetry, and between which there are no specific chemical interactions, such as hydrogen bonding, equation (110) and the theory on which it is based should furnish a satisfactory approximation to the truth.

The term D_{12} in equation (110) is the relatively small difference between two large quantities, so it cannot be very accurately evaluated from experimental values of energies of vaporization. However, a value of D_{12} obtained from heats of mixing can be employed to calculate heats of mixing at other concentrations. If A, B, and C are three liquids which form binary systems for which the theory holds, then $D_{AC} = D_{AB} + D_{BC}$.

It can be expected that, in liquid systems in which the molecules of different type undergo strong specific interactions, the simplifying assumptions on which equation (110) is based will not hold. Even in these cases, however, heats of mixing may be of considerable importance. Copley[209] and others have used heats of mixing as an indication of complex formation as a result of hydrogen bonding. In cases in which extensive hydrogen bonding takes place, the maximum heat of mixing is 10 to 100 times as large as in the nearly ideal cases studied by Vold[207] and of opposite sign. The concentration ratio at which the maximum heat of mixing is observed can be interpreted in terms of the structure of the complexes formed. Thus, the maximum in the case of chloroform, or fluorodichloromethane, with the dimethyl ether of ethylene glycol comes at a mole ratio of one, indicating that one molecule of halide is associated with one molecule of ether. In the case of either of these halides with the dimethyl ether of tetraethylene glycol, $CH_3O(CH_2CH_2O)_4$-CH_3, maximum heat evolution occurs when the mole ratio is three halide molecules to one ether molecule. These results indicate that only alternate oxygens in the ether molecules are available for hydrogen bonding, presumably because of steric hindrance.

2. Mixing Devices

A calorimeter designed for use with liquids can be applied to determining heats of solution, dilution, or mixing after incorporation of a suitable mixing device. Various designs for such devices will be mentioned here. Numerous authors[210] have employed thin glass bulbs holding one of the sub-

[209] G. F. Zellhoefer and M. J. Copley, *J. Am. Chem. Soc.*, **60**, 1343 (1938); M. J. Copley and C. E. Holley, *ibid.*, **61**, 1599 (1939); C. S. Marvel, M. J. Copley, and E. Ginsberg, *ibid.*, **62**, 3109 (1940); L. F. Audrieth and R. Steinman, *ibid.*, **63**, 2115 (1941); R. W. Spence, *J. Phys. Chem.*, **45**, 304 (1941). See also H. Hirobe, *J. Fac. Sci. Imp. Univ. Tokyo, Sect. I*, **1**, 155 (1925); D. B. McLeod and F. J. Wilson, *Trans. Faraday Soc.*, **31**, 596 (1935).

[210] F. Barry, *J. Am. Chem. Soc.*, **42**, 1911 (1920). B. H. Carroll and J. H. Mathews. *ibid.*, **46**, 30 (1924). W. Hieber and A. Woerner, *Z. Elektrochem.*, **40**, 256 (1934). T. F. Young and J. S. Machin, *J. Am. Chem. Soc.*, **58**, 2254 (1936). K. S. Pitzer, *ibid.*, **59**, 2365 (1937). H. Frahm and K. L. Wolf, *Z. physik. Chem.*, **A178**, 411 (1937). C. M. Slansky, *J. Am. Chem. Soc.*, **62**, 2430 (1940). J. C. Southard, *Ind. Eng. Chem., Ind. Ed.*, **32**, 442 (1940). C. J. H. Staverman-Pekelder and A. J. Staverman, *Rec. trav. chim.*, **59**, 1081 (1940). J. B. Conn, G. B. Kistiakowsky, R. M. Roberts, and E. A. Smith, *J. Am. Chem. Soc.*, **64**, 1747 (1942). R. B. Williams, *ibid.*, **64**, 1395 (1942).

stances.   The bulb is broken by various devices such as a rod extending down through the stirrer shaft or a set of claws which can be rotated from outside the calorimeter, or by being brought into contact with the rotating stirrer.   Permanent "dilution cups" have been employed by many workers. White and Roberts[211] have described a device particularly suited for use with solids.   A "boat" of Bakelite is supported from the calorimeter cover in a vertical position.   It is covered with a thin sheet of nitrocellulose which is waxed on.   The cover is pulled up to open the boat by means of a platinum wire going out through the cover of the calorimeter.   Pitzer[210] used a vertical glass tube with waxed-on closures of thin silver.   A glass rod extending down through the hollow stirrer shaft was used to rupture the silver sheets.   Partington and Soper[212] employed glass pipettes closed at the bottom with ground-glass stoppers which could be opened by a rod extending up through the elongated neck of the pipette.   Lange[205] employed submerged metal pipettes which could be opened at both ends so that good circulation of the liquid in the calorimeter through the pipette would be insured.   The design of the pipettes was such that they could be emptied, cleaned, and refilled without dismantling the calorimeter.   The pipettes employed by Kistiakowsky *et al.*[210] were of a similar type.   In the design of Young and Machin,[213] the pipettes were vertical silver tubes closed at each end with waxed-on silver covers which were pulled off by wires controlled from outside the calorimeter.   Gucker, Pickard, and Planck[214] used tantalum dilution cups with ground-in closures at each end.   The cups were opened in a very uniform way by a rather complicated lifting device so that the heat effect accompanying this process would be sufficiently constant. Lipsett, Johnson, and Maas[215] placed one of the substances to be mixed in a separate metal container within their calorimeter, which calorimeter was sitrred by being rotated about its axis; the inside container was so arranged that its cover fell off during the first revolution of the calorimeter.   Provision was made for catching the cover in clips so that it would be held from further motion inside the calorimeter.   Sturtevant[216] employed a tantalum dilution cup fastened to the calorimeter cover.   The cup contained a platinum–iridium bellows carrying a cylindrical cutter, and was closed by gold foil.   The cup was opened by applying about 10 pounds' pressure of nitrogen to the bellows through a small rubber tube attached to the cover of the

[211] W. P. White and H. S. Roberts, *J. Am. Chem. Soc.*, **59**, 1254 (1937).

[212] J. R. Partington and W. E. Soper, *Phil. Mag.*, **7**, 209 (1929).

[213] T. F. Young and J. S. Machin, *J. Am. Chem. Soc.*, **58**, 2254 (1936).

[214] F. T. Gucker, H. B. Pickard, and R. W. Planck, *J. Am. Chem. Soc.*, **61**, 459 (1939).

[215] S. G. Lipsett, F. M. G. Johnson, and O. Maas, *J. Am. Chem. Soc.*, **49**, 935, 1940 (1927).

[216] J. M. Sturtevant, *J. Phys. Chem.*, **45**, 127 (1941); *J. Am. Chem. Soc.*, **64**, 762 (1942).

calorimeter (see Fig. 33, page 427). This arrangement permitted opening of the dilution cup while the calorimeter contents were being stirred by oscillation of the calorimeter through 360°.

In any of these mixing devices, allowance must be made for the fact that the temperature of the contents of the mixing device will lag somewhat behind the temperature of the contents of the calorimeter if the temperature of the latter is changing. The magnitude of the necessary correction can be estimated by experiments in which both the mixing device and the calorimeter are filled with the same liquid.

In comparatively rough work, or in experiments in which the heat of mixing is large, the liquid to be added to the calorimeter may be contained in a vessel outside the calorimeter proper. Thus Vold[207] added one of the liquids to be mixed from a vacuum-jacketed flask; the temperature of this liquid was measured just before the addition so that a suitable correction could be applied if its temperature differed from that of the material in the calorimeter. Richards and Daniels[217] in their work on thallium amalgams added mercury from a water-jacketed pipette at a known temperature.

3. Corrections in Mixing Experiments

Calorimetric experiments in which two or more substances are mixed within the calorimeter are carried out in much the same way as other calorimetric procedures, and the corrections are evaluated by similar methods (see Section IV, page 333). Since processes of this sort are practically instantaneous, no especial difficulties arise. One correction, however, has been overlooked in some cases in which it is of significant magnitude. If the vapor pressures of the two substances to be mixed, and of the resulting mixture, are different, there will be some evaporation into or condensation from the air spaces in the system. For example, if a sodium chloride solution is added to pure water, there will be evaporation of water into the air originally over the salt solution and condensation of water from the air originally over the water. The magnitude of this effect is diminished by keeping the air spaces in the calorimetric and the mixing device as small as possible. The appropriate correction for this effect can be readily calculated from the vapor pressures and heats of vaporization of the initial and final solutions or liquids, and the volumes of the air spaces in the calorimeter.

4. Apparatus of Low or Moderate Sensitivity

In this and the following paragraphs will be found brief descriptions of a few calorimeters which have been applied to the determination of heats of

---

[217] T. W. Richards and F. Daniels, *J. Am. Chem. Soc.*, **41**, 1732 (1919).

mixing, solution, or dilution. Zellhoefer and Copley[209] have described a very simple apparatus with which relatively large heats of mixing are measured with an accuracy of a few per cent. A rubber-stoppered copper mixing vessel fitted with a hand-operated stirrer is almost completely im-

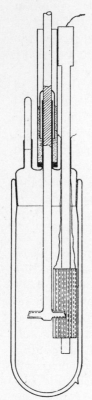

mersed in a Dewar flask containing diethyl phthalate. Also immersed in the diethyl phthalate is a pipette with delivery tube bent up and passing through the stopper of the mixing vessel. The contents of the pipette are forced into the mixing vessel by compressed air, the temperature rise of the diethyl phthalate being measured by a Beckmann thermometer. A heater in the calorimeter liquid serves for determining the electrical energy necessary to duplicate the heat of mixing. A fundamental weakness of this apparatus is the "dead" heat capacity of the relatively large amount of calorimeter liquid.

The simple apparatus used by Vold[207] gives about the same accuracy but with considerably smaller heats of mixing. Vold's calorimeter (Fig. 29) is a single Dewar flask with an evacuated ground-glass stopper carrying a mercury-sealed stirrer, a resistance thermometer, and a heater. The apparatus would be improved by including some mixing device, so the second liquid would not have to be added from a vessel outside the calorimeter. The Dewar calorimeter is submerged in a constant-temperature bath.

The calorimeters described by Pitzer[210] and Southard[210] also consist of Dewar flasks. These investigators used high-sensitivity resistance thermometers so that temperature measurements could be made to about 0.0001°.

Fig. 29.—
Simple calorimeter for
heats of mixing (Vold).

5. Apparatus of High Sensitivity

In the measurement of the minute heat effects met with in some dilution experiments, calorimeters of the greatest sensitivity are needed. These instruments have come to be called microcalorimeters, not because of their size (they usually contain about one liter of material), but because of their great sensitivity. For work of this sort, the differential twin calorimetric method (pages 342 and 367) is ideally suited, since the temperature differences to be measured are very small. The first important differential calorimeter of high sensitivity was described by Nernst and Orthmann.[218] These investigators employed a 100-junction thermel for measuring the

[218] W. Nernst and W. Orthmann, *Z. physik. Chem.*, **135**, 199 (1928).

temperature difference between the two calorimeters, and obtained a sensitivity of several microdegrees (1 microdegree = 10^{-6} degree).

The differential calorimeter has been brought to a high stage of development by Lange[205] and Gucker[214] and their collaborators. Further description and modification of the Lange type of calorimeter is given by Gulbransen and Robinson,[219] Ronneberg,[220] and Gall.[221] Slansky[210] has modified

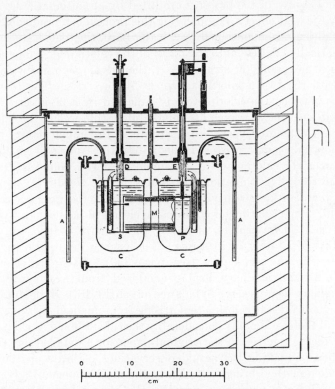

Fig. 30.—Differential adiabatic calorimeter of Gucker, Pickard, and Planck.

the apparatus so that it can be employed in the evaluation of heats of solution in nonaqueous solvents. In certain respects the calorimeter described by Gucker, Pickard, and Planck[214] is superior to that of Lange, its chief advantage being its wider range of applicability.

In Gucker's apparatus (Fig. 30), the calorimeters, C, of about one-liter

[219] E. A. Gulbransen and A. L. Robinson, *J. Am. Chem. Soc.*, **56**, 2637 (1934).

[220] C. E. Ronneberg, *Dissertation*, University of Chicago, 1935.

[221] J. F. Gall, *Dissertation*, University of Chicago, 1941.

capacity, are fabricated entirely of tantalum, which provides an excellent constructional material when strength and chemical inertness are important. The calorimeters have tightly ground-in covers of tantalum and are supported by dental floss (not shown) from the cover of the submarine jacket, being pulled up tightly against Lucite spacers, two of which, D and E, are shown in the figure. Each calorimeter contains, equidistant from its center, a stirrer, S, and a dilution pipette, P (capacity 60 ml.). The ground-in closures of the pipettes are lifted by an automatic device to insure that the heat effect accompanying this process is reproducible. Adiabatic conditions are maintained by a water bath, the temperature of which is automatically kept equal to the mean of the calorimeter temperatures by a photocell–galvanometer arrangement, the galvanometer of which is connected with the two adiabatic thermels, A, in series. The temperature difference between the calorimeters is indicated by a 60-junction copper–constantan thermel, M, which fits snugly into a thin well in the side of each calorimeter, extending nearly to its center. Preliminary tests indicated that this arrangement registered adequately the true temperature difference between the calorimeters. The main thermel is connected to a semiautomatic recording potentiometer and a highly sensitive galvanometer giving a temperature sensitivity of about one microdegree per millimeter deflection. Each calorimeter contains an electrical heater in a well welded to its cover. These heaters, of nearly the same resistance, can be energized either separately or in series. The energy input into each heater is measured in the usual way (see page 330). Each heater well contains also a small auxiliary heater energized from a separate battery. These auxiliary heaters serve to balance out slight drifts in the temperature difference between the calorimeters arising from unequal stirring or evaporation, and thereby simplify considerably the calculation of the data.

The reader is referred to the original paper for a detailed description of the method of making the actual observations of heats of dilution. A study of this method brings out clearly the most important advantage of the twin adiabatic procedure, namely, the almost complete elimination of the usual type of correction terms encountered in the ordinary calorimetric procedure.

The sensitivity of Gucker's apparatus is only slightly lower than that of Lange. The heat conduction between the calorimeters is only a small fraction of that in the Lange apparatus because of the relatively small number of junctions in the main thermel and the wide air gap between the calorimeters. The heat conduction between each calorimeter and the jacket is also only about half as large as with the unsilvered Dewar flask used in the Lange apparatus. It thus appears that Gucker's calorimeter can be applied with greater success to the measurement of relatively large heat effects.   The almost completely metallic construction of Gucker's calorimeter also makes it more suitable for observations of slow processes (see Section IX, page 423).

6.   Determination of Heats of Mixing by the Flow Method

Heats of mixing can be evaluated by the flow method.   The two liquids to be mixed flow at constant rates into a mixing chamber which is thermally isolated from its surroundings.   The heat of mixing is calculated from the temperatures of the two liquids before mixing, their rates of flow, and the temperature after mixing.   This method has been applied by Pratt.[222]   It is further described in Section IX (page 422).

IX.   HEATS OF CHEMICAL REACTIONS

The direct measurement of the heats of chemical reactions, other than combustion (Section VI, page 374), is a field of calorimetry which has received relatively little attention until recent years.   One of the chief reasons for this is the difficulty of making calorimetric observations on processes which are not complete within a few minutes.   Another reason is the fact that direct measurements cannot lead to significant results in cases which are complicated by side reactions.   Furthermore, many reactions take place only under conditions which are outside the scope of direct calorimetry.   There are, however, many reactions which are susceptible to direct calorimetric observation, and the data obtained from such measurements are of considerable importance.   We shall first point out some of the applications which have been made of directly determined heats of reaction, and then discuss the experimental methods available for measuring these heats of fast and of slow processes.   The methods for the indirect estimation of heats of reaction will be summarized in the last section.

1.   Applications

A.   HEATS OF FORMATION

If, in a given reaction, the heats of formation of all the substances involved but one are known, the heat of formation of that substance can be calculated from the heat of reaction.   In view of the great importance of heats of formation for the "master table of chemical thermodynamics" [223] (see page 349), this constitutes a most important general application of reaction heats.

---

[222] F. R. Pratt, *J. Franklin Inst.*, **185**, 663 (1918).
[223] F. D. Rossini, *Chem. Revs.*, **18**, 233 (1936).

B. HEATS OF HYDROGENATION

Kistiakowsky and coworkers[224] have determined the heats of hydrogenation of numerous compounds. In some cases, the heats of addition of chlorine and bromine have also been determined. The following examples illustrate the conclusions that can be drawn from such measurements: (1) An evaluation of the heats of hydrogenation of benzene, cyclohexadiene, and cyclohexane, together with estimates of the appropriate entropy changes, give the following free energies (298° K., 1 atm.):

$$\text{Benzene}_{(g.)} + \text{H}_{2\,(g.)} = \text{cyclohexadiene-1,3}_{(g.)}$$
$$\Delta F^0 = 13.6 \text{ kcal. per mole}$$

$$\text{Cyclohexadiene-1,3}_{(g.)} + \text{H}_{2\,(g.)} = \text{cyclohexene}_{(g.)}$$
$$\Delta F^0 = -17.7 \text{ kcal. per mole}$$

Since $\Delta F^0 = -RT \ln K$, where K is the equilibrium constant for a reaction, it is evident that cyclohexadiene is not obtainable from benzene by hydrogenation because the free energy change is such that only a negligible quantity of the product is present at equilibrium. It is, therefore, unnecessary to make assumptions concerning the relative rates of the successive steps in the hydrogenation of benzene to explain the absence of cyclohexadiene in the reaction product. (2) Support was found for the conclusion that rather large repulsive interactions exist between nonbonded atoms in a molecule. For example, the heat of hydrogenation of cyclopentene would seem to indicate that this molecule is less strained than cyclopentane, a conclusion strikingly at variance with the prediction based on the tetrahedral structure of the carbon atom. This apparently anomalous result can be understood when account is taken of the fact that, in the five-membered rings, the hydrogen atoms are held in the "eclipsed" position where their mutual repulsions are greater than when they are further apart as in the more usual "staggered" position.

C. HEATS OF REACTION IN CONNECTION WITH REACTION MECHANISMS

(1) The heats of several protein reactions have been measured.[225] For example, Conn, Gregg, Kistiakowsky, and Roberts determined the "heat of denaturation" of pepsin by alkali as the difference between the heats absorbed when native and denatured pepsins are treated with sufficient alkali to carry the pH to 9, where the denaturation is practically instantaneous. When varying initial pH values were used, so that the protein had already lost some of its enzymatic activity, the de-

[224] J. B. Conant and G. B. Kistiakowsky, *Chem. Revs.*, **20**, 181 (1937); G. B. Kistiakowsky, *et al.*, *J. Am. Chem. Soc.*, **60**, 440, 2764 (1938); **61**, 1868 (1939). See also R. B. Williams, *ibid.*, **64**, 1395 (1942).

[225] J. B. Conn, G. B. Kistiakowsky, and R. M. Roberts, *J. Am. Chem. Soc.*, **62**, 1895 (1940) (denaturation of hemoglobin). J. B. Conn, D. C. Gregg, G. B. Kistiakowsky, and R. M. Roberts, *ibid.*, **63**, 2080 (1941) (denaturation of pepsin). W. C. Boyd, J. B. Conn, D. C. Gregg, G. B. Kistiakowsky, and R. M. Roberts, *J. Biol. Chem.*, **139**, 787 (1941) (antibody–antigen reaction). G. Haugaard and R. M. Roberts, *J. Am. Chem. Soc.*, **64**, 2664 (1942) (enzymatic proteolysis).

crease in the "heat of denaturation" did not follow the same course as the decrease in the remaining enzymatic activity. It thus appeared that the calorimetric measurements were concerned with a different reaction caused by the alkali than were the enzymatic activity measurements. More recently, Bender and Sturtevant[226] re-examined this reaction, employing the extrapolation procedure described on page 423. When the reaction is carried out in a buffer solution at *constant* pH, a small heat absorption takes place, and the kinetics of the heat absorption are exactly the same as the kinetics of the loss of peptic activity. This result indicates that at about pH 6, with which Bender and Sturtevant worked, the heat-absorbing process is the same as the denaturation process, if the latter is taken to include any very rapid processes, such as ionization, accompanying the primary reaction. The heat of the reaction is a very strong function of the pH, approximately doubling between pH 6.2 and 6.4. Apparently the denaturation process itself changes with pH.

(*2*) Dilatometric, refractometric, and polarimetric determinations[227] of the rate of the mutarotation of α- and β-D-glucose show no observable deviations from the first-order rate law. From the heat evolved when α-glucose changes to the equilibrium mixture and that absorbed when β-glucose changes to the equilibrium mixture,[228] one can calculate the equilibrium constant for the reaction, on the assumption that no other forms of the sugar are involved in the equilibrium. Measurements at 25° and 35° led to $K_{35°}/K_{25°} = 0.949$, while a value of 0.984 is obtained by application of the van't Hoff equation (page 433) to the ΔH of the reaction α-glucose$_{(aq.)}$ = β-glucose$_{(aq.)}$. The difference of almost 4% is considerably larger than the experimental error. It is true that no account has been taken of the possibility that the activity coefficient of the glucose may differ considerably from unity, though it seems very unlikely that either of the above ratios could be significantly in error from this cause. It thus appears that the discrepancy is due to the existence of more than two forms of glucose in the equilibrium mixture.

D. HEATS OF NEUTRALIZATION AND IONIZATION

The heats of ionization of electrolytes are of interest in connection with the detailed study of the ionization process. Thus, the value of ΔH for an ionization reaction can be utilized to evaluate the change of the standard free energy of ionization or of the ionization constant with temperature (see page 433). From a knowledge of the heat and free energy of ionization, the entropy of ionization may be evaluated by the relation:

$$\Delta F^0 = \Delta H - T\Delta S^0 \tag{111}$$

When an aqueous solution of hydrochloric acid is mixed with a solution of sodium hydroxide, the resulting evolution of heat is almost entirely due to the combination

---

[226] M. Bender and J. M. Sturtevant, *unpublished work*.

[227] C. N. Rüber and J. Minsaas, *Ber.*, **59**, 2266 (1926). See also F. P. Worley and J. C. Andrews, *J. Phys. Chem.*, **32**, 307 (1928); H. S. Isbell and W. W. Pigman, *J. Research Natl. Bur. Standards*, **18**, 141 (1937).

[228] J. M. Sturtevant, *J. Phys. Chem.*, **45**, 127 (1941).

of hydrogen and hydroxyl ions to form water. This fact is utilized in determining the heat of ionization of water. In order to eliminate the effects resulting from the presence of the other ions in addition to the hydrogen and hydroxyl ions, it is necessary to extrapolate the results obtained at finite concentrations to infinite dilution. This extrapolation can be carried out in various ways.[229]

The heats of ionization of glycine and alanine have been measured[230] by observing the heats of reaction of the zwitterions with hydrochloric acid and sodium hydroxide:

$$Z^{\pm} + H^+ = ZH^+$$

$$\Delta H = -\Delta H_{A_1} \tag{112}$$

$$Z^{\pm} + OH^- = ZOH^-$$

$$\Delta H = \Delta H_{A_2} - \Delta H_W \tag{113}$$

where ΔH_{A_1}, ΔH_{A_2}, and ΔH_W are, respectively, the heats of the first and second ionizations of the dibasic acid, ZH^+, and the heat of ionization of water. The extrapolation of the data, in these cases, to infinite dilution could not be carried out directly because of the lack of data on the heats of dilution of the salts formed, so that somewhat less satisfactory procedures were resorted to. It is interesting to note that data on the heats of ionization of amino acids furnish important confirmation of the zwitterion hypothesis.[231]

2. Determination of the Heats of Fast Reactions

A. STATIC METHOD

The heat effect accompanying a reaction in a condensed phase can be determined by the ordinary methods of calorimetry[232] discussed in previous sections, provided the process is complete in a reasonably short time. The allowable magnitude of this period depends on several factors, such as the size of the heat effect, the desired accuracy, and the design of the calorimeter, particularly with respect to heat leakage. In some cases, accurate results have been obtained with reaction periods as long as one hour. However, in most cases in which reaction periods as long as this are encountered, it is better to employ the extrapolation procedure outlined on page 423,

---

[229] T. W. Richards and L. P. Hall, *J. Am. Chem. Soc.*, **51**, 731 (1929). K. S. Pitzer, *ibid.*, **59**, 2365 (1937). R. H. Lambert and L. J. Gillespie, *ibid.*, **53**, 2632 (1931).

[230] J. M. Sturtevant, *J. Am. Chem. Soc.*, **63**, 88 (1941), **64**, 762 (1942).

[231] D. I. Hitchcock in C. L. Schmidt, *Chemistry of the Amino Acids and Proteins*. C. C. Thomas, Springfield, Ill., 1938, p. 615.

[232] See, for example, W. Swietoslawski, *Diazocompounds, Thermochemical Investigation* (*Diazosoedinenîa, Thermokhimicheskoe Izsledovanie*, published in Russian with a summary in French), Ledentow's Society for Encouragement of the Development of Scientific Research, Moscow, 1917, 319 pp.; F. O. Rice and J. Greenberg. *J. Am. Chem. Soc.*, **56**, 2268 (1934) (reaction of ketene with alkali and alcohols); various references given earlier in this section.

not only because calorimetric errors are thereby reduced, but also because the procedure enables one to separate the heat effect of the mixing process from that of the main reaction, and to evaluate the kinetics of the latter. This extrapolation procedure can be employed only in cases in which the kinetics of the main heat evolution (as distinguished from the heat of the mixing process) are known or can be deduced from the experimental data.

Examples of the application of the static method are furnished by the neutralization reactions mentioned above.

Conn, Kistiakowsky, and Roberts[225, 233] have described a calorimeter specifically designed for liquid phase reactions, which has been successfully employed in cases in which the reaction period is as long as one hour. This apparatus is of the twin adiabatic type (page 342), though in the measurements so far reported it has been used as a single calorimeter, with the tare calorimeter simply supplying a fixed reference temperature. The design of the calorimeters is indicated in figure 31. A cylindrical gold can, A, of about 900-milliliters volume, is closed by a tightly fitting cover, B, a rubber gasket being used. The cover carries three wells (two of which are not shown) for a heater, an adiabatic thermel (20 junctions) between the calorimeter and the thermostat bath surrounding the submarine jacket, J, and the

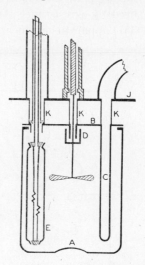

Fig. 31.—Liquid-phase calorimeter of Kistiakowsky and coworkers.

main thermel (50 junctions, in well C) which measures the temperature difference between the calorimeters. Each calorimeter is also equipped with an oil-sealed stirrer, D, and a mixing pipette, E. The design of the latter is such that either the calorimeter or pipette, or both, can be emptied and refilled without dismantling the apparatus.

An unusual feature of this apparatus is the support of the calorimeters in completely independent jackets submerged in the bath. This arrangement insures that the temperature of one calorimeter is not affected by that of the other. The temperature of the outer bath can be held constant, or made to follow closely the temperature of either calorimeter by means of an automatic control. The independent support of the two calorimeters necessitates an unusually long main thermel, the resistance of which is kept low by using relatively heavy wires in the middle portion of the thermel in the outer bath.

---

[233] See also J. B. Conn, G. B. Kistiakowsky, R. M. Roberts, and E. A. Smith. *J Am Chem. Soc.*, **64**, 1747 (1942) (hydrolysis of acid anhydrides).

B. FLOW METHOD

Flow calorimetry has been used in the determination of the heats of fast reactions. The chief limitation of the method is that it requires relatively large amounts of the reacting solutions. Keyes, Gillespie, and Mitsukuri[234] employed a vacuum-jacketed glass calorimeter equipped with mixing baffles. The temperature of the solution after reaction was measured by a resistance thermometer. As with the Scheel and Heuse (page 357) apparatus for measuring the heat capacities of gases, it was found that

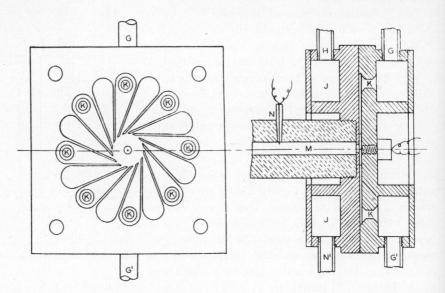

Fig. 32.—Mixing device, flow method for calorimetry of fast reactions (LaMer and Read). Left, view of rear face of plate; right, cross section of mixing device and reaction tube.

the temperature increase due to the reaction was proportional to the rate of flow, so that extrapolation to infinite rate was necessary. The heat losses in these experiments amounted to 2 to 7% of the total heat effect.

An ingenious modification of the flow method permits the estimation of both the velocities and the heats of reactions having half-periods as short as a few thousandths of a second. Two liquid streams moving at high velocity are very rapidly mixed and then flow through an observation tube which is fitted with thermocouples at appropriate intervals. This method

[234] F. G. Keyes, L. J. Gillespie, and S. Mitsukuri, *J. Am. Chem. Soc.*, **44**, 707 (1922). See also L. J. Gillespie, R. H. Lambert, and J. A. Gibson, *ibid.*, **52**, 3806 (1930).

has been developed largely by Roughton and his collaborators[235] and by LaMer and Read.[236] Particular attention must be given to the very rapid mixing of the solutions. The mixing device employed by LaMer and Read is shown in figure 32. One of the solutions enters through tubes *G* and *G'*, and is led through holes *K* into jets leading tangentially into the mixing chamber. The other solution enters through tubes *H* and *H'*, and is led into jets alternating with those for the first solution. The swirling motion thus imparted to the liquids in the mixing chamber results in rapid mixing. From the mixing chamber the solution passes into the hard rubber observation tube, *M*, of 6.35-millimeter bore, into which thermocouple junctions *N* are inserted at intervals. Experiments with a rate of flow of 100 centimeters per second in the observation tube indicated that mixing was complete by the time the solution reached the first thermocouple, that is, in less than 0.002 second. Indication of considerably higher rates of mixing has been obtained by Roughton in some forms of his apparatus. The results obtained have demonstrated that, at the higher rates of flow used in these experiments, the heat loss to the surroundings is negligible.

3. Determination of the Heats of Slow Processes

We shall include in our discussion processes the *calorimetric observation* of which requires measurements extending over relatively long periods of time. Thus, the catalytic hydrogenation of a gaseous olefin (page 418), even though it may be a rapid chemical reaction, requires more or less extended observations because of the necessity of passing a sufficient amount of the reacting gases over the catalyst to obtain an accurately measurable temperature rise.

A. EXTRAPOLATION METHOD

With very few exceptions,[225, 237] direct calorimetric determinations of heats of reaction have been confined to reactions which are essentially complete in considerably less than one hour. This is because of the difficulty of holding the calorimetric errors sufficiently low even when the adiabatic method is employed. The rate of heat evolution or absorption accompany-

---

[235] H. Hartridge and F. J. W. Roughton, *Proc. Cambridge Phil. Soc.*, 22, 426 (1925); 23, 450 (1926). F. J. W. Roughton, *Proc. Roy. Soc. London*, A126, 439, 470 (1930); *J. Am. Chem. Soc.*, 63, 2930 (1941). J. B. Bateman and F. J. W. Roughton, *Biochem. J.*, 29, 2622 (1935).

[236] V. K. LaMer and C. L. Read, *J. Am. Chem. Soc.*, 52, 3098 (1930).

[237] See, for example, W. Swietoslawski and A. Dorabialska, *Compt. rend.*, 185, 737 (1927); O. Meyerhof *et al.*, *Biochem. Z.*, 236, 326 (1931); 281, 292 (1935); 289, 87 (1937).

ing a chemical reaction falls off with the time.   Thus, in the case of a first-order reaction having a half-time of 30 minutes, the reaction is 75% complete after one hour, 93.8% after two hours, 98.4% after three hours, and 99.6% after four hours.   If one attempted to measure directly the total heat effect of the reaction with an accuracy of 0.5%, one would have to continue observations for at least four hours after mixing.   In the last three hours, during which approximately 75% of the calorimetric error is introduced, only 25% of the heat effect of the reaction itself would be obtained.   Furthermore, the transition, at the completion of the reaction, to a linear temperature change due only to stirring and thermal leakage would be so gradual that any of the usual methods (Section IV, page 333 *et seq.*) for evaluating the stirring and thermal leakage corrections would be very difficult to apply.

These difficulties can be largely eliminated by a simple extrapolation procedure, provided the rate of heat evolution or absorption follows a discoverable law, and the apparent calorimeter temperature does not lag appreciably behind the mean temperature of the calorimeter and its contents. This latter requirement will usually be met if an all-metal calorimeter of low heat capacity is employed, and temperature measurements are made by thermocouples or resistance thermometers of low lag.[238]   In some cases, it is not even necessary to stir the calorimeter after the initial mixing process is complete.   The extrapolation may be carried out for irreversible first-[239] and second-order[240] reactions.   Similar procedures can be developed which will apply to other types of reactions.

The principle of the extrapolation method is that calorimetric measurements are confined to the period between the completion of the mixing process and the point of approximately 75% completion of the reaction. From these data a value for the rate constant of the process is calculated which then allows extrapolation of the temperature observations back to the instant of mixing and forward to the completion of the reaction (infinite time).   The stirring and thermal-leakage corrections can be evaluated from a rating period run several half-times after the start of the reaction. In the case of a first-order reaction having a half-time of 30 minutes, the observations during the reaction period need to extend over only one hour, or even less.   No further observations are needed until the final rating period, which could safely be started five or six hours after mixing, and

---

[238] See the discussion of thermometer lag by D. R. Harper, *Natl. Bur. Standards (U. S.), Bull.* 8, 659 (1912).   Among other things, it is shown by Harper that the lag of a critically damped galvanometer behind an e. m. f. changing linearly with time is independent of the rate of change of the e. m. f.

[239] J. M. Sturtevant, *J. Am. Chem. Soc.*, 59, 1528 (1937).

[240] J. M. Sturtevant, *J. Am. Chem. Soc.*, 64, 77 (1942).

which should be of approximately the same length as the reaction period. It is evident that, in experiments of this type, the adiabatic method (preferably with automatic adiabatic control) should always be employed, so that variations in the leakage modulus of the calorimeter will not cause serious errors (see page 341).

First-Order Reactions.—Readings of the calorimeter temperature (which may be expressed in microvolts or ohms) are taken at times t_1, $t_2 = t_1 + \Delta t$, and $t_3 = t_1 + 2\Delta t$ after the start of the reaction. Suppose these readings, after application of any corrections, are μ_1, μ_2, μ_3. It has been shown by Roseveare[241] that, for a first-order reaction:

$$k = \frac{1}{\Delta t} \ln \frac{\mu_1 - \mu_2}{\mu_2 - \mu_3} \tag{114}$$

Further calculation leads to the result:

$$\mu_0 - \mu_\infty = \frac{(\mu_1 - \mu_2)(\mu_2 - \mu_3)}{\mu_1 + \mu_3 - 2\mu_2} \left(\frac{\mu_1 - \mu_2}{\mu_2 - \mu_3}\right)^{t_2/\Delta t} \tag{115}$$

where $\mu_0 - \mu_\infty$ is the total temperature change for the reaction. The accuracy of $\mu_0 - \mu_\infty$ is highest when Δt is about 0.7 or 0.8 times the half-period of the reaction and t_1 is about 0.5 or 0.6 times Δt. Several sets of three readings should be taken. If the reaction rate has a high temperature coefficient and the observations extend over a considerable temperature range, the above expressions must be modified[239] to allow for the variation of k. The value of μ_∞ is calculated by means of the relation:

$$\mu_\infty = \frac{\mu_1\mu_3 - \mu_2{}^2}{\mu_1 + \mu_3 - 2\mu_2} \tag{116}$$

so that one can readily evaluate μ_0. If the (corrected) temperature of the calorimeter just before the reactants are mixed is μ_0', the temperature change due to the mixing process is given by $\mu_0' - \mu_0$. It is, of course, assumed that the heat capacity of the reacting system remains constant during the reaction. This is probably a valid assumption in the case of dilute solutions; in any event, the validity of this assumption can be tested by determining the heat of the reaction at two different temperatures, and employing the relation:

$$\left(\frac{\partial \Delta H}{\partial T}\right)_p = \Delta \bar{C}_p \tag{117}$$

where $\Delta \bar{C}_p$ is the difference between the sum of the partial molal heat capacities of the products and that of the reactants.

---

[241] W. E. Roseveare, *J. Am. Chem. Soc.*, **53**, 1651 (1931).

In the above development it has been assumed that the mixing process is complete in an interval of time short in comparison with the half-time of the reaction under investigation. Barry[242] has considered the case in which this condition is not fulfilled, and has described an extrapolation procedure which can be applied in such cases, providing the mixing process follows an exponential course the rate of which can be approximately determined.

Second-Order Reactions.—In the case of a second-order irreversible reaction, the kinetic equation is:

$$kt = \frac{1}{A - B} \ln \frac{B(A - Y)}{A(B - Y)} \tag{118}$$

where $A \neq B$ are the initial concentrations of the reactants, and Y is the concentration at time t of the reactant present in smaller stoichiometric amount. Application[243] of the methods of projective geometry leads to the following results:

$$\frac{B}{A} = \frac{\alpha(\mu_2 - \mu_3) - (\mu_1 - \mu_2)}{(\mu_2 - \mu_3) - \alpha(\mu_1 - \mu_2)} \alpha^{t_2/\Delta t} \tag{119}$$

$$\mu_\infty = \frac{\mu_3(\mu_1 - \mu_2) - \alpha\mu_1(\mu_2 - \mu_3)}{(\mu_1 - \mu_2) - \alpha(\mu_2 - \mu_3)} \tag{120}$$

$$\mu_0 - \mu_\infty = \frac{A}{A - B} \left[\frac{\mu_1(\mu_2 - \mu_3) - \alpha\mu_3(\mu_1 - \mu_2)}{(\mu_2 - \mu_3) - \alpha(\mu_1 - \mu_2)} - \mu_\infty \right] \tag{121}$$

$$k = \frac{1}{(A - B)\Delta t} \ln \alpha \tag{122}$$

In these equations μ_1, μ_2, and μ_3 are (corrected) temperature readings at times t_1, $t_2 = t_1 + \Delta t$, and $t_3 = t_1 + 2\Delta t$ after the instant of mixing. The quantity α may be calculated from equation (119) by successive approximations, and then used to evaluate μ_∞, $\mu_0 - \mu_\infty$ and k by equations (120), (121), and (122).

One of the most important advantages of these extrapolation procedures is the possibility of a direct comparison of the kinetics of the heat absorption or evolution with the kinetics, determined in some other manner, of the reaction to be expected in the system under study. In this way, it becomes possible to gain a more definite idea of the nature of the process the heat effect of which is being measured. This point has been illustrated above in connection with the denaturation of pepsin (page 419).

Surprisingly few examples are to be found in the literature of the appli-

[242] F. Barry, *J. Am. Chem. Soc.*, **42**, 1296, 1911 (1920).
[243] J. M. Sturtevant, *J. Am. Chem. Soc.*, **59**, 699 (1937).

cation of the above or equivalent procedures. Several papers[244] have reported calorimetric measurements in which the necessary information regarding the extent of the reaction was obtained from analytical determinations, or from rate constants measured by ordinary methods outside the calorimeter. Duclaux[245] showed that satisfactory rate constants for several reactions could be derived from calorimetric observations, but he made no attempt to evaluate the heats of these reactions from his data. Barry[242] apparently was the first to determine both rates and heats from the same data. His careful and thorough work dealt with the inversion of

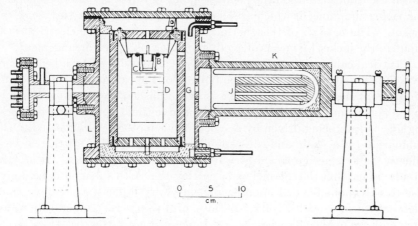

Fig. 33.—Calorimeter for slow liquid-phase processes (Sturtevant).

sucrose, and he obtained results which have since been confirmed.[230] Recently Batalin and Shcherbakov[246] and Wolf and Merkel[247] obtained moderately precise rate constants and heats of reaction from calorimetric measurements.

Sturtevant[226, 228, 239, 240] has investigated several reactions, employing the extrapolation method. The calorimeter used in the more recent work is illustrated in figure 33. The calorimeter can, D, constructed of tantalum, is supported by dental floss in an aluminum adiabatic jacket, G, which is in turn contained in a cast aluminum submarine, L, completely sub-

[244] H. T. Brown and S. V. Pickering, *J. Chem. Soc.*, **1897**, 756, 783. A. Tian, *Bull. soc. chim.*, **33**, 427 (1923); *J. chim. phys.*, **30**, 665 (1933). Bérenger-Calvet, *ibid.*, **24**, 325 (1927). E. Calvet, *ibid.*, **30**, 1, 140, 198 (1933). E. D. Coon and F. Daniels, *J. Phys. Chem.*, **37**, 1 (1933).

[245] J. Duclaux, *Compt. rend.*, **146**, 120 (1908). W. Tschelinzew, *Chem. Zentr.*, **83**, II, 1899 (1912).

[246] A. K. Batalin and I. A. Shcherbakov, *J. Gen. Chem. U.S.S.R.*, **10**, 730 (1940).

[247] K. L. Wolf and K. Merkel, *Z. physik. Chem.*, **A187**, 61 (1940).

merged in a constant-temperature bath of transformer oil. The calorimeter is closed by a tantalum cover, a tight seal being effected by a rubber gasket. The cover carries a tantalum dilution cup, B, the action of which has been described on page 412.

The temperature of the calorimeter is measured by a 30-junction thermel the "cold" junctions of which are contained in a lagged copper cylinder, J, in side arm K of the submarine. The "hot" junctions of this thermel are in the form of thin ribbon and are distributed over the surface of the calorimeter in close thermal contact with it. The temperature difference between the calorimeter and the jacket is indicated by a 20-junction thermel, the jacket junctions of which are distributed over the inside surface of the jacket. The e. m. f. of this thermel is used to control the electrical heat input to the jacket by means of a galvanometer–photocell arrangement.

Electrical calibration of the calorimeter is accomplished by a heater contained in a well (not shown) in the bottom of the calorimeter.[248] Stirring of the contents of the calorimeter is accomplished by rotating the submarine back and forth through 360° about five times per minute, the rocking mechanism being driven by a synchronous motor and connected to the submarine by a chain-and-sprocket drive. This type of stirring is very effective, and is accompanied by a relatively small heat effect. It has the disadvantage that the thermel wires cutting the earth's magnetic field give rise to galvanometer deflections which are very difficult to remove completely by compensating coils. Because of this, precise temperature measurements are made only while the calorimeter is not being rocked.

This calorimeter has been used with reactions having half-times as short as three minutes. With a sufficiently large heat effect, there should be no difficulty in studying reactions requiring several hours to reach half completion. Satisfactory results have been obtained in cases in which the total temperature rise was less than 0.001°, though in such a case the half-time should not exceed 20 or 30 minutes.

B. ORDINARY METHOD

By the term "ordinary method" is meant the usual procedure of extending the calorimetric measurements until the evolution or absorption of heat is essentially complete. The measurements themselves may be carried out by the adiabatic method or the method of constant jacket temperature.

Gas Phase Reactions.—An important gas phase reaction, the combustion of volatile substances, has been discussed in Section VI, page 391.

Kistiakowsky and coworkers,[224] in their investigation of the heats of hydrogenation and halogenation of unsaturated substances in the vapor state,

---

[248] J. M. Sturtevant, *J. Am. Chem. Soc.*, **64**, 762 (1942).

used a method[249] designed to minimize systematic errors resulting from adsorption effects and side reactions. A mixture of excess hydrogen and substance to be reduced is led under atmospheric pressure at a precisely controlled rate into A, a glass catalyst chamber (Fig. 34), where the reduction takes place and the reaction products are brought into thermal equilibrium with the calorimeter fluid by passage through a glass spiral, C. The products are then led out of the calorimeter, and are burned in an excess of oxygen; the carbon dioxide thus formed is absorbed in Ascarite, and serves as a measure of the amount of substance reduced. In some cases, copper is used as catalyst; other compounds require a platinum or a cobalt–nickel catalyst.

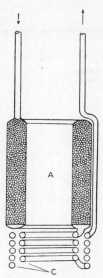

The catalyst chamber is contained in a calorimeter of more or less conventional design, diethylene glycol being employed as the calorimeter liquid so measurements can be made at temperatures as high as 150°. The calorimeter is suspended in a submarine jacket in a bath the temperature of which is automatically held close to that of the calorimeter, the adiabatic control being governed by a 12-junction thermel. The temperature of the calorimeter is measured by a 16-junction thermel, the reference temperature, supplied by a well-lagged "cold calorimeter" (see page 326), being close to that of the calorimeter.

The reduction is allowed to proceed until the temperature of the calorimeter rises at a constant rate. The reduction products are then burned and the carbon dioxide collected without any disturbance to the steady state of the calorimetric system until a sufficient temperature rise has been obtained. The energy equivalent of the calorimeter is determined, with hydrogen flowing through the

Fig. 34.—Catalyst chamber for heats of hydrogenation (Kistiakowsky and coworkers).

catalyst chamber, in the usual way by means of an electrical heater. The completeness of the reductions and the absence of side reactions were carefully investigated. The completeness of reduction was most convincingly shown by passing the reaction mixture first through a duplicate catalyst chamber outside the calorimeter and then through the chamber in the calorimeter; in such experiments, there was no observable heat effect produced in the calorimeter. The method has been developed to the point at which the factor most important in limiting the accuracy is the purity

[249] G. B. Kistiakowsky, H. Romeyn, J. R. Ruhoff, H. A. Smith and W. E. Vaughan, *J. Am. Chem. Soc.*, **57**, 65 (1935).

of the reactants.   The reproducibility of the calorimetric measurements
was usually of the order of $\pm 0.1\%$.

In the determination of the heats of addition of chlorine and bromine to

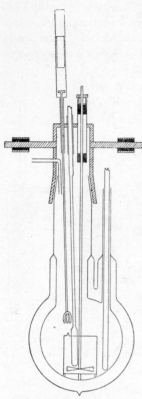

Fig. 35.—Calorimeter for
determining heats of hydrogenation of liquids (Wil-
liams).

some gaseous olefins,[250] the catalyst was calcium
chloride or calcium bromide, and the amount of
the reaction was determined by burning the gas
mixture from the calorimeter and determining
halogen acid in the combustion products.   The
hydrocarbon was always used in excess.   Tests
showed the reaction to be complete, and free
from any contamination by substitution.

Liquid Phase Reactions.—Williams[251] has
determined the heats of hydrogenation of some
unsaturated compounds in the liquid phase with
the calorimeter illustrated in figure 35.   Lister[252]
employed the same apparatus after some modification, to determine the heats of addition of
bromine[253] to some cyclic olefins in carbon tetrachloride solution.   Williams' calorimeter is a
spherical Dewar flask, of about 500-milliliter
capacity, with two necks.   The smaller neck
carries the resistance thermometer used in measuring the calorimeter temperature, while the
other one ends in a ground joint.   A brass head
fits over this joint, and carries the shaft of the
propeller stirrer, an electric heater, a gas inlet,
and a device for holding and breaking the ampoules which contain the substance to be hy-
drogenated.   The calorimeter is so supported by
the side arms on the brass head that it can be
shaken by means of an eccentric driven by a synchronous motor, in order to insure sufficiently
rapid hydrogenation.   The calorimeter is immersed almost up to the ground
joint in a constant-temperature water bath.   Williams found that results
having a precision of about 0.5% could be obtained with this apparatus.

[250] J. B. Conn, G. B. Kistiakowsky, and E. A. Smith, *J. Am. Chem. Soc.*, **60**, 2764
(1938).

[251] R. B. Williams, *J. Am. Chem. Soc.*, **64**, 1395 (1942).   See also H. E. Bent, G. R.
Cuthbertson, M. Dorfman, and R. E. Leary, *ibid.*, **58**, 165 (1936);   B. L. Crawford and
G. S. Parks, *ibid.*, **58**, 373 (1936).

[252] M. W. Lister, *J. Am. Chem. Soc.*, **63**, 143 (1941).

[253] Measurements of this same sort were reported by W. Louguinine, *Compt. rend.*, **150**,
915 (1910).

Heat-Flow Method.—The heats of slow processes, including those having small heat effects, can be measured by the so-called heat-flow method.[254] The calorimeter is supported within a constant-temperature jacket. A multijunction thermel measures the temperature difference between the inside surface of the jacket and the outside surface of the calorimeter. The heat exchange between the calorimeter and the jacket should, in most cases, be more rapid than with the usual types of calorimeters. The optimum rate for this exchange depends on the magnitude and the kinetics of the heat change to be measured. The calorimeter itself can usually be made considerably smaller than is practicable in other calorimetric procedures. The measurement consists in observing the calorimeter–jacket temperature difference as a function of time. If the heat exchange follows Newton's cooling law, the rate of gain of heat by the calorimeter from the jacket is:

$$dq/dt = \kappa(T_j - T) \tag{123}$$

where T_j and T are, respectively, the temperatures of the jacket and the calorimeter. It is evident that the total heat absorbed by the calorimeter between times t_1 and t_2 is:

$$\Delta q = \kappa \int_{t_1}^{t_2} (T_j - T)dt \tag{124}$$

where the integration will usually be performed graphically. If $T_j - T = 0$ at t_1 and at t_2, the heat of the process occurring between these two times is equal to Δq. If $T_j - T = 0$ at t_1 but is different from zero at t_2, account must be taken of the heat capacity of the calorimeter and its contents. If this quantity is represented by C, the heat of the process is given by $\Delta q + C(T_j - T_2)$.

The chief weaknesses in this method are the errors which arise from inconstancy of the leakage modulus of the calorimeter, and the difficulty of initiating the reaction in the calorimeter. The simple treatment given above will not hold if there are appreciable temperature gradients within the calorimeter. The method has been employed in observations extending over periods several days in length.

4. Indirect Determination of Heats of Reaction

A. FROM CALORIMETRIC DATA

Heats of reaction are frequently calculated from heats of combustion (see Section VI, page 374 *et seq.*). It was pointed out previously that the re-

---

[254] W. Swietoslawski and J. Salcewicz, *Compt. rend.* **199**, 935 (1934); R. Sandri, *Monatsh.*, **68**, 415 (1936). J. L Magee and F. Daniels, *J. Am. Chem. Soc.*, **62**, 2825 (1940), have employed this method with their calorimeter designed for photochemical reactions.

sults of such calculations are in most cases relatively inaccurate because of the large magnitude of heats of combustion compared with other heats of reaction (see the discussion of the sucrose inversion, page 379) and that this situation is somewhat improved when heats of reaction are inferred from heats of solution (page 407) because of the smaller magnitude of heats of solution.

Heats of reaction are sometimes evaluated from other heats of reaction. For example, the hydrogenation data of Kistiakowsky *et al.*[224] for butene-1 and *cis*-butene-2 give a value for the heat of isomerization of butene-1 to *cis*-butene-2 of -1.77 kcal. per mole. It is interesting to note that this difference is about 6% of either heat of hydrogenation, while it is only 0.3% of either heat of combustion.

B. FROM OTHER THERMODYNAMIC DATA

The heat of a reaction can be evaluated from other thermodynamic data in several ways. If the free energy and entropy changes accompanying an isothermal process are known, the change in heat content is given by the fundamental relation:

$$\Delta H = \Delta F + T \Delta S \tag{125}$$

If this expression is differentiated with respect to temperature, and use is made of the relations:[255]

$$\left(\frac{\partial H}{\partial T}\right)_p = C_p = T\left(\frac{\partial S}{\partial T}\right)_p \tag{126}$$

it follows that:

$$\left(\frac{\partial \Delta F}{\partial T}\right)_p = \frac{\Delta F - \Delta H}{T} \tag{127}$$

Here, the subscript p means that the pressure on *each* substance is to be the same whether we are working at one temperature or another; the process under consideration is not necessarily one which takes place at constant pressure. Thus, if the process is $A = B$, and the pressure on substance A is one atmosphere and that on substance B is ten atmospheres at one temperature, these same pressures must be used at other temperatures. From equation (127) it is readily found that:

$$\frac{\partial(\Delta F/T)}{\partial(1/T)} = \Delta H \tag{128}$$

This equation provides a method for evaluating heats of reaction from free energy data alone. In the case of a reversible reaction, the free energy change accompanying the process with all reactants and products in their standard states, that is, the standard free energy, can be determined from the equilibrium constant:

$$\Delta F^0 = -RT \ln K \tag{129}$$

[255] G. N. Lewis and M. Randall, *Thermodynamics and the Free Energy of Chemical Substances.* McGraw-Hill, New York, 1923, pp. 57, 132, 172.

Substitution of this relation in equation (128) gives the familiar van't Hoff equation:

$$\frac{\partial \ln K}{\partial(1/T)} = -\frac{\Delta H}{R} \tag{130}$$

or

$$\frac{\partial \ln K}{\partial T} = \frac{\Delta H}{RT^2} \tag{131}$$

The ΔH value obtained from equilibrium data is of course the *standard* change in heat content.

An important method for determining heats of reaction is based on the observation of the e. m. f. of a reversible galvanic cell. According to the Gibbs-Helmholtz equation:

$$\frac{\Delta H}{\mathbf{NF}} = T\frac{\partial \mathbf{E}}{\partial T} - \mathbf{E} \tag{132}$$

In this equation, $\mathbf{F}$ is the Faraday equivalent, $\mathbf{N}$ is the number of Faraday equivalents passing through the cell when the cell reaction takes place, ΔH is the heat of this reaction, and $\mathbf{E}$ is the reversible electromotive force of the cell. Numerous illustrations of the application of this method will be found in the literature.[256]

Note

The author wishes to acknowledge his great indebtedness to Dr. F. D. Rossini, of the National Bureau of Standards, and to Dr. E. L. Skau, of the Southern Regional Research Laboratory of the Department of Agriculture, who have kindly offered their criticisms on parts of the manuscript, and particularly to his colleague, Dr. S. E. Wood, of Yale University, who has read over the entire manuscript and made numerous helpful suggestions.

---

[256] See especially H. S. Harned and B. B. Owen, *Physical Chemistry of Electrolytic Solutions*. Reinhold, New York, 1943.

General References

American Institute of Physics, *Temperature, Its Measurement and Control in Science and Industry*. Reinhold, New York, 1941.

Bichowsky, F. R., and Rossini, F. D., *The Thermochemistry of Chemical Substances*. Reinhold, New York, 1936.

Burton, E. F., Grayson Smith, H., and Wilhelm, J. O., *Phenomena at the Temperature of Liquid Helium*. Reinhold, New York, 1940.

Eucken, A., *Energie- und Wärmeinhalt*. Vol. VIII, Part 1, of Wien-Harms *Handbuch der Experimentalphysik*, Akadem. Verlagsgesellschaft, Leipzig, 1929.

Lewis, G. N., and Randall, M., *Thermodynamics and the Free Energy of Chemical Substances*. McGraw-Hill, New York, 1923.

MacDougall, F. H., *Thermodynamics and Chemistry*. 3rd ed., Wiley, New York, 1939.

Ostwald-Luther, *Physikochemische Messungen*. 4th ed., Akadem. Verlagsgesellschaft, Leipzig, 1925.

Parks, G. S., and Huffman, H. M., *The Free Energies of Some Organic Compounds*. Reinhold, New York, 1932.

Partington, J. R., and Shilling, W. G., *The Specific Heats of Gases*. Van Nostrand, New York, 1924.

Steiner, L. E., *Introduction to Chemical Thermodynamics*. McGraw-Hill, New York, 1941.

Taylor, H. S., and Glasstone, S. M., editors, *Treatise on Physical Chemistry*. 2nd and 3rd eds., Van Nostrand, New York, 1931 and 1942.

Washburn, E. W., *J. Research Natl. Bur. Standards*, **10**, 525 (1933).

Weber, R. L., *Temperature Measurement and Control*. Blakiston, Philadelphia, 1941.

Wenner, R. R., *Thermochemical Calculations*. McGraw-Hill, New York, 1941.

White, W. P., *The Modern Calorimeter*. Chem. Catalog Co., New York, 1928.

CHAPTER XI

MICROSCOPY

Edwin E. Jelley, *Eastman Kodak Company*

I.   INTRODUCTION

Largely through the efforts of Chamot and Mason and of Winchell in the United States, and of Hartshorne and Stuart in Great Britain, there has been a growing tendency during recent years for chemists to avail themselves of microscopic techniques, especially those which depend on the use of the polarizing microscope.   Petrographic-microscopic methods which were originally developed for the identification of minerals in thin sections have, in the course of time, been extended to the study of crushed minerals, crystals of inorganic compounds, and crystals of organic compounds. It is this last-mentioned field with which we are concerned, a field in which the optical crystallographer is, unfortunately, several hundred thousand compounds behind the synthetic organic chemist.

The objects of crystallographic microscopy are two; first, to record and classify optical data of pure organic compounds so that other workers will be able to identify them by their optical properties, various physical properties, and such analytical data as are obtainable from the size of sample available; and second, to be able to identify an unknown crystal as one of a limited number of "possibles" by a rapid technique. There is little hope that compilations of optical data of organic compounds will ever be so near completion that optical data *alone* will serve as a means of positive identification, since the number of known organic compounds is increasing at an ever-increasing rate, whereas chemists with sufficient optical experience to guarantee the reliability of their determinations of optical constants are not often able to devote their time to this task. However, the second object of crystallographic microscopy can often be of service in the organic laboratory by enabling the chemist to check the purity of a compound, to follow the course of a reaction, and to check on identifications made by other means. The study of thermal phenomena under the microscope will often explain apparently discordant results by revealing an unsuspected polymorphism, dynamic isomerism, or loss of solvent of crystallization. However, in crystallographic microscopy, as in so many other fields of physical science, there is no substitute for a sound knowledge of fundamentals and no short cut to experience.

The optical properties of crystals of organic compounds vary more, as a function of wave length, than those of the majority of minerals and inorganic crystals. This is particularly true of aromatic compounds in general, and is the reason why the author has devoted special attention to optical dispersion. The section on the microscopy of colored crystals is a new presentation of the optics of absorbing crystals in the light of present-day color chemistry.

As this chapter is being written, the electron microscope is opening up a new domain in microscopy. One of the outstanding characteristics of the electron microscope is its combination of very high resolving power with unusually great depth of field, thus, with 60-kilovolt electrons a resolving power of about $0.005\ \mu$ is attained with a depth of field of about $2\ \mu$ and a cone of illumination of $1°$. It is interesting to compare these values with those of the best apochromatic optical objective, with a focus of about two millimeters and an illuminating cone of $135°$ in oil; such an objective has a maximum resolving power of about $0.16\ \mu$ and a corresponding depth of

focus of 0.2 μ. The electron microscope has, therefore, about thirty times
the resolving power of the best possible with the optical microscope together
with ten times its depth of focus; the electron microscope gives an orthographic projection of a small crystal, whereas the optical microscope, with
its 135° cone of vision, sees at least five sides of a cube at once, the image
in consequence being difficult to interpret. This possibility of obtaining
orthographic projections, singly or in stereo pairs, of minute crystals is
very attractive to the chemical microscopist. What remains to be determined, however, is the effect of the high vacuum combined with a powerful electron beam on crystals of various types of organic and inorganic
compounds. That this aspect of electron microscopy needs careful study
is shown by the occasional publication of electron micrograms of crystals
having, apparently, curved edges.

II. POLARIZING MICROSCOPES

1. General Principles

A microscope is a compound magnifying instrument in which a lens
system known as the *objective* projects a real, inverted, and enlarged image
of an object; this image in turn is magnified by a second magnifying lens
system known as the *eyepiece*. The objective and eyepiece are supported
in optical alignment and at a constant distance from each other by the
body tube of the microscope. The object to be viewed under magnification
is supported on a stage which has an aperture through which light is ad-
mitted to it. Focusing of the image is accomplished by moving the body
tube up and down with respect to the object stage. The *coarse adjustment*
is usually a rack and pinion mechanism, a complete rotation of the coarse
adjustment head moving the body from 18 to 24 millimeters, depending on
the make of the microscope. The *fine adjustment* is an arrangement of
screws and levers, cams, inclined planes, or the like which imparts a very
slow movement to the body, usually one complete rotation of the fine adjustment head moving the body 0.1 millimeter. In order to gain resolving
power and freedom from diffraction effects it is necessary to illuminate the
object with a cone of light comparable with the collecting power of the
objective. This is accomplished by a third lens system known as the
substage condenser, which causes a beam of light reflected in the appropriate direction by the microscope mirror to converge on the object. The
substage condenser must be equipped with some means of regulating the
angle of the illuminating cone, since microscope objectives in general, and
high-power dry ones in particular, will only give a reasonable measure of
freedom from flare when the angle of the illuminating cone is restricted to a

certain optimum value. In the case of a biological microscope, the cone of illumination is controlled by means of an iris diaphragm below the condenser.

Microscope objectives are classified according to their degree of chromatic correction into three main types. *Achromatic* objectives, constructed of crown glass converging lenses and flint glass diverging ones, are able to bring light of two widely separated wave lengths to the same focus. Their lack of chromatic correction for intermediate and extreme wave lengths gives rise to the so-called *secondary spectrum.* Achromats are spherically corrected for one wave length only. *Fluorite* objectives, containing, as their name suggests, one or more fluorite lenses, give a less pronounced secondary spectrum and an over-all improvement in spherical aberration. *Apochromatic* objectives also employ fluorite lenses, but their construction is such that three wave lengths come to the same focus while they are spherically corrected for two wave lengths. For general microscopy there can be no doubt of the great superiority of apochromats, but few apochromats can be used for polarized-light work because of the anomalous birefringence of most naturally occurring fluorite.

Objectives can be corrected only for one image distance. If the distance of the image from the rear focal plane of an objective, of focus f millimeters, is l millimeter, $(l/f) - 1$ diameters is the *initial magnification* produced by the objective. This image is again magnified by the eyepiece to give a virtual image. By a generally accepted convention, the virtual image is considered to be formed 250 millimeters from the rear focal plane of the eyepiece, so that the *power* of an eyepiece is given by $250/f'$, where f' is its focal length. Thus, the magnification, M, of the microscope as a whole is given by the expression:

$$M = 250 \; l/ff' \tag{1}$$

In actual practice, objectives, with the exception of a few of the lowest powers, are made *parfocal*. This necessitates having a longer image distance with high powers than with low ones. It is therefore customary for manufacturers to specify the initial magnification of objectives for a given *mechanical tube length*, which is the over-all length of the body tube, measured from the upper end of the eyepiece adapter to the shoulder against which the objective seats. The working distance of an objective is the clear distance between the metallic rim holding the front lens of the objective and the upper surface of a cover glass 0.18 millimeter thick when the microscope is focused on an object beneath the cover.

The numerical aperture of a microscope objective (N.A.) is the sine of the angle α made by the most oblique rays entering the objective with the optical axis of the microscope, multiplied by the refractive index of the medium in which the objective is immersed:

$$\text{N.A.} = n \sin \alpha \qquad (2)$$

For dry objectives, the immersion medium is air, so that N.A. = sin α.

In order to convert a microscope to a polarizing microscope it is necessary to polarize the light entering the substage and to insert another polarizing prism, known as the *analyzer*, above the objective. The analyzer may be arranged to slide in the body tube above the objective, or be mounted in a cap which fits over the eyepiece. An ordinary type of substage condenser cannot be used with a polarizing prism, since the prism would need to be very large in order not to obscure part of the back lens of the condenser; consequently a substage condenser of a modified design is often employed. Other necessary features of a polarizing microscope are a graduated rotating stage and crosswebs in the eyepiece which are accurately aligned with the vibration directions of the polarizer and analyzer. The optical principles involved are discussed on pages 457–468.

2. Petrographic Microscopes

The most elaborate polarizing microscopes are those designed for petrographic research. The determination of the optical properties of crystals, such as those occurring in thin sections of minerals, necessitates very frequent changes from orthoscopic to conoscopic methods of observation. The orthoscopic observation of a crystal employs the ordinary optical system of the microscope with the addition of a polarizer and an analyzer; a low-power objective (4–10×) is used in conjunction with a low-power condenser which provides a narrow cone of illumination over a relatively large area. The conoscopic method of examination involves the study of the interference figure formed at the back focal plane of a high-power objective of large numerical aperture, and requires the use of a condenser of equal or greater aperture. The back focal plane of the objective is imaged in the eyepiece with the aid of an auxiliary lens, the Bertrand lens, which is inserted between the objective and the eyepiece. Petrographic microscopes are so constructed that the change from one method of observation to the other is easily carried out.

A typical example of a modern petrographic microscope is the Bausch & Lomb LC model shown in figure 1. It has a graduated stage which rotates on ball bearings and which is fitted to take a mechanical stage and other equipment. The analyzer prism slides in and out of the body tube between a parallelizing lens system of the type first described by Becher[1];

---

[1] S. Becher, *Ann. Physik*, **47**, 285 (1915).

this lens system insures freedom from astigmatism and permits the analyzer to be inserted and withdrawn without change of focus, of magnification, or of location of the image. The change from a low-power to a high-power condensing system is effected by turning a knurled head which swings the high-power condensing system into place. This mechanism is shown in

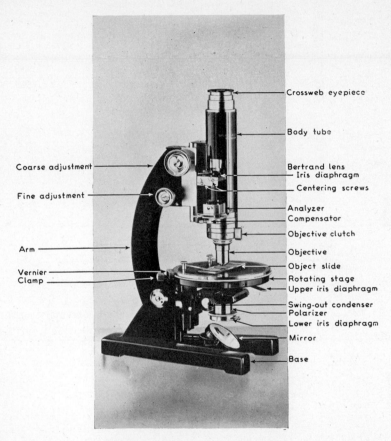

Crossweb eyepiece

Body tube

Coarse adjustment

Bertrand lens
Iris diaphragm

Centering screws

Fine adjustment

Analyzer
Compensator

Objective clutch

Arm

Objective

Object slide

Vernier
Clamp

Rotating stage
Upper iris diaphragm

Swing-out condenser
Polarizer
Lower iris diaphragm

Mirror

Base

Fig. 1.—Petrographic microscope.

figure 2. Each objective is carried in its own centering collar which is readily attached to a special nosepiece, so that any number of precentered objectives may be readily interchanged. Under normal working conditions the objectives remain centered indefinitely. The Bertrand lens slides into the body tube in a focusing sleeve. It is equipped with centering screws and an iris diaphragm for the optical isolation of the interference figures of small crystals. A slot, provided with a dust cover, is placed just beneath the analyzer for the accommodation of a quartz wedge, first-order-red selenite, quarter-wave mica, and other forms of compensator.

High-power
  condenser

Low-power
  condenser

Upper iris
  diaphragm

Shutter for
oblique illumination

Swing - out
  mechanism

Polarizer

Lower iris
  diaphragm

Fig. 2.—Swing-out condenser.

3. Chemical Microscopes

Chemical microscopes are polarizing microscopes of simple and robust design according to specifications originally laid down by Chamot and Mason.[2] They differ principally from the more elaborate petrographic instruments described above in that they are not equipped with a built-in Bertrand lens. The best models are equipped with a swing-out high-aperture condenser system, which, as already explained, greatly facilitates the study of interference figures. Most makers of chemical microscopes are able to supply either a cap analyzer or an analyzer which slides in the body tube. The latter is decidedly preferable for workers who wear glasses. In place of the Bertrand lens a pinhole diaphragm or an auxiliary lens above the eyepiece, known as a Becke lens, is used. The self-contained conoscopic apparatus of the type discussed on page 483 (Fig. 26) is worthy of special consideration since the microscopy of organic compounds depends a great deal on the study of interference figures given by small crystals.

Further improvements in optical properties of polarizing filters of the Polaroid type will no doubt lead to a simplification in the optical system of the chemical microscope for use in the organic chemical laboratory, since

[2] E. M. Chamot and C. W. Mason, *Handbook of Chemical Microscopy.* 2nd ed., Vol. I, Wiley, New York, 1938, p. 55.

the thinness of a Polaroid analyzer and its freedom from astigmatism render unnecessary a system of parallelizing lenses.

Chamot and Mason recommend the use of an accurately centered revolving nosepiece, or one with individually centerable openings, for three objectives. This is a sound practice, since most chemical microscopy, apart from more or less fundamental research on the optical properties of crystals, can be carried out with three objectives.

4. Accessories

The choice of accessories for chemical microscopy is naturally governed by the extent of the optical investigations to be undertaken. The minimum requirements for useful work in the organic laboratory are: a chemical microscope equipped with a swing-out high-power condenser and apparatus for the observation of conoscopic interference figures of small crystals; an accessory for determining optical sign, such as a quarter-wave mica plate, a first-order-red selenite plate, a quartz wedge or a Johannsen compensator; a triple nosepiece equipped with three parfocal and centered strain-free objectives and two or three eyepieces with cross hairs and focusing eye lenses. The optical characteristics of a selection of Bausch & Lomb strain-free achromatic objectives are given in table I by way of illustration. A similar range of objectives is made by other manufacturers of polarizing microscopes.

TABLE I

OBJECTIVES FOR POLARIZING MICROSCOPE

Initial magnification	Focus, mm.	N.A.	Working distance, mm.	Type
4×	32	0.10	38	Dry
6×	22.7	0.17	15.5	Dry
10×	16	0.25	7.0	Dry
21×	8	0.50	1.6	Dry
45×	4	0.85	0.3	Dry
or 36×	4	0.95	0.25	Dry
97×	1.8	1.25	0.14	Oil immersion

When only three objectives are to be employed in a nosepiece, the author's preference is for a 6×, 21×, and 45× (N.A. = 0.85). It is important to note that different manufacturers employ different tube-length corrections for their objectives. Low-power objectives up to 10× initial magnification are not at all critical with respect to tube-length correction, but objectives of over 30× initial magnification are very critical. It is not a sound policy to equip a laboratory with an odd collection of microscope accessories.

Focusing crossweb eyepieces are supplied with magnifications, calculated on a 250-millimeter image distance, of $5\times$, $7^1/_2$ or $8\times$, $10\times$, $12^1/_2\times$, and sometimes higher. When only two eyepieces are to be chosen, the author's preference is for a $5\times$ and $10\times$. A very useful addition is a $7.5\times$ eyepiece with a focusing eye lens to take a micrometer disk. This is used for estimating the optic axial angle in air $(2E)$ of biaxial crystals (see pages 507–510).

A mechanical stage is a very great convenience. It enables one to remove a slide from the microscope, apply some physical or chemical treatment to it, and return it to the same position on the microscope stage. This particular application is useful when studying the action of heat on extremely small particles. The slide is allowed to cool before being returned to the microscope. More obvious uses of a mechanical stage are to aid in the systematic exploration of a large number of minute crystals and to render easier the task of centering them on the cross hairs for conoscopic examination. A mechanical stage with a very fine adjustment over a limited travel is particularly advantageous for the study of very small crystals. An adjustment of this type is provided by the built-in mechanical stage of the Bausch & Lomb LD petrographic microscope designed by F. E. Wright.

For work on colored crystals, a dichroscope eyepiece of the Wollaston-prism type (page 513) is convenient, though not absolutely necessary. It is essential to have a good microscope lamp equipped with a water-cooling cell and a set of Wratten M filters. A source of monochromatic light, such as a sodium-vapor lamp for $\lambda = 589$, or a mercury-vapor lamp equipped with Wratten filters Nos. 77A and 58 for $\lambda = 546$ is very useful for the preliminary conoscopic examination of absorbing crystals and for studying optic normal, obtuse bisectrix, and uncentered interference figures.[3] A monochromator with a wave-length scale, such as the Bausch & Lomb Laboratory Wave-Length Spectrometer, with the eyepiece shutters in position and the eyepiece removed, or replaced by a single lens of about two-inch focus is invaluable for determination of dispersion of birefringence and the dispersion of extinction commonly met with in monoclinic and triclinic crystals of colored organic compounds (see pages 506 and 518).

Thermal studies under the microscope require a hot stage. Many present users of this very useful accessory must construct their own. Since only low-power orthoscopic observations are made with a hot stage, an inexpensive microscope may be used for this purpose. It is advantageous to keep the hot-stage microscope with its own objectives exclusively for thermal studies, since such work impairs the strain-free characteristics

[3] E. E. Jelley, *Ind. Eng. Chem., Anal. Ed.*, **13**, 196 (1941).

of objectives to be used for birefringence determinations. A particularly useful piece of equipment is a copper bar heated at one end so that a temperature gradient is maintained along it, in the manner employed for melting-point determinations by Dennis and Shelton.[4] This bar is used for recrystallizing substances from the melt at temperatures not far removed from the melting point.

III. MICROSCOPY OF THERMAL PROPERTIES

1. Melting Points. Hot Stages

The microscope may be used as an aid to the study of thermal phenomena. For this purpose it is necessary to equip it with a hot stage for the study of substances which are solid at room temperature, and a cold stage for the study of substances which are liquid above $-40°$ C. Most of the heating stages on the market have been designed for biological work and are only suitable for temperatures below $100°$ C., which renders them of very limited application in chemical work.

Hot stages suitable for determining melting points have been described by numerous investigators, in particular by Kofler and Kofler,[5] whose book also gives a list of references. Two simple and effective designs have been described by Chamot and Mason.[6] One of these is quite easily constructed. It consists of a block of aluminum $3 \times 4 \times \frac{1}{2}$ inch thick, having a $\frac{3}{4}$-inch hole through the center. The upper and lower surfaces are recessed to receive thin glass windows. A hole is drilled through one edge to permit the insertion of a thermometer or thermocouple. About two meters of No. 20 B & S Nichrome wire is wrapped around the aluminum plate in two layers insulated from each other and from the plate by asbestos paper. The outer layers of insulation are made sufficiently thick to avoid excessive conduction of heat to the microscope stage. The insulation is cut away to allow for the removal and replacement of the glass windows which are held in place by separate pieces of asbestos board having openings only just large enough to permit of illumination and observation of the specimen to be heated. Zscheile and White[7] have described a heating stage constructed of two copper blocks, the lower of which is electrically heated, in which provision is made for passing a stream of nitrogen through the heating cavity in order to avoid oxidation of the material being ex-

[4] L. M. Dennis and R. S. Shelton, *J. Am. Chem. Soc.*, **52**, 3128 (1930).

[5] L. Kofler and A. Kofler, *Mikroskopische Methoden in der Mikrochemie.* Haim, Vienna, 1936. L. Kofler and H. Hilbck, *Mikrochemie*, **9**, 38 (1931); **15**, 242 (1934).

[6] E. M. Chamot and C. W. Mason, *Handbook of Chemical Microscopy.* 2nd ed., Vol. I, Wiley, New York, 1938, pp. 201, 203.

[7] F. P. Zscheile and J. W. White, *Ind. Eng. Chem., Anal. Ed.*, **12**, 436 (1940).

amined. The temperature of the heating chamber is determined thermo-electrically by means of an iron–constantan couple and a Leeds & Northrup precision potentiometer. A heating rate of 0.3° C. per minute is recommended.

Cold stages consist of a suitably insulated chamber which can be cooled by means of a liquid circulating at low temperature. A thoroughly practical design has been described by Chamot and Mason.[8] A cooling system capable of reaching very low temperatures with this stage has been described by Mason and Rochow.[9] The cold stage is useful in the determination of melting points and polymorphism of many organic compounds which are liquid at ordinary temperature. At temperatures below the dew point of the atmosphere, the condensation of moisture or ice on the windows may be a source of trouble, which, however, may be overcome by allowing a slow stream of dry air or nitrogen to impinge on both upper and lower windows. In low-temperature work, it is particularly necessary to guard against heating the specimen by the absorption of energy from the illuminating beam: a heat absorbing filter, or a deep water cell containing a very dilute solution of cupric sulfate will considerably reduce this heating effect.

Both hot and cold stages are best used on a microscope with a detachable rotating stage, or on a simple biological microscope equipped with "Polaroid" polarizer and analyzer. Hot stages in particular should be used with caution on the rotating stage of a polarizing microscope. In any case, the hot stage should be removed from the microscope as soon as the observations have been completed.

Use of Polarized Light.—A particular advantage of determining melting points under the microscope is that the phenomena of fusion are directly observable. With the majority of organic crystals the transition from solid to liquid state is very sharply defined and is unmistakable. Except in those very rare cases in which the crystal is isotropic, the use of a polarizer and analyzer on the microscope is of particular service, as the disappearance of birefringence is usually a definite indication of fusion. However, there are three conditions under which a crystal may lose its birefringence at a temperature below the melting point:

(*1*) It may have an isotropic polymorph, as in the case of carbon tetrabromide which becomes isotropic at 46.9 and melts at 92.5°.

(*2*) It may change into an opaque mass of disoriented crystals of a polymorph as in the case of *s*-di(*m*-nitrophenyl) urea, which crystallizes from 95% alcohol in three polymorphs, according to temperature. One

---

[8] E. M. Chamot and C. W. Mason, *Handbook of Chemical Microscopy*. 2nd ed., Vol. I, Wiley, New York, 1938, p. 205.

[9] C. W. Mason and T. G. Rochow, *Ind. Eng. Chem., Anal. Ed.*, **6**, 367 (1934).

becomes opaque at 60°, and another at about 180°; all three melt at 242°.

(*3*) It may lose solvent of crystallization and become opaque.

It is desirable, therefore, to supplement observation under crossed nicols by observations with the analyzer removed, or else rotated to the parallel position.

As with melting-point determinations by nonmicroscopic methods, the crystals must be thoroughly dry, or erroneous results may be obtained. The melting point as determined under the microscope is usually lower than that obtained in the usual way, probably because of the ease with which onset of fusion is observed. However, Kofler and Kofler[5] point out the possibility that water of crystallization may be readily lost when a minute quantity of a compound is heated between a microscope slide and cover glass, so that the higher melting point of the anhydrous substance is measured, whereas the lower value of the hydrate is obtained when the substance is heated in a capillary tube.

2. Polymorphism

Substances which exhibit more than one crystalline form are said to be polymorphous, and are often referred to as di, tri, etc., -morphous when they possess two, three, or more forms. Polymorphous crystals of the same substance differ one from the other in their physical properties, but nevertheless yield identical liquids and vapors. In general, polymorphous modifications are readily distinguishable from isomers, since the latter usually yield different liquids and vapors when heated. However, there are many known cases of isomeric compounds which are tautomeric, that is, they are more or less easily interconvertible. The conversion of tautomers may take place spontaneously, or it may need the presence of a catalyst. This phenomenon is also known as *dynamic isomerism*.

Polymorphs may be divided into two classes: those which are enantiotropic, and those which are monotropic. *Enantiotropic* polymorphs interchange reversibly on changing the temperature, each form having its own stability range of temperature. *Monotropic* polymorphs, on the other hand, do not interchange reversibly on changing the temperature: one form is unstable, and the other stable, at all temperatures. Although microscopic examination is usually carried out at atmospheric pressure, a study of typical pressure–temperature diagrams is a help to a clear understanding of the phenomena. In figure 3, curves for the polymorphs, *I* and *II*, and the liquid, *L*, of an enantiotropic system are given. In this diagram, the conditions under which form *I* is stable are represented by the area to the left of boundary *I tt'*; form *II* is stable under the conditions denoted by area $t'tf_2f_2'$. On gradually heating crystal form *I* at atmospheric pressure, it remains unchanged, except for slight loss by vaporization, until temperature t is reached, when it changes over to crystal form II. On further heating, form II melts at temperature f_2. In the complete absence of supercooling, the liquid solidifies at f_2 to form II, and form II changes to form I at t. However, many organic substances supercool considerably: in the case under consideration the vapor-pressure curve of the supercooled liquid would continue in the direction $f_2 \rightarrow f_1 \rightarrow x$. In the complete absence of form II, form I may persist above the transition temperature until its melting point, f_1, is reached; similarly, form II may supercool below the transition temperature.

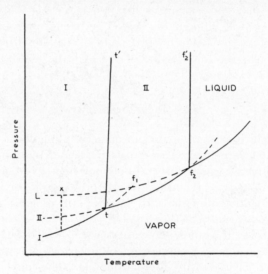

Fig. 3.—Pressure–temperature diagram of an
enantiotropic substance.

Monotropic polymorphs are characterized by the fact that one form is stable at all temperatures below its melting point and never exhibits transformation into the second form, while the second form has a lower melting point and is metastable at all temperatures below that. The pressure–temperature diagram of a monotropic substance is given in figure 4, in which the stable form, II, has melting point f_2, and the metastable form, I, has melting point f_1. Curves $II\ f_2$ and $I\ f_1$, if extrapolated, meet at a point, t, representing the hypothetical transition point which cannot be attained experimentally because it lies above both melting points.

Ostwald[10] has formulated a general rule, the *law of successive reactions*, which, in connection with crystallization from supercooled liquids and from

[10] W. Ostwald, *Z. physik. Chem.*, **22**, 306 (1897).

supersaturated solutions, implies that the form which crystallizes out is not the most stable one, but the one which can be reached with the minimum loss of free energy. In a dimorphous system, this, of necessity, is the meta-stable form. If in the pressure–temperature curve of an enantiotropic dimorphous substance given in figure 3 the liquid had supercooled to point x, the nearest state would be II, which is in its metastable region at x. Contact with stable form I would cause the transformation of II into I. Similarly, in the case of the monotropic dimorphous system shown in figure 4, liquid supercooled to y would crystallize to the metastable form. On heating, this form would melt at f_1. A good example of this phe-

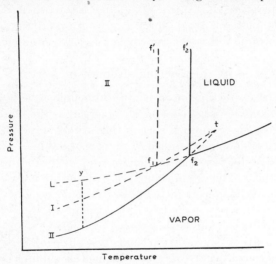

Fig. 4.—Pressure–temperature diagram of a monotropic substance.

nomenon is supplied by benzophenone, as first reported by Zincke.[11] If the stable orthorhombic modification, which melts at 48.5°, is heated to about 60°, and then cooled, it does not crystallize in the stable modification, but remains liquid. Occasionally, a monoclinic modification will crystallize from the supercooled liquid: this metastable modification has a melting point of 26.5°. Inoculation of the supercooled liquid with the metastable solid causes immediate crystallization to this modification.

The displacement of transition and melting points with increase of pressure is so small that it need not be considered in connection with microscopic work. When a substance possesses more than two poly-morphous forms, these may be all enantiotropic or all monotropic, or some may be enantiotropic and the rest monotropic. With many organic com-

---

[11] T. Zincke, *Ann.*, **159**, 381 (1871).

pounds the transformations of the different modifications take place readily unless the cooling has been too rapid and severe supercooling has taken place. Supercooling may be avoided by having the cooling liquid in contact with crystals of stable and metastable modifications. Thus, Dippy and Harts- horne[12] recommend a preliminary crystallization from a melt of a sub- stance under a microscope cover glass. The central portion of the cover is then heated to remelt the crystals, either by means of a small gas flame, or by contact with the heated end of a small metal rod. In preliminary ob- servations, the establishment of a temperature gradient across a small area of the slide enables different enantiotropic forms to exist together in the right temperature zone of the crystalline layer, whereas under similar conditions a stable monotropic form always grows at the expense of the unstable monotropic form over the whole temperature range.

3. Dynamic Isomerism

Care must be exercised not to confuse dynamic isomerism with poly- morphism. Dynamic isomerism, or tautomerism, is the more or less ready change of one isomer to another, such as that of the α- and β-benzaldoximes and α- and β-acetaldoximes studied by Bancroft and his associates.[13] The two isomers have different melting points, and each can lower the melting point of the other. The establishment of equilibrium may be fairly rapid, or may be relatively slow as in the case of anisaldoxime studied by Skau and Saxton.[14] A microscopic study of the isomerism of acetaldehyde 2,4- dinitrophenylhydrazone has been reported by Bryant.[15] An isomer melting at 168–170° C. was obtained by repeated crystallization from 95% ethanol; the other isomer, melting at 157°, was obtained by sublimation. When the second modification came in contact with the first, liquefaction occurred through the lowering of the melting point. Crystallization from the melt gave an equilibrium mixture melting near 148°. The thermal behavior of a dynamic isomer is that of two different substances mutually inter- convertible. The rate of interconversion may be greatly modified by traces of catalysts, such as acids. This often accounts for an apparently erratic behavior.

4. Glass Formation

When a melt is cooled quickly it may supercool to form a vitreous mass or "glass," which may remain in this state for hours, days, or even years.

---

[12] J. F. J. Dippy and N. H. Hartshorne, *J. Chem. Soc.*, **1930**, 725. N. H. Harts- horne and A. Stuart, *ibid.*, **1931**, 2583.

[13] W. D. Bancroft, *J. Phys. Chem.*, **2**, 143, 245 (1898); **3**, 144 (1899).

[14] E. L. Skau and B. Saxton, *J. Phys. Chem.*, **37**, 197 (1933).

[15] W. M. D. Bryant, *J. Am. Chem. Soc.*, **60**, 2814 (1938).

The physical properties of such a glass are those of a liquid of extremely high viscosity. It is optically isotropic unless subjected to mechanical strain. A glass does not possess a true melting point: heating often induces crystallization, or, if crystallization does not take place, the glass softens and finally regains the fluidity of the normal liquid. The phenomenon of crystallization on heating is very well shown by aceto-β-naphthalide, a substance which melts at 132–134° C. and solidifies to a clear glass when cooled suddenly. On warming a microscope slide preparation of the vitreous substance, crystals radiate from a number of centers, a growth which, however, is instantly checked by recooling the slide.

5. Mesomorphism

Usually, crystals have well-defined melting points at which the crystal changes into a clear liquid. However, many substances are now known which pass through an intermediate state on heating the crystals: at a definite temperature they melt to a liquid—often turbid—showing many optical properties usually associated with crystals, and at a higher temperature suddenly change to a normal, clear liquid. A number of different names have been proposed for this intermediate state, such as "liquid crystal,"[16] "anisotropic liquid,"[17] "paracrystal,"[18] and "mesoform."[19] However, the term "mesomorph" is used here in the interests of uniform terminology. Under this system of nomenclature, *thermotropic mesomorphism* refers to the production of states intermediate between crystal and liquid by means of heat, contrasted with *lyotropic mesomorphism*, as defined by Lawrence,[20] in which the intermediate phase is produced by the forces of solvation.

Thermotropic mesomorphs exist in two well-defined states, the smectic and the nematic. The smectic state may be considered as being solid in two dimensions and liquid in one, and the nematic state as solid in one dimension and liquid in two. At first glance it might be assumed that the maximum number of mesomorphous states possible with a single substance would be two. Vorländer[21] has pointed out that polymorphism is possible with mesomorphs; thus, *p*-(*p*-phenetolazoxy)-benzoic acid phenyl ester forms three mesomorphs, and N,N'-terephthaloyl-*bis*-*p*-aminocinnamic acid

---

[16] O. Lehmann, *Flüssige Kristalle und ihr scheinbares Leben*, Voss, Leipzig (1921), gives full references to Lehmann's work in this field.

[17] V. Fréedericksz and V. Zolina, *Trans. Faraday Soc.*, **29**, 919 (1933).

[18] F. Rinne, *Trans. Faraday Soc.*, **29**, 1008 (1933).

[19] A. S. C. Lawrence, *J. Roy. Microscop. Soc.*, **58**, 30 (1938).

[20] A. S. C. Lawrence, *Trans. Faraday Soc.*, **29**, 1016 (1933).

[21] D. Vorländer, *Trans. Faraday Soc.*, **29**, 913 (1933).

ethyl ester forms no less than four different mesomorphs. Recent systematic studies by Weygand and Gabler[22] on the effect of molecular structure on mesomorph formation have revealed many such cases, an example being p-nonoxybenzalphenetidine, which forms one nematic and two smectic forms having transition points of 115°, 84°, and 79° C.

A third type of mesomorph, which is related to the smectic type, is known as the *cholesteric* type. Many cholesterol derivatives, such as the acetate, benzoate, and bromide, exhibit an extraordinary optical phenomenon in the mesomorphous state: when the crystalline substance is heated it melts to an isotropic liquid. On cooling this melt, a mesomorph is formed which shows brilliant colors by reflected light. Touching the cover glass during this stage of the cooling aids in the development of the colors. This reflected light is circularly polarized. In this state, the substance shows enormous optical rotatory power—sometimes a million times that of quartz of similar thickness! A few other substances have been reported to show this strange optical phenomenon, *e. g.*, amyl p-(cyanobenzalamino)-cinnamate.

It should be noted that the mesomorphous state may be either enantiotropic as in the cases of p-azoxyanisole and p-azoxyphenetole, or monotropic as in the cases of cholesteryl esters and anisal-p-aminoacetophenone. Furthermore, a mesomorph does not necessarily behave as a liquid. Supercooling may so increase its viscosity that it becomes, in effect, an anisotropic "glass" made up of a patchwork of oriented molecules. A good example is 1-benzeneazo-4-anisalaminonaphthalene, first studied by Vorländer, Kreiss, and Kuhrmann.[23]

The observation of mesomorphs is readily carried out with a hot stage if care is taken to avoid too rapid heating or cooling. Special microscopes for the study of "liquid crystals" have been constructed by some European manufacturers according to specifications by Lehmann. Usually, the microscope stage is fitted with a small gas jet which is used to heat the microscope slide bearing the substance under examination. A very simple heating device was used by Bernal and Crowfoot.[24] It consisted of a movable stage, across the central aperture of which was stretched a Nichrome wire which could be heated by the current from a battery or transformer. The specimens were prepared by fusion, using a microscope cover glass for a support and a wedge-shaped splinter of cover glass, 10 millimeters long and 1 millimeter wide at its wider end, as a cover. When the heated wire was

---

[22] C. Weygand and R. Gabler, *Naturwissenschaften*, **27,** 28 (1939).

[23] D. Vorländer, G. Kreiss, and C. Kuhrmann, *Z. angew. Chem.*, **43,** 13 (1930). See also D. Vorländer, *Chemische Kristallographie der Flüssigkeiten*, Akadem. Verlagsgesellschaft, Leipzig, 1924.

[24] J. D. Bernal and D. Crowfoot, *Trans. Faraday Soc.*, **29,** 1032 (1933).

placed across the wedge, a sharp temperature gradient—up to 100° C. or more—was obtained in the width of the microscope field in which all the phases of the substance could be simultaneously viewed in equilibrium. Bernal and Crowfoot also used strips of mica as covers; the mica has a marked orienting effect on nematic mesomorphs. Observations of uncovered surfaces can conveniently be made with this apparatus. Although this arrangement is no more suited to the exact determination of transition points than is the Lehmann microscope, it does enable the phenomena associated with the smectic and nematic states to be observed much more easily than is possible with a hot stage of the type used for melting-point determinations.

The differentiation between nematic and smectic mesomorphs is not too difficult after some experience has been gained by working with known substances. The following is a guide to the principal differences between the two states when observed under a microscope, within the temperature range of stability: the nematic mesomorphs are much more fluid than smectic mesomorphs, and are markedly oriented by solid surfaces, in contrast to the behavior of smectic mesomorphs which are not so oriented. When the nematic mesomorph is formed by cooling the true (isotropic) liquid, it first appears in anisotropic droplets of circular contour, while angular bodies (*bâtonnets*) are characteristic of the smectic state under similar conditions. The nematic state in bulk is often isotropic when quiescent; but movement causes alignment of the thread-like aggregates, with the production of strong anisotropy, and, in the case of colored substances, dichroism. Uncovered layers of smectic mesomorphs show a terraced structure; thus, thallous soaps exhibit the layer structure known as "Grandjean's terraces," and many other smectic substances exhibit a curious terraced structure of droplets known as *gouttes à gradins*. Smectic mesomorphs in thin layers between a microscope slide and cover glass often exhibit a characteristic focal conic structure. This behavior is very clearly shown by ethyl *p*-azoxybenzoate beween 114° and 120° C.

During the last few years, much valuable work has been done by Weygand and his collaborators, Gabler, Bircan, Lanzendorf, and Hoffmann, on new compounds exhibiting thermal mesomorphism, and on the influence of various substituents and groups.[25] Undoubtedly, a more detailed optical study of these new compounds will add to our understanding of mesomorphism.

---

[25] C. Weygand and R. Gabler, *J. prakt. Chem.*, **151**, 215 (1938); *Naturwissenschaften*, **27**, 28 (1939); *Z. physik. Chem.*, **B47**, 148 (1941); *J. prakt. Chem.*, **155**, 332 (1940). C. Weygand, R. Gabler, and N. Bircan, *ibid.*, **158**, 266 (1941). C. Weygand and W. Lanzendorf, *ibid.*, **155**, 221 (1938). C. Weygand and J. Hoffman, *Z. physik. Chem.*, **B50**, 124 (1941).

6. Loss of Solvent of Crystallization

The above discussion of the thermal properties of organic compounds has been limited to substances which do not lose solvent of crystallization on heating. The behavior on heating of a crystal containing solvent of crystallization depends on the boiling point of the solvent and the various forces binding it in the crystal lattice. Among the many possibilities are: (a) the crystal gives up its solvent, which is lost by evaporation; (b) the solvent is liberated, and then dissolves part of the unsolvated crystal; (c) the crystal melts to form a solution of the substance in the solvent; and (d) a part of the solvent is liberated with the formation of a new crystal phase containing a smaller molecular proportion of solvent of crystallization.

The presence of a low-boiling solvent of crystallization may often be detected by heating some of the substance in a capillary tube, the upper part of which is kept cold. Condensed droplets may be tested by their solvent action on different highly colored materials. For example, crystals of potassium permanganate yield an intense purple solution with droplets of water, a weak purple with methanol, a faint purple with ethanol, and no color at all with benzene. Many simple unsulfonated azo dyes are insoluble in water, but are very soluble in alcohols, and may also be used as indicators. Another useful way of detecting solvent of crystallization is by heating the crystals under a heavy aliphatic hydrocarbon, such as Petrolatum liquid u.s.p. XI. As the solvent is driven off, it forms bubbles in the immersion liquid. If a substance crystallizes in the same form from a number of different solvents, it is almost a certainty that no solvent of crystallization is present.

IV. OPTICS OF TRANSPARENT CRYSTALS

1. Geometry and Optics

A. CRYSTAL SYSTEMS

Although a knowledge of geometric crystallography is a necessary foundation for the study of crystal optics, an adequate presentation of the subject would require far more space than is available here. The reader is therefore referred to standard works on crystallography and mineralogy, and to Chapter XII, "Determination of Crystal Form," by M. A. Peacock, and Chapter XIII, "Crystallochemical Analysis," by J. D. H. Donnay.

For the purposes of optical study it is convenient to consider crystals as belonging to one of the following seven systems:

Triclinic, having three unequal axes inclined at unequal angles other than 90° to each other. These axes are designated a, b, and c, c being the vertical axis; b is the side-to-side axis which is longer than the front-to-back axis a. The angle between b and c is designated α, that between a and c is β, and that between a and b is γ. The elements of the triclinic system may therefore be expressed as $a \neq b \neq c$, $\alpha \neq \beta \neq \gamma \neq 90°$.

Monoclinic, having three unequal axes; a and c are inclined to each other; b is at right angles to a and c ($a \neq b \neq c$, $\beta \neq 90°$, $\alpha = \gamma = 90°$).

TABLE II

THE THIRTY-TWO CLASSES OF CRYSTALS, ARRANGED IN ORDER OF SCHOENFLIES SPACE-GROUPS

Schoenflies		Class No.	System, class, and symmetry
			Triclinic
1	C1	1	Asymmetric: no elements of symmetry
2	S2	2	Pinacoidal: 1A2/cP[a]
			Monoclinic
3–6	CS	3	Domal: 1P
7–9	C2	4	Sphenoidal: 1A2 (polar)
10–15	C2h	5	Prismatic: 1A2/P
			Orthorhombic
16–37	C2v	7	Pyramidal: 1A2, 2P
38–46	V, D2	6	Bisphenoidal: 3A2
47–74	Vh, D2h	8	Bipyramidal: 3A2, 3P
			Tetragonal
75–76	S4	10	Bisphenoidal: 1A4/cP
77–88	Vd, D2d	14	Scalenohedral: 1A4/cP, 2A2, 2P
89–94	C4	9	Pyramidal: 1A4
95–100	C4h	12	Bipyramidal: 1A4/P
101–112	C4v	13	Ditetragonal pyramidal: 1A4, 4P
113–122	D4	11	Trapezohedral: 1A4/4A2
123–142	D4h	15	Ditetragonal bipyramidal: 1A4/P, 4A2, 5P
			Trigonal
143–146	C3	16	Pyramidal: 1A3
147–148	C3i	17	Rhombohedral: 1A3, cA6
149–154	C3v	20	Ditrigonal pyramidal: 1A3, 3P
155–161	D3	18	Trapezohedral: 1A3/3A2
162–167	D3d	21	Ditrigonal scalenohedral: 1A3/3A2, 3P
168	C3h	19	Bipyramidal: 1A3/P
169–172	D3h	22	Ditrigonal bipyramidal: 1A3/P, 3A2, 4P
			Hexagonal
173–178	C6	23	Pyramidal: 1A6
179–180	C6h	25	Bipyramidal: 1A6/P
181–184	C6v	26	Dihexagonal pyramidal: 1A6, 6P
185–190	D6	24	Trapezohedral: 1A6/6A2
191–194	D6h	27	Dihexagonal bipyramidal: 1A6/P, 6A2, 7P
			Cubic
195–199	T	28	Tetrahedral pentagonal dodecahedral: 4A3, 3A2
200–206	Th	30	Dyakisdodecahedral: 4A3, 3A2, 3P
207–212	Td	31	Hextetrahedral: 4A3, 3A2, 6P
213–220	O	29	Pentagonal icositetrahedral: 4A3, 3A4, 6A2
221–230	Oh	32	Hexoctahedral: 4A3, 3A4, 6A2, 9P

[a] A2, A3, A4, and A6 indicate axes of digonal, trigonal, tetragonal, and hexagonal symmetry, respectively. 3A2 should be read as "three digonal axes." P indicates a plane of symmetry; the slanted line means "at right angles to"; c before A or P indicates a compound axis or plane, respectively. It should be noted that 1A2/cP is the same thing as a center of symmetry.

Orthorhombic, having three unequal axes mutually at right angles ($a \neq b \neq c$, $\alpha = \beta = \gamma = 90°$).

Tetragonal, having two equal axes with a third longer or shorter. The three axes are mutually at right angles ($a_1 = a_2 \neq c$, $\alpha = \beta = \gamma = 90°$).

Trigonal (or rhombohedral), having three equal axes equally inclined at other than a right angle ($a_1 = a_2 = a_3$, $\alpha = \beta = \gamma \neq 90°$). This system may also be referred to the axes of the hexagonal system.

Hexagonal, having three equal axes mutually at 120° in one plane, with a longer or shorter axis perpendicular to this plane. The equal axes are designated a_1, a_2, and a_3, and the perpendicular axis c.

Cubic, having three equal axes mutually at right angles.

These seven systems of crystals are subdivided on the basis of their symmetry into 32 classes. These are given in order of Schoenflies space-groups in table II. The class number is that given by Tutton, by Hartshorne and Stuart, and by Gibb. (See General References.)

In table II the numbers of the space-groups in Schoenflies classical system have been given in order to simplify correlation with x-ray crystal structure determinations, with the aid of the "Synoptical Table of the Nomenclatures of Schoenflies, Wyckoff, and of Mauguin," given by Bragg.[26]

Miller Indices.—The relative lengths of the axes of a crystal are usually expressed in terms of b, which is taken as unity. Thus, $a:b:c = a/b:1:c/b$. The intercepts of any face on the a, b, and c axes are expressed in terms of these parameters. Suppose that the linear intercepts on these three axes are p, q, and r for a particular face, then the intercepts in terms of the parameters are pb/a, q, rb/c. The Miller indices of this particular face are a/pb, $1/q$, and c/rb, multiplied by a factor which brings them to their simplest whole-number relationship. In general, the Miller indices are written in the form (hkl); when two of the indices are zero, the other is, of course, unity; this is the case of a face which cuts one axis only. The *law of rational intercepts* states that the intercepts on the axes made by any face can always be expressed as rational multiples of the parameters. In goniometry, the parametric ratios are chosen so as to give the simplest Miller notation for the chief forms on the crystal.

Forms.—All crystal faces which are similarly oriented with respect to the axes of a crystal are referred to as a form. Forms consisting of two parallel faces are known as *pinacoids*. Forms consisting of 3, 4, 6, 8, or 12 faces parallel to the c-axis are known as *prisms*. Forms parallel to a horizontal axis and intercepting the other two axes are known as *domes*. Forms intercepting three axes are known as *pyramids*. The number of faces possible in a form depends on the symmetry of the crystal; for example, in the triclinic system the highest possible number is two and in the cubic system it is 48. However, some of the classes of a system may exhibit a half, or even a quarter, of the maximum number of faces in a

---

[26] W. L. Bragg, *The Crystalline State*. Vol. I, Macmillan, New York, 1934, pp. 342–346.

form of the highest symmetry of the crystal system. These are said to be *hemihedral* and *tetartohedral*, respectively, as compared with the highest symmetry class which is said to be *holohedral*. In certain classes, crystals may be differently terminated at opposite ends of a crystallographic axis, and are said to be *hemimorphic*. In classes which have either no symmetry, or only axes of symmetry (classes 1, 4, 6, 9, 11, 16, 18, 23, 24, 28, and 29), *enantiomorphous* forms may occur and the crystals may exhibit dextro and levo types.

Habit and Twinning.—It is to be emphasized that the geometry of crystal form is concerned with interfacial angles. Unequal growth of certain faces may make two crystals of the same substance look dissimilar, but the angles between corresponding pairs of faces are constant. Factors which change the external shape are:

(*1*) Variations in the development of different forms may completely change the shape of crystals of a given compound. A striking example, familiar to students of mineralogy, is that of calcite which occurs naturally in acute and obtuse rhombs, hexagonal prisms, and many types of scalenohedra. All these varieties are built from the same unit cell of calcite; all readily cleave to form the $(10\bar{1}1)$ rhomb; all, when unstrained, have the same optical properties. Variations in the forms exhibited by crystals of a given compound may often be due to variations in the solvent from which they were crystallized, or even to the presence of an impurity in the mother liquor. Two well-known examples are those of sodium chloride, which normally exhibits only cubic (100) faces but develops octahedral (111) faces when grown from solutions containing urea, and potash alum, which normally exhibits (111) faces but develops (100) faces when grown from solutions to which some sodium hydroxide has been added.

(*2*) Different faces of the same form may develop unequally. This gives rise to distorted crystals which, in extreme cases, become lamellar or acicular even though they may belong to the cubic system. An example is provided by the tabular crystals of octahedral silver bromide.

(*3*) Under certain conditions it is not easy to recognize multiple twinning. The twinned crystals may simulate higher symmetry than that of the untwinned crystals. Two main types of multiple twinning may occur: multiple twinning on a pinacoid is known as polysynthetic twinning; multiple twinning on a prism produces cyclic twins.

The general shape of a crystal, as governed by the relative development of certain forms, or of particular faces of one form, is referred to as the *crystal habit*.

B. POLARIZED LIGHT

In studying the optical properties of crystals we are concerned with the wave nature of light. Light consists of transverse electromagnetic waves; by virtue of the transverse nature of these waves they possess a vector property known as polarization. As ordinarily emitted by the sun or a lamp, light consists of a mixture of waves having every possible vibration plane: it is, however, possible to polarize light so that every ray has the same vibration direction. In former times, the *plane of polarization* was defined as the plane of incidence in which the polarized light was most copiously reflected. This plane is at right angles to the direction of the electrical vibrations, which are now recognized as being responsible for the chemical and photographic effects of light; consequently, the vibration plane of polarized light is defined as the direction of the electric vector. Wood[27] uses the term "plane of polarization" as synonymous with the vibration plane, a very desirable procedure which is not yet followed in all works on mineralogy and petrography.

C. OPTICALLY ISOTROPIC CRYSTALS

Crystals of the cubic system in general are optically isotropic, that is to say, they have a single refractive index regardless of the direction of light through them, and of its plane of polarization. They share this property with true liquids and unstrained glasses. A very few cubic crystals are known which possess optical rotatory power—the best known example is sodium chlorate which rotates the plane of polarization of sodium light 3° 1′ per millimeter of thickness, some crystals being levo-, and some dextrorotatory. Apart from these rare exceptions, it may be stated that a flat plate of an isotropic substance does not affect the plane of polarization of light passing perpendicularly through it, so that a flat plate of an isotropic substance does not brighten the microscope field with crossed nicols in any position of rotation of the stage. This is true no matter what the orientation of the plate is with respect to the crystal axes. However, steeply inclined interfaces can rotate the vibration plane to an extent dependent on the vibration azimuth of the incident light, so that such interfaces may appear gray or white between crossed nicols.

D. OPTICALLY ANISOTROPIC CRYSTALS

Crystals of the remaining six classes of crystal symmetry possess the property of double refraction, whereby light passing through such crystals is, in general, resolved into two beams, polarized at right angles, which travel through the crystal at different velocities. The velocity of light in any medium is inversely proportional to the refractive index of that medium. If n is the refractive index of that medium, V the velocity of light in it, and V_a the velocity of light in air, then:

$$n = V_a/V \tag{3}$$

Consequently, it may be stated that, in general, an optically anisotropic crystal has two refractive indices for each and every ray direction other than along an optic axis.

Optically anisotropic crystals form two principal groups, known as *uniaxial* and *biaxial*, respectively. There are various ways of representing the optical properties of these two classes of crystals. The best known geometric construction is Fletcher's[28] *optical indicatrix*, in which the ray and wave-normal surfaces are derived from an ellipsoid of revolution for uniaxial crystals and a triaxial ellipsoid

---

[27] R. W. Wood, *Physical Optics*. 3rd ed., Macmillan, New York, 1934, p. 329.
[28] L. Fletcher, *The Optical Indicatrix*. Frowde, London, 1892.

for biaxial crystals. The ray–velocity surface is a three-dimensional representation of the two velocities corresponding to each ray direction; the wave-normal–velocity surface represents the pair of velocities for each wave-normal. The logical construction for the purposes of the crystallographer and chemical microscopist, however, is the surface derived by plotting the pair of refractive indices for each direction of the wave-normal, since the direction of light traveling through a crystal is that of the wave-normal. The ray direction is a purely mathematical concept so far as ellipsoidal wave fronts are concerned; the relation between a corresponding ray and wave-normal direction is shown diagrammatically in figure 5. We shall now consider the wave-normal–refractive index diagrams for the two groups of optically anisotropic crystals.

Uniaxial Crystals.—With crystals of the tetragonal, trigonal, and hexagonal systems, one of the sheets of the wave-normal–refractive index surface is a sphere, as in an optically isotropic medium; the other is an ellipsoid of rotation which touches the sphere at the poles of its axis. Its equatorial diameter may be greater or less than that of the sphere, in which cases the crystals are said to be positively or negatively uniaxial, respectively (Fig. 6). The wave with the spherical front is known as the *ordinary ray*, since it obeys the ordinary (Snell's) law of refraction; consequently, in our wave-normal–refractive index diagram the radius of the sphere is known as the ordinary refractive index and is usually represented by the symbol n_ω or its abbreviation, ω. The wave with the ellipsoidal front is known as the *extraordinary ray*, since it does not in general obey Snell's law because of the difference between the ray and wave-normal directions. The refractive index for the extraordinary ray varies from n_ω along the

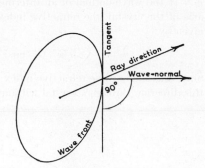

Fig. 5.—Corresponding ray and wave-normal directions.

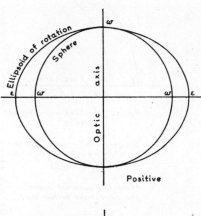

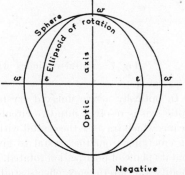

Fig. 6.—Refractive-index–wave-normal surface of positive and negative uniaxial crystals.

optic axis to its maximum or minimum value of n_ϵ, or ϵ, at the equator of the ellipsoid. The intermediate values of the refractive index are sometimes designated n_e. If the wave-normal of an intermediate ray makes an angle θ with the optic axis of the crystal, the refractive index of the crystal for the extraordinary ray is given by:

$$n_e = \sqrt{[\epsilon^2\omega^2/(\epsilon^2 \cos^2 \theta + \omega^2 \sin^2 \theta)]} \tag{4}$$

Since there is but one refractive index along the optic axis, light is transmitted in this direction through a crystal without modification.

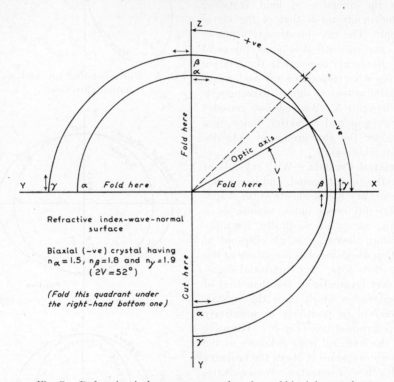

Fig. 7.—Refractive-index–wave-normal surface of biaxial crystals.

In optically active uniaxial crystals, plane-polarized light traveling along the optic axis is resolved into two circularly polarized (right-handed and left-handed) beams which traverse the crystal with slightly different velocities. They recombine on emerging from the crystal to give plane-polarized light which, however, has had its plane of polarization rotated. The phenomenon of optical rotation does not modify the interference effects studied with the polarizing microscope, and will not, therefore, be considered further in this chapter. Optical rotatory power is dealt with in Volume II, Chapter XIX, "Polarimetry," by W. Heller.

A very important and easily memorized rule is that the extraordinary ray vibrates

in the plane of the optic axis, which in turn coincides with the c crystallographic
axis of trigonal, tetragonal, or hexagonal symmetry.

Biaxial Crystals.—The refractive index–wave-normal surface of a biaxial
crystal is more complicated than that of a uniaxial crystal. It is shown diagrammatically in figure 7, which should be traced on tracing paper, cut, and folded,
as indicated on the diagram to yield one octant of a three-dimensional representation. The folded diagram should look like figure 8. In this diagram, the three
coordinate axes, X, Y, and Z, are the principal vibration directions corresponding
to the smallest, intermediate, and highest refractive indices, which are designated

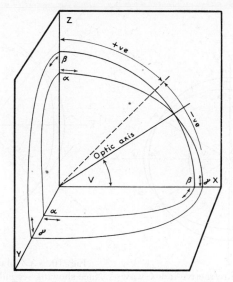

Fig.   8.—Refractive-index–wave-normal
surface of biaxial crystals (folded diagram).

n_α, n_β, and n_γ, respectively. (Winchell uses the symbols N_p, N_m, and N_g.) The
abbreviations α, β, and γ should not be used unless the context makes it clear that
the angles between the a-, b-, and c-axes of a triclinic crystal are not being referred
to. The most important principal plane of our refractive index diagram is the
XZ plane, shown in full in figure 9. It consists of a circle of radius n_β which cuts
an ellipse which has a semimajor axis of n_γ and a semiminor axis of n_α at points
A_1, A_2, $\bar{A}_1$, and $\bar{A}_2$. The directions A_1—$\bar{A}_1$ and A_2—$\bar{A}_2$ are the *primary optic axes*,
usually referred to as the *optic axes*. Light traveling along the optic axes of a
colorless biaxial crystal does not change its state of polarization. The refractive
index for waves traveling along an optic axis is obviously n_β.

If, instead of employing a refractive index–wave-normal diagram, we show the
velocity of the waves in the XZ plane as a function of the ray direction, we then
have a circle of radius $1/n_\beta$ which cuts an ellipse having a semimajor axis of $1/n_\alpha$
and a semiminor axis of $1/n_\gamma$ at points S_1, S_2, $\bar{S}_1$, and $\bar{S}_2$ (Fig. 10). The directions

$S_1—\bar{S}_1$ and $S_2—\bar{S}_2$ are known as the *secondary optic axes*. Rays which travel through a crystal along a secondary optic axis deviate according to their plane of polarization; the rays for all possible planes of polarization form a hollow cone of small angle which diverges from the point of emergence. This effect is known as *external conical refraction*. In a solid model of the ray–velocity surface, it can be seen that the four points of emergence of the secondary optic axes are in conical depressions, "dimples," in the surface. A plane surface tangent to the ray surface in these locations makes contact everywhere in a ring; this means that all the rays within a hollow cone have the same wave-normal. This effect is known as *internal*

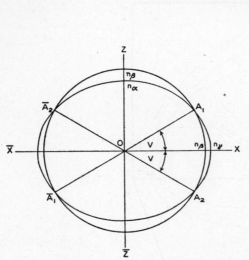

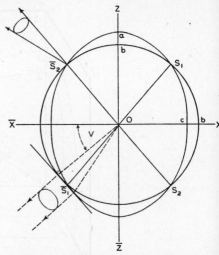

Fig. 9.—*XZ* plane of refractive-index–wave-normal surfaces showing the primary optic axes of a biaxial crystal.

Fig. 10.—*XZ* plane of ray–velocity surface showing secondary optic axes, external (upper left) and internal (lower left) conical refraction.

conical refraction. The angle of the cones is very small in most minerals and inorganic crystals, but may be large with crystals of aromatic compounds having extremely large values of $(n_\gamma - n_\alpha)$ and a large value of $2V$. The phenomena of external and internal conical refraction are of no practical significance in petrography and chemical microscopy.

The optic axial angle is expressed as $2V$, where V is the angle between an optic axis and the principal vibration direction X or Z, whichever is the nearer. It is nearer to X for negative biaxial crystals and nearer to Z for positive ones; this is equivalent to stating that for negative biaxial crystals $(n_\gamma - n_\beta)$ is less than $(n_\beta - n_\alpha)$ and for positive ones, greater.

The principal vibration directions in the plane of the optic axes are known as the *bisectrices* or *median lines*. The acute bisectrix, Bx_a, or first median line, makes an acute angle with each optic axis; it is X for negative and Z for positive crystals. The obtuse bisectrix, Bx_o, or second median line, is Z for negative and X for positive crystals. In orthorhombic crystals the principal vibration directions, X, Y, and Z coincide with the crystallographic axes. In monoclinic crystals one of the principal vibration directions coincides with the crystallographic ortho-axis b, whereas in triclinic crystals the principal vibration directions are without necessary relationship to the directions of the crystallographic axes.

The relation between V and the principal refractive indices is readily derived from the refractive index–wave-normal diagram in figure 9, in which the elliptical curve has the following equation in polar coordinates:

$$\frac{\cos^2 \theta}{\gamma^2} + \frac{\sin^2 \theta}{\alpha^2} = \frac{1}{r^2} \tag{4}$$

For a negative crystal V is the angle XOA. For a positive crystal it is the angle ZOA. If we call these angles V_n and V_p, respectively, we have:

$$\frac{\cos^2 V_n}{\gamma^2} + \frac{\sin^2 V_n}{\alpha^2} = \frac{1}{\beta^2} = \frac{\sin^2 V_p}{\gamma^2} + \frac{\cos^2 V_p}{\alpha^2} \tag{5}$$

Solving for V_n and V_p:

$$\sin^2 V_n = \cos^2 V_p = \alpha^2(\gamma^2 - \beta^2)/\beta^2(\gamma^2 - \alpha^2) =$$
$$(\gamma^2/\beta^2 - 1)/(\gamma^2/\alpha^2 - 1) \tag{6}$$

When γ is less than 0.1 greater than α, we may assume that $\alpha^2(\gamma + \beta) \doteqdot \beta^2(\gamma + \alpha)$ and obtain the simple *approximate* formula:

$$\sin^2 V_n = \cos^2 V_p \doteqdot (\gamma - \beta)/(\gamma - \alpha) \tag{7}$$

E. INTERFERENCE COLORS

An important property of doubly refracting crystals is that they exhibit interference effects in polarized light when three conditions are satisfied: the light entering the crystal must be polarized; the crystal must be so oriented that it splits the light into two beams, vibrating in planes at right angles, which traverse the crystal with different velocities; the emerging beams must be brought into the same plane of vibration by means of another polarizing prism, which is termed the *analyzer* when used for this purpose. This interference is easily understood by means of vector diagrams. In figure 11, the amplitude and vibration plane of a polarized light wave are represented by the length and direction of vector A. This wave is resolved into two waves (represented by vectors B and C) vibrating at right angles by the crystal. Vectors B and C are resolved in the vibration plane of the analyzer, which in this diagram is taken as being perpendicular to that of A, and we get vectors D and E. In figure 12, the analyzer plane coincides with that of A. The former case is that of *crossed nicols* and the latter that of *parallel nicols*. For crossed nicols the waves have the same amplitude, since $OD = OE = OA \cdot \sin \theta \cos \theta$, while with parallel nicols $OD = OA \cdot \cos^2 \theta$ and $OE = OA \cdot \sin^2 \theta$, which are only the same when $\theta = 45°$. Moreover, with crossed nicols the vectors are at $180°$, which means that a phase difference of $\lambda/2$ has been introduced between the two waves.

We must now consider the effect of the difference in length of the optical paths traversed by the two waves within the crystal. If the thickness of the crystal is l and its two refractive indices are n_1 and n_2, the path difference of the two waves is $l(n_1 - n_2)$. For our present purpose we are interested in the phase difference, δ. Expressed in degrees:

$$\delta = 360l(n_2 - n_1)/\lambda \tag{8}$$

where λ is the wave length of the light. In order to determine the amplitude of the light emerging from the analyzer we make use of another simple vector diagram.

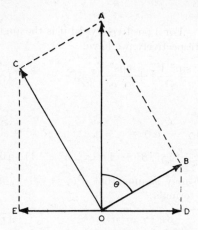
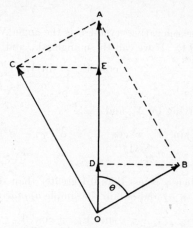

Fig. 11.—Vector diagram for crossed nicols.

Fig. 12.—Vector diagram for parallel nicols.

The case of crossed nicols is shown in figure 13. One of the vectors is retarded by an angle, δ, to give vector E'. The vector sum of E' and D is F, whose scalar, the distance OF, is the required amplitude:

$$OF = 2OA \cdot \sin\theta\cos\theta\sin\frac{\delta}{2} \tag{9}$$

If θ is varied with δ remaining constant, OF is a maximum for $\theta = 45°$. This position of the crystal is known as the $45°$ or *diagonal position*. In this position, $OF = OA \cdot \sin\frac{\delta}{2}$. Since the intensity of light is proportional to the square of the amplitude, we may write

$$I = I_0 \sin^2\frac{\delta}{2} \equiv I_0(1 - \cos\delta)/2 \tag{10}$$

where I_0 is the original intensity and I that transmitted by a crystal, having a phase retardation δ, between crossed nicols. It will be noticed that OF becomes zero for all values of δ when $\theta = 0°$, $90°$, $180°$, and $270°$; hence, when a crystal is rotated between crossed nicols through 360°, there are four positions in which light is not transmitted.   These are known as the *extinction positions*.   We shall now consider the effect of varying δ with θ remaining constant.   When δ is 0° or 360°, $\sin\dfrac{\delta}{2}$ is zero, so that OF is zero.   The maximum value of OF occurs for $\delta = 180°$, or for any number of complete revolutions plus 180°; this may be expressed as $\delta = (2n + 1)\pi$ radians for maximum transmission and $\delta = 2n\pi$ for darkness.

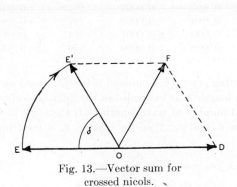

Fig. 13.—Vector sum for crossed nicols.

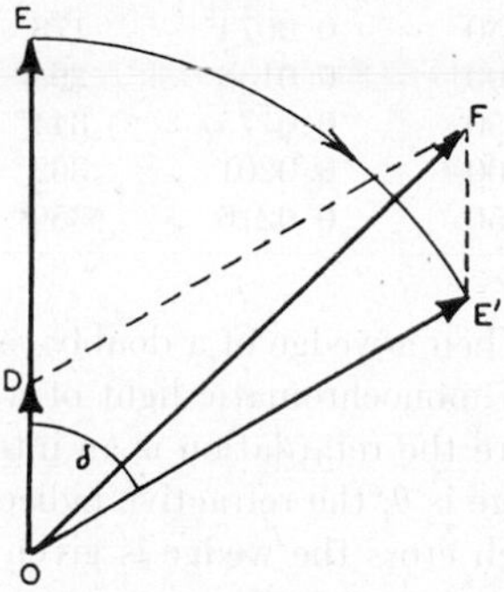

Fig. 14.—Vector sum for parallel nicols.

The case of parallel nicols is treated in figure 14.   As before, vector E is retarded by an angle, δ, to give vector E', which when added to D gives F, whose scalar, the distance OF, is the amplitude of the transmitted wave.

$$OF = \sqrt{[\sin^4\theta + \cos^4\theta + 2\sin^2\theta\cos^2\theta \cdot \cos\delta]} \qquad (11)$$

This expression can only equal zero when two conditions are simultaneously fulfilled, namely, $\cos\delta = -1$ and $\theta = 45°$.   For $\theta = 0°, 90°, 180°$, and $270°$, $OF = 1$, which means that the maximum light is transmitted.   We obtain the following expression for the light transmission of a crystal in the 45° position between parallel nicols:

$$I = I_0(1 + \cos\delta)/2 \equiv I_0\cos^2\frac{\delta}{2} \qquad (12)$$

It will be noted that the sum of the intensities transmitted by crossed and by parallel nicols is I_0.   Since this is true for all values of δ, it follows that the interference colors obtained in the two cases are exactly complementary.   As a practical example of the use of the above formulas, a comparison is given in table III of the transmissions of optic normal sections of benzil and quartz, 30μ thick, between crossed nicols.

The results in table III are plotted in figure 15, which clearly shows that the benzil transmits practically only the blue, while the quartz section of the same thickness transmits most of the spectrum and appears a slightly yellowish white.   The transmission maximum of benzil is not 100% because of absorption of the extraordinary ray; this is indicated by the dotted lines in the figure.

TABLE III

TRANSMISSION OF BENZIL AND QUARTZ BETWEEN CROSSED NICOLS

λ, mμ	Benzil			Quartz		
	$\epsilon - \omega$	δ	I/I_0	$\epsilon - \omega$	δ	I/I_0
420	0.0000	0°	0.000	0.0094	242°	0.745
450	0.0074	178°	1.000	0.0094	226°	0.847
500	0.0138	298°	0.265	0.0093	201°	0.967
550	0.0175	344°	0.019	0.0092	187°	0.996
600	0.0201	362°	0.000	0.0091	164°	0.981
650	0.0216	359°	0.000	0.0090	150°	0.933

When a wedge of a doubly refracting crystal is examined between crossed nicols with monochromatic light of wave length λ, it extinguishes the light at positions where the retardation is an integral number of wave lengths. If the angle of the wedge is θ, the refractive indices are n_1 and n_2; then the spacing, d, of the fringes which cross the wedge is given by:

$$d = \lambda/(n_1 - n_2) \tan \theta \qquad (13)$$

If $(n_1 - n_2)$ were the same for all values of λ, d would be directly proportional to λ. Such a wedge, when examined between cross nicols with white light, would

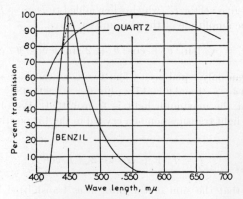

Fig. 15.—Transmission of 30 μ optic normal sections of quartz and benzil between crossed nicols.

present *Newton's color scale*, which is the order of the interference colors shown by reflection from an air gap between two plane glass surfaces in contact at one edge and separated by about one micron at the opposite edge. The interference colors shown by a trace of lubricating oil on a wet road very nearly follow Newton's color scale; the very slight departure is caused by the dispersion of the oil. With crystals, the dispersion of birefringence may be very large and the departure from Newton's color scale considerable. When d is greater for shorter wave lengths than for longer ones, the interference colors are said to be *anomalous*, as in the case of benzil discussed above. This subject is discussed further under the heading of dispersion (page 469).

F. POLARIZING PRISMS

It will be sufficient for our present purpose to consider the action of the square-ended polarizing prism constructed of calcite so oriented that its optic axis is perpendicular to the length of the prism. This category includes the Glan-Thompson

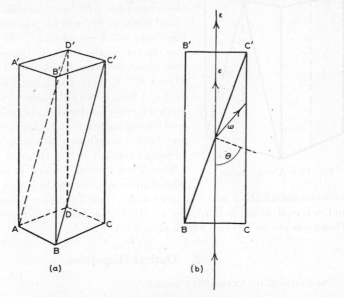

Fig. 16.—Glan-Thompson prism.

and Glazebrook prisms[29] which differ only in regard to the direction of the optic axis of the calcite with respect to the diagonal film of low-index cement. In figure 16a, the calcite is cut to yield a square prism of calcite, $ABCD$, $A'B'C'D'$. The optic axis is in direction AD (Glan-Thompson) or AB (Glazebrook). All the so-called Glan-Thompson prisms of German construction examined by the author have the optic axis in the *diagonal* direction, AC or BD.[30] The prism of calcite is cut along diagonal plane $ABC'D'$, and the two parts are ground and polished, then cemented with a medium of refractive index as near as possible to ϵ (1.4864). In

[29] R. Glazebrook, *Phil. Mag.*, **15**, 352 (1883). S. P. Thompson, *ibid.*, **12**, 349 (1881); **21**, 476 (1886). P. Glan, *Reportorium Exptl.-Physik (Carl's)*, **16**, 570 (1880).

[30] See E. E. Jelley, *J. Roy. Microscop. Soc.*, **62**, 93 (1942).

the past, raw linseed oil has been used as a cement. Recently, Bausch & Lomb have used a special resin transparent down to 300 mμ.[31]

The action of the prism is easily understood from the diagram in figure 16b, in which we consider the case of light entering the prism at normal incidence. The light is split into an ordinary and an extraordinary component which travel without deviation until they meet cementing film BC'. Since the refractive index of this film is roughly the same as that of ϵ, the extraordinary ray goes on through the prism. However, the refractive index of calcite for the ordinary ray is 1.6584. If, therefore, θ, which for normal incidence on the prism face equals angle CBC', is such that $\sin \theta > 1.4864/1.6584$, that is, if $\theta > 63.7°$, then the ordinary beam will

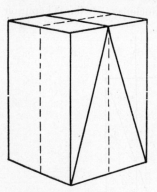

be totally reflected. In practice it is absorbed by a black varnish on the vertical sides of the prism. However, when CBC' is *exactly* 63.7°, only rays inclined towards BC' will be polarized, since only for these rays will θ exceed 63.7°. In actual construction, therefore, the angle is increased. It can be shown that the prism has its widest angular aperture when CBC' is about 76.1°, but this means a prism having a length to width ratio of about 4:1, which is often inconveniently long. Glan-Thompson prisms used for top-analyzers and other similar petrographic uses have a length to width ratio of 2.75:1, which means a value of CBC' of 70°.

Fig. 17.—Ahrens prism.

The Ahrens' prism,[32] which is so widely used in petrographic microscopes, is shown in figure 17. It has twice the width of face compared with a Glan-Thompson prism of equal length and so is equivalent, as illustrated by the broken lines in the figures, to four Glan-Thompson prisms of equal length placed side by side.

2. Optical Dispersion

A. DISPERSION OF REFRACTIVE INDEX

The refractive index of any substance depends on the wave length of the transmitted radiation. This property is known as the dispersion of refraction, and is possessed by all substances in varying degree. Dispersion of refraction is often expressed as the inverse relationship:

$$\nu = (n_D - 1)/(n_F - n_C) \tag{14}$$

where n_D, n_F, and n_C are the refractive indices for the sodium D ($\lambda = 5893$ Å.), hydrogen F ($\lambda = 4861$ Å.), and hydrogen C ($\lambda = 6563$ Å.) lines. However, the constant ν does not take into account the shape of the dispersion curve: two substances might have the same values of n_D and ν and yet have different refractive indices for the extreme red and violet ends of the spectrum. The principal

[31] W. M. D. Bryant, *J. Am. Chem. Soc.*, **65**, 96 (1943).
[32] C. D. Ahrens, *J. Roy. Microscop. Soc.*, **1886**, 397.

refractive indices of uniaxial and biaxial crystals are usually subject to differing degrees of dispersion.

B. DISPERSION OF BIREFRINGENCE

The birefringence of a crystal may be expressed as the difference between the two refractive indices for light traveling in any given direction through it. This means that the birefringence of a crystal is a function of the ray direction. In the case of uniaxial crystals, the dispersion of birefringence is very nearly independent of ray direction and for all practical purposes may be considered as constant. Theoretically, a slight deviation is possible with crystals possessing widely different values of n_ω and n_ϵ, together with widely different dispersions of the two principal refractive indices. With biaxial crystals, both the birefringence and the dispersion of birefringence are dependent on ray direction. This is particularly true of the dispersion of birefringence of crystals viewed in a direction close to that of an optic axis, as the directions of the optic axes of biaxial crystals may vary considerably with change of wave length. For this reason, a measurement of the birefringence of a biaxial crystal is useless unless the orientation of the direction of viewing with respect to the wave surface is also recorded.

C. DISPERSION OF OPTIC AXES

The directions of the two optic axes of a biaxial crystal are usually different for different wave lengths. The nature and extent of this dispersion of the axes is of considerable importance in identifying organic compounds.

Two different effects may be combined in the dispersion of the optic axes. The first of these effects is a change of optic axial angle with change of wave length, and is best referred to as "differential dispersion of indices" since the optic axial angle is governed by the ratio of the three principal refractive indices. If the dispersion of one of the indices differs markedly from the other two, the crystal may be uniaxial at a specific wave length, whereby crossed axial plane dispersion must result. Further, it is possible for a biaxial crystal to change sign. This occurs when $2V$ passes through $90°$. The second effect, which can be present only with monoclinic and triclinic crystals, is a dispersion of the principal vibration directions of the wave surface.

Orthorhombic Dispersion.—With orthorhombic crystals, the dispersion of the optic axes is due solely to differential dispersion of the principal indices of refraction, and the principal vibration directions are constant for all wave lengths. All three of the principal vibration directions of orthorhombic crystals coincide with crystallographic axes. Consequently, orthorhombic dispersion is characterized by the fact that the optic axial plane does not change, and the two axes converge or diverge equally with change of wave length. There are two special cases of orthorhombic dispersion which deserve attention. The first of these, *crossed axial plane* dispersion, occurs when the optic axial angle decreases to zero at some point in the spectrum. At this point, the Y vibration direction interchanges with X or Z, and the optic axial angle then increases in a plane at right angles to its former one. In the second special case, the optic axial angle is $90°$ at some point in the spectrum, so that X is the acute bisectrix for one end of the spectrum, and Z is for the other end. This is equivalent to saying that the sign of birefringence is changed at the particular wave length.

Crossed axial plane dispersion is shown by a number of substances, among which may be mentioned p-nitrobenzaldehyde,[33] picrates of various amines,[34] the high-temperature polymorphs of o-dinitrobenzene and 1,8-dinitronaphthalene, and the low-temperature form of dibenzoylmethane.[35]

The wave length for which the crystal becomes uniaxial may vary widely with change of temperature if all of the principal refractive indices are fairly close together.

Monoclinic Dispersion.—This is characterized by the fact that only one of the principal vibration directions must necessarily coincide with a crystallographic axis for all wave lengths. The particular crystallographic axis is that which is at right angles to the plane of the other two, and is called the ortho- or b-axis. Any one of the three principal vibration directions of the wave surface may be coincident with the b crystallographic axis, so that three principal types of dispersion result.

Case 1. Crossed Dispersion.—This type of dispersion results when the acute bisectrix (X of negative, and Z of positive crystals) is fixed, whereby the plane of the optic axes rotates about the acute bisectrix. Mitchell and Bryant[34] have recently found a number of amine picrates which exhibit this property in marked degree.

Case 2. Horizontal Dispersion.—This type of dispersion results when the obtuse bisectrix (X of positive, and Z of negative crystals) is fixed. This results in the plane of the optic axes being displaced horizontally in the acute interference figure. It should be noted that a substance which shows horizontal dispersion of the axes in the acute figure must show crossed dispersion in the obtuse figure and vice versa, so that, in the special case where axial angle $2V$ is 90° for some particular wave length, the birefringence changes sign, and the two acute interference figures show horizontal and inclined dispersion, respectively. A good example of this effect is provided by stilbene,[31] which shows horizontal dispersion in the visible spectrum down to 4070 Å., and crossed dispersion in the ultraviolet.

Case 3. Inclined Dispersion.—Inclined dispersion results when the normal to the optic plane (Y) is fixed. Both acute and obtuse interference figures show displacement in the plane of the optic axes. Good examples of inclined dispersion are provided by o-nitroacetanilide,[36] and hexamethylenetetramine picrate.[34]

In addition to the dispersion of the principal vibration directions, the optic axial angle also may vary with change of wave length, so that the interference figure may be quite complex when viewed with white light. It is theoretically possible for the optic axial angle to become zero at some point in the spectrum, and then to increase in a direction at right angles. This would result in a modified form of crossed

---

[33] N. H. Hartshorne and A. Stuart, *Crystals and the Polarising Microscope.* Arnold, London, 1934, p. 197.

[34] J. Mitchell, Jr., and W. M. D. Bryant, *J. Am. Chem. Soc.*, **65**, 128 (1943).

[35] E. E. Jelley, *unpublished work.*

[36] E. E. Jelley, *J. Roy. Microscop. Soc.*, **56**, 101 (1936).

axial plane dispersion in which inclined dispersion would become horizontal and vice versa. However, crossed dispersion would remain crossed dispersion under these conditions. Perhaps the finest example of monoclinic crossed axial plane dispersion is α,α'-dipyridyl which was recently studied by Bryant.[37] This substance is uniaxial at about 4150 Å., and exhibits horizontal dispersion for shorter wave lengths and inclined dispersion for longer wave lengths. The various types of monoclinic dispersion are summarized in table IV.

TABLE IV
TYPES OF MONOCLINIC DISPERSION

$b =$	Sign	Acute	Obtuse	Acute[a]	Obtuse[a]
X	—	Crossed	Horizontal	Crossed	Horizontal
X	+	Horizontal	Crossed	Inclined	Inclined
Y	—	Inclined	Inclined	Horizontal	Crossed
Y	+	Inclined	Inclined	Horizontal	Crossed
Z	—	Horizontal	Crossed	Inclined	Inclined
Z	+	Crossed	Horizontal	Crossed	Horizontal

[a] After crossed axial plane dispersion has taken place. The obtuse bisectrix changes place with Y.

Triclinic Dispersion.—With triclinic crystals, all three principal vibration directions of the wave surface may vary with change of wave length. Since the axes of the wave surface bear no relationship to the crystallographic axes, the dispersion of the principal vibration directions has no element of symmetry, so that the acute interference figure could present the appearance of a mixture of horizontal and crossed, horizontal and inclined, etc., monoclinic dispersion. Dispersion of the optic axial angle also occurs, and crossed, axial plane dispersion is theoretically possible where the axial angle becomes zero for some particular wave length. The dispersion of the optic axes would possess the characteristic asymmetry of the triclinic system at wave lengths both longer and shorter than the point of uniaxiality. So far as the author is aware, triclinic crossed axial plane dispersion has not yet been observed, but it must be remembered that a small measure of monoclinic or triclinic dispersion combined with crossed axial plane dispersion can only be detected by careful measurements in monochromatic light of various wave lengths.

Change of Sign in Uniaxial Crystals.—In uniaxial crystals, the direction of the optic axis is constant for all wave lengths, so that in a centered uniaxial interference figure differential dispersion of the ordinary and extraordinary rays gives rise to a departure from the "Newton's rings" series of colors. It is possible for the dispersion of the lesser refracted ray to be so much greater than that of the more highly refracted one that at some specific wave length the two refractive indices become equal, and then change places. This means that the sign of birefringence changes on passing through the wave length for which the crystal is isotropic. This effect is shown by benzil,[31, 38] which is isotropic at 4205 Å., optically positive for longer, and optically negative for shorter, wave lengths.

[37] W. M. D. Bryant, *J. Am. Chem. Soc.*, **63,** 511 (1941).
[38] E. E. Jelley, *Phot. J.*, **74,** 514 (1934).

3. Molecular Structure and Optical Properties

Since a crystal of an organic compound consists of a regularly arranged group of identical molecules, the shape of the molecule and its polar characteristics play a large part in determining the optical properties of the crystal. Rod-shaped molecules, such as those of long-chain hydrocarbons and their simple derivatives, have a greater refractive index for light vibrating along their length than for transverse vibrations. If such molecules are approximately parallel to one another in the crystal, the crystal is positive biaxial or positive uniaxial. However, considerable inclination of molecules in one crystal layer relative to those in an adjacent layer changes the sign of the birefringence. The refractive indices of crystals built from rod-shaped molecules are not very high unless the molecule contains highly refractive substituents, such as bromine, iodine, or sulfur. As with the refractive index of liquids, a conjugated double bond linkage causes an increase in the indices.

Planar molecules, particularly those with conjugated chain ring systems such as benzene and naphthalene derivatives, confer two high principal refractive indices (n_β and n_γ) on their crystals, so that, in general, crystals of carbocyclic substances possess large values for their maximum birefringence ($n_\gamma - n_\alpha$). Exceptions to this general rule may result when molecules in different planes are staggered with respect to each other. When this occurs, n_γ and n_β are lower, and n_α is higher, than is usual for this class of compound. The effect of substituents is of considerable interest, inasmuch as the dispersion of refractive indices and of principal vibration directions are often greatly modified. Heavy atomic substituents, such as bromine, iodine, and selenium increase both the refractive indices and their dispersion, but polar substituents such as amino, nitro, carbonyl, and thiocarbonyl often affect the dispersion of the optical properties so strongly that striking abnormalities are exhibited by the crystals. The optical properties of salts of a colored aromatic compound may differ markedly among themselves, a property which is often of importance in establishing the identity of a colorless acid or base which itself is not well characterized optically but which will yield a crystalline salt with a colored base or acid, respectively.

V. MICROSCOPY OF TRANSPARENT CRYSTALS

1. Preparation of Crystals

There is no single method of preparing crystals of a substance for optical examination which can be adopted as a standardized technique, since there is such wide variation in the physical properties of organic compounds. It is, however, possible to lay down some general principles as a guide.

A. CRYSTALLIZATION FROM SOLVENTS

Among the various ways of crystallizing a substance from a solvent, the following are the most useful:

(1) Slow evaporation of the solvent. This method is useful for recrystallizations on microscope slides. The rate of evaporation of very

volatile solvents can be slowed down by covering the preparation with a watch glass. Care should be taken to prevent the absorption of water vapor from the air when working with acetone or methanol. An effective way of doing this is to allow the evaporation to take place in a desiccator containing a drying agent and an evaporating basin half filled with an absorbent such as butyl phthalate. Activated charcoal may also be employed for this purpose. The main usefulness of recrystallizations on microscope slides is that they are often a rapid means of checking the purity of a substance when the impurity has different optical properties. However, where the object is to obtain well-formed crystals, it is usually better to perform the crystallization in a small beaker.

(2) Cooling a saturated hot solution.

(3) Dilution of a solution of the substance with a nonsolvent. For example, by the addition of water to alcohol solutions, or of ligroin to benzene solutions.

(4) Salting out substances from their solutions. Thus sulfonates may be thrown down as sodium salts by the addition of a large quantity of sodium chloride or sodium sulfate to their solutions. From the microscopic point of view, sodium chloride has the advantage that it forms easily recognizable isotropic crystals of square or rectangular outline, so that crystals of the organic substance are readily picked out under polarized light.

(5) Precipitation of free acid or base. Crystals suitable for optical study may sometimes be obtained by the addition of a mineral acid to aqueous solutions of salts of organic acids, and by the addition of a strong alkali to aqueous solutions of salts of organic bases.

B. CRYSTALLIZATION BY SUBLIMATION

Substances which have an appreciable vapor pressure at temperatures below their melting point are often readily crystallized by sublimation. The method is useful with substances which do not readily crystallize from solvents, and particularly as a means of separating small quantities of a volatile substance from a large bulk of a relatively nonvolatile one. The rate of sublimation of a substance depends not only on its vapor pressure at the operating temperature, but also on the temperature and distance from the condensing surface and on the atmospheric pressure. Much can be accomplished by an experienced worker without the aid of elaborate apparatus: material may be sublimed from one object slide to another, or from a small watch glass to an object slide. With such simple apparatus there are three important rules for successful operation: (1) avoid drafts; (2) use a small source of heat such as a microburner or a small coil of electrically heated Nichrome wire; (3) heat the specimen very slowly. It is sometimes desirable with substances of low melting point or great volatility to cool the object slide which receives the sublimate by means of a small block of aluminum or a small vessel containing water. However, condensation on too cold a surface may cause the crystals to be too small for useful observation. Mixtures of two volatile substances may be fractionally sublimated if their volatilities differ appreciably, but care must be taken to heat the mixture very slowly and evenly, the sublimate being received on a series of object slides which are laid down in sequence as obtained, sublimate side up. The progress of sublimation can be watched under the microscope, and the temperature range of sublimation observed with the aid of a hot stage; applications of this method are discussed in Kofler and Kofler.[39] Various types of apparatus have been devised to facilitate sublimation under reduced pressure; a list of references is given in Chamot and Mason.[40]

C.   CRYSTALLIZATION FROM MELT

The preparation of crystal films of organic compounds by cooling the fused substance as a thin film under a cover glass has some very useful applications. The crystals may be made as thin as desired, and, quite often, a variety of optical orientations are obtained in the same slide so that the interference figures can be observed to the best advantage. The usual way of preparing microscope slides by fusion is to place a few milligrams of substance on an object slide and cover it with a No. 1 cover glass. It is then heated very slowly, the temperature being raised up to the melting point, and then held there until fusion is complete. The slide is cooled slowly. It is sometimes necessary to seed the edge of the preparation by touching it with a trace of the solid substance on the point of a needle. After the substance has solidified, it may be recrystallized by cautiously melting the substance under about three-quarters of the cover glass. The slide is then allowed to cool slowly. The solid substance seeds the melt and much larger uniform areas of crystal are formed. A metal bar heated at one end and cooled at the other forms a very convenient hot plate for fusion work. It is easily calibrated for temperature gradient, so that it becomes a simple matter to crystallize a melt at any desired temperature. Under certain conditions it is an advantage to solidify the fusion preparation very suddenly; this is the case with substances which normally crystallize to yield a single optical orientation as revealed by convergent polarized light. Very rapid crystallization will often result in the forma-

[39] L. Kofler and A. Kofler, *Mikroskopische Methoden in der Mikrochemie*. Haim, Vienna, 1936.

[40] E. M. Chamot and C. W. Mason, *Handbook of Chemical Microscopy*. 2nd ed., Vol. I, Wiley, New York, 1938, p. 347.

tion of some crystals with a different orientation, after which the preparation may be partly remelted and then slowly cooled to give larger crystals of the new orientation.

The fusion method is particularly valuable as a rapid means of comparing a known with an unknown substance. Very small quantities of the two substances are melted at opposite edges of a cover glass, and are allowed to flow under the cover so that they meet somewhere near the center (Fig. 18). The slide is slowly cooled, preferably on a heated bar, and the known substance is seeded. The course of crystallization may then be watched with a hand magnifier or a low-power bench microscope in order to observe whether the crystals continue their growth with undiminished velocity at the boundary between the known and unknown substance. If the two substances are identical, the crystals will continue past the boundary, and if the slide is then heated from one end of the boundary, so as to establish a temperature gradient across the slide from A to B, the two substances will melt simultaneously.

Fig. 18.—Comparison fusion slide.

The optical properties of the crystals which are determinable, such as retardation and optical orientation, do not exhibit any discontinuity at the boundary if the two substances are identical. Likewise, polymorphic transitions are not checked at the boundary. It should be remembered that a small proportion of an impurity in either the known or the unknown substance may differentially slow up the crystallization and diminish the degree of perfection of the crystals obtained. If the two substances are dissimilar, various differences may occur. Where the substances are dissimilar and not isomorphous, crystals will grow through the known substance and stop at the boundary. Even if the crystallization of the known creates sufficient disturbance at the boundary to start crystallization of the unknown, the rate of growth and optical properties of the crystals will present a discontinuity at the boundary. On melting back the substance, differences on either side of the boundary will be apparent, and also in the narrow boundary region where the two substances have mixed for there is the possibility that eutectics or even definite addition compounds may be formed. In comparison slides in which the known and unknown are isomorphous, a slight slowing up of crystallization at the boundary may often be observed, and the crystals which grow in the narrow region of mixing are usually not so well formed as those of the pure known and unknown. Some pairs of substances are not easily differentiated by fusion comparison methods: for example, p-dichlorobenzene and p-dibromobenzene, 2,4-dichloro-1-naphthol and 2,4-dibromo-1-naphthol.

The author[35] has used an interferometric method employing half-silvered slides and cover slips as a rapid means of comparing the refractive indices at the boundary, of a crystal which has grown from a known into an unknown substance, by studying the interference fringes given in plane-polarized monochromatic light. Both the object slide and the cover glass need to have fairly good optical surfaces, since the best results are given when the two half-silvered surfaces are parallel. Particularly good results are given by slides and covers constructed from optically worked plates of fused quartz, which have been given a light coating of platinum by cathodic sputtering. The platinum as first deposited is very easily removed by rubbing; but after the coated slides have been heated to 700° C. and slowly cooled in a muffle furnace, the coat becomes very resistant. When a single substance, such as β-bromonaphthalene is fused between the two platinized surfaces and is then allowed to crystallize, the individual crystals show only very broad interference bands when examined with a low-power microscope in polarized monochromatic light. The same interference pattern is observed with β-chloronaphthalene. If, however, a mixed slide is prepared with β-chloronaphthalene on one side, and β-bromonaphthalene on the other, and if some mixing has occurred at the boundary, crystals growing through the boundary suffer a change of refractive index. This change is shown in polarized monochromatic light, such as sodium ($\lambda = 589$ mμ) or mercury ($\lambda = 546$), when the crystal is in the extinction position and the analyzer has been withdrawn. Under these conditions, the crystal in the boundary zone shows some closely spaced interference bands. The position, and sometimes the spacing, of the bands change when either the crystal or the polarizer is rotated through 90°. If the two refractive indices presented by the "known" part of the crystal are n_1 and n_2, and those of the "unknown" part are n_1' and n_2', and if the crystal has a thickness of d mμ, then the number of bands in the boundary zone is $2d (n_1' - n_1)/\lambda$ and $2d (n_2' - n_2)/\lambda$, respectively (n_1' and n_2' being taken as greater than n_1 and n_2). With a preparation 0.03 millimeter thick, a refractive index difference of 0.01 gives a single interference band. Under favorable conditions, fractions of a band can be estimated.

D. MOUNTING

Fusion slides do not require mounting, and may be made reasonably permanent by ringing the cover circle with liquid glue, diluted 1:1, or a casein cement. Varnish, gold size, shellac, marine glue, and asphalt varnish usually tend to dissolve the crystals and diffuse into the preparation.

Crystals which have been separated from their mother liquor, or which have been prepared by sublimation, need to be mounted in order to reduce refraction effects to a minimum. Three conditions must be fulfilled by the mountant: (*1*) it must not dissolve the crystals; (*2*) it must have a refractive index reasonably near the mean refractive index of the crystals; (*3*) it should be as viscous as possible at room temperature. The first condition is not easy to fill, so far as permanent mounts are concerned. Of two mountants which have a low solvent action for many classes of organic compounds, liquid petrolatum (u.s.p. heavy grade) is too fluid, and glycerol–jelly has too low a refractive index in most cases. An alternative is saturating a medium of suitable viscosity and refractive index with the substance under study, a convenient way being to dissolve some of the substance in a drop of hot mountant on an object slide, cool it to about 50° C., place some well-formed crystals in it, and cover with a No. 1 cover glass. The slide is then placed under gentle pressure and allowed to cool to room temperature. Many commercial synthetic resins are now available which, either alone or in admixture, are suitable for making semipermanent mounts. The following list of mountants used by the author is given by way of illustration:

(*1*) 15 grams of hard Canada balsam in 10 milliliters of α-bromonaphthalene; $n_D = 1.59$.

(*2*) Arochlor No. 1262; $n_D = 1.65$.

(*3*) 10 grams of hard Canada balsam in 30 milliliters of Arochlor No. 1254; $n_D = 1.61$.

(*4*) 20 grams of polystyrene in 40 milliliters of α-bromonaphthalene; $n_D = 1.66$.

(*5*) Plasticizer E, 47.7% chlorine; $n_D = 1.51$.

Composition (*4*), polystyrene in α-bromonaphthalene, has some special advantages: it has a low solvent action; it is viscous at room temperature; and its refractive index remains approximately constant at 1.66 during its slow hardening by evaporation of the α-bromonaphthalene. The author prepares this medium as follows: 40 ml. of α-bromonaphthalene is poured over 20 g. of polystyrene resin contained in a tall-form 200-ml. beaker. A short stirring rod is placed inside the beaker, which is then covered with a watch glass to prevent evaporation of the solvent. The beaker is maintained at 70° C. for about a week, with occasional stirring until the mixture is homogeneous. It is then allowed to remain undisturbed in the hot-air oven for a further three or four days to allow undissolved solid material to settle, and is finally decanted into a clean, dry, wide-mouth bottle.

It is sometimes possible to dissolve a substance to be crystallized in the mounting medium at a temperature just above the melting point of the substance. This may be accomplished by heating them together on an object glass, stirring the droplet with a needle to effect thorough mixing, covering with a No. 1 cover circle, and then cooling to a few degrees below the melting point of the substance by means of a heated bar. The preparation is allowed to crystallize slowly—reheating if necessary to dissolve most of the crystals and then recooling to get a better regulated growth. Some experimentation is necessary to get the optimum proportion of crystal to mountant. If the preparation is too cold during the crystallization process, the crystals may depart considerably from their normal habit.

E. METHODS OF CHANGING OPTICAL ORIENTATION

It is often necessary to change the orientation of a crystal in order to study an acute bisectrix interference figure, or the extinction colors presented by some particular orientation. This operation is readily carried out on preparations mounted in a viscous medium, such as an Arochlor with or without an admixture of Canada balsam, or the polystyrene–bromonaphthalene medium (4) referred to above. Specially designed rotation apparatus is sometimes useful for certain types of work. Three simple designs are illustrated in Hartshorne and Stuart.[41] The Fedorov universal stage may be used for determining optical axial angles of moderately large crystals in fusion slides, the general technique being the same as that employed with rock sections in petrographic work. However, the limited usefulness of the universal stage does not justify the high cost of a suitable petrographic microscope and the necessary accessories for routine microscopy in an organic laboratory.

2. Orthoscopic Examination

By orthoscopic examination we mean the examination of the image of the crystal in ordinary light, in polarized light, or between crossed nicols. When the crystal is of sufficient size, a low-power objective and very narrow cone of illumination should be used. The crystalline form, habit, and cleavage should be observed with the analyzer withdrawn; it is not necessary to remove the polarizer for these observations. If the crystal is mounted in a medium of medium refractive index, its relief may vary considerably when either the microscope stage or the polarizer is rotated; this effect is dealt with under the heading of refractive index determination (pages 489–501).

A. EXTINCTION ANGLES

When a crystal is rotated on the microscope stage between crossed nicols, it passes through an extinction position every 90°, as has been explained on

---

[41] N. H. Hartshorne and A. Stuart, *Crystals and the Polarising Microscope.* Arnold, London, 1934, p 130.

page 464.   Extinction is classified under three headings: *parallel, symmetrical,* and *oblique.*   These are illustrated in figures 19a, b, and c, respectively.   Parallel and symmetrical extinction are characteristic of all possible orientations of crystals of the hexagonal, trigonal, tetragonal, and orthorhombic systems.   Symmetrical extinction is symmetrical in that the vibration planes of polarizer or analyzer bisect the edge angles presented by the crystal; irregular development or distortion may cause the crystal to deviate markedly from the ideal form, but the bisection of edge angles still holds.   Parallel, and more rarely, symmetrical, extinction also occur in monoclinic crystals viewed exactly at right angles to the crystallographic

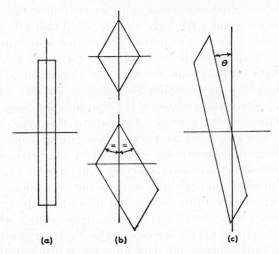

(a)   (b)   (c)

Fig. 19.—Extinction: (a) parallel; (b) symmetrical;
(c) oblique.

ortho-axis b, but its occurrence in other orientations of monoclinic crystals, or in any orientation of triclinic crystals, is fortuitous.   Oblique extinction occurs in all orientations of triclinic crystals and in all orientations of monoclinic crystals other than those in which ortho-axis b is at right angles to the line of vision, occurrence of parallel extinction being fortuitous.   In the case of oblique extinction, the extinction angle is the angle, less than 45°, between the most prominent or characteristic crystal edge of the crystal at extinction and the nearest vibration plane of analyzer or polarizer.   An important aspect of extinction angles in the study of organic crystals is that of *dispersed extinction.*   Dispersed extinction is most clearly seen with thick crystals when a very narrow cone of illumination and a powerful light source are used.   When the dispersion is slight, the color of crystal changes from brownish to bluish on passing through the extinction position, whereas brilliant colors are seen when the dispersion is large. Dispersed extinction can occur in triclinic crystals and in monoclinic crystals not in their position of parallel extinction. Under no circumstances can dispersed extinction occur in crystals of higher than monoclinic symmetry.

In elongated crystals, such as those of columnar or acicular habit, the character of the elongation is regarded as positive or negative according to whether it corresponds to the higher (slow ray), or lower (fast ray), refractive index, respectively. In uniaxial crystals, the direction of elongation is of necessity the crystallographic c-axis, since the tetragonal or hexagonal axes are equal. We have already noted that vibrations parallel to the c-axis are those of the extraordinary ray, consequently positive and negative uniaxial crystals show positive and negative elongation, respectively. With orthorhombic crystals, the elongation is negative if it takes place in the X principal vibration direction, positive for the Z direction and both positive and negative if the elongation is along Y, depending on the orientation of the crystal. Crystals of this type, when rotated through 360° along a horizontal axis, pass alternatively through two positive and negative elongations, separated by four extinction positions which occur when the visual axis coincides with an optic axis. With crystals of the monoclinic and triclinic systems the elongation is regarded as positive or negative according to whether it most nearly agrees with the direction of higher or lower refractive index, respectively; when the direction of elongation most nearly corresponds to Y, the crystals exhibit both positive and negative elongation, depending on their orientation.

3. Conoscopic Examination

The conoscope is a device for determining the nature of the wave surface of a crystal. Its principle is shown diagrammatically in figure 20, in which a roughly parallel beam of light is polarized and is then passed through a converging lens which brings it to a focus within the crystal, which we will suppose to be a plate of calcite cut perpendicular to the optical axis. The light diverging from the crystal is rendered parallel by a collecting lens and passes through an analyzer, crossed with respect to the polarizer, which causes interference to occur. As seen from above, the condensing lens looks like a flat disk. The center of the disk is illuminated by light which has passed perpendicularly through the crystal; its circumference is illuminated by light which has passed obliquely through the crystal. This illuminated disk is therefore an orthographic projection of a segment of the wave surface as refracted into air.

If we bear in mind that the vibration direction of the extraordinary ray is in the optic axial plane, we can readily understand the formation of the *interference figure* of our optic axial section of calcite, since all radii of the circular disk represent vibration directions of the extraordinary rays hav-

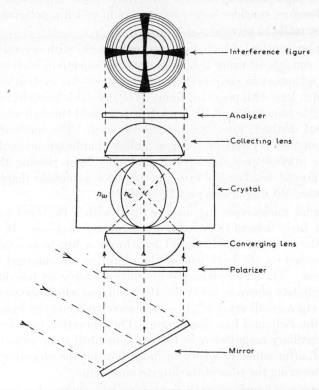

Fig. 20.—Formation of interference figure.

ing directions through the crystal indicated by their location on the disk of the interference figure. The center of the figure appears dark because it is made up of rays which have traveled along the optic axis of the crystal. The radii of the figure which have the same, or very nearly the same, directions as the vibration planes as the polarizer and analyzer must appear dark, since along these directions the crystal is at extinction. If monochromatic light is used, a series of concentric dark rings will appear. These occur for directions in which the retardation of the crystal is an integral number of wave lengths as explained on page 465. The ratio of the di-

ameters of the 1st, 2nd, 3rd......rings is roughly $1:\sqrt{2}:\sqrt{3}$.......
In white light the rings form an ascending series of interference colors.

In actual practice, single lenses are not favored as convergers and collecting lenses because of their bad spherical aberration and relatively small angular aperture. It is very desirable, particularly when working with small crystals, to be able to view them orthoscopically and then, with the minimum of manipulation, to view their conoscopic interference figures. We shall therefore consider some of the ways in which a polarizing microscope can be made to serve as a conoscope.

The simplest method, which, however, only works with crystal plates of large area, consists in using a high-power dry objective, such as a four-millimeter achromat in conjunction with a condensing system capable of filling its back lens with polarized light. The crystal is brought into focus, the eyepiece is removed, and the back lens is viewed through an analyzer. A small, but distinct, interference figure is seen. The method may be applied to smaller crystals by using a pinhole diaphragm over the draw-tube of the microscope; this insures that only light passing through a particular crystal reaches the eye. In place of a pinhole diaphragm, a Wright crossed-slit diaphragm may be used.[42]

Petrographic microscopes are usually fitted with a Bertrand lens which slides in the body tube of the microscope below the eyepiece. In conjunction with the eyepiece the Bertrand lens forms a low-power microscope which is focused on the back lens of the objective, an enlarged image of which is seen. The more elaborate instruments have an iris diaphragm fitted immediately above or below the Bertrand lens which serves to isolate the light from a small crystal. It is necessary to focus the image of the crystal on the Bertrand lens diaphragm. This operation may require the use of an auxiliary magnifier over the eye lens until some experience has been gained, after which it is easy to judge how far the objective must be raised by observing the edge of the interference figure.

The interference figures of small crystals may be observed on an ordinary "biological" microscope, by equipping it with Polaroid polarizer and analyzer and a Johannsen lens.[43] A Johannsen lens is made by drawing out a heated glass rod to hair-like thinness and breaking the glass filament into pieces 3 or 4 cm. in length. The ends of these filaments are fused by brief heating in the edge of a Bunsen flame in order to form spherical globules. On examination under the microscope, some spherules will be found which

---

[42] F. E. Wright, *Methods of Petrographic-Microscopic Research, Carnegie Inst. Wash. Pub.* No. 158, 1911, p. 59.

[43] A. Johannsen, *Manual of Petrographic Methods.* McGraw-Hill, New York, 1918, p. 454.

are free from bubbles and are less than 0.1 mm. diameter. The crystal is first focused under a 16-mm. or 8-mm. objective and a 5× or 10× eyepiece and is brought into the center of the field. The small spherical lens is then placed in contact with the cover-glass, directly over the crystal. On racking up the objective, a plane of focus is reached in which an interference figure is seen. The angle of the cone of rays making up the interference figure is, of course, the same as that of the cone of illumination given by the substage condenser, consequently the diaphragm on the Abbé condenser should be fully opened. The maximum angle of the cone of rays visible in a Johannsen lens is approximately 90°, which corresponds to a numerical aperture of 0.7.

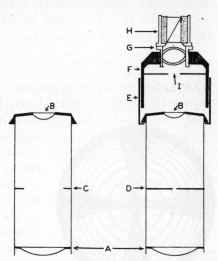

Fig. 21.—Conoscopic apparatus for use with student-type microscope.

Another way of observing the interference figures of crystals is to magnify the Ramsden's disk given by a low-power (5×) eyepiece by means of a high-power (20×) lens usually known as a Becke–Klein magnifier. The author[35] has found it better to employ two 5× eyepieces equipped as in figure 21. Each eyepiece has a field lens, A, and an eye lens, B. One of the eyepieces (shown at the left of the figure) is equipped with cross webs in the field diaphragm, C; this eyepiece is used for orthoscopic observations in conjunction with a cap analyzer. The other eyepiece is provided with a pinhole aperture in the center of the diaphragm, D, which replaces the usual field diaphragm. This eyepiece is converted to a conoscopic apparatus by inserting it in sleeve E, in which slides fitting F, which carries a 20× or a 30× magnifier, G, and analyzing prism H. A reticle with a micrometer or coordinate scale may be fitted in a diaphragm, I, at the focus of G. In using the apparatus, the image of the crystal under study is first centered and focused on the cross webs of the orthoscopic eyepiece, which is then withdrawn from the microscope body tube. The conoscopic apparatus is then inserted, and is rotated to an extinction position with respect to the substage polarizer. The interference figure is focused by sliding fitting F in sleeve E.

The angle, θ, of the cone of light within the crystal which is represented by the diameter of the conoscopic interference figure is related to the numerical aperture of the objective, and the mean refractive index n

presented by the particular orientation of the crystal by the following approximate relationship:

$$\theta = 2 \sin^{-1} (N.A./n)$$

It is obviously advantageous to use an objective with as high a numerical aperture as possible for the purpose of studying the general nature of the wave surface of a crystal, such as a 4-mm. objective of N.A. = 0.85 or 0.95. A wider conoscopic angle may be obtained by the use of a 1.8-mm. oil-immersion objective of N.A. = 1.25 or 1.30, but this entails the use of an oil-immersed condenser, which is rather a messy operation since in this case a return from conoscopic to orthoscopic observation necessitates the removal of the condenser and cleansing of the slide.

B. UNIAXIAL INTERFERENCE FIGURES

Two types of centered uniaxial figures are possible: the optic axial figure, the formation of which has been described above, and the optic normal figure. The optic axial figure is very easily recognizable by its consisting of a black cross and a number of concentric circles of rising order of interference. The appearance of the uniaxial figure in monochromatic light is shown in figure 22. The number of circles in the figure increases with increase of thickness and of birefringence of the crystal, and with increase of numerical aperture of the objective used. The determination of the sign of a uniaxial crystal is quickly made by inserting a birefringent plate of known fast and slow vibration directions in the 45° position between the objective and analyzer of the conoscopic system when *compensation* or extinction takes place in a spot in each of two opposite quadrants. These are, of course, the quandrants where the fast and slow vibrations of the crystal correspond to the slow and fast vibrations, respectively, of the compensator. Since we know that the vibration direction of the extraordinary rays are radii in the figure, we can at once tell whether ϵ is fast (uniaxial negative) or slow (uniaxial positive): when the crystal is positive, the pair of quadrants in which compensation occurs is at right angles to the pair of quadrants in the slow direction of the compensator; for negative crystals the compensation occurs in the same pair of quadrants. With thick basal sections of uniaxial crystals possessing marked optical rotatory power, the center of the uniaxial cross is replaced by a bright field, the color of which depends on the

Fig. 22.—Interference figure of uniaxial crystal.

thickness and optical rotatory power of the substance. A perfectly centered optic axial figure does not change when the microscope stage is rotated; if the optic axis is not quite perpendicular to the plane of the section, the center of the figure describes a circle on rotating the stage but the uniaxial cross does not rotate.

The uniaxial optic normal figure, with the crystal in the 45° position between crossed nicols, shows a slight variation in interference color in the outer parts of alternate quadrants. The interference color is lower at the edges of the quadrants in the direction of the optic axis of the crystal and higher at the edges of the other pair of quadrants than it is in the middle of the field (Fig. 23a). If a thick crystal presenting the optic normal figure

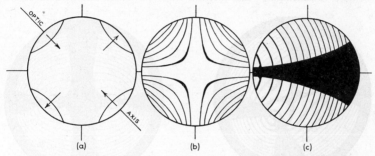

Fig. 23.—Interference figures of uniaxial crystals: (a) optic normal, white light; (b) optic normal, monochromatic light; (c) uncentered figure, monochromatic light.

is examined in the 45° position, the field appears uniformly white; with monochromatic light a series of hyperbolic interference bands appear, as shown in Fig. 23b. When the crystal is rotated to an extinction position, the field of view, with the exception of the edges of the four quadrants, is uniformly dark. On rotating the stage a few degrees either way of the extinction position a pair of broad dark bands rapidly move out of the field, an effect which has caused the optic normal figure to be termed a *flash figure*. Uncentered uniaxial figures in the 45° position show an eccentric series of bands of rising interference, the center of which may, of course, be outside the conoscopic field. In the extinction position a single dark brush crosses the field (Fig. 23c). A uniaxial brush is *always* parallel to the vibration plane of either the polarizer or the analyzer.

C. BIAXIAL INTERFERENCE FIGURES

Three types of centered biaxial figures are possible: the acute bisectrix (Bx_a), obtuse bisectrix (Bx_o), and optic normal figures. The *optic normal* ("flash") figure is indistinguishable from the uniaxial optic normal figure when $2V$ is small.   When $2V$ is in the region of 90°, the edges of all four quadrants show the same slight increase of retardation, so that the figure presents a symmetrical appearance.   The acute bisectrix figure is the most important of those presented by biaxial crystals, since it permits the estimation of the optic axial angle with a fair degree of accuracy (see pages 507–510).

The appearance of an *acute bisectrix* figure for a crystal in the 45° position is shown in figure 24.   In the extinction position, the appearance changes to that shown in figure 25.   The points of emergence of the optic axes are marked by the "eyes" of the figure, which are points of zero retardation and must, therefore, appear dark for any position of rotation of the microscope stage.   Johannsen[44] has termed these points in the interference figure

Fig. 24.—Biaxial interference
figure: 45° position.

Fig. 25.—Biaxial interference
figure: extinction position.

melatopes.   Surrounding the melatopes are bands of equal retardation. which correspond successively to retardations of λ, 2λ, 3λ, ...   In monochromatic light these bands are black; in white light they form a rising series of interference colors.   The apparent distance apart of the melatopes in a centered acute bisectrix figure depends on: (*1*) the numerical aperture of the objective used;   (*2*) the optic axial angle, $2V$, of the crystal; and (*3*) its refractive index, n_β, along the optic axis.   The curves in figure 26 give the maximum observable values of $2V$ for objectives of various numerical apertures as a function of n_β.   Two *isogyres* pass through the melatopes; with the crystal in the 45° position they form two hyperbolic brushes with their convex side toward the acute bisectrix.   The smaller $2V$, the greater is the curvature of the isogyres; for $2V = 90°$ the isogyres are straight.   When the stage is rotated, the isogyres rotate in the opposite direction.   If, instead of rotating the stage, the nicols are rotated synchronously then the isogyres rotate in the same direction as the nicols, but twice as fast. It follows, therefore, that the isogyres of a biaxial crystal, unlike those of a uniaxial one, do not remain parallel to the vibration planes of the polarizer and analyzer. This fact often permits one to judge whether a crystal is uniaxial or biaxial when only an uncentered conoscopic figure can be obtained.

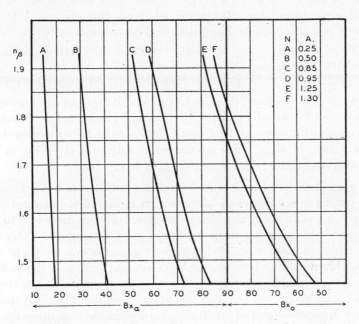

Fig. 26.—Conoscopic field of various microscopic objectives.

The appearance of a centered obtuse bisectrix figure depends very much on the optic axial angle. When $2V$ is nearly $90°$, it resembles that of an acute bisectrix figure with the melatopes just outside the conoscopic field. When $2V$ is nearly $0°$, the figure is practically indistinguishable from that given by the optic normal. The appearance may, of course, be anywhere between these two extremes. One other type of biaxial conoscopic figure is of particular importance, namely, that in which a single optic axis emerges in the field of view. The *single* brush establishes beyond doubt that the crystal is biaxial; its curvature when the crystal is in the $45°$ position renders possible a rough estimation of $2V$; and, from its movement when a compensator is inserted between the objective and the analyzer, the sign of the crystal may be determined by one of the methods given below.

It is convenient to classify conoscopic interference figures of biaxial crystals into the groups *centered*, *displaced*, and *uncentered*, according to whether two, one, or no symmetry planes pass through the center of the figure. Using this classification, we find that the following are essential relationships between the type of biaxial figure and the face upon which a crystal rests.

Centered figures are given by (100), (010), and (001) plates of orthorhombic crystals and by (010) plates of monoclinic crystals. Centered figures by other monoclinic orientations are fortuitous.

Displaced figures are given by (hk0), (h0l) and (0kl) orthorhombic plates and by (100), (001), and (h0l) monoclinic plates.

Uncentered figures are given by (hkl) orthorhombic plates; by (hk0), (0kl) and (hkl) monoclinic plates and by all orientations of triclinic crystals. Centered and displaced figures with triclinic crystals are fortuitous. In the above classification any two, or all three, of the Miller indices denoted by h, k, l, may be alike; thus, an uncentered figure is given by an orthorhombic crystal resting on a pyramid (111) face.

The sign of a biaxial crystal is determined with the aid of some sort of compensating device, such as a quarter-wave mica, a first-order red selenite (gypsum), a quartz wedge or a Berek compensator. One method is to rotate the crystal, which for this purpose should show an acute bisectrix figure, to its extinction position and then to insert a quarter-wave mica of known fast and slow directions between the objective and analyzer; the melatopes and isogyres now appear bright, and a black spot appears below the optic axial plane on one side of the field and above it on the other. If the black spots are in the same pair of quadrants as those in the slow direction of the mica, the crystal is negative, whereas it appears in the adjacent pair of quadrants for a positive crystal. A convenient way of using a first-order red selenite (gypsum) plate is by rotating the crystal to that 45° position in which its optic axial plane is in the same direction as that of the slow component of the selenite. The isogyre or isogyres appears red, which shades to yellow on its convex side and blue on its concave side for positive crystals and to blue on its convex side and yellow on its concave side for negative crystals. This method can obviously be used when only a single isogyre appears in the field, provided, however, that $2V$ is not so nearly equal to 90° that the isogyre is devoid of curvature.

When a quartz wedge of the Wright or Johannsen type, or a Berek compensator (described on page 502) is used to determine the sign of a crystal, it is well to adopt the routine of placing the crystal in the 45° position for which its optic axial plane coincides with the slow vibration direction of the wedge or compensator. Then, on inserting the wedge or rotating the Berek compensator to either side or its normal (30 graduation) position, the isogyres appear to move toward Z. It follows, therefore, that when the isogyre moves in the direction of its convex side the crystal is positive, and that movement in the concave direction shows that the crystal is negative. This method is equally applicable to figures presenting a single isogyre. When an undoubted obtuse bisectrix figure is studied by this means, the unseen concave sides of the isogyres will face the center of the figure. On sliding in the wedge, or on rotating the Berek compensator, the color fringes will move along the optic axial plane towards the center of the figure if the crystal is negative, and out from the center towards the optic axes if the crystal is positive.

It is advisable, when working with unfamiliar polarizing microscopic equipment, to check the above techniques on known crystals. A basal section of calcite, or a fusion slide of sodium nitrate, provides a convenient example of a negative uniaxial substance. A cleavage plate of muscovite ("ordinary") mica, or a fusion slide of piperonal, provides a convenient example of a negative biaxial crystal. The piperonal preparation presents both acute and obtuse bisectrix figures.

4. Determination of Refractive Indices

A. CRYSTAL ORIENTATION

Refractive index determinations with the microscope are usually made by the immersion method in which a very narrow axial cone of illumination is used. The orientation of the crystal is therefore given by the center of the interference figure. In the great majority of polarizing microscopes, the vibration direction of the polarizer is in the $N–S$ direction (to and from the observer), or, in the case of microscopes with synchronous rotation of the nicols, it is easily set in this position. This position of the vibration plane of the polarizer will therefore be assumed in the following discussion. Isotropic crystals, having a single refractive index, do not require special orientation.

Uniaxial crystals have two principal indices, n_ω and n_ϵ. Optic normal orientations present both. For n_ω, set the crystal at extinction with its crystallographic c-axis (direction of the optic axis) $E–W$ and withdraw the analyzer. For n_ϵ set c in $N–S$ position. Centered optic axis figures (basal plates) give n_ω only for all settings.

Biaxial crystals. Centered acute bisectrix, obtuse bisectrix, and optic normal figures indicate that two optical symmetry planes intersect in the center of the figure. Consequently, crystals giving these conoscopic figures present two of the three principal refractive indices. Displaced figures present only one principal index and uncentered figures do not present any.

The particular refractive index for plane-polarized light transmitted through a biaxial crystal in an extinction position is readily deduced by considering the type of interference figure in conjunction with the following rules:

(1) When the convergent polarized light interference figure shows that axial rays are transmitted along the acute or obtuse bisectrix, the crystal is at extinction when the plane of the optic axes is in the N–S or E–W position. The vibration at right angles to the plane of the optic axes is n_β regardless of whether the figure is that of the acute or obtuse bisectrix, and the vibration in the plane of the optic axes must therefore be for n_α or n_γ, depending on whether or not it corresponds to a lower or a higher index than n_β, respectively. It follows therefore that, when a crystal showing a centered bisectrix figure is rotated to an extinction position, and the analyzer prism and converger are withdrawn, light is transmitted through the crystal with a velocity corresponding to n_α, n_β, or n_γ. The various possibilities are given in table V.

TABLE V

OPTICAL ORIENTATION

Interference figure	Sign	Direction of optical axial plane	Index
Acute bisectrix	Positive	N–S	α
Acute bisectrix	Positive	E–W	β
Acute bisectrix	Negative	N–S	γ
Acute bisectrix	Negative	E–W	β
Obtuse bisectrix	Positive	N–S	γ
Obtuse bisectrix	Positive	E–W	β
Obtuse bisectrix	Negative	N–S	α
Obtuse bisectrix	Negative	E–W	β

(2) When convergent polarized light gives a centered optic normal or "flash" figure, one of the extinction positions presents the lowest principal index, n_α, and the other presents the highest index, n_γ.

(3) One principal index is presented by crystals which give a displaced interference figure, since an optical symmetry plane passes through the center of the figure. Possible cases are: obtuse and acute bisectrix figures, either positive or negative in sign, when displaced in the plane of the optic axes, present n_β when the direction of the optic axial plane is E–W, and the transmitted light is vibrating N–S. Obtuse and acute bisectrix figures when displaced laterally present n_α or n_γ when the optic axial plane is N–S (see Table V). In the case of crystals giving an optic normal flash figure displaced along a principal plane, a very simple rule gives the principal index presented: the crystal is placed at extinction with the optic normal E or W of the microscope axis; the N–S vibration direction then

corresponds to n_α or n_γ, depending on whether this is the "fast" or "slow" direction.

B. IMMERSION METHODS

The immersion method of determining the refractive indices of small crystals may be said to date from the work of Maschke,[45] who described the appearance of crystals immersed in liquids of differing refractive indices. Becke[46] first described the movement of fringes of light seen around immersed crystals when the microscope objective was raised or lowered, an effect now known as the Becke line.   Schroeder van der Kolk[47] did much to popularize the immersion method of determining the refractive index of

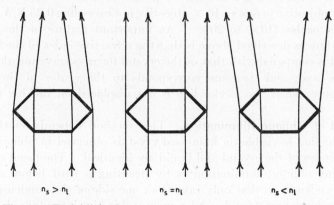

$n_s > n_l$ $n_s = n_l$ $n_s < n_l$

Fig. 27.—Becke line of prism with index n_s in liquid with index n_l.

crystalline substances.   Stated simply, the immersion method consists of matching a refractive index of a crystal with that of a liquid whose refractive index is either known or can be measured; and the many variations in present day procedure depend on alternative methods of ascertaining when the index has been matched, and of measuring the refractive index of the liquid.   There are two principal methods of comparing the refractive index of a transparent solid with that of a liquid in which it is immersed: the central illumination method which makes use of the Becke line effect, and the method of oblique illumination.

Method of Central Illumination.—This method depends on the fact that a crystal or crystal grain having a prismatic or lenticular cross section

[45] O. Maschke, *Ann. Physik Chem.*, **145**, 549 (1872); *ibid.*, [N. S.] **11**, 722 (1880).

[46] F. Becke, *Sitzber. Akad. Wiss. Wien*, **102**, 358 (1893).

[47] J. L. C. Schroeder van der Kolk: *Kurze Anleitung zur mikroskopischen Krystallbestimmung*, Wiesbaden, 1898, p. 11; *Tabellen zur mikroskopischen Bestimmung der Mineralien nach ihrem Brechungsindex*, Wiesbaden, 1906.

does not deviate axial light rays when immersed in a liquid having an identical refractive index, whereas the rays are deviated if the crystal and immersion liquid differ in refractive index.   The nature of this deviation is readily understood from the diagram in figure 27, which shows that rays passing through a prismatic (or lenticular) edge of a crystal are bent toward the crystal if it has a higher index than that of the liquid, and away from the crystal if it has the lower index.   Consequently, when the microscope system is racked *upward*, the band of light from the crystal edges appears to move toward the substance with the *higher* refractive index.   These Becke-line phenomena are best observed by using: a bright source of light, preferably monochromatic; a narrow cone of light from the polarizer such as is given by a low-power condenser stopped down; a low-power objective (a 6 × or 10 × objective not exceeding 0.25 N.A.) and a high-power ocular (10× to 20×).   An important feature of the Becke-line procedure as described above is that the refractive index of the immersion liquid is compared with that of the crystal for rays traveling along the microscope axis, and therefore corresponds to the center of the interference figure, when the Becke line is not displaced on racking up the objective.

Method of Oblique Illumination.—This method depends on the fact that no shading is visible on immersed crystals observed in oblique light when the index of the crystal and liquid are identical.   The usual method of obtaining oblique illumination is by inserting a card below a high-aperture condenser so that only rays from one side of the condenser pass through the immersed crystal.   A low-power objective is used for observing the shading on the crystal, which appears on the side facing the direction in which the card is inserted if the crystal has the higher refractive index, and on the opposite side if it has the lower index.   The substage condenser should be racked up fully.   This method of oblique illumination is open to the objection that the rays used in the test do not pass axially through the crystal; although the error so introduced is small with crystals of low birefringence, it may be appreciable with substances of high birefringence, such as are common among aromatic compounds.   Saylor[48] has discussed the sources of error both in the Becke-line method of central illumination and the method of oblique illumination.   He found the latter to be unreliable with strongly birefringent crystals, and described a much improved method employing two diaphragms—one inserted below the converger element of the condenser from the right-hand side so as to obscure about half the aperture, and the other, a stop covering the right-hand half of the back lens of a 3.2× objective.   Saylor recommends that

---

[48] C. P. Saylor, *J. Research Natl. Bur. Standards*, **15**, 277 (1935).

the vibration plane of the beam of polarized light should be horizontal
(*E–W*) rather than vertical (*N–S*) as is commonly used with Becke-line
methods.

C. IMMERSION LIQUIDS

Adjusting the Refractive Index of the Immersion Liquid.—The Becke-
line effect, and the shadows in oblique light tell us when the refractive
index of a liquid is higher or lower than that of the immersed solid. In
fact, with some experience, the difference between them can be estimated
to 0.1. The problem of the immersion method is, therefore, to adjust
the refractive index of the liquid so that it substantially matches that of
the immersed solid. The following is a list of methods which can be used
for this purpose.

(*1*) *By changing the immersion liquid.* This is usually accomplished
by having a set of liquids of known refractive index going from about
1.360 to 1.780 in steps of about 0.005. The most expeditious way of
working with such a set of liquids is to start with one of $n = 1.55$, and use
it as a mountant for crystals held between an object slide and cover glass.
The interference figures of the crystals should be studied in order to make
sure that principal indices are being determined. It is then noted, by
examination in central or oblique illumination, whether the principal
indices of the crystal are higher or lower than the index of the liquid.
Liquids nearer to the estimated indices are then tried on another preparation of the crystals; and this operation is repeated until finally each of
the indices is matched to within 0.005. If an index of the crystal falls
between those of two liquids, it is usually possible to judge the index to
0.002. It should be remembered, however, that inaccurate orientation of
the crystal and temperature changes during the manipulations can introduce an error of greater magnitude than 0.002. Where only a very small
quantity of crystalline material is available, it is advantageous to use
volatile immersion media which have been redistilled, since in this case one
liquid may be allowed to evaporate before the next is applied to the same
preparation. The high-index melts used by Larsen and Berman[49] for
determining the refractive index of minerals are unsuitable for refractive
index work on organic compounds.

(*2*) *By varying the temperature of the immersion liquid.* Of the various
methods which have been developed to permit the use of fewer liquid
standards with a given specimen, that of changing the refractive index of
the liquid by varying its temperature has possibly found most favor

---

[49] E. S. Larsen and H. Berman, "Microscopic Determination of the Nonopaque
Minerals," *U. S. Geol. Survey Bull.* No. 848 (1934).

amongst petrographers. The thermal variation method was originated by Gaubert,[50] and is based on the fact that the temperature coefficient of refractive index, dn/dT, of a liquid is considerably greater than that of most minerals and inorganic compounds. In principle, the transparent or translucent substance is immersed in a liquid of slightly higher refractive index, and the temperature of the system is then raised slowly to the point at which central or oblique illumination test shows that the indices of liquid and solid are equal. Both Emmons[51] and Saylor[52] have described heating cells for this purpose. That of Saylor has the special advantage of thinness, so that it permits the use of conoscopic observation of an immersed crystal in order to determine if one or both of its vibration directions are on optical symmetry planes, and, therefore, correspond to principal indices.

(3) *By varying the wave length of the light used for observation.* Posnjak and Merwin[53] originated the method of adjusting the refractive index to that of the immersed solid by using a monochromator as a light source, and by varying the wave length until the central or oblique illumination test shows that a match has been obtained. By working with an overlapping series of liquids of known refractive index and dispersion, it is possible to obtain values for the refractive index of a given solid at various temperatures.

The last two methods (*2* and *3*) of varying the refractive index of an immersion liquid have been combined in the *double variation* method of Emmons,[54] who has also devised a universal stage technique which employs a special lower segment with a water-circulation device for regulating the temperature. The universal stage is used for orienting the crystals or crystal fragments which are held between a pair of cover glasses "oiled" to the segments with an appropriate immersion fluid. In the absence of a specially equipped universal stage, the necessary determination of the optical orientation may be carried out in convergent polarized light with the Bertrand lens if a Saylor heating cell is used, as this cell is, of course, equally usable for the double variation method.

(*4*) *By mixing two nonvolatile liquids on the microscope slide.* The author[55] proposed the system of mixing two substantially nonvolatile liquids of widely separated refractive indices in a cavity on a microscope object glass, varying their proportion until the refractive index of an

[50] P. Gaubert, *Bull. soc. franç. minéral.*, **45**, 89 (1922).

[51] R. C. Emmons, *Am. Mineral.*, **13**, 504 (1928).

[52] C. P. Saylor, *J. Research Natl. Bur. Standards*, **15**, 97 (1935).

[53] E. Posnjak and H. E. Merwin, *J. Am. Chem. Soc.*, **44**, 1970 (1922).

[54] R. C. Emmons, *Am. Mineral.*, **11**, 115 (1926); **13**, 504 (1928); **14**, 414, 441. 482 (1929).

[55] E. E. Jelley, *J. Roy. Microscop. Soc.*, **54**, 234 (1934).

immersed solid has been matched. Some of the liquid is then transferred to the prism of a microrefractometer, and its refractive index is read. Provided that the immersion liquids, microscope, and microrefractometer have stood in the workroom to reach room temperature to within $\pm 2°$, no temperature control is necessary. For work with crystals of inorganic compounds and organic compounds of low solubility, the liquids originally chosen are given in table VI. However, since this work was published,

TABLE VI

LIQUIDS FOR DETERMINATION OF REFRACTIVE INDEX

	Substance	Boiling point, deg. C.	d_4^{20}	n_D^{20}	dn/dT
1	Ethyl oxalate	73° at 10 mm.	1.0793	1.410	0.00048
2	Ethyl citrate	180° at 11 mm.	1.1369	1.443	0.00036
3	n-Butyl phthalate	155° at 10 mm.	1.0388	1.492	0.00032
4	α-Bromonaphthalene	148° at 16 mm.	1.4876	1.658	0.00048
5	α-Iodonaphthalene	160° at 14 mm.	1.7344[a]	1.702	0.00047
6	Methylene iodide	180° at 760 mm.	3.325	1.742	0.00068

[a] d_4^{15}.

the author has substituted di-n-butyl carbonate, $n_D^{20} = 1.411$ for diethyl oxalate and tri-n-butyl citrate, $n_D^{20} = 1.445$, for triethyl citrate. There are now available a large number of commercial plasticizers which will serve for the lower refractive index range.

The mixing of the liquids is readily carried out by stirring with a glass rod drawn out to about a millimeter diameter at the stirring end. The liquids can be handled conveniently in small hypodermic syringes, which are well adapted for transferring small amounts of liquid to the slide excavation in which the mixing is performed.[56] Since the refractive index of the liquid is determined after a match has been obtained, the liquids used need not be pure—the only necessary condition is that their refractive index shall not change within a few minutes exposure to the air.

The refractive index of a mixture of two liquids of different volatilities and refractive index may be regulated by differential evaporation. This method is particularly applicable to Clerici's method of determining refractive indices by means of the apparatus described below. Promising results have been obtained with this method by using the following mixtures:[57]

(*1*) Two volumes of diethyl carbonate and one volume of α-iodonaphthalene has $n_D^{20} = 1.491$, which rises on evaporation of the ethyl carbonate to 1.702.

---

[56] R. N. Titus, *private communication.*

[57] E. E. Jelley, *unpublished work.*

(*2*) Two volumes of *n*-butyl acetate and one volume of α-iodonaphthalene has $n_{\mathrm{D}}^{20} = 1.497$, which rises on evaporation to 1.702.

(*3*) Two volumes of *n*-heptane and one volume of α-iodonaphthalene has $n_{\mathrm{D}}^{20} = 1.492$, which rises on evaporation to 1.702.

(*4*) By substituting *n*-butyl phthalate for α-iodonaphthalene in the above formulas, liquids are obtained having a refractive index of about 1.42, which rises on evaporation to 1.49.

Similarly, the refractive index of mixtures of methylene iodide and Merwin's solution[58] may be adjusted by allowing the methylene iodide to evaporate, whereby the index is raised. Merwin's solution consists of methylene iodide saturated with sulfur, iodoform, stannic iodide, arsenic triiodide, and antimony triiodide. A rather deep cell was used for the "variation-by-evaporation" technique, which worked well with moderately large crystals. Once the index corresponding to a known vibration direction had been obtained, some of the liquid was transferred by means of a micropipette (constructed from a medicine dropper) to a modified prism on the author's microrefractometer described below.

The solubility of many crystalline organic compounds in organic immersion media—especially methylene iodide, frequently imposes a restriction on the number of methods of matching the refractive index of the crystal with that of the liquid. Thermal variation methods can rarely be used, partly because the solvent action of the media is much more rapid at higher temperatures, and partly because dn/dT of the crystal may be appreciable. The wave-length variation method sometimes fails because $dn/d\lambda$ is of the same order of magnitude as that of organic immersion liquids. Where sets of known liquids are used, these may be saturated with the compound under study and recalibrated with an Abbé refractometer.[59] One particular advantage of the author's technique of varying the refractive index by mixing two liquids, or by differential evaporation, is that any moderate degree of dissolution of the solid is automatically compensated for, since the refractive index is measured after the match has been obtained. Certain aqueous and glycerol solutions of highly refractive inorganic salts, particularly of potassium mercuric iodide, are useful immersion media. Sonstadt's or Thoulet's solution[60] is prepared by dissolving 230 grams of potassium iodide and 270 grams of mercuric iodide in 80 milliliters of water, and then cautiously evaporating on a steam bath until a crystalline film forms on the surface of the liquid. The clear portion is decanted. It has a refractive index of about 1.72. It should be noted that this solu-

[58] H. E. Merwin, *J. Wash. Acad. Sci.*, **3**, 35 (1913).

[59] W. M. D. Bryant, *J. Am. Chem. Soc.*, **65**, 96 (1943).

[60] A. Johannsen, *Manual of Petrographic Methods*. McGraw-Hill, New York, 1918, pp. 250, 519.

tion contains 2.33 times as much potassium iodide as that required to form potassium mercuric iodide (KHgI$_3$). If an excess of mercuric iodide is used, a solution of potassium mercuric iodide is obtained which has a considerably lower refractive index. The author prepared aqueous solutions of various alkali mercuric iodides of the general formula $\overset{\text{I}}{\text{M}}HgI_3$, saturated at 20° C. These had the following refractive indices:

$$
\begin{array}{cccc}
\overset{\text{I}}{\text{M}} = & \text{Li} & \text{Na} & \text{K} \\
n_\text{D}^{20} = & 1.620 & 1.621 & 1.615
\end{array}
$$

Dunningham[61] studied the system KI–HgI$_2$–H$_2$O and found that the solid phase, K$_2$HgI$_4$, does not exist, contrary to the statements in many textbooks. The author[57] has confirmed, by means of a microscopical study of the crystals which separated from Sonstadt's solution on evaporation, that only KI and KHgI$_3$ are found at 30° C. The principal objection to Sonstadt's solution is its very poisonous and corrosive nature.

Nonprincipal Refractive Indices.—In chemical work, particularly with monoclinic and triclinic crystals, it is often useful to measure the refractive indices corresponding to the two vibration directions presented by some well-defined and easily recognizable crystallographic orientation of the crystal. This is especially true of crystals having a lamellar or tabular habit, since such crystals usually present the same orientation, and measurements of the refractive indices presented are of value in identification work. For purposes of publication, such indices should be accompanied by an accurate sketch showing the crystallographic, and, if possible, the optical orientation.

D. MEASURING REFRACTIVE INDEX OF IMMERSION LIQUID

When the refractive index of the immersion liquid has been adjusted by either the method of mixtures or the method of evaporation, it becomes necessary to determine its refractive index. The quantity of liquid worked with is usually so small that the index must be measured on a single drop. The choice of method employed is usually governed by the optical apparatus available.

Wright[62] gave an account of known methods and of several original methods. The first three of his methods depend on the use of easily constructed hollow prisms which are used on a spectrometer or goniometer. The fourth method uses an Abbé–Pulfrich crystal refractometer. A drop of liquid is placed on the horizontal surface of the hemisphere and is covered with a piece of matt tinfoil, which is made by pressing the smooth foil onto

---

[61] A. C. Dunningham, *J. Chem. Soc.*, **105**, 368 (1914).
[62] F. E. Wright, *J. Wash. Acad. Sci.*, **4**, 269 (1914).

ground glass by means of a pencil eraser. Its function is to prevent the appearance of troublesome interference bands which are present when the thin film of liquid is bounded by a substantially plane liquid–air interface. "Dull" and "medium" grades of aluminum foil work equally well. The author has tried Wright's fourth method on a Bausch & Lomb Abbé refractometer with excellent results. However, the dividing line is not easily seen when reflecting matt foil is used, but it is readily seen if black or dark foil is used, such as oxidized copper foil or sulfided silver or lead foil. For nonaqueous immersion liquids, a piece of gelatin-coated black paper serves very well, provided that it has been pressed flat. Advantages of this technique are that the lower prism of the Abbé can be closed, and the temperature control used, and that the dispersion of the liquid is compensated for

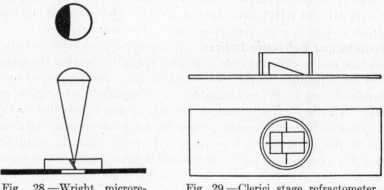

Fig. 28.—Wright microre-   Fig. 29.—Clerici stage refractometer.
      fractometer.

by the Amici prisms, the degree of rotation of which can be used in computing the dispersion, v. It should be remembered, however, that the prisms of the Abbé refractometer are constructed of heavy flint glass which is rather easily scratched; hence the foil, or coated black paper, should be kept free from dust.

Wright's fifth method is an ingenious application of the critical-angle method of determining refractive indices. The apparatus, which is shown diagrammatically in figure 28, is in effect a miniature pair of Abbé prisms. The prisms have a refractive index of 1.92, and an angle of 60°. The lower prism has a ground surface, and the upper prism a polished one. A drop of the immersion liquid is placed in the gap between the two prisms. A low-power objective is focused on the top surface of the cell, and the Bertrand lens of the microscope is introduced. The field is then seen to be divided into light and dark portions separated by a color fringe, if white light is used. In monochromatic light, which today is conveniently obtained from sodium-vapor and mercury-vapor lamps, the dividing line is sharp. Its position depends on the refractive index of the immersion liquid, and is recorded by means of a filar micrometer. The apparatus is calibrated with known liquids. Wright's sixth, seventh, eighth, and ninth methods are alternative forms of critical-angle apparatus for use with the petrographic microscope, and do not appear to have gained much popularity.

Clerici's method[63] employs a cell containing a prism mounted over an index line, as shown diagrammatically in figure 29. When the cell is filled with immersion liquid, the compound glass–liquid prism displaces the

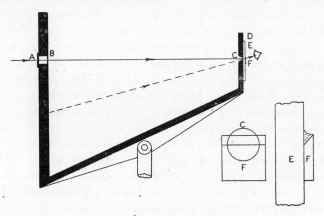

Fig. 30.—Jelley microrefractometer.

image of the index line by an amount which is a function of the refractive index of the liquid. The displacement is measured at moderate magnification with a filar micrometer eyepiece. The setup can be calibrated by means of known liquids. Viola[64] improved Clerici's method by using a double prism with its apex vertically over the index line. Nichols[65] uses two prisms cemented side by side, and sloping in opposite directions. Both Viola's and Nichols' methods have the advantage that the displaced lines are at the same focus, whereas in Clerici's original design the greater the displacement the greater the difference in focus. Wright[62] found that Clerici's method was accurate to only ±0.005, and that Viola's modification was somewhat more accurate. Nichols claims an accuracy of ±0.001.

The author[55] described a new type of microrefractometer which is a self-

[63] E. Clerici, *Atti accad. Lincei*, **16**, 336 (1907); **18**, 351 (1909).

[64] C. Viola, *Atti accad. Lincei*, **19**, 192 (1910).

[65] L. Nichols, *Natl. Paint Bull.*, **1**, 12 (1937).

contained, direct-reading instrument. Its optical principle is shown in figure 30. Light from a fixed slit, A, passes through a narrow slot in a scale, B, which is graduated in refractive index. The slit is viewed through aperture C in stage plate D. Over the aperture is placed a plate of glass, E, about one millimeter thick which supports microprism F. The microprism, which is obtained by beveling one edge of an optically worked cover glass at 45°, is placed with the bevel facing the glass plate. The lower (obtuse) edge of the bevel is placed approximately midway over the aperture in the stage plate, and parallel with the slit. A drop of the immersion liquid is placed in the bevel so as to form a compound glass–liquid prism. On looking through the aperture, a deviated image of the slit is seen superimposed on an undeviated image of the scale. This image of the slit which is obtained with white light is spread out into a spectrum, the position of the yellow on the scale giving the approximate value of n_D. With sodium light, the principal image is bordered by a number of diffraction bands. A form of the apparatus was made and sold by E. $Leitz$ ($London$) $Ltd.$ under the name of the Leitz-Jelley Microrefractometer, which incorporated two improvements suggested by the author. The first of these was a didymium (Nd + Pr) glass filter over the slit for use with white light. When this is used, the spectrum image of the slit is seen to be crossed by two sharp bands, the one nearer the red giving the value of n_D to ±0.001. The second improvement was a transparent index which moved over the scale and was set to correspond with the didymium band. The refractive index could then be read, and checked, at leisure.

Two other modifications of the Jelley microrefractometer have appeared which, however, both employ the same optical principle. These are the modification of Edwards and Otto,[66] which is calibrated by known liquids instead of the more accurate, but less convenient, method of optical computation, and that recently made and sold in the United States under the name of Fisher refractometer.

In its original form, the microrefractometer was used to measure the refractive index of about 0.1 cubic millimeter, or 0.0001 milliliter. The Leitz-Jelley instrument had a more robust prism, and needed about 0.0005 milliliter of liquid. In the original publication, the author suggested two special uses of the microrefractometer in chemical microscopy: checking the purity of a micro quantity of liquid by measuring its refractive index as it evaporates, and characterizing organic compounds by determining n_D at their melting point. A modification of the Fisher refractometer with a heating stage for carrying out this measurement has been described by Frediani.[67]

[66] A. E. Edwards and C. E. Otto, *Ind. Eng. Chem.*, *Anal. Ed.*, **10**, 225 (1938).

[67] H. A. Frediani, *Ind. Eng. Chem.*, *Anal. Ed.*, **14**, 439 (1942).

A modification of the author's microprism, shown in figure 31, permits the use of the microrefractometer with volatile liquids.[68] This enclosed prism, which has a side 0.1–0.4 millimeter, will hold the liquid in the vertical position and so can be used with a vertical slit and horizontal scale. A direct-reading, self-contained microrefractometer eases the work of determining refractive indices by the immersion method. There does not appear to be any good reason why the Wright prism (Wright's fifth method, described on page 498) could not be built into a simplified Abbé-type refractometer without Amici prisms. This could be used with monochromatic light.

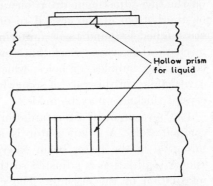

Hollow prism for liquid

Fig. 31.—Microprism for volatile liquids.

5. Determination of Birefringence and Its Dispersion

A. COMPENSATORS

It is necessary to distinguish between the *principal birefringences* which are the differences between principal indices, for example, $n_\omega \sim n_\epsilon$ of uniaxial crystals, $n_\gamma - n_\alpha$, $n_\gamma - n_\beta$, and $n_\beta - n_\alpha$ of biaxial ones, and the nonprincipal birefringence presented by some known crystallographic orientation of a crystal. In organic chemical microscopy, it is often possible to grow relatively large crystal plates by crystallization from a melt; and quite frequently these crystal plates have a constant optical orientation. Consequently, measurements of birefringence on such plates can be of value in comparing an unknown substance with a known one. Principal birefringences are of value in estimating n_γ and sometimes n_β of aromatic substances which usually are beyond the range of measurement by the immersion technique.

We have seen (pages 463–467) that polarized light entering a crystal not in the extinction position is resolved into two beams vibrating at right angles which travel with different velocities, so that one ray is retarded relative to the other. The distance by which the one ray is retarded on its emergence from the crystal is known as the retardation of the crystal for that particular direction of light transmission. Retardation is given by the expression:

$$R = t(n_2 - n_1) \tag{15}$$

where t is the thickness of the crystal, n_2 is the higher index, and n_1 the lower.

---

[68] E. E. Jelley, *unpublished work*.

(R and t are, of course, expressed in the same units, such as mm., μ or mμ.) If n_2 and n_1 are principal indices, it follows that R/t is a *principal birefringence*. Measurements of retardation can usually be made without much difficulty on small crystals, but the measurement of thickness is another matter. At first sight it might appear to be possible to orient the crystal so that only rays corresponding to n_α (or the lower index of a uni-axial substance) were transmitted, and then to note the distance traversed on the fine-adjustment drum on racking up the microscope from a focus on the bottom of the crystal to one on the top. However, in practice, the method is found to be quite inaccurate, for a variety of optical and mechanical reasons. Sometimes crystals prepared by the fusion method contain air bubbles, or holes, which extend from the object slide to the cover glass; in this case, a somewhat less inaccurate measurement of the crystal thickness may be made.

The measurement of retardation is usually made with the aid of a compensator. A compensator is a means of introducing a known re-tardation in the faster beam emerging from a crystal. The amount of known retardation is adjusted so that it neutralizes, or compensates, the retardation of the crystal. The earliest type of compensator was the quartz wedge of Biot,[69] which suffered from the disadvantage that the thin end still had an appreciable retardation. Wright[70] combined a quartz wedge with a parallel plate having a retardation corresponding to that of the middle of the wedge, but with its fast vibration direction at right angles to that of the wedge. The Wright combination wedge has zero retardation in the center, with increasing retardation on either side—one side having its fast vibration parallel, and the other at right angles, to the length of the wedge. This wedge, which is usually engraved to give direct readings of retardation, is particularly useful when used with the Wright universal ocular[71] in which it slides in the focal plane of the ocular. The Johannsen[72] wedge is somewhat similar but has zero birefringence at one end. The Berek compensator,[73] which is an improvement on the earlier one of Niki-tin,[74] consists essentially of a thin plate of calcite cut perpendicularly to the optical axis which is rotated about a diameter by means of a graduated drum. This compensator is inserted in a slot over the microscope objective and so does not entail the use of an analyzer over the eyepiece.

---

[69] See A. Johannsen, *Manual of Petrographic Methods*. McGraw-Hill, New York, 1918, p. 366.

[70] F. E. Wright, *J. Geol.*, **10**, 33 (1902).

[71] F. E. Wright, *Am. J. Sci.*, **29**, 416 (1910).

[72] A. Johannsen, *Am. J. Sci.*, **29**, 436 (1910).

[73] M. Berek, *Centr. Mineral. Geol.*, **1913**, 388, 427, 464, 580.

[74] W. Nikitin, *Z. Kryst.*, **47**, 378 (1910).

Compensators do not work well with substances having a strong dispersion of birefringence, as the compensation point is often masked by color effects, particularly at higher retardations. The problem cannot be solved by using monochromatic light because compensation occurs at wave-length intervals in monochromatic light, and only the difference of the retardation from the nearest integral multiple of wave lengths can be determined. However, the strong dispersion of birefringence of many organic crystals makes measurements of this dispersion highly desirable as a means of characterization of organic compounds.

B. MICROSPECTROGRAPH

In order to overcome the difficulty of determining the compensation point at a number of wave lengths, the author[75] has worked out three methods of determining the dispersion of birefringence of organic compounds which melt without decomposition, and one which is applicable to crystals which are not recrystallizable by fusion. These methods were designed primarily for use with the grating microspectrograph, three different designs of which have been described in the publications referred to above. In view of the increasing interest in optical methods of identifying organic compounds it seems desirable to summarize the methods here:

Method 1.—A square or rectangular piece of No. 2 or No. 3 cover glass is placed on an object slide, which is preferably, but not necessarily, made of optically worked fused quartz. Another square of cover is placed so that one edge rests on the first cover and the other on the slide. Some crystals of the substance to be studied are placed near the sloping cover slip, and the slide is then heated on a hot plate until the substance melts and is drawn under the sloping cover glass to form a wedge of liquid. The preparation is then cooled and, if necessary, seeded by touching the liquid with some solid substance on a needle. Usually the preparation needs careful "melting back," until crystal remains only under one corner of the thin end of the wedge. The slide is then allowed to cool very slowly in order to obtain crystals of uniform orientation. Such a wedge preparation shows ascending orders of retardation when examined in polarized light (crossed nicols) with a low-power objective. The image of the wedge is focused on the slit of the microspectrograph so that the slit cuts through the color bands at right angles. Spectrograms are then made on Panatomic-X 35-mm. film. From these spectrograms the dispersion is readily obtained by one of two methods. The first is applicable when many interference bands are visible. A line is ruled through the spectrogram

[75] E. E. Jelley, *Phot. J.*, **74**, 514 (1934); *J. Roy. Microscop. Soc.*, **56**, 101 (1936); *Ind. Eng. Chem., Anal. Ed.*, **13**, 196 (1941). See also E. M. Chamot and C. W. Mason, *Handbook of Chemical Microscopy*, 2nd ed., Vol. I, Wiley, New York, 1938, pp. 183–186.

in a position corresponding to the thick end of the wedge crystal, as in figure 32. Irregularities in the crystal cause many lines to run through the length of the spectrum: one of these should be chosen as a guide for the ruled line, thereby avoiding errors due to aberrations of the optical system. A wave-length scale is then attached to the spectrogram, and the wave lengths, λ_n, λ_{n+1}, λ_{n+2}, ..., at which the nth, $(n + 1)$th, $(n + 2)$th, ... interference bands cross the ruled line are recorded. The reason for using a wedge is, of course, that the value of n is immediately given if the extreme tip of the wedge appears in the spectrogram. The value of the retardation

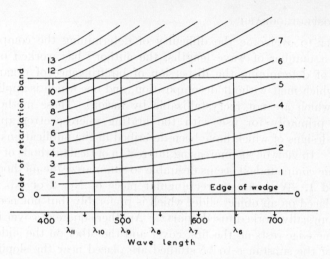

Fig. 32.—Computation of dispersion of birefringence from spectrogram.

for any wave length, λ_n, at which an interference band of the nth order intersects the ruled line is $n\lambda_n$, and the corresponding birefringence is $n\lambda_n/t$, where t is the thickness of the wedge at the corresponding point. The values of $n\lambda_n$ are plotted against λ, if necessary, to obtain the value of the retardation for sodium light ($\lambda = 589.3$). The curve is then redrawn with the values of the retardation at various wave lengths being expressed relative to that of $\lambda = 589.3$, which is taken as unity. In this way, we avoid the need for measuring the thickness of the wedge. The manner of using a monochromator for this method is explained later in this chapter. It should be noted that the wedge crystal can be used for determining the value of the birefringence in monochromatic light if the slope of the wedge is known: thus, if the slope of the wedge is θ, and the distance between two bands (measured by means of a micrometer eyepiece) is d for a wave length λ, the birefringence for that wave length is $\lambda/d \tan \theta$. Since the angle of the wedge is small, usually about $2°$, it is necessary to measure it to within $\pm 1'$ if reasonable accuracy is desired.

Method 2.—A small planoconvex lens, preferably of fused silica, and an optically worked object slide of fused silica are required. The microspectrograph is calibrated for any given microscope setup (usually the lowest power the microscope will give) by photographing the Newton's rings given in sodium light, with the slit of the microspectrograph wide open. If transmitted light is used, the upper surface of the object slide and the convex surface of the lens must either be half-silvered or else coated with a thin dye film which strongly reflects sodium light. By far the best dye of those studied is 1,1'-diethyl-2,2'-cyanine chloride, which is used as a 1% solution in a mixture of 9 parts of methanol and 1 part of water. When a drop of this solution is applied to each surface, it spreads out and evaporates to leave a film of dye having a very sharp absorption band at 578 mμ, and, in consequence, a very high refractive index for sodium light. The Newton's rings produced by dye-treated surfaces are quite as good as those obtained with half-silvering. In order to prepare lens crystals, the lens is placed convex side down on the object slide and touching a little of the substance under study. The slide is then heated in order to melt the substance and cause it to flow under the lens. The slide is then cooled and seeded, if necessary, to crystallize the melt. It is usually necessary to melt back the crystals until only a trace remains solid, and then cool very slowly in order to obtain well-formed crystals. When such a preparation is examined with crossed nicols in monochromatic light, a series of dark rings is seen, corresponding to retardations of λ, 2λ, 3λ, etc., whose radii are proportional to 1, $\sqrt{2}$, $\sqrt{3}$, etc. When more than one optical orientation is presented, different series of rings are apparent: thus piperonal may give rings corresponding to $n_\beta - n_\alpha$, and rings of about four-and-a-half times the diameter corresponding to $n_\gamma - n_\beta$. However, it may happen that the orientation does not correspond to an axis of the wave surface, so that rings do not correspond to a principal birefringence. In this case, the measurements of dispersion are only of value if the substance always presents the same orientation in a lens crystal; fortunately, this is often the case. The image of the lens crystal is thrown on the slit of the microspectrograph, care being taken to assure that the slit passes through the center of the figure. From a comparison of the Newton's rings and the interference spectrogram, the birefringence of the substance can be determined for all wave lengths from 400 to 660 mμ with panchromatic film, and in the infrared with suitably sensitized film or plates.

Method 3.—This method employs "droplet crystals" and has the advantage of simplicity, but the disadvantage that it gives the dispersion of birefringence only. Fragments of the substance under study, weighing between 0.1 and 10 mg. are fused on a microscope slide. On cooling, the droplets crystallize to yield wedge-shaped crystals, which are examined as in Method 1.

Method for Substances not Recrystallizable by Fusion.—The method of computing the retardation–λ graph, and of deriving the dispersion of birefringence which is described under Method 1 is readily applied to crystals which possess either a crystallographically or an artificially produced wedge-shaped edge. The crystals should be mounted in a medium having an index not too far removed from the mean of the two indices presented. Some of the viscous Arachlors, and mixtures of Arachlors with Canada balsam, and the other viscous media mentioned earlier in this section, are very useful. If possible the crystal is rolled under the cover glass until its interference figure shows that a principal birefringence is presented. Since the purpose of the wedged part of the crystal serves merely to indicate the order of the retardation bands, the wedge may be quite crude; even a rounded end of a crystal obtained by dissolving one end of the crystal will serve.

C. MONOCHROMATOR

A small monochromator, such as the Bausch & Lomb Laboratory Wave-Length Spectrometer, may be used for determining the dispersion of birefringence of crystals having a wedge-shaped edge. The microscope is illuminated with light from the exit slit of the monochromator. An appropriate crystal, whose optical orientation has previously been determined conoscopically with white light, is brought to the center of the field and is placed in the 45° position. The light from the monochromator is thrown on the crystal so that the wedge-shaped edge is illuminated, as well as a flat thick part of the crystal which is imaged on the cross webs. The wave-length drum is turned to the extreme red and is then brought slowly back until the part of the crystal on the cross webs is at extinction. The order of the retardation band, n, and wave length, λ_n, are noted. The wave length of the light is shortened until the crystal is again dark and the wave length λ_{n+1} for the $(n + 1)$th retardation band is noted. This operation is repeated for the entire spectrum. The computation of dispersion and its graphical expression are carried out as described above. The lens method may be used for determining the value of the birefringence for sodium 589 mμ or mercury 546 mμ in order to convert the values of dispersion of birefringence into birefringences at various wave lengths.

Approximate values of dispersion of birefringence may be obtained with the aid of a microspectroscope having a wave-length scale. A crystal with a wedge-shaped edge is used, as in the method described above, to determine the order of the retardation band; the wave lengths, λ_n, λ_{n+1}, λ_{n+2}, ... at which the nth, $(n + 1)$th, $(n + 2)$th bands cross the spectrum are noted, and the necessary computations are made.

Rarely, crystals are examined in which the birefringence is greater in the red than in the blue. In these cases care must be exercised so that the right order is ascribed to the retardation bands. Benzil, referred to on page 466, is a substance which falls into this category. Other examples are to be found in crystals showing crossed axial plane dispersion; the birefringence for the acute bisectrix of such crystals passes through zero at the wave length of uniaxiality. Since the retardation bands on either side of this wave length have the order 1, 2, 3, ... etc., it is not necessary to have a wedge-shaped edge to the crystal in order to determine its dispersion of birefringence.

6. Determination of Optic Axial Angles and Their Dispersion

A. VISUALLY

The precision with which optic axial angles may be measured varies within wide limits depending on the direction of the axes with respect to the morphology of the crystal. The most favorable condition is that in which both axes appear in the convergent polarized light interference figure, as in this case the measurement can be made with relatively simple apparatus. When neither, or only one axis appears in the interference figure, a reasonably accurate determination is very time consuming and requires a universal stage. Universal-stage methods could not be adequately described in this chapter; for a description of them, the reader is referred to books by Wright, Johannsen, and Winchell and Emmons.[76]

The optic axial angle is designated as $2V$. This is the acute angle between the primary optic axes within the crystal. The angle of the axes as measured in air from a crystal plate cut normal to the acute bisectrix is $2E$. When an oil-immersion condenser and objective are used, the angle is $2H$. The relations between these angles are:

$$\sin E = n_\beta \sin V \tag{16}$$

and for an immersion oil with $n_D = 1.515$:

$$\sin H = 0.66 \sin E \tag{17}$$

One of the most used methods is that of Mallard,[77] which is based on the

---

[76] F. E. Wright, *Methods of Petrographic-Microscopic Research, Carnegie Inst. Wash. Pub. No. 158*, 1911. A. Johannsen, *Manual of Petrographic Methods*, 2nd ed., McGraw-Hill, New York, 1918. A. N. Winchell and R. C. Emmons, *Microscopic Characters of Artificial Minerals*, 2nd ed., Wiley, New York, 1931.

[77] E. Mallard, *Bull. soc. ind. minéral. St.-Etienne*, **5**, 506 (1882).

observation that the distance between the optic axes as measured on the interference figure with any particular microscope system is proportional to sin E, the sine of half the optic axial angle in air. This relationship is usually expressed as:

$$D = K \sin E \tag{18}$$

where D is the measured distance and K is known as Mallard's constant, which is determined from a known crystal, or by an apertometer. The accuracy of Mallard's method is usually greater with thicker crystals. Wright has shown that Mallard's method may be applied to uncentered acute bisectrix figures by the use of a double screw micrometer eyepiece,[78] or an eyepiece fitted with a coordinate micrometer scale.[79]

Centered acute bisectrix figures having $2E$ so large that the axes fall outside the interference figure may be measured by Wright's modification[80] of Michel Lévy's method. In this method, a circle of reference is introduced into the interference figure. This is effected by introducing a glass plate having a circle (or concentric circles) into the focal plane of the eyepiece, or at a conjugate focus, such as the back lens of the objective, or the upper iris diaphragm of the petrographic swing-out condenser. A crystal of known $2E$ is placed in the crossed (extinction) position, and the stage is rotated until the isogyres are tangential to the reference circle. The angle of rotation, ϕ, is noted. The constant, C, for the particular microscope system is given by:

$$C = \sqrt{\sin 2\phi \cdot \sin E} \tag{19}$$

With C determined, the value of $2E$ for another crystal plate can be determined noting the new value of ϕ, and substituting in the equation:

$$\sin E = C/\sqrt{\sin 2\phi} \tag{20}$$

Johannsen and Phemister[81] have described a more accurate method in which a plate of substance of known $2E$, such as a plate of muscovite mica, is fixed in the diagonal position upon the uppermost lens of the condensing system. The object slide with the crystal of unknown $2E$ is placed on the microscope stage so that its optic axial plane is parallel to that of the mica. The ease and accuracy of this operation are increased if the microscope is provided with synchronous rotation of the nicols, since in this case the mica is brought to extinction by rotating the nicols through 45°. The crystal of unknown $2E$, which has been roughly oriented with the aid of

[78] F. E. Wright, *Am. J. Sci.*, **24**, 336 (1907).

[79] F. E. Wright, *Am. J. Sci.*, **31**, 97 (1911); *J. Wash. Acad. Sci.*, **1**, 60 (1911).

[80] F. E. Wright, *Am. J. Sci.*, **20**, 288 (1905).

[81] A. Johannsen and T. C. Phemister, *J. Geol.*, **32**, 81 (1924).

the Bertrand lens, is then rotated to exact extinction and the nicols are brought back to the former direction.   The Bertrand lens is again inserted, and the stage is rotated; the confused interference figure at first seen changes until, at the end point, the dark brushes come into view because the isogyres of the unknown substance have been superimposed on those of the mica.   If we designate as ϕ the angle through which the stage has been rotated, then:

$$\sin E \text{ of unknown} = \sin E \text{ of known} / \sqrt{\sin 2\phi} \qquad (21)$$

When a single optic axis appears in the interference figure, a rough estimate of $2V$ may be made from the curvature of the isogyre.   Wright[82] has computed the trace of the isogyre for centered and uncentered optic axis figures for $n_\beta = 1.6$ and $2V = 15°, 30°, 45°, 60°, 75°$, and $90°$.

Accurate measurements of optic axial angles have been made by rotating crystals in a trough filled with a liquid having a refractive index of n_β. The axis of rotation must be normal to the optic axial plane, that is, about the Y axis.   Except in favorable cases, the orienting of the crystal is a difficult operation.   A simple stage goniometer combined with a thin cell has been described by Wood and Ayliffe.[83]   This apparatus has the advantage that it can be used with the high-power objective and condenser necessary for observing the convergent polarized light interference figure, so that the mounting of the crystal is not so critical.   It should be possible, by using the Wood–Ayliffe goniometric apparatus on a microscope equipped with a calibrated micrometer eyepiece for measuring the direction of emergence of the optic axes in a plane normal to that of rotation, to compute $2V$ with fair accuracy on crystals rotated about an axis making a considerable angle with Y.   Bryant[84] has used a modification of this apparatus for measuring optic axial angles.

B. PHOTOGRAPHICALLY

Since, as already mentioned, the dispersion of the optic axes of crystals is usually much more marked with organic than with inorganic compounds, the measurement of this property is important.   Bryant, who has done so much work in this field, has lately adopted a photographic method of recording the dispersion.[85]   The principle is quite simple: the interference figure which should, of course, show both optic axes, is photographed with

[82] F. E. Wright, *Methods of Petrographic-Microscopic Research*, Carnegie Inst. Wash. *Pub.* No. 158, 1911, pp. 168–170.

[83] R. G. Wood and S. H. Ayliffe, *J. Sci. Instruments*, **12**, 194 (1935).

[84] W. M. D. Bryant, *J. Am. Chem. Soc.*, **60**, 394 (1938).

[85] W. M. D. Bryant, *J. Am. Chem. Soc.*, **63**, 511 (1941).

various wave lengths of monochromatic light, using a micrometer ocular in order to obtain a reference scale. The photographs are measured in order to determine: (a) the nature of dispersion of the axes of the wave surface; and (b) the variation of $2E$ or $2H$ as a function of λ.

In his publications dealing with the grating microspectrograph, the author has drawn attention to the value of having a wide spectrum, in which lines corresponding to the various wave lengths are straight, for obtaining a photographic record of the dispersion of optic axes. Unfortunately, the accuracy of the method is offset by the disadvantage that it cannot be used for measuring monoclinic inclined or horizontal dispersion, or for triclinic dispersion. As mentioned earlier, crossed axial-plane dispersion occurs in orthorhombic, monoclinic, and triclinic crystals when the dispersions of the principal refractive indices are so different that, at some particular wave length, n_β changes places with n_α or n_γ This wave length, often referred to as the "wave length of uniaxiality," may be determined by using a monochromator as a source of illumination for the convergent polarized light system, or by the use of the microspectrograph. The temperature coefficients of the principal refractive indices are usually different, which means that the λ of uniaxiality may vary with change of temperature.

VI. MICROSCOPY OF COLORED CRYSTALS

1. Theory

A. PLEOCHROISM AND DICHROISM

Colored crystals of other than cubic symmetry are usually, although not invariably, *pleochroic*, that is to say, the degree of absorption of light of any wave length by unit thickness of the crystal is a single-valued function of the vibration direction with reference to the crystal orientation. The amplitude, A, of a ray which has traversed a thickness, d, of an absorbing medium is given by:

$$A = A_0 e^{-2\pi\kappa d/\lambda} \tag{22}$$

where λ is the wave length in the medium, A_0 is the incident amplitude, and κ is the *absorption index*. Since intensity I is proportional to the square of the amplitude, we may write the absorption formula as:

$$I = I_0 e^{-4\pi\kappa n d/\lambda_0} \tag{23}$$

where n is the refractive index of the medium and λ_0 is the wave length in air of the incident light.

In the most general case, monochromatic light incident on a plate of an absorbing crystal is resolved into two elliptically polarized rays. The ellipses have the same ratio of major to minor axes and the same direction of rotation but have their major axes at right angles. However, light vibrating along a vibration plane of the crystal plate is transmitted as plane-polarized light and can, therefore, be extinguished by the analyzer in the crossed position. The crystal section has refractive indices of n_1 and n_2 and absorption indices of κ_1 and κ_2, respectively, for its two extinction directions. Differently oriented sections of the same crystal present different values of n_1, n_2, κ_1, and κ_2. These values vary with change of wave length, the absorption indices in particular being liable to wide variations. Just as we can construct a refractive index–wave-normal surface as an aid to visualizing the nature of double refraction in a crystal, so we can construct an absorption index–wave-normal surface. For a perfectly transparent crystal the absorption surface would be a geometrical point, while for an absorbing optically isotropic crystal it would be a sphere of radius κ. With uniaxial crystals the absorption surface for the ordinary ray is a sphere of radius κ_ω, and for the extraordinary ray it is an ovaloid varying between κ_ω along the optic axis and κ_ϵ along the optic normal. Usually crystals of positive birefringence have $\kappa_\epsilon > \kappa_\omega$, while those of negative birefringence have $\kappa_\omega > \kappa_\epsilon$. This is equivalent to stating that the higher absorption is usually associated with the higher refractive index. With biaxial orthorhombic substances the absorption surface resembles that of the refractive index–wave-normal surface in that there are two directions for which the two absorption indices are the same. These directions do not coincide, except by chance, with the optic axes, and have no particular significance. What is important is that the principal axes of the absorption surface of an orthorhombic crystal coincide with X, Y, and Z of the refractive index surface which in turn coincide with the crystallographic symmetry. Only one of the principal absorption axes coincides with a principal vibration direction in a monoclinic crystal, and this is the one which in turn coincides with the b crystallographic direction. The complete optical asymmetry of crystals of the triclinic system is shown also in the absorption surface, since the principal absorption axes do not, except by chance, coincide with the principal vibration axes.

It is convenient at this point to discuss briefly the meaning of the terms *dichroism*, *trichroism*, and *pleochroism*. In petrography and chemical microscopy, dichroism has two meanings: any crystal or mineral section which changes in color when rotated on the microscope stage in polarized light (analyzer withdrawn) is said to be *dichroic;* the term is applied in a more specific sense to absorbing uniaxial crystals which exhibit two extreme colors with optic normal sections viewed in polarized light vibrating parallel to, and normal to, the plane of the optic axis, respectively. In this latter sense, an absorbing orthorhombic crystal may be *trichroic* when it exhibits three different absorptions corresponding to the X, Y, and Z vibration directions. Absorbing monoclinic and triclinic crystals may be *trichroic* only if there is no appreciable dispersion of the principal axes of vibration and absorption. Usually, at least so far as crystals of dyes are concerned, dispersion of these axes is present. This dispersion causes the crystals to exhibit a great many colors on changing their orientation in plane-polarized light. Such crystals are said to be *pleochroic*. The term "pleochroism" is also used to describe the absorption phenomena of colored uniaxial and biaxial crystals in general.

B. OPTICAL PHENOMENA OF PLEOCHROIC CRYSTALS

Ordinary Light.—Most of the optical studies of strongly pleochroic crystal have hitherto been made on naturally occurring substances, especially the uniaxial minerals chlorite and tourmaline, and the biaxial minerals cordierite, epidote, andalusite, and glaucophane, and on that very curious group of highly colored crystals of the platinocyanides first studied by Haidinger.[86]

Plates of equal thickness cut at different orientations from a colored uniaxial crystal appear different when viewed by transmitted ordinary light. The maximum difference is shown by sections normal to, and parallel to, the optic axis, respectively. If, for example, a uniaxial crystal transmitted only red for the ordinary ray and only green for the extraordinary ray, the optic axis section would appear red. The optic normal section would appear yellow, since half of the transmitted light would be red and the other half green. A mixture of red and green light appears yellow.

Similarly, plates of equal thickness cut normal to the principal vibration axes of a trichroic orthorhombic crystal appear different when viewed by transmitted ordinary light. Thus, half the light incident on a plate cut normal to X suffers an absorption corresponding to the Y vibration (and absorption) axis, and the other half suffers an absorption corresponding to the Z axis, whereas plates cut normal to Y have a mixture of absorptions corresponding to X and Z and those normal to Z have a mixture of absorptions corresponding to X and Y. An example of pleochroism visible in ordinary light is afforded by a fusion slide of azobenzene.

Plane-Polarized Light.—The light transmitted by a section of a pleochroic crystal is readily resolved into its two components, except in the case of monoclinic and triclinic crystals showing dispersed extinction, by successively rotating the section on the stage of the polarizing microscope to extinction positions in adjacent quadrants, and removing either the polarizer or analyzer in order to observe the color of the transmitted light for each of the two vibration planes of the section. However, this technique, which is the one commonly adopted by the chemical microscopist, is not very good for showing slight degrees of dichroism. Haidinger[87] introduced the *dichroscope*, which is substantially a prism of calcite interposed between a square aperture and a focusing lens. The calcite splits the light from the aperture into two beams polarized at right angles, whereby two images of the square are seen in approximate contact. The plane of vibration of the ordinary image is parallel to the junction between the two squares, that of the extraordinary images is perpendicular to this junction. Many modifications of the dichroscope have been reported in the literature which cover improvements such as rotating specimen holders with two mutually perpendicular axes of rotation for studying pleochroism. A similar device has been used as an eyepiece dichroscope, in which the square

---

[86] W. Haidinger, *Ann. Physik Chem.*, **68,** 302 (1846); **70,** 571 (1847); **71,** 321 (1847); **76,** 99, 294 (1849); **77,** 89 (1849); **81,** 572 (1850). See also F. Pockels, *Lehrbuch der Kristalloptik.* Teubner, Berlin, 1906, p. 441.

[87] W. Haidinger, *Ann. Physk Chem.*, **65,** 1 (1845). See also A. Johannsen, *Manual of Petrographic Methods.* 2nd ed., McGraw-Hill, New York, 1918, p. 325.

aperture was in the image plane of the microscope.[88] The usual construction in present-day eyepiece dichroscopes is to equip a Huygens' eyepiece with a diaphragm having a square aperture, which is placed near the field lens, and a Wollaston prism which is placed just beneath an eye lens with focusing adjustment. The Wollaston prism splits a beam of light into two beams, polarized at right angles, which deviate equally from the microscope axis, so that when the eye lens is properly adjusted for focus two squares are seen in approximate contact. The innermost side of each square is strongly fringed with yellow, and the outermost with blue, but this is not quite so objectionable as the appearance in the Haidinger type of dichroscope eyepiece, where the extraordinary image is strongly fringed with yellow on the side nearest the ordinary image, and fringed with blue on the other side, since in addition the focus is different for the two images. It is necessary to check the vibration planes of the two images of the Wollaston-prism type of dichroscope eyepiece; they may be parallel and perpendicular to the dividing line of the field, or at $+45°$ and $-45°$. This check is readily made on the microscope with the polarizer in position.

The dichroscope eyepiece is used without polarizer or analyzer. Daylight is an unsatisfactory illuminant for a microscope employing a dichroscope eyepiece because it may have an appreciable plane-polarized component.

Convergent Ordinary Light.—If a section of a pleochroic uniaxial crystal cut perpendicular to the optic axis is viewed conoscopically in convergent ordinary light, the direction of the optic axis is indicated by a small spot different in color from the rest of the field. The apparent diameter of the spot diminishes as the thickness of the section is increased, and its boundary becomes more sharply defined. Seen in monochromatic light, it is lighter than the surrounding field if the ordinary ray is less strongly absorbed than the extraordinary one, and conversely. It is possible for the optic axis to appear as a dark spot at one wave length, and as a light spot at another.

Optic axial sections of biaxial crystals exhibit a dark brush, perpendicular to the optic axial plane, which is intercepted by a bright spot on the axis.

Convergent Plane-Polarized Light.—The most important conoscopic observations of pleochroic crystals are made in convergent plane-polarized light. *Absorption figures* are obtained by the use of the polarizer (or analyzer) alone. *Interference figures* are obtained by the use of crossed polarizer and analyzer, as they are with transparent crystals.

The absorption figure of a uniaxial crystal, as seen with light comprising a fairly narrow band of the spectrum, may present either of two appearances. If the absorption of the ordinary ray is less than that of the extraordinary ray, a brush is seen which is parallel to the plane of vibration of the polarized light; the brush is intercepted by a bright spot on the optic axis. With most polarizing microscopes the vibration plane of the polarizer is in the *N–S* position (vibrations to and from the observer), so that it is in this position that the brush appears. If, however, the absorption of the ordinary ray exceeds that of the extraordinary ray, the brush

---

[88] C. Leiss, *Die optischen Instrumente der Firma R. Fuess.* Engelmann, Leipzig, 1899, p. 220.

is perpendicular to the plane of polarization and is continuous through the optic axis. With a uniaxial crystal having different absorption spectra for the ordinary and extraordinary rays, the parallel $(N-S)$ brush with the bright axial spot appears at some wave lengths, and the perpendicular $(E-W)$ continuous brush at others. When examined with white light, the conoscopic absorption figure of such a crystal consists of a pair of differently colored brushes at right angles, that corresponding to the ordinary ray being perpendicular to the plane of polarization and continuous. Magnesium platinocyanide is an example of this type; its conoscopic absorption image consists of a violet continuous brush perpendicular to the vibration plane of the polarizer and a red brush at right angles which fades out on the optic axis.

The interference figure of an optic axial section of a pleochroic uniaxial crystal consists of dark cross and some rings, if sufficient light is transmitted for them to be visible. This is the case when the absorption of the ordinary ray is slight and the number of rings which can be seen depends on the degree of absorption of the extra-ordinary ray. When the absorption is appreciable, the rings are indistinct because they are produced by the interference of two elliptically polarized rays of different intensities which cannot give extinction. When the ordinary ray is very strongly absorbed, the conoscopic interference figure is uniformly dark.

The absorption figures of pleochroic biaxial crystals are observed conoscopically in plane-polarized light. The following considerations apply to orthorhombic crystals and to monoclinic and triclinic crystals showing only slight dispersion of the principal vibration directions.

Optic Axial Absorption Figures.—In absorbing biaxial crystals, the absorption suffered by light traveling along an optic axis depends on its plane of vibration. The vibration planes of an optic axial section are in the plane of the optic axes (the XZ plane) and perpendicular to it (the Y axis), respectively. Let us call the corresponding absorption indices κ_p and κ_y. When the section is viewed cono-scopically in monochromatic light vibrating in the plane of the optic axes, a con-tinuous brush is seen in this plane if $\kappa_p > \kappa_y$, whereas the brush is perpendicular to this plane and is intercepted by a bright spot on the optic axes if $\kappa_p < \kappa_y$. When the section is viewed in light vibrating perpendicularly to the optic axial plane, a continuous brush is seen in the optic axial plane if $\kappa_p < \kappa_y$, while the per-pendicular brush intercepted by the bright axial spot is seen if $\kappa_p > \kappa_y$. The figures seen with white light are colored; the colors are different from the two extinction positions.

Acute Bisectrix Absorption Figures.—When an acute bisectrix section is viewed conoscopically in plane-polarized white light vibrating perpendicularly to the optic axial plane, a band of uniform color, corresponding to the Y absorption, goes straight across the figure along the optic axial plane. On either side of this band the color changes, since these parts of the conoscopic figure comprise vibrations ap-proaching the Z direction with negative crystals, and the X direction with positive ones, so that the color of these outer parts of the figure changes symmetrically from the center to the sides of the field, with abrupt changes in the region of the optic axes. When the same section is viewed in white light vibrating in the optic axial plane, a band of uniform color crosses the conoscopic figure through the acute bisectrix, perpendicular to the optic axial plane. In the case of optically negative crystals, this color corresponds to the X absorption; with optically positive ones it corresponds to the Z absorption. On either side of this band the color changes towards that for the Z direction with negative crystals, and that for the X direction with positive ones. The changes in the region of the optic axes are abrupt. The colored band corresponding to the Y direction, which is seen in white light vibrating perpendicular to the optic axial plane, is very much narrower than that corresponding to the X or Z band seen when either the crystal or the plane of polarization is rotated 90°.

Obtuse Bisectrix Absorption Figures.—When an obtuse bisectrix section is viewed conoscopically with white light vibrating perpendicular to the optic axial plane, the narrow colored band, corresponding to the Y absorption, crosses the figure along the optic axial plane. The rest of the figure shades towards the color corresponding to the X absorption for optically negative crystals, and to the Z absorption for optically positive ones. When either the crystal or the plane of polarization is rotated 90°, a broad band of color passes through the center of the figure, perpendicular to the optic axial plane. Its color corresponds to the Z absorption for optically negative crystals, and to the X absorption for optically positive ones.

Uncentered figures presenting one axis show the colored band along the optic axial plane, corresponding to the Y absorption.

Optic Normal Sections.—When an optic normal section is viewed conoscopically in plane-polarized light, the absorption figure is uniformly colored. The two extreme colors, corresponding to the X and Z absorptions, are obtained when the crystal is rotated to extinction positions perpendicular to each other.

The interference figures of pleochroic biaxial crystals in monochromatic light differ in certain respects from those of transparent crystals. For wave lengths at which the absorption is negligible the interference figures are perfectly normal, whereas with moderate absorption the isogyres are intercepted by bright spots on the optic axes unless vibration directions of the crystal coincide with the vibration planes of the polarizer and analyzer. The optic axial bright spots are brightest when the crystal is in the diagonal position, when the lemniscates nearest the optic axes also have moderately bright spots at their points of intersection with the optic axial (XZ) plane. The bright spot effect is not usually visible in thick crystal plates having a very strong absorption in one region; such plates give a fairly normal interference figure by their transmitted light. It follows that the conoscopic interference figures of absorbing crystals are profoundly influenced by their thickness.

Dispersion of the optic axial angle causes dispersion of the optic axial brushes, but does not affect the appearance of bands of uniform color seen in the conoscopic absorption figures along YZ, XZ, and XY planes for X, Y, and Z vibrations. However, dispersion of the principal vibration directions, such as may occur with monoclinic and triclinic crystals, causes the absorption spectrum of the crystal to become a function of the vibration direction. Instead of there being three principal absorption spectra, the absorption maxima may vary continuously with change of vibration direction.

This type of dispersed pleochroism is strikingly shown by microscopical preparations of pinakryptol green, the photographic desensitizing dye. A few milligrams of pinakryptol green is dissolved in a drop of pyridine on an object slide. The slide is warmed to hasten the evaporation of the pyridine and to prevent its dilution by atmospheric moisture. The droplet is spread out with a glass rod so that the crystals which form are extremely thin. Many of the crystals have irregular contours (anhedral), but they all show the dispersed pleochroism. Viewed orthoscopically by transmitted ordinary white light, they appear a dull olive green. By substituting plane-polarized light, the crystals show many colors on rotating the microscope stage, passing consecutively through dull red, orange, yellow, green, blue, and purple. As would be expected, these crystals show strong dispersion of extinction. Although crystals showing dispersed pleochroism must of necessity show dispersed extinction, the converse is not necessarily true.

C. MEASUREMENT OF ABSORPTION

The absorption index, κ, was defined on page 510. It is the ratio of the amplitude of light at any instant to its amplitude one radian of a vibration earlier. Other constants expressing the absorption of light by a medium can be derived from the absorption index. Two which are common in crystal optics are the *absorption coefficient*, k, which is numerically equal to $n\kappa$ where n is the refractive index, and the *extinction modulus*, m, which is numerically equal to $4\pi n\kappa \cdot \log_{10} e/\lambda_0$, where λ_0 is the wave length in air.

In computing κ, k, or m from measurements of transmission, the loss of light by reflection must be taken into account. For an absorbing medium bounded by air the transmission is given by the expression:

$$T = I/I_0 = [16n^2/(n + 1)^4] \cdot 10^{-md} \tag{24}$$

where n is the refractive index, m is the extinction modulus, and d is the thickness, from which we obtain:

$$m = [2 \log_{10} 4n/(n + 1)^2 - \log_{10} T]/d \tag{25}$$

When an absorbing medium is mounted between two pieces of glass with a mounting medium having refractive index n', the transmission, T', is measured relative to that of two pieces of glass separated by the same mounting medium. If $n'' = n/n'$, we have:

$$m = [2 \log_{10} 4n''/(n'' + 1)^2 - \log_{10} T']/d \tag{26}$$

The extinction modulus, absorption index, or absorption coefficient of plates of weakly absorbing crystals, such as cobalt copper sulfate, cobalt potassium sulfate, and other substances of similar absorption, have been determined by cutting suitably oriented plates of the crystal and measuring the absorptions for the two vibration directions of each plate on a spectrophotometer. (For references, see Pockels.[89]) Berek[90] has described a slit microphotometer which may be used with

[89] F. Pockels, *Lehrbuch der Kristalloptik*. Teubner, Berlin, 1906, pp. 403–408.

[90] M. Berek, *Optische Messmethoden im polarisierten Auflicht*, Deut. mineral. Gesellschaft, Berlin, 1937. Reprinted from *Fortschr. Mineral. Krist. Petrog.*, **22**, 1–104 (1937).

transmitted polarized light. This instrument gives satisfactory results on crystals about one millimeter across when a mercury-vapor lamp is used in conjunction with the appropriate Wratten filters as a source of monochromatic light. What is needed, however, is a combined microphotometer and monochromator designed to function with the polarizing microscope.

Measurements on crystals with very strong selective absorption, such as organic dyes, are hardly ever possible because crystals of the required thickness (often not more than a few microns) cannot be grown of a sufficient area for use with low magnification. From what has been said above on conoscopic absorption figures, it will be realized that the cone of illumination must not exceed a few degrees when the principal absorptions of an acute bisectrix section are being measured. It is essential that only light which has passed through the crystal be permitted to enter the microscope objective; this means that an image of a distant exit pupil of a monochromator must be thrown on the crystal. The ordinary plane mirror of the microscope gives a double image and should, therefore, be replaced by a surface aluminized one. The swing-out type of substage condenser cannot be used if the polarizing prism is equipped with a cylindrical correcting lens, but an adequate polarizer can be constructed from any type of polarizing prism, over which is mounted a short focus achromatic lens. The Bausch & Lomb 21 × achromat with an iris diaphragm is a good lens for this work, especially if the crystals are mounted between two microscope cover glasses so that the correction of the lens is disturbed as little as possible. The crystal preparation is fixed to a $1'' \times 3''$ slide of Bakelite with a half-inch hole in the center. As the light entering the condenser is very nearly parallel, an ordinary nicol prism is quite satisfactory as a polarizer. Since accurate measurements of crystal thickness are rarely possible, quite large errors in the absolute values of the extinction modulus are to be expected. However, the wave length of the absorption maximum and the shape of the absorption curve are obtainable even when the thickness of the crystal is not known.

D. MEASUREMENT OF DICHROISM

The degree of dichroism at any particular wave length of a section of a pleochroic crystal is conveniently expressed by $m_2 - m_1$, the difference between the two extinction moduli. Let us suppose that the extinction moduli of the section are m_1 and m_2, the corresponding intensities of the transmitted beams are I_1 and I_2 for an incident intensity of I_0, and the thickness of the crystal is d. Since the original unpolarized light is resolved into two beams by the crystal, we have:

$$I_1 = I_0 \cdot 10^{-m_1 d}/2 \tag{27}$$

$$I_2 = I_0 \cdot 10^{-m_2 d}/2 \tag{28}$$

so that:

$$\log_{10} I_1/I_2 = (m_2 - m_1)d \tag{29}$$

Hence the dichroism can be determined by measuring the ratio of intensities of the two transmitted beams and the thickness of the crystal section.

The simplest optical method of determining dichroism on the microscope consists of the use of a dichroscopic eyepiece of the Wollaston-prism type over which rotates an analyzing prism on a graduated circle. Neither the polarizer nor the body-tube analyzer of the microscope is used during the actual measurement, although a polarizer must be used for the purpose of orienting the crystal so that its vibration planes coincide with those of the dichroscope images. It is absolutely essential that only light which has passed through the crystal be allowed to enter the microscope, in order to avoid the very serious errors which result from lens flare (page 528) when the objective is flooded with light. The microscope is illuminated with monochromatic light, which, because of the small field and narrow cone of illumination required, is conveniently provided by a Bausch & Lomb Laboratory Wave-Length Spectrometer. If the intensities of the two adjacent images comprising the dichroscope field are I_1 and I_2, and the vibration plane of the analyzer makes an angle θ with the vibration plane of the image with intensity I_1, then $I_1/I_2 = \tan^2 \theta$. Substituting in equation (29) above, we obtain:

$$m_2 - m_1 = (2 \log \tan \theta)/d \tag{30}$$

The readings are repeated at a number of wave lengths in order to obtain the curve for dichroism. No correction has been applied for the loss of light by reflection at the two crystal faces in the above formula. Such a correction could be applied, but it would fail to take account of light reflected back from the microscope objective to the upper surface of the crystal and back again into the microscope system. The most practical solution is mounting the crystals in a medium having a refractive index about halfway between the two indices for the crystal section, when the reflection error becomes negligible.

As with other crystal optical measurements, measurements of dichroism are valueless unless the optical orientation of the crystal section is known. The principal dichroisms are those of optical normal sections which give $m_z - m_x$, and bisectrix sections which give $m_z - m_y$ (negative acute, and positive obtuse), and $m_y - m_x$ (positive acute, and negative obtuse). Obviously, if the dichroism is known for two principal sections, the third is obtained from the sum or difference of the other two. Dichroism curves are obtained by plotting dichroism against wave length.

E. METALLIC REFLECTION

Metallic reflection is reflection of the larger part of the incident light. The reflecting power, R, of a plane surface of a substance is defined as the ratio of the intensity of the reflected light to that of the incident light for normal incidence. If the substance has refractive index n and absorption index κ:

$$R = [(n - 1)^2 + n^2\kappa^2]/[(n + 1)^2 + n^2\kappa^2] \tag{31}$$

Obviously R approaches unity as κ increases and as n increases above unity or decreases below it. Metals have high values of κ and consequently reflect a large part of the incident light, whereas the reflecting power of a transparent substance is only considerable if its refractive index is high. Thus, for $\lambda = 589$ mμ, silver and platinum have reflecting powers of 0.93 and 0.70, respectively, while those of water, window glass, and diamond are 0.023, 0.04, and 0.172, respectively, the high reflecting power of the diamond being due to its high refractive index (2.417). In general, any face of an anisotropic absorbing crystal has different reflecting powers for its two vibration directions.

Metallic reflection is of interest to the organic chemical microscopist because this type of reflection occurs with a great many dyes. Very strongly colored crystals of dyes have large values for one or more of the principal absorption indices with correspondingly high refractive indices on the long wave-length side of the absorption band. Berek[90] has evolved microscopical methods of determining the reflecting power and double reflection of anisotropic absorbing crystals. One of these methods employs his slit microphotometer. Another uses a specially constructed elliptical analyzer. The success of these methods owes much to Berek's ingenious modification of the vertical illuminator. In place of a simple right-angled prism, he uses a *compensating prism*, which is constructed of glass having a refractive index of $\sqrt{3}$. Plane-polarized light entering the prism suffers three internal reflections and emerges as plane-polarized light for all azimuths of the plane of vibration. This work does not appear to have been extended to the study of dyes, possibly because of the difficulty of growing dye crystals with optically flat faces. However, a qualitative study of the phenomena exhibited by dye crystals under vertical illumination is of interest.

The double reflection of the different faces of an absorbing anisotropic crystal may be observed in three ways. First, the crystal may be examined by vertical illumination with plane-polarized light. The crystal is conveniently mounted on a simple rotation device, such as a dissecting needle pushed horizontally through a cork which is supported on a $1'' \times 3''$ object slide. An ordinary prism vertical illuminator gives fairly satisfactory results if the light entering it is polarized in the plane of incidence, or perpendicular thereto, by a "Polaroid" polarizing filter or by a nicol. A cover-glass vertical illuminator may be used with polarized light vibrating perpendicular to the plane of incidence, *i. e.*, at right angles to the microscope body tube.[91] A low-power objective, such as a $6\times$ achromat should be used. The presence of double reflection is demonstrated by rotating the microscope stage. The second way is to use ordinary light with the vertical illuminator, but to examine by means of a rotating analyzer, or to rotate the crystal and use a fixed analyzer. The third way is to use ordinary light for vertical illumination and to analyze the double reflection with a dichroscope eyepiece.

Doubly reflecting crystals may also be studied by vertical illumination with crossed nicols. An ordinary prism or cover-glass vertical illuminator can be used if the vibration plane of the polarizer is in the correct azimuth. With the cover-glass reflector, the most intense reflected beam of plane polarized light is obtained when the vibration plane of the polarizer is perpendicular to the plane of incidence. If, therefore, the light enters the vertical illuminator along a path directly towards the observer (N–S), the analyzer is in the crossed position when its vibration plane is in this same (N–S) direction. This is 90° from the usual setting of the analyzer.

[91] E. E. Jelley, *J. Roy. Microscop. Soc.*, **54**, 18 (1934).

The prism vertical illuminator may be used with the same polarizer setting, or with one parallel to the plane of incidence. This latter setting has the advantage that, when the light enters the illuminator directly towards the observer $(N–S)$, the analyzer is crossed in the customary $E–W$ position. The setting of the polarizer can be checked by observing the darkness of the field when the microscope is focused on a clean microscope slide. The polarization effects of a face of a doubly reflecting crystal as seen by vertical illumination with crossed nicols are as follows:

(*1*) On rotating the microscope stage the crystal goes through four extinction positions, 90° apart, in one complete revolution, unless the crystal is monoclinic or triclinic with the particular face being studied showing appreciable dispersion of its vibration directions. Such dispersion of the vibration directions gives vivid, and often characteristic, colors in place of extinction. In the four diagonal positions the image has maximum brightness.

(*2*) If the reflecting power for one vibration direction is considerably greater than for the other, the crystal in the diagonal position appears the same color as that observed with polarizer or analyzer alone for the vibration direction of the stronger reflection.

(*3*) If the two reflections are both high and of not greatly different intensity, interference colors may be produced which are unrelated to either the absorption or the reflection of the crystal. The colors result from the interference of the resolved components of two *elliptically* polarized rays, and are in consequence less saturated than the interference colors of the first and second orders obtained with transmitted light from colorless crystals between crossed nicols. A good example of this type of interference is given by the mineral marcasite, the orthorhombic form of FeS_2. A polished specimen of this mineral exhibits curious pastel colors with crossed-nicol vertical illumination.

The reflecting power of a plane surface of an absorbing substance is changed to some degree by immersing it in a medium of refractive index n_m. The change is slight with metals having a high absorption index, this being the case for silver ($\kappa = 20.6$), chromium ($\kappa = 4.9$), and cadmium ($\kappa = 5.0$). An easily perceptible lowering of reflecting power occurs with metals having a somewhat lower absorption index, such as nickel ($\kappa = 1.86$) and tungsten ($\kappa = 0.94$). (The above values of κ are for $\lambda = 589$ mμ.) The loss of reflecting power with many metals is greater at shorter wave lengths, since κ is usually lower in this region. Crystals of dyes have considerably lower absorption indices than those of metals; even the highest value of κ rarely exceeds 0.1 and is usually much lower, so that the effect of immersion is great. The reflecting power for any vibration direction is lowered when the corresponding refractive index is greater than $\sqrt{n_m}$, and is a minimum when it is n_m. When, however, the refractive index is less than $\sqrt{n_m}$, the reflecting power is increased. Both of these effects can occur for one vibration direction of a single face of a crystal, since the refractive index is abnormally high for the long-wave side of an absorption band, and abnormally low for the short-wave side. This lowering of reflecting power on the long-wave side of an absorption band together with an increase on the short-wave side in the immediate vicinity of the absorption band, gives rise to a color shift towards the blue as well as to an increase of color saturation. The effect is present with dyes having a narrow and intense absorption band in the middle of the visible spectrum.   Examples occur in the cyanine class of photographic sensitizing dyes.   This effect is also shown by amorphous films of some readily accessible dyes, such as basic fuchsin, pararosaniline hydrochloride, and the various methyl violets; the films are prepared by rapidly drying thin layers of saturated alcohol solutions of the dyes on glass plates.   It should be noted that, with crystals embedded in a mounting medium between an object slide and cover glass, approximately 4% of the vertically incident white light is reflected by the top surface of the cover glass when a dry objective is used.   This white light is mixed with the light reflected from the crystal and reduces its color saturation; it can be eliminated, when desired, by using a prism of small angle (10–15°) as a cover.

F.   COLOR AND CONSTITUTION

Textbooks on petrography usually divide colored minerals into two classes: *idiochromatic*, in which the color is due to the absorption of the mineral itself; and *allochromatic*, in which the coloring matter is suspended in the mineral as minute inclusions.   In chemical microscopy, the colored crystals with which we are concerned are idiochromatic.

The absorption of light by a substance, crystalline or otherwise, is due to electron transitions for some frequency range (or ranges) of the electromagnetic waves which constitute light.   The absorption of an individual molecule or ion is modified by its environment; the greatest modification usually occurs when the molecules or ions are packed in a crystal lattice.   We shall first consider the principal types of absorbing ions and molecules, and classify them as *atomic, atomic-molecular*, and *molecular absorbers*.

Atomic absorbers have an incomplete subshell of electrons which is shielded by completed subshells.   This is, of course, the electronic structure of the rare earth elements, atomic numbers 58–71, inclusive.   Salts of the rare earth elements are remarkable for the narrowness of their absorption bands.   In crystals, even at room temperature, the absorption bands are very narrow, some of them appearing as lines comparable in width to the broader lines in the solar spectrum.   Rawlins[92] has pointed out that the sharpness of these absorption bands is due to the shielding of the incomplete 4f group of electrons by the completed 5s and 5p of the triply ionized atoms.   A good example of this type of absorption spectrum is afforded by neodymium sulfate octahydrate crystals.[93]

Atomic-molecular absorbers are present in molecules or ions having an atom with an unshielded incomplete subshell.   Elements with this type of electronic structure are the metals with atomic numbers 22–29, 41–46, 73–79, and 92.   Not only are transitions possible for electrons in lower levels to the incomplete subshell of such an atom, but transitions may also occur between this subshell and coordinated groups surrounding it.   Consequently, the absorption spectrum of a compound of one of these elements also depends on the nature of the coordinated groups.   The

[92] F. I. G. Rawlins, *Trans. Faraday Soc.*, **25**, 762 (1929).

[93] M. H. Dufet, *Bull. soc. franç. minéral.*, **24**, 373 (1901).   See also E. E. Jelley, *Nature*, **136**, 335 (1935).

very wide range of colors displayed by bivalent and trivalent cobalt compounds illustrates this fact. In certain ions, such as CrO_4^{--}, MnO_4^-, and UO_2^{++}, there is an empty subshell immediately below the valency electron level, so that orbital transitions from lower levels to the otherwise empty subshell are possible. Brode[94] considers that the coordinated shell of oxygen atoms in the permanganate ion shields the third subshell, and that this accounts for the well-defined structure of some seven components in its principal absorption band. However, the four oxygen atoms of the chromate and manganate ions do not afford any substantial degree of shielding.

Molecular absorbers are the type encountered in colored organic compounds. Such compounds are highly unsaturated structures in which resonance occurs between two or more electronic configurations of the molecules. A conjugated double bond system is present in the great majority of colored organic compounds, either in the form of carbocyclic or heterocyclic nuclei, or as chains such as $\left(\begin{smallmatrix} -C=C \\ H \ \ H \end{smallmatrix}\right)_n$ and $-N=N-$. Usually, both conjugated ring and chain systems occur in the same molecule. In general, the frequency at which conjugated chain and ring systems absorb is lower the greater the number of atoms in the conjugated system. The resonance frequency is also lowered by attaching polar groups such as $-NO_2$, $-CN$, $-NR_2$, $=O$, $=S$, $-NO$, and $-OH$ to the terminal atoms in conjugated systems. Ketenes represent a rare type of a resonating consecutive double bond chain of atoms. Detailed discussions on resonance in its relation to the color and constitution of organic compounds have been given by Lewis and Calvin[95] and by Brooker.[96] The color of free radicals results from transitions between an incomplete shell of a carbon or nitrogen atom and other atoms or groups attached to it; the absorbing system is therefore of the atomic-molecular type of the present classification.

It is of interest to consider the effect of environment on the absorption of molecules, with particular reference to the absorption of crystals. When the molecules of a light-absorbing substance are so far apart in space that there is no appreciable interaction between them, the absorption spectrum consists of many thousands of sharp lines arranged in bands which result from the superimposition of many quantized levels of rotational and vibrational energy on the energy of the various electron transitions. The energy absorbed by such isolated molecules is re-emitted as resonance radiation.[97]

At somewhat higher vapor pressures the resonance radiation ceases, for the potential energy of electrons in higher levels is translated into energy of vibration and rotation of other molecules with which the excited molecule collides, but the character of the absorption remains substantially unchanged. However, when the absorbing molecules are in a liquid or solid, molecular collisions result in a considerable broadening of the fine structure of the absorption bands. At room tem-

[94] W. R. Brode, *Chemical Spectroscopy.* 2nd ed., Wiley, New York, 1943, p. 267.

[95] G. N. Lewis and M. Calvin, *Chem. Revs.*, **25**, 273 (1939).

[96] L. G. S. Brooker, *J. Am. Chem. Soc.*, **62**, 1116 (1940); **63**, 3192, 3203, 3214 (1941); **64**, 199 (1942); *Rev. Modern Phys.*, **14**, 275 (1942).

[97] R. W. Wood, *Physical Optics.* 3rd ed., Macmillan, New York, 1934, pp. 616–647.

perature the absorption bands may still show several moderately sharp maxima, but the fine structure entirely disappears.   The influence of dipole moment, refractive index, and other factors on the molar extinction coefficient and position of the absorption maximum of dyes in solution is discussed by Sheppard and coworkers[98] in a paper on the effects of environment and aggregation on the absorption spectra of dyes.

In crystals of an absorbing compound, the molecules or ions are arranged in a regular manner, and the absorption may become quite complicated.   The effect of packing an atomic absorbing system, such as the neodymium sulfate octahydrate mentioned above, in a crystal lattice is to make the absorption bands much narrower than they are for the same absorbing ion in aqueous solution or in a glass, such as neodymium glass.   Spedding[99] has shown that the grouping of the absorption lines of a rare earth salt depends on the crystal symmetry of the substance.   The absorption spectrum of atomic-molecular absorbers is not usually greatly changed in a crystal lattice unless strongly polar ions, such as NO_3^-, are also present.   The platinocyanides, referred to on page 512, are a marked exception to this rule; the $Pt(CN)_4^{--}$ ion in aqueous solution and in anhydrous crystals is colorless, whereas crystals containing water of crystallization are very strongly colored and exhibit metallic reflection for certain wave lengths.   The color is deeper the greater the number of moles of water of crystallization per $Pt(CN)_4^{--}$ ion, as is shown in table VII.   Apparently the water molecules and platinocyanide ions are involved in an electronic resonance mechanism which is a characteristic of the lattice structure of the crystals.

TABLE VII

COLORS OF PLATINOCYANIDE CRYSTALS

Substance	H_2O per $Pt(CN)_4^{--}$	Color by transmission	Metallic reflection
$Ag_2Pt(CN)_4$	0	Colorless	None
$HgPt(CN)_4$	0	Colorless	None
$(NH_4)_2Pt(CN)_4H_2O$	1	Colorless	Blue-violet
$(NH_4)_2Pt(CN)_42H_2O$	2	Yellow	Blue
$K_2Pt(CN)_43H_2O$	3	Yellow	
$BaPt(CN)_44H_2O$	4	Green and yellow pleochroic	
$MgPt(CN)_45H_2O$	5	Deep yellow	
$MgPt(CN)_47H_2O$	7	Purple and red pleochroic	Blue and green
$Y_2[Pt(CN)_4]_321H_2O$	7	Red, yellow, green, and colorless pleochroic	Blue and green

The absorption spectrum of molecular absorbers may be very greatly changed in a crystal lattice.   When all the molecules in the unit cell of the crystal have the same orientation, there is considerable interaction between neighboring molecules, and the absorption spectrum for the Z vibration direction suffers considerable broadening both to longer and to shorter wave lengths.   With this disposition of the molecules in the crystal lattice, both the birefringence and the pleochroism are

[98] S. E. Sheppard, *Rev. Modern Phys.*, **14**, 303–340 (1942).

[99] F. H. Spedding, *J. Chem. Phys.*, **5**, 160 (1937); *Phys. Rev.*, **50**, 574 (1936).

extreme. Usually, however, the molecules are arranged so that they can be considered as belonging to two interpenetrating lattices in which they are differently inclined. This "staggering" of the molecules considerably affects the absorption characteristics of the crystal. In general, the color of a crystal composed of an unionized molecule, such as phenol blue or a merocyanine dye,[100] is similar to that of the substance dissolved in a liquid with a high refractive index and large dipole moment. However, when the dye is a salt, the electromagnetic field of the ion attached to the dye may exert a very considerable influence on the light-absorbing properties of the crystal. This is especially true of basic dyes of the cyanine[101] class. Crystals of the chlorides of these dyes are not very different in color from their solutions, but the colors of crystals of the perchlorates of these dyes are often quite different from those of their solutions. This is particularly true of crystals whose principal refractive indices are very close together; not only is their absorption weak, but also the absorption maximum is often shifted toward the violet end of the spectrum, an effect clearly shown by different salts of 1,1'-diethyl-2,2'-cyanine, which vary from the deep red halides to the pale straw-colored trithionate.[102]

2. Preparation of Colored Crystals

The preparation of colored crystals for microscopic observation is complicated by the necessity of obtaining crystals thin enough for examination by transmitted light and yet of sufficient area to permit of easy observation of their pleochroism and optical orientation. Crystals of lamellar habit are ideal for examination; the difficulty is, of course, that such crystals present only one optical orientation. The habit of crystals of organic compounds is often different for different solvents, but the possibility that the crystal may contain solvent of crystallization or exist in polymorphous forms must be kept in mind. Since much of the microscopy of colored organic crystals consists of comparing known with unknown crystals, it is important the same salts of acidic and basic dyes should be compared after crystallization from the same solvent under identical conditions of evaporation or cooling.

A. BASIC DYES

The choice of anion depends on the solubility of the dye. By far the most generally useful salts are the perchlorates, which usually show strong pleochroism. The perchlorates are prepared by precipitating the dye from an aqueous or alcoholic solution by the addition of a large excess of sodium perchlorate solution. When the quantity of dye is very small, its perchlorate may be collected in a filter tube, rinsed with a drop or two of water, and then recovered by extracting the filter with methanol or other

---

[100] C. E. K. Mees, *Theory of the Photographic Process.* Macmillan, New York, 1942, p. 1035.

[101] C. E. K. Mees, *op. cit.*, p. 992.

[102] E. E. Jelley, *Ind. Eng. Chem., Anal. Ed.*, **13**, 196 (1941).

suitable solvent. With very soluble dyes, a larger anion is an advantage, such as that of Reinecke salt, $[Co(CNS)_4(NH_3)_2]^-$. Other well-characterized crystals of basic dyes are the picrates, in which the strong blue absorption of the picrate anion is little changed by the presence of the dye cations in the crystal, while the absorption of the cation may be completely changed.

B. ACID DYES

The alkali and alkaline earth salts of sulfonated dyes do not always form crystals suitable for microscopic study. In this case it is best to prepare the free acid and add an excess of a volatile alkali such as ammonia or morpholine. Well-characterized crystals can often be obtained by double decomposition with salts of bulky cations such as $[Co\ en_3]Cl_3$, $[Co(NH_3)_6]Cl_3$, $[Zn\ en_2]SO_4$, $[Cu\ en_2]Cl_2$ where en indicates ethylenediamine. An excess of the metallic coordination compound is used to precipitate the dye complex, which is then collected and recrystallized from water. Silver–thiourea complexes of acid dyes are readily obtained by adding to the dye solution an excess of a 1% aqueous solution of thiourea previously saturated with silver chloride.[103]

C. EVAPORATION

As with colorless crystals, the evaporation of a solvent may yield crystals suitable for study. The simplest case is that of the slow evaporation of a pure solvent such as n-hexane, benzene, or water. Evaporation from a small beaker gives crystals more suitable for the study of crystal form than of optical properties, whereas evaporation of a film of solution on an object slide will often yield crystals thin enough, and of sufficient area, for optical study. Both types of crystal are usually necessary in order to correlate the geometric and optical characteristics. Complicated organic compounds, such as dyes in general, crystallize very slowly, so that the rate of evaporation must be retarded lest the preparation dry before the crystals have time to grow to a satisfactory size. Object-slide preparations should be covered with a watch glass and protected from drafts so that the evaporation takes from 15 to 60 minutes. Extremely concentrated solutions may be handled by the object-slide technique; thus nitrobenzene and pyridine are useful solvents for cyanine dyes. Use may be made of the property of certain solvents of not wetting glass in order to collect traces of a dye left on an object slide by the evaporation of a wetting solvent such as acetone, alcohol, or water. A small globule of the nonwetting solvent is rolled over the object slide with the aid of a very thin glass rod until it

---

[103] E. E. Jelley, *unpublished work.*

has picked up sufficient dye, and is then allowed to evaporate. Evaporation of mixed solvents, in which the more volatile constituent is also the best solvent, is a very useful method of growing crystals of dyes. For example, dyes insoluble in water, but soluble in dilute alcohol, may be crystallized by allowing their solution in dilute alcohol to evaporate; the percentage of alcohol in the mother liquor falls, and the dye crystallizes out from solution.

D. COOLING

When a substance is substantially more soluble in a given solvent at high than at low temperatures, it may be recrystallized by cooling its hot saturated solution. This principle may often be applied to the micro-recrystallization of dyes on an object slide. The liquid chosen should be such that the solubility of the dye has a very high temperature coefficient, such as pyridine and quinoline for acid dyes, α-bromonaphthalene for many basic dyes, triethylbenzene for nonionized dyes of low solubility. With this method of crystallization, polymorphous varieties of both unsolvated and solvated crystals may occur. The cooling should in any case be slow—over a one- or two-hour period at least.

E. DILUTION WITH A NONSOLVENT

Addition of a nonsolvent to a solution of a dye will throw it out of solution if there is an appreciable affinity between the molecules of the solvent and the nonsolvent. Typical systems of this nature are alcohol (solvent) diluted with water (nonsolvent) and pyridine or nitrobenzene (solvents) diluted with benzene or cyclohexane (nonsolvents). The nonsolvent must be added very slowly to the solvent, since too rapid precipitation yields very small and aggregated crystals. A convenient way of carrying out crystallization by dilution is to place the more or less saturated solution of the dye, contained in a microbeaker or a cavity in an object slide, in a desiccator containing a beaker of nonsolvent. Dilution from the vapor phase then takes place very slowly and evenly, and good crystals are formed in a few days.

Probably the method of Vesce[104] of growing dye crystals is a dilution method. He uses 93% sulfuric acid as a solvent for both sulfonated and unsulfonated azo dyes. Some of the powdered dye is stirred into a drop of acid on an object slide and the slide is then covered. Crystals form after several minutes and may subsequently change; the general appearance of the crystals serves for their characterization. The formation of the

---

[104] V. C. Vesce, in J. J. Mattiello, *Protective and Decorative Coatings*. Vol. II, Wiley, New York, 1942, pp. 124–163.

crystals and their subsequent modification could be due to dilution of the sulfuric acid with water from the atmosphere. The method does not, however, lend itself to a study of the optical properties of the crystals.

F. DIFFUSION METHOD

A modification of the dilution method has proved itself particularly useful for the preparation of large areas of strongly absorbing crystals of cyanine dyes.[103] A milligram or so of dye is dissolved in a drop of nitrobenzene and the concentrated solution of dye is transferred to a clean object slide. The droplet is covered with a cover circle 18 or 22 millimeters in diameter, when it spreads out to form a somewhat irregular film approximately 10 millimeters in diameter. Some xylol balsam, warmed if necessary, is run round the edge of the cover circle with the aid of a turntable, and the slide is stored for some days at 35° to 45° C., when crystals will usually form. The thickness of the crystals is limited by the distance apart of the cover and object glass, and may be between 10 and 100 μ. This method, which has given particularly good results with perchlorates of cyanine dyes, has the advantage that the crystals are grown and mounted in a single operation.

3. Methods of Examination

A. ORTHOSCOPIC

The morphology of the crystal should first be studied as far as possible, and then observations on the nature of the extinction between crossed nicols should be made. Organic dyes in crystalline form rarely have a symmetry higher than orthorhombic, and consequently are quite likely to show one or more types of optical dispersion, often to an extreme extent. Most triclinic crystals, and monoclinic crystals viewed along other than a perpendicular to the ortho-axis *b*, show some dispersion of extinction. The nature and extent of this dispersion should be noted. Observations on pleochroism should be made on crystals in their extinction positions, when they possess them. It should be remembered that dye crystals often have an abnormally high reflectivity as a consequence of very strong selective absorption. This may completely change the apparent pleochroism of crystals viewed with a dry objective when the field is filled with light, since light is reflected from the front glass surface of the objective to the top surface of the crystal and thence back into the microscope. Crystals which should appear very deep blue or purple for one vibration direction often appear a bright yellowish green. A striking example of this effect was shown by 1,1'-diethyl-2,2'-cyanine perchlorate crystallized from nitrobenzene by the diffusion method. When examined with a 10×

objective in a narrow cone of polarized light, they presented colorless and pale brown pleochroism, whereas the true pleochroism was colorless and deep red, as was demonstrated by restricting the field of illumination until it fell within the crystal.[102] The only certain way of studying the pleochroism of organic crystals with strong selective absorption is to restrict the area of illumination so that it falls entirely within the crystal being studied (see page 518).

B.   CONOSCOPIC INTERFERENCE FIGURES

The conoscopic examination of colored crystals between crossed nicols follows the general lines of that of transparent crystals discussed on pages 480–489. Preliminary work is best carried out with monochromatic sodium ($\lambda = 589$ mμ) or mercury ($\lambda = 546$) light, if the crystals are sufficiently transparent to this region of the spectrum. Crystals transmitting the red end of the spectrum are best examined with tungsten light filtered through a Wratten No. 29(F), or a combination of No. 29(F) and No. 35 (D). If one or both of the optic axes appear in the interference figure as seen with monochromatic light, it is then profitable to change over to white light. The interference figure appears more recognizable when the crystal is in the extinction position. Crossed axial plane dispersion is quite common in crystals of dyes, particularly magenta and purple ones, and dispersion of two or three of the principal vibration directions is fairly common, so that the interpretation of the interference figure is often impracticable. However, it is this complexity of the interference figures of dyes which makes them all the more useful as a qualitative basis of comparison of known with unknown substances for the purposes of identification. The appearance of the interference figure of a crystal of a dye depends on the thickness of the crystal. With crystals thin enough to have only weak absorption very brilliant color effects, due to a combination of optical dispersion and absorption, are often exhibited, while with thick crystals an almost monochromatic band of light is transmitted and the interference figure appears to be fairly normal.

C.   CONOSCOPIC ABSORPTION FIGURES

The absorption figures of small dye crystals are usually difficult to obtain, but are a valuable aid in their study and optical characterization. Absorption figures are obtained by using either the polarizer or the analyzer in the conoscopic mode of examination. The principal practical difficulty is lens flare, which arises from the circumstance that the microscope objective is usually flooded with light which has passed round the crystal, whereas in the study of the corresponding interference figure this light is extinguished by the analyzer. Obviously the difficulty is diminished by using an objective with as small a field of view as possible. A 2-mm. oil-immersion objective and 1.40 N.A. oil-immersion condenser give the clearest absorption figures. If the illuminated area can be restricted to fall within the crystal under examination, lens flare is eliminated; however, this usually needs a polarizing substage of special construction.

Conoscopic absorption figures are of great value in determining whether or not a number of crystals presenting different dichroism when examined orthoscopically are different orientations of the same crystalline modification.

D. MICROSPECTROGRAPH

The author's microspectrograph is well adapted to the study of pleochroism, both orthoscopically and conoscopically. Neither the polarizer nor the analyzer of the microscope is used for microspectrography; instead, the image of the crystal or its conoscopic disk is projected on the slit of the microspectrograph, and a Wollaston prism is inserted in the collimated light beam to produce two adjacent spectra corresponding to the vibration planes of the crystal. In order to set a crystal so that its vibration planes agree with the vibration planes of the Wollaston prism, the microscope polarizer is temporarily inserted and rotated until it extinguishes one of the images given by the Wollaston, the crystal is rotated to extinction, and the polarizer is withdrawn.

E. VERTICAL ILLUMINATION

Large crystals of dyes having strong selective absorption are conveniently studied by vertical illumination with a $6\times$ or $10\times$ objective. Some form of simple rotation apparatus is essential for orienting the crystal; the reflected light is analyzed as explained on page 519. The extreme colors of the crystal are sometimes quite characteristic, and different, for homologous dyes.

General References

Beck, C., *The Microscope.* Beck, London, 1938.

Berek, M., *Optische Messmethoden im polarisierten Auflicht.* Deut. mineral. Gesellschaft, Berlin, 1937. Reprinted from *Fortschr. Mineral. Krist. Petrog.*, **22**, 1–104 (1937).

Chamot, E. M., and Mason, C. W., *Handbook of Chemical Microscopy.* 2nd ed., Vols. I and II, Wiley, New York, 1938 and 1940.

Dana, E. S., and Ford, W. E., *Textbook of Mineralogy.* 4th ed., Wiley, New York, 1932.

Drude, P., *Theory of Optics*. Translated by C. R. Mann and R. A. Millikan. Longmans, Green, New York, 1929.

Gibb, T. R. P., Jr., *Optical Methods of Chemical Analysis*. McGraw-Hill, New York, 1942.

Groth, P., *Optical Properties of Crystals*. Translated by B. H. Jackson. Wiley, New York, 1910.

Hartshorne, N. H., and Stuart, A., *Crystals and the Polarising Microscope*. Arnold, London, 1934.

Johannsen, A., *Manual of Petrographic Methods*. 2nd ed., McGraw-Hill, New York, 1918.

Larsen, E. S., and Berman, H., "Microscopic Determination of the Nonopaque Minerals," *U. S. Geol. Survey Bull.* No. 848 (1934).

Kraus, E. H., Hunt, W. F., and Ramsdell, L. S., *Mineralogy*. 3rd ed., McGraw-Hill, New York, 1936.

Pockels, F., *Lehrbuch der Kristalloptik*. Teubner, Berlin, 1906.

Rinne, F., and Berek, M., *Anleitung zu optischen Untersuchungen mit dem Polarisationsmikroskop*. Jänecke, Leipzig, 1934.

Rogers, A. F., and Kerr, P. F., *Optical Mineralogy*. McGraw-Hill, New York, 1942.

Tutton, A. E. H., *Crystallography*. 2nd ed., Vols. I and II, Macmillan, New York, 1922.

Wahlstrom, E. E., *Optical Crystallography*. Wiley, New York, 1943.

Winchell, A. N., *Elements of Optical Mineralogy*. 5th ed., Vol. I, Wiley, New York, 1937.

Winchell, A. N., and Emmons, R. C., *Microscopic Characters of Artificial Minerals*. 2nd ed., Wiley, New York, 1931.

Winchell, A. N., *Optical Properties of Organic Compounds*. Univ. of Wisconsin Press, Madison, 1943.

Wood, R. W., *Physical Optics*. 3rd ed., Macmillan, New York, 1934.

Wooster, W. A., *Text-book on Crystal Physics*. Macmillan, New York, and Cambridge Univ. Press, London, 1938.

Wright, F. E., *Methods of Petrographic-Microscopic Research, Carnegie Inst. Wash. Pub.* No. 158, 1911.

CHAPTER XII

Determination of
CRYSTAL FORM

M. A. PEACOCK, *University of Toronto*

I. INTRODUCTION

In changing from a fluid state to a solid state, the great majority of chemical substances assume the crystalline state, in which the constituent atoms of the compound are bound together in an orderly arrangement by inherent forces of mutual attraction and repulsion. Normally, this process commences at many points in the crystallizing fluid, and the resulting solid is an aggregation of crystals with boundaries that are more or less irregular due to mutual contact. When carefully controlled, crystallization may be confined to few centers, giving individual crystals whose boundaries are due to the undisturbed interaction of the growing crystals and the surrounding fluid. Such crystals have polyhedral form, which was formerly implied by the word "crystal," and within such crystals the orderly internal atomic arrangement extends without interruption from the center to the surface.

Crystals of a given chemical compound are characterized above all by constancy of properties, and therefore the chemist interested in isolating and describing a compound in the solid state has always striven to obtain a crop of well-formed crystals on which to determine such specific properties as composition, specific gravity, and melting point. Formerly, the geometrical and optical properties of laboratory crystals were determined with equal care, since these gave the closest attainable insight to the crystal structure. But now that x-ray analysis permits the actual determination of the internal arrangement, geometrical and optical crystallography have become relatively neglected by the chemist, and the crystal form and optical behavior of laboratory crystals are frequently dismissed by brief, inadequate, even erroneous, descriptive terms.

There are good reasons for returning to a closer study of the external geometry of artificial crystals: angular measurements may permit the identification of an unrecognized crystalline substance by means of a determinative method treated by Donnay in Chapter XIII (page 561) of this book; x-ray crystallography is built directly on the foundation of geometrical crystallography, and therefore a consideration of the elements of geometrical crystallography may usefully precede the treatment of x-ray diffraction given by Fankuchen in Chapter XIV (page 585); and finally the study of crystal form in relation to crystal structure is bringing valuable results of a general theoretical nature. This chapter proposes, therefore, to give a partial outline of the theory of geometrical crystallography and working directions in goniometry, especially for the two practical purposes mentioned above. For the sake of brevity, completeness must be sacrificed; necessary formulas will be presented without proof; and, where alternative nomenclatures or viewpoints would be offered in a fuller treatment, a considered preference must be given here without supporting argument. These defects may be sufficiently remedied by the references that accompany this chapter.

II. CRYSTAL LATTICE

In the orderly internal arrangement which characterizes a crystal, the constituent atoms behave, in first approximation, like spheres with constant radii which are different for different kinds of atoms. Since a chemical compound is typically composed of only a few kinds of atoms in simple rational proportions, and the congregation of the atoms is caused by forces connected with their integral electronic structures, it is natural that the crystal should consist of a repetition of a three-dimensional pattern composed of a relatively small number of atoms.

This may be illustrated in two dimensions by the imaginary plane structure (Fig. 1) assumed by a compound, AB_2. This consists of a repetition of a plane pattern contained by a parallelogram defined by any point in the plane, say A_0, and two neighboring, identically surrounded points, say A_1, A_2, which do not lie in a line with A_0. A_0, A_1, A_2, . . . are called identical points, and the structure comes to self-coincidence by translation, parallel to itself, from one point to any other such point.

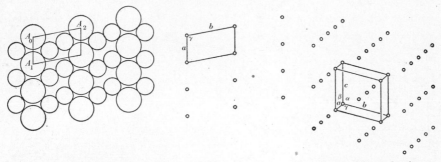

Fig. 1.—Plane structure.   Fig. 2.—Plane lattice.   Fig. 3.—Space-lattice.

An array of identical points in the plane structure (Fig. 1) gives the plane lattice (Fig. 2), and it is clear that the same lattice results whatever point in the structure is taken as the origin. The lattice is defined by a parallelogram which has the full symmetry of the structure. The smallest and least oblique parallelogram, with sides a, b, and included angle γ, is the standard choice, but other parallelograms may be chosen under special circumstances. Similarly, the array of identical points in an actual three-dimensional structure makes a space-lattice (Fig. 3), normally defined by the smallest and least oblique parallelepiped which has the full symmetry of the structure, in this case the parallelepiped with sides a, b, c, and the included angles α, β, γ. Again for special purposes, other parallelepipeds may be chosen to define the space-lattice. The chosen parallelepiped, or unit cell, contains one or more than one complete structural pattern, and is thus representative of the entire crystal. The determination of the absolute dimensions of the unit cell and the actual positions of all the atoms within it is attempted by a structural analysis by means of x-rays; the simpler geometrical relations with which we are here concerned may be properly explained and understood with reference to the crystal lattice in place of the crystal structure.

III. CRYSTAL FORM IN RELATION TO CRYSTAL LATTICE

1. Crystal Faces and Lattice Planes

A portion of a crystal is shown in plan in figure 4. The shortest horizontal lattice periods are a, b, and therefore the lattice lines OA, OB are taken as axes. For simplicity let the third axis, OC, be vertical. The crystal is bounded by vertical faces DE, EF, FG. Face DE cuts axis OA and is parallel to axes OB, $OC;$ it may therefore be denoted by the

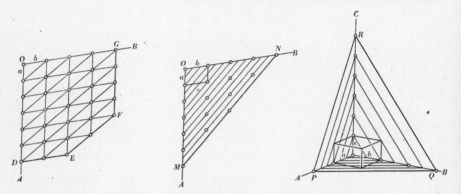

Figs. 4, 5, 6.—Crystal faces and lattice planes.

smallest integral intercepts $1 \infty \infty$. Similarly, face FG may be denoted by intercepts $\infty 1 \infty$, and EF by $1 1 \infty$. In figure 5, vertical plane MN has the smallest integral intercepts $3\ 2\ \infty$, and in the three-dimensional, general case in figure 6, plane PQR has the intercepts $2\ 3\ 6$.

Crystal faces were early denoted by their intercepts, but it was found that integers proportional to the reciprocals of the intercepts, the indices of Miller, are more fundamental and convenient, and these are now universally used both in geometrical and in x-ray crystallography. The crystal faces in figures 4, 5, and 6 thus receive the following notation, the Miller indices (hkl) being written in parentheses:

Face	Intercepts	Indices
DE	$1 \infty \infty$	(100)
FG	$\infty 1 \infty$	(010)
EF	$1 1 \infty$	(110)
MN	$3\ 2\ \infty$	(230)
PQR	$2\ 3\ 6$	(321)

Returning to figures 4 to 6, it will be noted that each crystal face is the outermost lattice plane of a set of lattice planes which are parallel, equidistant, and geometrically equivalent; and it will be observed that each of these sets of lattice planes subdivides the sides of the unit lattice cell, a, b, c, into h, k, l, equal parts, respectively. The Miller indices of a set of lattice planes, or the corresponding crystal face, may thus be usefully defined as the numbers of parts into which the set of planes subdivides the axial periods of the lattice.

From figures 4 to 6 it is further apparent that each set of lattice planes has its proper spacing and point density. These quantities are directly proportional and they can be calculated or obtained graphically[1] from the lattice elements, a, b, c, α, β, γ, and the Miller indices, h, k, l. It will be seen also that, in a general way, the spacings and point densities decrease with increase in the complexity of the indices of the lattice planes.

2. Laws of Crystallography

We may now state the laws of crystallography and understand them in terms of the crystal lattice.

Law of Romé de l'Isle.—*The angles between corresponding faces on different crystals of one species are constant.* Since different crystals of one species have identical lattices, and crystal faces are lattice planes, it is self-evident that corresponding interfacial angles must be constant. While the Law of Constant Angles is thus an axiom of normal crystal structure, it is not, according to Fankuchen, obeyed by some organic structures, notably the proteins.

Law of Haüy.—*Crystal faces make simple rational intercepts on suitable crystal axes.* Since crystal faces are lattice planes, it is axiomatic that the intercepts are whole numbers. Simple indices, as noted above, are associated with relatively large point densities, and it is reasonable that crystal faces should be predominantly those which are relatively densely occupied with lattice points.

Law of Bravais.—*The relative importance of crystal forms is proportional to the point densities or spacings of the respective lattice planes.* This statement is nearly equivalent to Haüy's law and therefore the two laws are sometimes linked as the law of Haüy–Bravais. Because point density, or spacing, can be expressed exactly, whereas simplicity of indices can be indicated only in a general way, as by the sum of the indices, Bravais' generalization is the more specific. The law was not widely accepted, since the crystal lattice could be determined only by assuming the truth of the law. Now that the lattice can be determined directly by x-ray dif-

---

[1] M. A. Peacock, *Z. Krist.*, **A100**, 93 (1938).

fraction, the truth of the law as a first approximation has been repeatedly confirmed in special cases.[2]

Law of Donnay–Harker.—*The relative importance of crystal forms is proportional to the spacings of the respective lattice planes as given by their indices in space-group notation.*[3] This important generalization has been remarkably confirmed in many special cases.[4] It agrees with the law of Bravais in recognizing that form importance is dependent in the first place on lattice plane spacing; and it states that the importance is further modified in keeping with the division of certain spacings by 2, 3, 4, or 6, caused by symmetry operations involving translations. These symmetry operations determine the ultimate symmetry type or space-group of the crystal, and they require that the indices of the affected sets of planes be multiplied by 2, 3, 4, or 6, giving multiple indices or indices in space-group notation. For further information on space-groups, see page 591.

3. Crystal Edges and Lattice Lines

Two nonparallel crystal faces meet in a line which is called an edge or axis; it coincides with the row of lattice points or the lattice line common

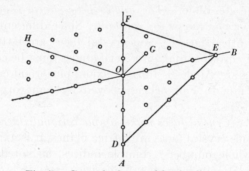

Fig. 7.—Crystal edges and lattice lines.

to the intersecting lattice planes. A lattice line is one of a set of parallel lattice lines with a common direction and period. Figure 7 represents a portion of a crystal bounded by faces (001), (110), and ($\overline{4}30$). *DE*, the edge between (001) and (110), is equivalent to the lattice line joining origin

---

[2] M. A. Peacock and D. A. Moddle, *Mineralog. Mag.*, **26**, 105 (1941). M. A. Peacock and R. B. Ferguson, *Univ. Toronto Studies, Geol. Ser.*, **48**, 65 (1943). J. D. H. Donnay, *Trans. Roy. Soc. Canada*, **37**, IV, 43 (1943).

[3] J. D. H. Donnay and D. Harker, *Am. Mineral.*, **22**, 446 (1937).

[4] J. D. H. Donnay, *Acad. roy. Belg., Bull. classe sci.*, **23**, 749 (1937); *Am. Mineral.*, **26**, 195 (1941); *Trans. Roy. Soc. Canada*, **34**, IV, 33 (1940); *ibid.*, **35**, IV, 51 (1941); *ibid.*, **36**, IV, 37 (1942). E. D. Taylor, *Am. Mineral.*, **25**, 123, 327 (1940). J. A. Tremblay, *J. Washington Acad. Sci.*, **32**, 327 (1942).

O to lattice point G whose coordinates are [$\bar{1}10$]. The Miller indices [uvw] of lattice line OG, or crystal edge DE, are therefore [$\bar{1}10$]. Similarly, crystal edge EF receives the indices of lattice line OH, namely [$\bar{3}40$], and in like manner a crystal edge inclined to all three lattice axes is denoted by the coordinates of the first lattice point [uvw] on the parallel lattice line passing through the origin.

From figure 7 we see that each set of lattice lines has its own period, which is the distance between successive points in the line, and consequently its own point density, which is the reciprocal of the period. These can be calculated from a, b, c, α, β, γ, and u, v, w, or obtained graphically. Also, increasing complexity of indices [uvw] is accompanied by increase in period, and therefore decrease in point density. This bears on a useful alternative statement of the law of Bravais: *The rate of crystal growth in any lattice direction is proportional to the point density in that direction.* In figure 7, for example, suppose that plane (001) has the greatest point density in the lattice; according to the usual statement of the law of Bravais, it will be the largest face. But if this plane has the greatest point density it will contain the two densest lattice lines, [100] and [010]. According to the alternative statement of the law of Bravais, crystal growth will be most rapid in these directions, and therefore face (001) will again be the largest. This fundamental law of crystal growth is most clearly displayed in habitually elongated crystals, in which the shortest period coincides with the direction of elongation, and in habitually tabular crystals, in which the plane of tabular development contains the two shortest lattice periods.[5]

IV. LATTICE TYPES, SYSTEMS, AND SYMMETRIES

1. Lattice Types

Owing to the tendency of the atoms of a crystallizing compound to adopt symmetrical arrangements, the crystal lattice may be of one or another of a number of special types. Including the general type, there are 14 possible lattice types, all of which are frequently represented by actual crystals. In each of these lattice types one can, of course, draw a simple or primitive cell by joining any lattice point to the three nearest lattice points (all four not lying in one plane), and completing the parallelepiped. When this is done, it is found that, in seven of the lattice types, the simple cell displays the full symmetry of the lattice[6] and consequently the simple cell is properly taken as the unit cell whose edges and angles define the lattice. In the

---

[5] L. G. Berry, *Univ. Toronto Studies, Geol. Ser.*, **48**, 25 (1943).

[6] The symmetry of the hexagonal lattice is displayed by an hexagonal prism consisting of three simple cells, as in figure 8F.

seven remaining types, the simple cell shows less symmetry than the lattice as a whole, but a multiple cell does exhibit the full symmetry, which is the same as that of one of the seven simple lattices shown in figure 8.

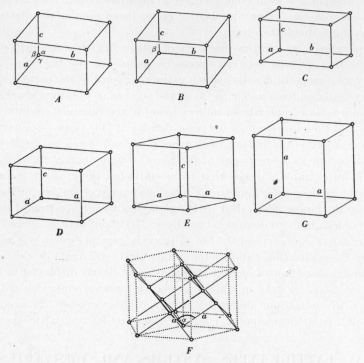

Fig. 8.—Simple lattice types: *A*—triclinic; *B*—monoclinic; *C*—orthorhombic; *D*—tetragonal; *E*—hexagonal; *F*—rhombohedral; *G*—cubic.

2. Lattice Systems

When crystals are classified according to their lattice types, we obtain seven lattice systems corresponding to the seven simple lattice types. These are listed in table I, which also gives the lattice elements and the lattice symmetries. The elements are written in two forms: first, the absolute cell dimensions, as obtained by x-ray measurements; and second, the relative cell dimensions, or geometrical elements, as found by goniometry. The elements in parentheses are those having special values in the special lattice types. The lattice symmetries will be briefly explained in the next section (page 540).

Some notes on the setting of the lattice cells in the several systems may be useful here.

In the triclinic system, also called anorthic, a unit cell determined roentgenographically or by geometrical means may be set up in 24 different ways with conventional right-handed axes of coordinates. A desirable unique setting is obtained by following the rules: $c < a < b$; α and β obtuse.[7] In this setting, in keeping with the law of crystal growth, the crystal will tend to be elongated parallel to the c-axis and flattened parallel to the plane containing the c-axis and the a-axis, which slopes downward directly toward the observer. This results in a satisfactory appearance to the crystal and the practical convenience of a prominent axis of adjustment and plane of reference in goniometry.

TABLE I

LATTICE SYSTEMS

System	Elements		Symmetry
Triclinic	$a\ \ b\ \ c;\ \ \alpha\ \beta\ \gamma$ $a:b:c;\ \ \alpha\ \beta\ \gamma$		$\bar{1}$
Monoclinic	$a\ \ b\ \ c;\ \ \beta\ (\gamma = \alpha = 90°)$ $a:b:c;\ \ \beta$		$2/m$
Orthorhombic	$a\ \ b\ \ c$ $a:b:c$	$(\alpha = \beta = \gamma = 90°)$	$2/m\ 2/m\ 2/m$
Tetragonal	$a\ \ c$ $a:c$	$(b = a;\ \alpha = \beta = \gamma = 90°)$	$4/m\ 2/m\ 2/m$
Hexagonal	$a\ \ c$ $a:c$	$(b = a;\ \gamma = 120°;\ \alpha = \beta = 90°)$	$6/m\ 2/m\ 2/m$
Rhombohedral	$a;\ \alpha$ α	$(b = c = a;\ \beta = \gamma = \alpha)$	$\bar{3}\quad 2/m$
Cubic	a	$(b = c = a;\ \alpha = \beta = \gamma = 90°)$	$4/m\ \ \bar{3}\ \ 2/m$

In the monoclinic system, sometimes named monosymmetric, the axis normal to the plane containing the inclined axes is set left-and-right and named the b-axis by fixed convention; one of the inclined axes is set vertically and named the c-axis, and the other inclined axis, the a-axis, slopes downward toward the observer. The rule $c < a$ gives an unique setting which is suitable if c is the shortest lattice period and consequently the axis of elongation. When b is the shortest period, and the crystal is consequently elongated in this direction, $c > a$ is often preferred.

The rule $a < b$ is always applied in the orthorhombic or rhombic system, and the unique setting $c < a < b$ is often suitable. However, when one cell edge is much greater than the others, and the crystal is consequently tabular parallel to the plane containing the shorter edges, the rule $a < b < c$ is often preferred. The simple tetragonal lattice can be set in only one way, with the unique c-axis vertical and an a-axis left-and-right. The unique c-axis of the hexagonal lattice is set vertically and one of the a-axes is set left-and-right.

---

[7] J. D. H. Donnay, *Am. Mineral.*, 28, 313, 507 (1943).

When the rhombohedral system, also named trigonal, is treated as independent of the hexagonal system, the lattice cell has been set up and the axes named in a variety of ways. However, the practical convenience of describing rhombohedral crystals in hexagonal notation recommends the setting in figure 8, in which the rhombohedral lattice may be regarded as a "centered" hexagonal lattice. In this setting, the edges of the rhombohedral cell, a, radiate upward from a common origin, with one edge rising directly toward the observer. The geometrical relations of the hexagonal and rhombohedral lattices are further explained elsewhere.[8] In the cubic system, often called isometric, there is no choice of setting.

In the foregoing section, the recommendations regarding the setting of crystal lattice cells lead to the normal or conventional settings which are generally preferred, if there is no good reason for adopting other settings. The practicing crystallographer, however, frequently encounters special cases for which an abnormal or unconventional setting seems preferable. These occur particularly in series of structurally related crystals belonging to different systems, when settings are naturally chosen to bring out the structural relations.

3. Lattice Symmetries

The important subject of crystal symmetry must be abbreviated here to a description of the seven lattice symmetries. These are combinations of symmetry operations which do not involve translations, namely, rotation and rotation-inversion. Rotation as a symmetry operation means rotation about an axis through $2\pi/n$, where $n = 1, 2, 3, 4, 6$. The possible rotation axes are thus 1-fold (no symmetry), 2-fold, 3-fold, 4-fold, 6-fold, and these are conveniently denoted simply by the numerals 1, 2, 3, 4, 6. Rotation-inversion means rotation about an axis followed by inversion through a point on the axis, the two parts of the operation being inseparable. The rotation-inversion axes, or briefly, inversion axes, are denoted by the over-scored numerals, $\bar{1}, \bar{2}, \bar{3}, \bar{4}, \bar{6}$. The 1-fold inversion axis is simply the symmetry center. The 2-fold inversion axis is equivalent to a mirror (symmetry, or reflection) plane m perpendicular to the axis, and this symbol is always used in place of $\bar{2}$.

The symmetry symbols of the lattice systems (Table I) are self-explanatory combinations of the foregoing symbols for the simple symmetry elements. The combination n/m means an n-fold axis normal to an m-plane. The actual disposition of the symmetry elements in each of the lattice symmetries is shown in figure 9, in which the axes of symmetry are denoted by appropriate numerals and the planes of symmetry by full lines.

---

[8] M. A. Peacock and M. C. Bandy, *Am. Mineral.*, **23**, 315 (1938).

These are drawn in the stereographic projection which is explained later (page 545).

The lattice symmetries are only seven of the 32 symmetries which are possible by combining symmetry operations without translations.[9] These 32 symmetries are the 32 classes of morphological crystallography or the 32 point groups of mathematical crystallography. The 32 classes divide

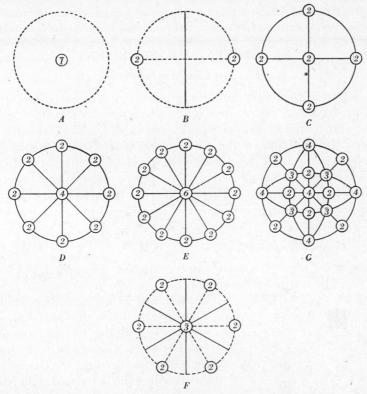

Fig. 9.—Lattice symmetries: A—triclinic ($\bar{1}$); B—monoclinic ($2/m$); C—orthorhombic ($2/m\,2/m\,2/m$); D—tetragonal ($4/m\,2/m\,2/m$); E—hexagonal ($6/m\,2/m\,2/m$); F—rhombohedral ($\bar{3}\,2/m$); G—cubic ($4/m\,\bar{3}\,2/m$).

into two groups: the seven holohedral classes, or lattice symmetries, each of which has the whole symmetry of the respective lattice type; and the remaining 25 merohedral classes, each of which has only a part of the symmetry of the respective lattice. We can give no further consideration here to the merohedral classes beyond noting that it is now more important than ever to try to determine the crystal class from the crystal form, since this knowledge is frequently needed in determining the space-group and structure of a crystal by means of x-rays.

A crystal which possesses symmetry will be bounded by one or more groups of symmetrical or equivalent faces. These are called crystal forms. In the ideal crystal equivalent faces are equal, but in actual crystals they are more or less unequal in size due to imperfect conditions of growth. However, these inequalities do not affect the angular relations of the faces or their normals; and in speaking of crystal symmetry the symmetry of the ideal crystal or the symmetry of the face-normals is always meant.

V. CRYSTAL MEASUREMENT

1. Goniometers

The determination of crystal form rests on crystal measurement on some form of goniometer. Large or rough crystals can be measured approximately with a simple contact goniometer—a divided semicircular plate with a contact bar hinged at the center of its straight edge. Small crystals with bright plane faces are needed for accurate measurements, which are made with a reflecting goniometer. Two types of reflecting goniometer are in common use, the single-circle type and the two-circle type; a three-circle goniometer was devised and used by Smith,[10] but the instrument is not widely used.

A. SINGLE-CIRCLE GONIOMETER

A schematic plan of a single-circle reflecting goniometer is given in figure 10. The instrument consists of a horizontal divided circle, *1*, whose

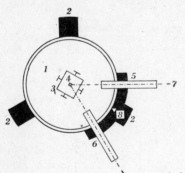

Fig. 10.—Single-circle goniometer.

vertical axis bears in a fixed stand, *2*. The circle carries crystal holder, *3*, which is provided with two rocking motions and two horizontal motions for adjusting and centering the crystal, *4*. To the stand are attached the horizontal collimator, *5*, and telescope, *6*, which are fixed at a convenient angle with their axes meeting in the axis of the circle. The collimator is provided with a signal slit and diaphragms and a fixed lens system. The telescope contains the cross hairs and lens systems for viewing the crystal or the image of the signal reflected from a crystal face. Light is provided by an enclosed 100-watt lamp with a short filament, *7*, and the circle is read to $1'$ or $\frac{1}{2}'$ at the index and vernier, *8*.

[10] G. F. H. Smith, *Mineralog. Mag.*, **14**, 1 (1904).

A crystal zone is an assemblage of faces intersecting in parallel edges whose direction is the zone-axis. The single-circle goniometer gives interfacial angles—angles between face-normals—in the zone whose axis is adjusted to the axis of the instrument. To obtain angles to the other faces of the crystal, it must be readjusted and measured zone by zone. This is inconvenient and sometimes very difficult, and, although a great mass of accurate goniometric data has been obtained with single-circle instruments, minute imperfect crystals and complicated intergrowths present almost insuperable difficulties. These are much reduced with the two-circle goniometer, which gives the angular relations of all the faces on one crystal termination with a single adjustment of the crystal.

B. TWO-CIRCLE GONIOMETER

The principle of the two-circle goniometer is indicated in the simplified plan in figure 11. It resembles a single-circle goniometer (explanatory numbers *1–8* as in Fig. 10), with a vertical post attached to the horizontal circle; this carries the bearing of the second, vertical, circle, *9*, whose horizontal axis, *10*, meets the vertical axis of the horizontal circle at the intersection of the axes of the collimator and telescope. The vertical circle is provided with an index and vernier, *11*, fixed to a supporting arm. The crystal holder is attached to the axis of the vertical circle, and thus the crystal can be turned about two mutually perpendicular axes and the position of any face on one termination

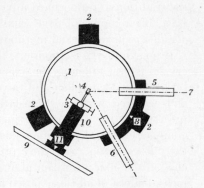

Fig. 11.—Two-circle goniometer.

is given by two coordinate angles. Only one adjustment of the crystal is made, and each face is brought to reflection only once.

Reflecting goniometers are not as yet made in the United States or Canada, but it is hoped that an American instrument maker will undertake the manufacture of a small and accurate two-circle instrument suitable both for geometrical and x-ray crystallography. In the meantime, chemists may obtain the use of suitable instruments, preferably the two-circle goniometer of Goldschmidt,[11] in a mineralogical laboratory or museum.

2. Selection, Mounting, and Measurement

The crystals best suited for goniometric work are those showing the least malformation or imperfection of the crystal faces. The range of size that

[11] V. Goldschmidt, *Z. Kryst.*, **21**, 210 (1893); **29**, 333 (1898).

can be used is about 0.1 to 10 mm., with perhaps 1 mm. as the preferred smallest dimension. The quality of the faces is more important than the size; with practice, crystals only a few tenths of 1 mm. in size are easily and accurately measured on the two-circle goniometer, provided the faces are bright planes.

A suitable crystal having been picked out with the help of a binocular microscope, it is sketched in one or more positions with reasonable fidelity. The most useful points of view are in the directions of the most prominent zone-axes. A rapid examination with the polarizing microscope may aid in determining the symmetry and in revealing the presence of intergrowths. The use of the microscope with laboratory crystals is treated by Hartshorne and Stuart,[12] and by E. E. Jelley in Chapter XI, "Microscopy."

The crystal may show evident symmetry, in which case a good general rule is to mount it with its axis of highest symmetry approximately parallel to the mounting pin which fits into the crystal holder. For this purpose the traditional, rather hard mixture of beeswax and pitch may be replaced by a softer more adhesive wax.[13] The mounting of very small or fragile crystals requires special methods, discussed in chapter XIV (page 612).

If no symmetry is apparent, the axis of the most prominent zone of the crystal is best taken as the axis of adjustment. The mounting pin is then set in the crystal holder and the crystal is adjusted with the rocking screws and centered with the translation screws until the selected zone-axis is precisely in the axis of the instrument. On the horizontal single-circle goniometer, the chosen zone-axis is now vertical, and measurement around the chosen initial zone may proceed. In the two-circle instrument, the chosen zone-axis is horizontal, in the axis of the vertical circle, and complete measurement of all the exposed faces of the crystal is made without further adjustment of the crystal. In both cases the angle or angles of a face are read when the instrument is set so that the image of the signal reflected from the crystal face lies on the cross hairs.

With faces of excellent quality, repeated measurements will not differ by more than one minute of arc, and in such cases the geometrical form of the crystal lattice can be determined, as described on page 549, with the highest attainable accuracy. When the faces are poor or bad, the reflecting goniometer can give only rough measurements leading to an approximate determination of the crystal lattice. In such cases the interpretation of the crystal form may be aided by measurements on the microscope, as described in chapter XI (page 435), and by a roentgenographic determination of the unit cell.

---

[12] N. H. Hartshorne and A. Stuart, *Crystals and the Polarising Microscope, a Handbook for Chemists and Others.* Arnold, London, 1934.

[13] *Central Scientific Company,* Chicago, 11450, wax, universal, red, is suitable.

VI. PROJECTIONS

When the measurement of a crystal has been completed, the next step is preparing a projection, which is a representation of the face-normals on a plane. Two projections are in common use, each having its particular usefulness and advantages; both are derived from the spherical projection, obtained by placing the crystal at the center of a sphere and projecting the face-normals to the surface of the sphere.

1. Stereographic Projection

Figure 12 shows the crystal at the center C, of a sphere of radius r, with the axis of the initial zone of measurement, SCN, vertical. CD is the trace of the horizontal plane through C; this is the plane of the stereographic projection. CP is any face-normal meeting the sphere at P. The join PS cuts plane CD in Q, which is the stereographic projection point or pole of the crystal face. If the face-normal makes an angle ρ with the vertical, the stereographic distance CQ equals $r \tan \frac{1}{2} \rho$. When $\rho = 90°$, as for all faces in the initial zone, the stereographic pole is on the equatorial circle, which is called the primitive circle of the projection. When ρ is greater than $90°$, as for the face-normal CP', the stereographic pole is outside the primitive circle, at Q'. In the case shown, where the lower face is symmetrical to the upper face by reflection in the plane of the projection, the pole of the lower face is conventionally represented by a small ring Q'' surrounding pole Q of the upper face.

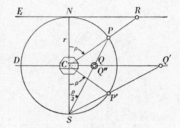

Fig. 12.—Construction of the stereographic and gnomonic projections.

Accurate constructions are available for plotting single-circle measurements in stereographic projection, but for most practical purposes rapid projection with the help of the stereographic net is sufficiently accurate. This net (Fig. 13) is the stereographic projection of a system of great circles meeting in a horizontal diameter, and a system of small circles normal to this diameter. A radius of 10 centimeters and an angular interval of $2°$ is convenient.[14] A great circle is the intersection of the sphere and a central plane; and, since the normals to the faces in a zone lie in a central plane, the face-poles lie on a great circle. A small circle is the intersection of the sphere with a noncentral plane; it is the locus of points at a fixed angular distance from a point on the sphere.

---

[14] Such stereographic nets may be obtained from the *University of Toronto Press*, Toronto 5, Canada.

Single-circle angles are conveniently plotted on a piece of transparent paper which can revolve on the net about a needle at its center. Angles between faces in the initial zone are laid off directly on the primitive circle. An inclined face, C, fixed by angles to two nonparallel vertical faces, A, B, is plotted by bringing A to one end of the horizontal diameter of the net and tracing the appropriate small circle, and repeating with B; the two

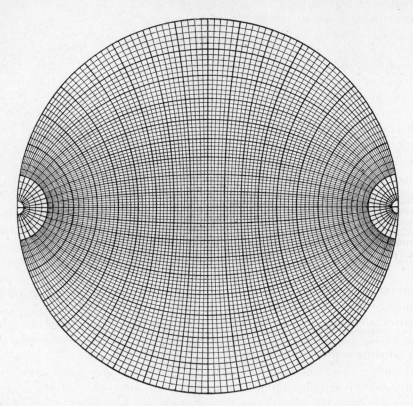

Fig. 13.—Stereographic net. (Reprinted by permission from "Optical Crystallography" by E. E. Wahlstrom, published by John Wiley & Sons, Inc.)

small circles intersect in the pole of C. Faces in a known inclined zone are plotted after turning the paper until the zone-circle lies on a great circle of the net.

The angles given by the two-circle goniometer are φ, ρ, respectively azimuth and polar distance with reference to the axis of the initial zone and a datum plane in the initial zone. These angles are directly comparable to geographic longitude and colatitude; and they are easily plotted on the stereographic net, or by using the simple construction in figure 14, in which the stereographic pole Q is fixed by angle φ and length CQ equals r tan $\frac{1}{2}\rho$.

The stereographic projection is invaluable in problems involving reorientation. The entire projection may be reoriented to bring any desired axis vertical by turning the upper sheet until the pole of the new vertical axis lies on the front–rear diameter of the net, and then moving every point through an equal angle along its appropriate small circle until the pole of the new vertical axis reaches the center of the net.

2. Gnomonic Projection

Returning to figure 12, NE is the trace of the horizontal plane touching the sphere at N; this is the plane of the gnomonic projection. The face-normal CP, produced to cut plane NE, gives the gnomonic projection point or pole R. If ρ is the polar distance of the face,

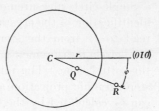

Fig. 14.—Stereographic and gnomonic poles plotted by two-circle angles.

then the gnomonic distance of R from the center of the projection is $NR = r$ tan ρ. Single-circle measurements can be plotted in gnomonic projection by way of the stereographic projection, using the construction in figure 14. Through stereographic pole Q draw radius CQ, measure CQ, and obtain ρ from the equation $CQ = r$ tan $\frac{1}{2}\rho$; the gnomonic pole R lies on the same radius at the distance $CR = r$ tan ρ. When $\rho = 90°$, as for faces in the initial zone, a face is represented by a radius parallel to the face-normal. Any inclined central plane cuts the gnomonic plane in a straight line, and consequently an inclined zone is represented by a straight line on the projection.

The gnomonic projection is particularly useful for indexing the measured faces by inspection. In figure 15, $a(100)$, $b(010)$, $c(001)$, have been chosen as the axial planes whose intersections give the directions of axes a, b, c, of the crystal lattice; and plane $p(111)$ has been chosen as the parametral plane whose intercepts on the axes are $a:b:c$. This defines the gnomonic net with periods p_0', q_0'. The Miller indices (hkl) of any pole on the projection are proportional to the coordinates of the pole in the gnomonic net, the third coordinate being unity. For example, the gnomonic coordinates of pole r are $\frac{1}{2}$ $\frac{3}{2}$ (1); the Miller indices are thus (132). Similarly, $d(021)$, $e(201)$, $q(131)$, are indexed by inspection. Faces of the vertical zone, whose in-

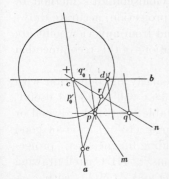

Fig. 15.—Gnomonic projection.

dices are of the type $(hk0)$, are indexed by the ratio of their gnomonic coordinates, the third term being zero, as, for example, $m(110)$, $n(130)$. The letters used for crystal faces and forms are arbitrary, only a, b, c, and m being regularly used with the indices given.

3. Interfacial Angles for Identification

Single-circle measurements will give all or most of the angles needed for identification of the crystal. Angles which have not been measured can be read to 1° from the stereographic projection on the stereographic net. Two-circle measurements will in general give only the interfacial angles in the initial zone. The missing angles can likewise be obtained from the stereographic projection and net; or the angle δ between any two faces can be calculated by the formula:

$$\cos \delta = \cos \rho_1 \cos \rho_2 + \sin \rho_1 \sin \rho_2 \cos (\varphi_2 - \varphi_1)$$

where $\varphi_1 \rho_1$ and $\varphi_2 \rho_2$ are the coordinate angles of the two faces.

4. Crystal Drawing

The morphological description of a crystal is not complete without a geometrical drawing showing the relative development of the forms. The old method of drawing crystals on the axial cross is difficult, especially if the drawing attempts to portray a particular crystal or if an unusual viewpoint is required. With the introduction of Goldschmidt's method of crystal drawing with the help of the gnomonic projection, accurate drawings of ideal or actual crystals in any system and from any viewpoint are easily and rapidly constructed. For short descriptions of this recommended method, see Porter[15] and Palache.[16]

For graphical work in crystallography, particularly in connection with the two-circle goniometer, the following equipment will be found useful: a good drawing board (24″ × 30″) or drawing table; a true hardwood or light steel straightedge (36″) and 30°–60° triangle (15″); a set of good drawing instruments; a small pin chuck for holding fine needles; projection paper (24″ × 16″) with $\frac{1}{2}$° azimuth divisions[17]; 7H Castell drawing pencils; cardboard or celluloid scales of $r \tan \rho$ and $r \tan \frac{1}{2} \rho$ with $r = 5$ cm. and 10 cm. Several types of useful crystallographic protractors have been described, the latest by Fisher.[18] For crystallographic calculations. Bruhns' seven-place tables[19] are convenient.

[15] Mary W. Porter, *Am. Mineral.*, **5**, 89 (1920).

[16] C. Palache, *Am. Mineral.*, **5**, 96 (1920).

[17] Supplied by the *University of Toronto Press*, Toronto 5, Canada.

[18] D. J. Fisher, *J. Geol.*, **49**, 292 (1941).

[19] K. C. Bruhns, *New Manual of Logarithms to Seven Places of Decimals*. Rev. ed., Powner, Chicago, 1936.

VII. DETERMINATION OF SYSTEM, FORMS, AND ELEMENTS

Having chosen a good crystal, adjusted it with reference to a suitable initial zone, measured it on a single-circle or two-circle goniometer, and plotted the measurements in stereographic or gnomonic projection, we may proceed to the actual determination of the crystal form. This involves, at the minimum, determining the crystal system, choosing the axial planes and parametral plane, indexing all the forms on the crystal, and calculating the geometrical elements of the chosen lattice from the measured angles. These essential steps will be illustrated by projections of ideal simplicity in each of the lattice systems.

1. Triclinic System

Figures 16 and 17 show, respectively, a stereographic and a gnomonic projection of the upper half of a triclinic crystal in the preferred conven-

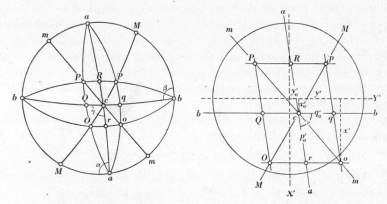

Fig. 16.—Stereographic projection of a triclinic crystal.   Fig. 17.—Gnomonic projection of a triclinic crystal.

tional orientation (axes $c < a < b$; angles α and β obtuse). The triclinic character shows in the absence of any axis of symmetry or plane of symmetry in the projections. In the stereographic projection, the conventional setting causes the pole of $c(001)$ to lie in front and usually to the right of the center, while the relation $cq < cr < 45°$ is approximately true. The gnomonic net is oblique and excentric with $c(001)$ in front and usually to the right of the center and the approximate relation $q_0' < p_0' < 1$ (radius of the sphere of projection).

With a, b, c, as the axial planes and o as the parametral plane, the remaining forms receive the simplest indices, which is a good indication, in the triclinic system, that the proper simple cell of the crystal lattice has been chosen. The forms shown in both projections then receive the indices:

$a(100)$, $b(010)$, $c(001)$, $m(110)$, $M(1\bar{1}0)$, $q(011)$, $Q(0\bar{1}1)$, $r(101)$, $R(\bar{1}01)$, $o(111)$, $O(1\bar{1}1)$, $p(1\bar{1}1)$, $P(\bar{1}\bar{1}1)$, using conventional form-letters.

The geometrical elements of the crystal are calculated from single-circle measurements by the methods of spherical trigonometry. The most convenient fundamental angles are five of the six angles, ab, bc, ca, oa, ob, oc (Fig. 16). From these, the following six angles are calculated—oca, ocb, oab, oac, obc, oba, as, for example:

$$\cos^2 \tfrac{1}{2}(oca) = \sin s \sin (s - oa)/\sin oc \sin ca$$

where $s = \tfrac{1}{2}(oa + ac + co)$; then:

$$a : b = \sin oca : \sin ocb$$
$$b : c = \sin oab : \sin oac$$
$$c : a = \sin obc : \sin oba$$

and $\alpha = 180° - cab$, $\beta = 180° - abc$, $\gamma = 180° - bca$.

A practical example of the measurement, projection, and calculation of a triclinic crystal from single-circle measurements is given by Tutton.[20]

In the calculation of geometrical elements from two-circle measurements and the gnomonic projection (Fig. 17), all the measured angles are conveniently taken into account, and the results are likely to be more accurate than those based on five interfacial angles. The procedure is as follows:

(1) Reduce the azimuth measurements to the azimuth of $b(010)$ as the prime meridian.

(2) Obtain the rectangular linear coordinates, x', y', for each pole on the gnomonic plane from the equations:

$$x' = \sin \varphi \tan \rho; \quad y' = \cos \varphi \tan \rho$$

(3) From x', y', derive the best mean values of the five elements of the gnomonic projection, x_0', y_0', p_0', q_0', ν, by plane trigonometry.

(4) Calculate the polar elements, p_0, q_0, $(r_0 = 1)$, λ, μ, (ν given), from the formulas:

$$\tan \varphi_0 = x_0'/y_0'; \quad \tan \rho_0 = x_0'/\sin \varphi_0 = y_0'/\cos \varphi_0$$

where φ_0, ρ_0, are the coordinate angles of the pole $c(001)$;

$$p_0 = p_0' \cos \rho_0; \quad q_0 = q_0' \cos \rho_0$$
$$\cos \lambda = y_0' \cos \rho_0; \quad \cos \mu = (x_0' \sin \nu + y_0' \cos \nu) \cos \rho_0$$

The geometrical elements are then obtained by the formulas:

$$a : b : c = \sin \lambda/p_0 : \sin \mu/q_0 : \sin \nu/r_0$$
$$\sin^2 \tfrac{1}{2} \alpha = \sin s \sin (s - \lambda)/\sin \mu \sin \nu$$
$$\sin^2 \tfrac{1}{2} \beta = \sin s \sin (s - \mu)/\sin \nu \sin \lambda$$
$$\sin^2 \tfrac{1}{2} \gamma = \sin s \sin (s - \nu)/\sin \lambda \sin \mu$$

where $s = \tfrac{1}{2}(\lambda + \mu + \nu)$.

[20] A. E. H. Tutton, *Crystallography and Practical Crystal Measurement*. Macmillan, London, 1911, p. 286.

These geometrical relations are further explained by Palache[21] and Peacock,[22] and a practical example of the application of the two-circle method to a triclinic crystal is given by Borgström and Goldschmidt.[23]

2. Monoclinic System

A monoclinic crystal is represented in the projections, figures 18 and 19, which show the single symmetry plane $b(010)$ indicating the monoclinic symmetry, and the relations, $ab = bc = 90°$, $ca < 90°$. The gnomonic net is rectangular and excentric, with the projection elements x_0', p_0', q_0'. The forms shown receive the simplest indices, $a(100)$, $b(010)$, $c(001)$, $m(110)$, $q(011)$, $r(101)$, $R(\overline{1}01)$, $o(111)$, $p(\overline{1}11)$.

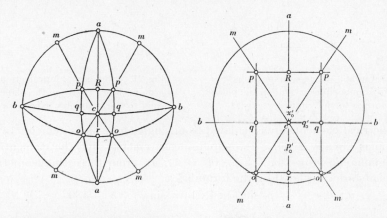

Fig. 18.—Stereographic projection of a monoclinic crystal on the plane normal to the vertical axis.

Fig. 19.—Stereographic projection of a monoclinic crystal on the plane normal to the vertical axis.

To obtain the geometrical elements from single-circle measurements, at least three independent angles are needed; the most convenient are cq, ca, am. With these angles the elements are:

$$a : b : c = \tan am : \sin ac : \tan cq; \quad \beta = 180° - ca$$

Two-circle measurements lead to the best mean values for the projection elements, x_0', p_0', q_0', from which the geometrical elements are obtained by the formula:

$$a : b : c = q_0'/p_0' \sin \beta : 1 : q_0'; \quad \cot \beta = -x_0'$$

Monoclinic crystals are often elongated with the symmetry axis, in which case it is convenient to take this axis as the axis of adjustment on the

[21] C. Palache, *Am. Mineral.*, **5**, 185 (1920).
[22] M. A. Peacock, *Am. J. Sci.*, **28**, 241 (1934).
[23] L. Borgström and V. Goldschmidt, *Z. Kryst.*, **41**, 63 (1906).

two-circle goniometer. The projections then appear as in figures 20 and 21, which are symmetrical to the 2-fold axis. The gnomonic net is oblique with a node, $b(010)$, at the center. Indexing proceeds as before and the

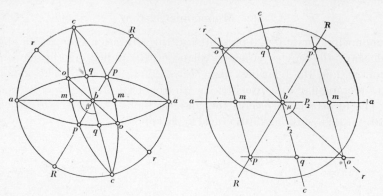

Fig. 20.—Stereographic projection of a monoclinic crystal on the plane normal to the symmetry axis.

Fig. 21.—Stereographic projection of a monoclinic crystal on the plane normal to the symmetry axis.

geometrical elements are calculated from single-circle measurements by the formulas already given. Two-circle measurements give the elements of the gnomonic projection, r_2, p_2, $(q_2 = 1)$, μ; from these the geometrical elements are calculated by the formula:

$$a : b : c = 1/(p_2 \sin \mu) : 1 : 1/(r_2 \sin \mu); \quad \beta = 180° - \mu$$

3. Orthorhombic System

Projections of an orthorhombic crystal (Figs. 22 and 23) show the two vertical planes of symmetry intersecting in the vertical 2-fold symmetry

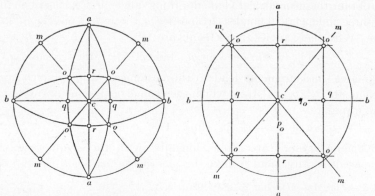

Fig. 22.—Stereographic projection of an orthorhombic crystal.

Fig. 23.—Gnomonic projection of an orthorhombic crystal.

axis. The gnomonic net is rectangular with a node at the center. The conventional setting ($c < a < b$) gives $cq < cr < 45°$ (Fig. 22) and $q_0 < p_c < 1$ (Fig. 23). The forms shown are $a(100)$, $b(010)$, $c(001)$, $m(110)$, $q(011)$, $r(101)$, $o(111)$. The geometrical elements may be obtained from two angles measured on the single-circle or two-circle goniometer:

$$a : b : c = \tan am : 1 : \tan cq$$

Two-circle measurements give the best mean values for the projection elements, p_0, q_0, ($r_0 = 1$), yielding the geometrical elements:

$$a : b : c = q_0/p_0 : 1 : q_0$$

4. Tetragonal System

Figures 24 and 25 are projections of a tetragonal crystal showing the four vertical symmetry planes intersecting in the vertical 4-fold axis. The

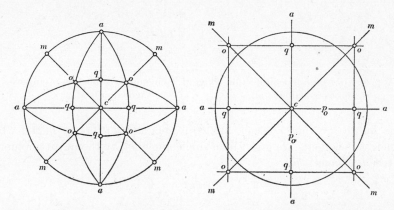

Fig. 24.—Stereographic projection of a tetragonal crystal.

Fig. 25.—Gnomonic projection of a tetragonal crystal.

gnomonic net is square with a node at the center. The angle cq may be greater or less than $45°$, and the projection element p_0 is thus greater or less than unity. The forms shown are $a(100)$, $c(001)$, $m(110)$, $q(011)$, $o(111)$. A single interfacial angle, or the mean value of the projection element p_0 ($r_0 = 1$), gives the geometrical element:

$$a : c = 1 : \tan cq = 1 : p_0$$

5. Hexagonal System

An hexagonal crystal is projected in figures 26 and 27, which show the six vertical planes of symmetry intersecting in the vertical 6-fold axis.

The gnomonic net is a 60° rhombic net with a node at the center. The forms are indexed with reference to 60° gnomonic axes and the projection element p_0 (Fig. 27). By this means, the indices $(hk.l)$ are obtained; the complete Bravais symbol $(hk\bar{i}l)$ is obtained by adding $i = h + k$. The

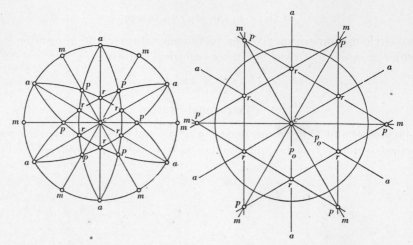

Fig. 26.—Stereographic projection of an hexagonal crystal.   Fig. 27.—Gnomonic projection of an hexagonal crystal.

forms shown are thus $c(0001)$, $a(10\bar{1}0)$, $m(11\bar{2}0)$, $r(10\bar{1}1)$, $p(11\bar{2}1)$. The geometrical elements are given by a single angle, or by the mean gnomonic projection element, p_0:

$$a : c = 1 : \tfrac{1}{2}\sqrt{3} \tan cr = 1 : \tfrac{1}{2}\sqrt{3}\, p_0$$

6. Rhombohedral System

A simple rhombohedral crystal is projected in figures 28 and 29, which show the three vertical symmetry planes intersecting in the vertical 3-fold axis. The gnomonic net is a system of equilateral triangles, rrr, sss, ttt, etc. To obtain the Miller indices (hkl) of a pole on the gnomonic projection, draw the three zone-lines, rr, and name their inner and outer sides $+h$, $+k$, $+l$, and $-h$, $-k$, $-l$, respectively. The indices of a pole on the gnomonic projection are proportional to the perpendicular distances from the pole to the three zone-lines, as shown in the case of $t(11\bar{1})$. The forms of a rhombohedral crystal may also be indexed with reference to hexagonal axes, exactly as in figure 27. In this way the forms in figures 28 and 29 receive the following rhombohedral and hexagonal indices: $c(111)(0001)$, $m(10\bar{1})(11\bar{2}0)$, $r(100)(10\bar{1}1)$, $s(110)(01\bar{1}2)$, $t(11\bar{1})(02\bar{2}1)$. The rhombohedral axial angle, α, is given by angle cr or the projection element, p_0, by the formulas:

$$\tan \tfrac{1}{2}\alpha = \sqrt{3} \cos cr; \quad \tan cr = p_0$$

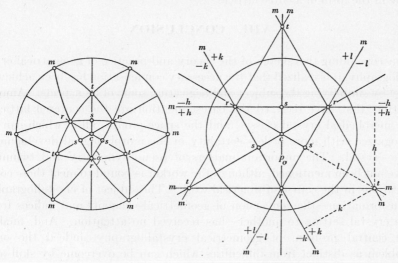

Fig. 28.—Stereographic projection of a rhombohedral crystal.

Fig. 29.—Gnomonic projection of a rhombohedral crystal.

7. Cubic System

Projections of a cubic crystal (Figs. 30 and 31) show four vertical symmetry planes intersecting in a vertical 4-fold axis, also four 3-fold axes

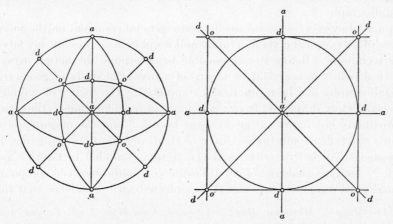

Fig. 30.—Stereographic projection of a cubic crystal.

Fig. 31.—Gnomonic projection of a cubic crystal.

emerging at o. The net is square with a node at the center and the projection element $p_0 = 1$. The forms shown are $a(100)$, $d(011)$, $o(111)$. There is no geometrical element to be calculated, since no variation is possible in the form of a cubic lattice.

VIII. CONCLUSION

In concluding this sketch of the theory and practice of geometrical crystallography, it is realized that the necessary condensation has been achieved only by simplifying the subject and neglecting some of its aspects. Among matters that have received the barest mention are the centered lattices, the merohedral crystal classes, and the space-groups, all of which can be recognized with more or less certainty in the morphological development of a crystal. The important matters of pseudosymmetry and twinning have not been mentioned, although the worker is bound to meet these complications in the course of practical work. The subject of crystallographic transformation—the conversion of geometrical elements and indices from one crystal setting to another—has received no attention. And, finally, the central problem of geometrical crystallography—indeed the only problem as distinct from difficulties which can be overcome by skill and patience—namely the discovery of *the* crystal lattice as distinct from *a* crystal lattice by geometrical means, has been glossed over in the foregoing examples by giving projections of such simplicity that no choice of lattice but the right one could reasonably be made. The adequate discussion of any of these topics would unduly expand this chapter. For information on these matters see the available textbooks and also recent mineralogical papers containing geometrical crystallography in connection with x-ray crystallography.[24]

It may, however, be useful to offer some general comment on the present status of geometrical crystallography and its place as a present-day laboratory technique. Before it was possible to determine the actual array of identical points in a crystal by means of x-rays, the study of geometrical crystallography had been practically completed. The theory of symmetry was completely developed from mathematical considerations; the general approximate law of crystal growth was known; and the majority of the known crystallized substances, more of them organic than inorganic, had been measured and described and the results compiled in Groth's great work.[25] Striking analogies of crystal form were found between compounds of analogous compositions; and it was inferred with confidence that these

---

[24] *Am. Mineral.*, *Mineralog. Mag.*, and *Contrib. Can. Min.* (*Univ. Toronto Studies, Geol. Ser.*) of the last few years.

[25] P. Groth, *Chemische Krystallographie.* 5 vols., Engelmann, Leipzig, 1906–1919.

analogies were due to similarities in the atomic or molecular structures which could not, however, be further revealed.

As x-ray crystallography developed, the symmetry theory of geometrical crystallography was adopted as a necessary tool for the new technique. Particularly the smallest subdivisions of symmetry, namely the 230 space-groups, assumed special significance; and tabulations of these groups with lists of all the possible types of atomic positions in each group soon became necessary aids in structural determination. Although many structures were, and still are, too complicated to be determined, the determination of the crystal lattice soon became a routine which could be carried out in every case with ease and certainty, given suitable material and equipment. Comparing this lattice with that inferred by goniometry, complete agreement was sometimes found: perhaps more often it was found that goniometry had led to a different lattice cell than that given by x-rays, and this showed, as was indeed suspected, that the existing methods of discussing goniometric results did not lead with certainty to the smallest cell of the crystal lattice but often gave a small multiple cell. Thus x-ray technique superseded goniometry as a positive means of finding the crystal lattice, and the natural tendency has been to neglect morphological results or at most to indicate the transformation required to bring them into line with the x-ray findings.

On the other hand, when it became clear that there is but one proper choice of lattice cell for a given crystal, it became of great interest to re-examine the morphology of crystals and to improve the methods of choosing the unit cell from geometrical data. Efforts in this direction have been fruitful. The arithmetic-harmonic rule provided a reliable means of finding the crystal lattice in the general (triclinic) case,[26] and the specialization of this rule for centered lattices and space-groups[27] gave an equally reliable procedure for the higher symmetries. The effectiveness of these improved procedures is best tested, as in the writer's laboratory, by making a considered choice of the lattice cell from geometrical data and then determining the cell directly by x-rays and comparing the independent results. The consistent agreement obtained thus far shows that the ambiguity of geometrical cell determinations can be practically overcome.

Crystal form is the logical external manifestation of crystal structure, and as a function of structure it deserves study and description, like every other function of the structure. Indeed, as the most immediate expression of the structure, crystal form should take its place immediately after crystal structure in the description of a crystallized substance, and without

---

[26] M. A. Peacock, *Am. Mineral.*, **22**, 210 (1937).

[27] J. D. H. Donnay, *Ann. soc. géol. Belg. Bull.*, **61**, 260 (1938); *Am. Mineral.*, **24**, 184 (1939).

question structure and form should be described with reference to one and the same lattice coordinates. A chemical laboratory engaged in structural work requires a goniometer to orient single crystals for x-ray photographs; with a little practice, a complete examination of the crystal form can be made and the results coordinated with the roentgenographic work. If a geometrical description has already been published, it should be transformed, if necessary, to the structural lattice. In this way the great body of careful goniometric work on organic substances could gradually be reworked for a future compilation of structural crystallography. In such a work the description of a crystalline substance might take the form of the following summary of the principal crystal properties of tartaric acid:[28]

TARTARIC ACID ($C_4H_6O_6$)

Symmetry. Monoclinic, sphenoidal, $C_2^2 - P2_1$
Lattice. $a = 7.693, b = 6.037, c = 6.195$Å., $\beta = 100°\ 17'$
$\quad\quad a:b:c = 1.2743:1:1.0262$
Structure. $Z = 2$. (Atomic positions, when known.)

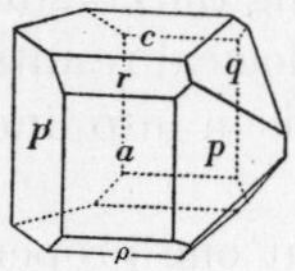

Forms (right crystals). $a(100), p'(1\bar{1}0), p(110), q(011), c(001), r(101), \rho(\bar{1}01), \kappa(0\bar{1}1), o(111), s(211), t(311)?, \omega(\bar{1}11), \omega'(\bar{1}\bar{1}1)$ (Fig. 32); left crystals symmetrical to right crystals by reflection in (010).

Twins. Twin axis [001].

Physical Properties. Cleavage (100) perfect; specific gravity 1.759; melting point 168–170° C.; strongly pyroelectric and piezoelectric.

Optical Properties.

Fig. 32.—
Crystal of *d*-
tartaric acid.

	(Na)	
$\alpha = b$	1.4961	Positive
$\beta:c\ +19\text{--}18°$	1.5359	$2V = 77°\ 09\frac{1}{2}'$
$\gamma:c\ -71\text{--}72°$	1.6055	$2E = 156°\ 36'$

Rotatory power in the optic axes of right crystals (degree/mm.): -8.5 (Li), -11.4 (Na), -14.2 (Tl).

For the present, the goniometric data on crystals can also be used in another way, namely, by recasting them according to a set of inflexible rules so as to give angular determinative data. This scheme, which was commenced before the era of x-ray crystallography and is now well advanced, is described by Donnay in the following chapter of this book.

In concluding this sketch of geometrical crystallography I am glad to acknowledge the kindness of Dr. J. D. H. Donnay and Dr. I. Fankuchen, who read the

[28] Cell dimensions by W. T. Astbury, *Proc. Roy. Soc. London*, **A102**, 506 (1923); remaining properties selected from P. Groth, *Chemische Krystallographie*, Vol. III, Engelmann, Leipzig, 1910, p. 303.

manuscript and suggested some improvements and additions which should make a mineralogist's essay more useful to organic chemists.

General References

Barker, T. V., *Graphical and Tabular Methods in Crystallography.*   Murby, London, 1922.

Friedel, Georges, *Leçons de cristallographie professées à la faculté des sciences de Strasbourg.*   Berger-Levrault, Paris, 1926.

Goldschmidt, Victor, *Kursus der Kristallometrie.*   Borntraeger, Berlin, 1934.

Groth, P., *Chemische Krystallographie.*   5 vols., Engelmann, Leipzig, 1906–1919.

Miers, Henry A., *Mineralogy.   An Introduction to the Scientific Study of Minerals.* 2nd ed., rev. by H. L. Bowman, Macmillan, London, 1929.

Tutton, A. E. H., *Crystallography and Practical Crystal Measurement.*   Vol. I, *Form and Structure;*   Vol. II, *Physical and Chemical.*   2nd ed., Macmillan, London, 1922.

CHAPTER XIII

CRYSTALLOCHEMICAL ANALYSIS

J. D. H. Donnay, *Hercules Powder Company*

I. INTRODUCTION

"Crystallochemical analysis" is the name given by Fedorov[1] to the determination of (noncubic) crystalline substances by means of goniometric data. Although, since the advent of x-ray diffraction methods in crystallography, the scope of "crystallochemical analysis" might well be expanded to include all methods of identification based on crystallographic constants, it seems best to retain the term in its original restricted sense.

Such a method of determination offers marked advantages:

(1) It requires only a very small amount of the substance to be identified —one crystal, a fraction of a millimeter in length, is sufficient, provided it is bounded by faces that reflect light. If the crystal faces give no reflections and the contact goniometer must be resorted to, the crystal should be larger, at least of the order of one centimeter.

---

[1] E. S. vonFedorow, *Mém. Acad. Sci. Russie*, **36** (1920); see also *Z. Kryst. Mineral.*, **50**, 513 (1912).

(*2*) The crystal is not destroyed by the analysis; all of the substance remains available for other tests.

(*3*) The method is rapid, the total time required for an analysis varying between half an hour and a few hours.

(*4*) A huge amount of crystallographic data accumulated in the past century are made available for determinative purposes. The number of substances forming good crystals that have been investigated to date by non-x-ray goniometry may be estimated to exceed 10,000, and possibly to approach 12,000. Of these, the vast majority are organic compounds.

(*5*) In most cases, the goniometric method of crystallochemical analysis does not overlap the x-ray methods. The latter, it is true, are able to cope with crystals devoid of reflecting faces and also with substances that crystallize in the isometric (cubic) system. The number of substances for which x-ray diffraction data are available, however, is still relatively small. The card index[2] for the determination of crystalline powders by the Hanawalt method comprises only 1200 substances, mostly inorganic compounds. According to a recent survey (1942) by Nowacki,[3] we know the absolute unit-cell dimensions and the space group for about 3000 substances.

Crystallochemical analysis is based on the Law of Constancy of Angles. The latter is easily understood now that we know the existence of the crystal lattice. The faces of a crystal are parallel to *nets* (lattice planes); and the edges, being the intersections of faces, are parallel to *rows* (lattice lines). The angle between two faces of a crystal is equal to the angle between two nets of its lattice. If the same two faces, that is to say—faces parallel to the same two nets, occur on another crystal of the same crystalline species (same chemical compound and, in case of polymorphism, same modification), then obviously the interfacial angle at the same temperature will have the same value. A similar explanation holds for the angle between two edges, the interzonal angle.

II. IDENTIFICATION AND DETERMINATION

Two different tasks[4] may confront the crystallographer engaged in analyzing an unknown substance. The "unknown" may be only partially so, in the sense that some information has already been gathered on its constitution, as by qualitative chemical analysis, microchemical tests, or spectrographic analysis. In this case, the task may reduce to checking

---

    [2] W. P. Davey, *Card Index File of X-Ray Diffraction Data*. Published jointly by Am. Soc. Testing Materials and Natl. Research Council, 1941.

    [3] W. Nowacki, *Helv. Chim. Acta*, **25**, 863 (1942).

    [4] P. Terpstra, *Natuurw. Tijdschr.*, **14**, 168 (1932).

one or a few possibilities—it is a problem of *identification*.   On the other hand, the substance studied may be totally unknown, without any information on its chemical composition; the problem is then truly one of *determination*.

The problem of identification is by far the simpler of the two.   There is no need to have any determinative catalogue based on a unique choice of the unit cell.   It is easy enough to look up the crystallographic description of the suspected substance in the literature and to compare the published angles with those one has measured.   For this purpose, Groth's five volumes[5] are the outstanding compendium, in which about 7200 crystalline substances (two-thirds of them organic compounds) are described and classified according to their chemical composition.   Although Groth gives interfacial angles only, other angles may, of course, be used for identification purposes.   By plotting the published data in stereographic projection, the coordinate angles (longitude φ and colatitude ρ) of the normal to any face can be obtained for comparison with angles measured on the unknown crystal by means of the two-circle goniometer.   Interzonal angles can be read from the projection and checked on the unknown crystal with a simple contact goniometer.   Another method, recently developed at the Hercules Experiment Station by the writer jointly with O'Brien,[6] can be applied in the case of microscopic crystals lying on a glass slide with a face parallel to the stage of the microscope.   The angles between edges or projections of edges (projections onto the plane of the stage) can be measured on the rotating stage; such angles are readily obtainable from the published interfacial angles by graphic constructions on the stereographic net.

Simple as they are, these methods of identification (of "checking hunches") by goniometry may be extremely valuable to the industrial chemist.   In order, however, to derive the fullest possible measure of usefulness from the published goniometric data, the latter should be made available in a systematic index to be used for determinative purposes.

Before a determinative index can be compiled, a choice of crystallographic constants must be made.   These constants may be the relative unit-cell dimensions (axial elements) or angles (interfacial, interzonal, or coordinate angles).   Even if they are cast in the form of angles, they are fundamentally related to the unit cell, whose shape controls the values of all angles and whose choice determines the Miller indices to be assigned to the various faces.   To say, for instance, that one of the angles to be used as determinative constants is the angle between faces (100) and (110) would be meaningless as long as the choice of axial elements has not been agreed upon.   In the last analysis, deciding on a selection of angles as

---

[5] P. Groth, *Chemische Krystallographie.*   Engelmann, Leipzig, 1906–1919.

[6] J. D. H. Donnay and W. A. O'Brien, *Microscope Goniometry.*   Unpublished.

determinative criteria will always involve, as a prerequisite, the selection of the unit cell.[7] The latter need not be the true (structural) unit cell; it may well be arbitrary, provided the rules governing its choice lead to a unique solution.

III. THE BARKER METHOD

1. Nomenclature and Determinative Constants

Barker[8] introduced a few concepts which simplify the discussion of his method. A *plane* is defined as a face direction. It corresponds either to one face only or to two parallel faces, whether these two faces are similar (equivalent) or not, whether they constitute a form or part of a form, or

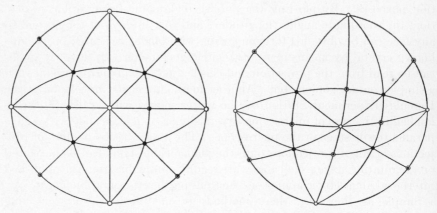

Fig. 1.—The 13 planes with simplest indices in isometric and triclinic systems.
○, cubic planes; ⊙, dodecahedral planes; ●, octahedral planes.

whether they belong to two different forms. *Similar* or *equivalent* faces are faces that have the same physical appearance, for instance, as to luster, striations, etched figures, and the like, regardless of some differences in their sizes and shapes. A *form* is defined as the assemblage of all similar faces on a crystal, as, for example, a cube, an octahedron, a dodecahedron.

By analogy with the isometric system terminology, the three axial planes, whose Miller symbols comprise two zeros and a one, are called the *cubic planes;* they are (100), (010), (001). Likewise the six planes whose symbols contain one zero and two ones are termed the *dodecahedral planes;* they are (011), (101), (110), (0$\bar{1}$1), ($\bar{1}$01), (1$\bar{1}$0). Finally, the four planes whose

[7] J. D. H. Donnay, G. Tunell, and T. F. W. Barth, *Am. Mineral.*, **19**, 437 (1934).

[8] T. V. Barker, *Systematic Crystallography, an Essay on Crystal Description, Classification and Identification.* Murby, London, 1930.

Miller indices are all ones are designated the *octahedral planes;* they are (111), $(\bar{1}11)$, $(\bar{1}\bar{1}1)$, $(1\bar{1}1)$. These 13 planes are called the *planes with simplest indices* (Fig. 1), the indices smaller than 2, positive or negative, being the simplest. This definition is somewhat modified in the hexagonal system, as will be seen later on. A plane whose symbol contains an index greater than one is called a *complex* plane. The following conventional letters have been adopted (Fig. 2) to designate the faces: $a(100)$, $b(010)$, $c(001)$, $q(011)$, $r(101)$, $m(110)$, $Q(0\bar{1}1)$, $R(\bar{1}01)$, $M(1\bar{1}0)$, $o(111)$, $p(\bar{1}11)$, $O(1\bar{1}1)$, $P(\bar{1}\bar{1}1)$. A primed letter refers to the face parallel to the unprimed one; for instance, $a'(\bar{1}00)$, $m'(\bar{1}\bar{1}0)$.

The choice of three axial faces, $a(100)$, $b(010)$, $c(001)$, and of one parametral face, that is, a face intersecting all three coordinate axes, for in-

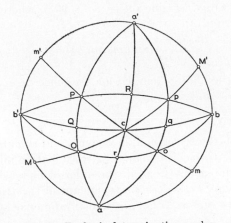

Fig. 2.—Barker's determinative angles.

stance any one of the "octahedral" faces, say $o(111)$, determines what the Miller symbols of all the remaining faces will be. This is easy to see (Fig. 2): Zone circles aca' and bcb' are given; zone circle co determines m on the primitive circle; zone circles aoa' and bob' determine the locations of q and r; zone circle qr intersects the primitive in M, whence the zone circle $MOcM'$ can be drawn; and the projection is easily completed. The pattern of the 13 planes with simplest indices, considered with a cubododecahedral zone vertical, is extremely important in the development of the Barker method. It can be visualized as a spherical quadrilateral resulting from the intersection of two lunes; the lunes point to two cubic planes; the diagonals of the quadrilateral meet the primitive circle in two dodecahedral planes. This pattern has been called the *normal pattern.*

Assuming one had a set of rules to make a unique choice of the axial and parametral faces, every crystallographer would be able to reach the same normal pattern (Fig. 2), which would be an unambiguous representation of the crystal. The rules will be given on pages 566–573. In order to avoid tedious calculations, or at least to reduce them to a minimum, Barker proposed the use of angular values, instead of the axial elements as determinative constants; namely, in the triclinic system, the interfacial angles, *cr, ra, am, mb, bq, qc*. It is immaterial whether these planes have all been observed or not. One of the angles is superabundant, since five angles are sufficient to determine the axial elements. The six Barker angles obey the relation:

$$\frac{\sin cr}{\sin ra} \cdot \frac{\sin am}{\sin mb} \cdot \frac{\sin bq}{\sin qc} = 1$$

Fewer angles are used in the more symmetric systems: four in the monoclinic system, *cr, ra, am, bq* (since $ab = bc = 90°$), where the following relation holds:

$$\frac{\sin cr}{\sin ra} \cdot \tan am \cdot \tan bq = 1$$

three in the orthorhombic system, *cr, am, bq* (since $ca = ab = bc = 90°$), where the relation reduces to:

$$\tan cr \cdot \tan am \cdot \tan bq = 1$$

and one only, *cr*, in the tetragonal, hexagonal, and rhombohedral systems. The substances are to be listed, in the determinative index, according to systems and, within each system, in the order of increasing values of one of the angles, chosen as *classification angle* (**am** in the triclinic and monoclinic systems, **cr** in the orthorhombic and the dimetric systems), which is printed in boldface.

2. Choice of Setting. Principle of Simplest Indices

The first step in the application of Barker's method is plotting the stereographic projection of all the faces from the angular measurements. The choice of the coordinate axes and of the parametral face is not to be guided by crystal-habit considerations, but will result from an analysis of the stereographic projection.

Try to give simplest indices to as many of the observed planes as possible. If this can be done in only one way (for instance, if all the observed planes are the 13 planes of figure 1), the *setting* is said to be uniquely determined. This means that it is known which planes are to be cubic, which dodecahedral, and which octahedral, although it is not known which of the three cubic planes is to be $a(100)$, nor which face is to become $a(100)$ and which $a'(\overline{1}00)$, and so on. In other words, the parallelopiped which is to be taken as the unit cell is determined, although the coordinate axes, which are the edges of the parallelopiped, are neither named nor directed. An example, chosen from the triclinic crystal system, will show how the Principle of Simplest Indices is put to work.

Consider the stereographic projection of naphthalene chloropicrate (Fig. 3), plotted according to the axial elements given in Groth.[9] Only nine forms are observed, yet two are given complex symbols: $Z'(\bar{1}21)$ and $X'(\bar{1}\bar{2}1)$. By means of a forward rotation about the diameter normal to (010), until the four-plane zone $b'Kcqb$ falls on the equatorial circle, the projection is given a new appearance (Fig. 4) in which the normal pattern of figure 2 is easily recognized. All the observed planes can be given "simplest indices"; even so, four poles of the normal pattern remain vacant. The unit cell defined by figure 4 satisfies Barker's Principle of Simplest Indices.

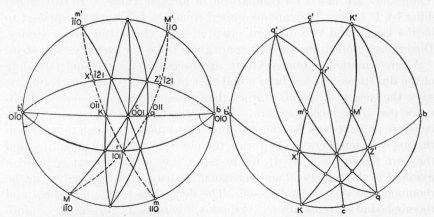

Fig. 3.—Naphthalene chloropicrate   Fig. 4.—Naphthalene chloropicrate
    (before reorientation).   (after reorientation).

The application of this principle may lead to ambiguity, in the sense that more than one setting may be found to give simplest indices to the same maximum number of observed planes. Ambiguity in the choice of the setting may occur in the case of *overdevelopment*, that is to say, when there are several settings having the same maximum number of planes with simplest indices, or in the case of *underdevelopment*, when less than 13 planes are observed and there are several ways of composing the normal pattern by adding nonobserved planes. Auxiliary rules are provided to remove the ambiguity in the choice of the setting. They are based on comparisons between angular values, for instance, that setting may be chosen in which angle ca (001:100) is nearest 90°. In this type of comparison, two angles are accounted equal if their values differ by 1° or less. Each in

[9] P. Groth, *Chemische Krystallographie.*   Vol. V, Engelmann, Leipzig, 1919, p. 365.

turn is supposed to be the larger and the two settings are worked out.   If
two angles are actually equal, that is, if the angles are between identical
or equivalent faces, the ambiguity persists and the next rule is tried.   The
auxiliary rules will be given under each crystal system.

3.   Orientation of Setting

Additional rules determine the orientation of the setting, once the latter
is uniquely selected.   They are concerned with naming and directing the
axes, or, the equivalent, deciding which of the axial planes will be c and
which a, which of the c faces will be (001), and which of the a faces will be
(100).   Such rules completely determine the orientation of the setting.
Again they are based on comparison of angular values.   If two angles
differ by $1°$ or less, they are accounted equal, each in turn is supposed to
be the larger, and two different orientations of the setting are necessary.
Directions for orienting the setting are given below for each crystal system.

A few remarks on nomenclature are necessary for the understanding
of the directions.   It has been noted that little heed is paid to symmetry,
since the concept of *planes* (rather than those of *faces* and *forms*) domi-
nates the whole Barker system.   In keeping with this viewpoint, all the
faces are projected, on the stereographic projection, as though they were in
the upper hemisphere.   The forms thereby lose their individualities and
they are loosely designated; for instance, any inclined form is called a
pyramid in the tetragonal and hexagonal systems, a rhombohedron in the
rhombohedral system, and so on.   The definitions of the hexagonal and
rhombohedral systems are not orthodox according to present-day standards.   In the Barker system, any crystal with a single threefold symmetry axis is treated as rhombohedral.   Only if a crystal has a single
sixfold symmetry axis is it considered hexagonal.

4.   Auxiliary Rules to Remove Setting Ambiguities

A. TETRAGONAL SYSTEM

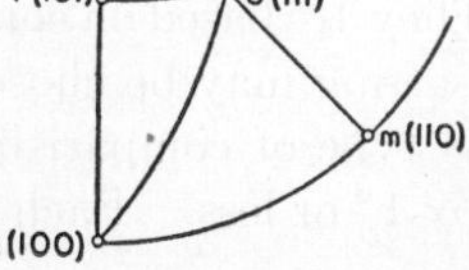

Fig. 5.—Tetragonal system.

The fourfold symmetry axis is taken as the c-axis.   The planes
with simplest indices (Fig. 5) are: $c(001)$, $r(101)$,
$a(100)$, $m(110)$, $o(111)$.   The classification angle
is **cr**.

Rule for Ambiguous Cases.— *Underdevelopment.*—If only one pyramid is present, it is
labeled $r(101)$.

Overdevelopment.—That setting is chosen for
which **cr** is closest to $45°$.

B.   HEXAGONAL SYSTEM

The sixfold symmetry axis is taken as the c-axis.   The planes with simplest indices (Fig. 6) are: $c(0001)$, $r(10\bar{1}1)$, $a(10\bar{1}0)$, $m(11\bar{2}0)$, $o(11\bar{2}1)$.   Remember that the third index is superabundant.   The classification angle is **cr**.

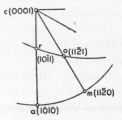

Fig. 6.—Hexagonal system.

Rules for Ambiguous Cases.— *Underdevelopment.*—If only one pyramid is present, it is labeled $r(10\bar{1}1)$.

Overdevelopment.—That setting is chosen for which **cr** is closest to $49°\ 6'$.

C.   RHOMBOHEDRAL SYSTEM

The threefold symmetry axis is taken as the c-axis.   The planes with simplest indices in rhombohedral notation (Fig. 7) are: $c(111)(0001)$, $r(100)(10\bar{1}1)$, $a(10\bar{1})(11\bar{2}0)$, $e(110)(01\bar{1}2)$, $o(11\bar{1})$ $(02\bar{2}1)$.   The classification angle is **cr**.

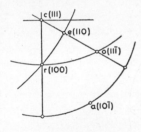

Fig. 7.—Rhombohedral system.

Rules for Ambiguous Cases.— *Underdevelopment.*—If only one rhombohedron is present, it is labeled $r(100)(10\bar{1}1)$.   Two rhombohedra tautozonal with $c(111)(0001)$ are labeled $e(110)(01\bar{1}2)$ and $o(11\bar{1})(02\bar{2}1)$.   Two rhombohedra, one of which truncates the other, are labeled $r(100)$ $(10\bar{1}1)$ and $o(11\bar{1})(02\bar{2}1)$.

Overdevelopment.—That setting is chosen for which **cr** is closest to $54°\ 45'$.

D.   ORTHORHOMBIC SYSTEM

The three mutually perpendicular symmetry directions are taken as coordinate axes.   (A symmetry direction is either a 2-axis or the perpendicular to a mirror.)   The setting is oriented by placing the hypo-tetragonal zone vertical, with am smaller than mb.   (The hypo-tetragonal zone is that cubo-dodecahedral zone in which the angle between a cubic and a dodecahedral plane is closest to $45°$.)   The planes with simplest indices (Fig. 8) are: $c(001)$, $r(101)$, $a(100)$, $m(110)$, $b(010)$, $q(011)$, $o(111)$.   The Barker angles are: **cr**, am, bq, with **cr** as classification angle.

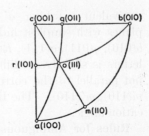

Fig. 8.—Orthorhombic system.

Rules for Ambiguous Cases.— *Underdevelop-*

ment.—If only one cubo-dodecahedral zone is developed, so that only one axial ratio can be determined, this zone is taken as **cra**, with **cr** smaller than **ra**. In this case, the only angle that can be given is **cr**, the classification angle.

Overdevelopment.—To choose from equally simple settings apply the following rules in order: *(1) am* nearest 45°, *(2) bq* nearest 45°, *(3) cr* nearest 45°.

Remarks.—Barker used *cr*, instead of *bq*, in rule *(2)*. The change was proposed[10] in view of the fact that *cr*, being the classification angle, should have as wide a range as possible. Rule *(3)* was added by Spiller and Hey.

E. MONOCLINIC SYSTEM

The symmetry direction is taken as the *b*-axis. For convenience, the stereographic projection is made on the *b*(010) plane. The setting is oriented by taking *ca* smaller than 90°, with *cr* smaller than *ra*, which is

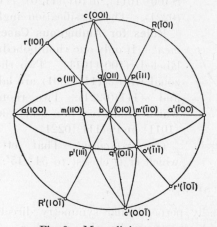

Fig. 9.—Monoclinic system.

equivalent to taking *ca'* larger than 90°, with *cR* smaller than *Ra'*. The planes with simplest indices (Fig. 9) are: *c*(001), *r*(101), *a*(100), *m*(110), *b*(010), *q*(011), *o*(111), *R*($\bar{1}$01), *p*($\bar{1}$11). The convention relative to primed letters is slightly modified; some primed letters represent faces that are not parallel to the corresponding unprimed ones (Fig. 9), for instance: *m*(110), *m'*($\bar{1}$10). The Barker angles are *cr*, *ra*, **am**, **bq**, with **am** as classification angle.

Rules for Ambiguous Cases.—A number of problems may occur in

[10] P. Terpstra, J. D. H. Donnay, J. Mélon, and W. J. van Weerden, *Z. Krist,* **A87,** 281 (1934)

cases of underdevelopment. Although they can all be solved in a straight-forward manner, they will require more detailed explanations. Some definitions must be introduced.

A zone is called a *three-plane zone*, a *four-plane zone*, etc., according to the number of planes it contains. A four-plane zone is said to be *harmonic* when four faces, *p*, *q*, *r*, *s*, taken in order (Fig. 10), satisfy the cotangent formula:

$$2 \cot pr = \cot pq + \cot ps$$

which can easily be expressed geometrically as: $2AR = AQ - SA$, whence $SA + AR = AQ - AR$ or $SR = RQ$ (Fig. 10). It is thus easy to check

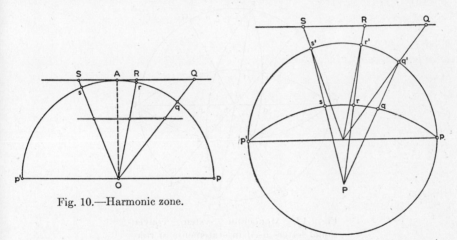

Fig. 10.—Harmonic zone.

Fig. 11.—Checking an harmonic zone.

whether a zone is harmonic—on a parallel to the first face-normal, the other three face-normals must intercept equal segments. If the zone to be checked is not the equatorial zone (Fig. 11), it is rotated into the equator around the first face-normal. This may be done on the stereographic net or, more simply, by joining pole *P* of the zone to face poles *q*, *r*, *s*, and producing to the equatorial circle. A cubo-dodecahedral zone (for instance, zone *arcR* in figure 9) is harmonic, and so is a cubo-octahedral zone (for example, zone *aoqp* in figure 9). A three-plane zone is transformed into an harmonic four-plane zone by the insertion of a fourth plane, harmonically, in the largest interfacial angle. This is known as the *Principle of Largest Angle Truncation*. Likewise a four-zone bundle, constituted by four zones having one plane in common, may be harmonic. The four zones that meet in a cubic plane form an harmonic zone bundle (for example, zones *raR′*, *omp′*, *qbq′*, *pm′o′*, which all intersect in the plane *c*, in figure 9). A three-zone bundle is transformed into an harmonic bundle by the insertion of a fourth zone, harmonically, in the largest interzonal angle. This is known as the *Problem of the Free Zone.*

A form oblique to the *b*-axis is called a *terminal form*. It consists of two planes (for instance, *o* and *o'* in figure 9) tautozonal with *b*. The zone is called a *polar zone*. The planes lie on a diameter which determines the location of a plane on the equator. The *b* plane is not a terminal form; its presence or absence is immaterial to the systematic problem. The various cases of underdevelopment are distinguished according to the number of terminal forms, such as can be given simplest indices. In order to

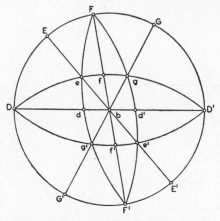

Fig. 12.—Monoclinic system, conventional letters used in statements of rules.

simplify the statements of rules, Barker designates the planes, prior to the choice and orientation of the setting, by certain conventional letters (Fig. 12).

Underdevelopment.—(*1*) Three Terminal Forms. The Free Zone Problem suffices to remove any ambiguity.

(*2*) Two Terminal Forms. Let *d* and *e* be two planes (Fig. 13) such that angle *dbe* is acute. Three equatorial planes (*D, E, F*) are located by zones *bdD, beE, deF*. If the fourth equatorial plane, *G*, is not developed, it is inserted harmonically in the largest of the three angles, *DE, EF, FD'*. The only case of ambiguity arises (Fig. 14) when *G*, either developed or inserted, falls between *D* and *E*. The latter are then taken as axial planes, which makes *d* and *e* dodecahedral.

(*3*) One Terminal Form. Let *d* be the one terminal; it defines *D* on the equator. If *E, F, G* are developed, *d* is considered dodecahedral, which makes *D* and *F* axial. If only two equatorial planes besides *D* are developed, insert the fourth one harmonically (Principle of Largest Angle Truncation).   If only one equatorial plane besides D is present, it is labeled (001), while d is taken as (110) and D as (100); in this case, two angles are given, ca and **am**, the latter being the classification angle.   If no equatorial plane besides D is present, which may happen in the case of an incomplete crystal, D is taken as (100), d as (110), and **am** is the only angle given.

(4)   No Terminal Form.   Such substances are listed separately in the index.   The classification angle becomes **ca**, supplemented if possible by

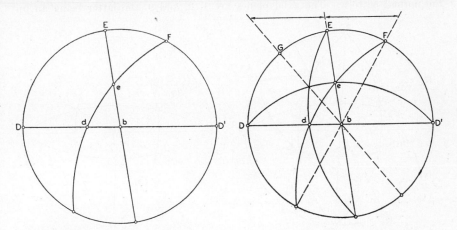

Fig. 13.—Two terminals (data).   Fig. 14.—Two terminals (solution).

cr and ra.   If D, E, F, G are developed, either D, F, or E, G are taken as axial, according to whether DF or EG is closer to 90°.   If only three equatorial planes are developed, apply the Principle of Largest Angle Truncation to create a fourth one.   If only two equatorial planes are present, they are considered axial, and **ca** is the only angle given.

Overdevelopment.—To choose from equally simple settings, apply the following rules in order: *(1) ca* nearest 90°, *(2) cr* nearest 45°, *(3) bq* nearest 45°, *(4) am* nearest 45°.

Remarks.—The rules for monoclinic overdevelopment, barely sketched by Barker, had to be recast.[10]   Rule *(4)* was added by Spiller and Hey.

EXAMPLE

Suppose an unidentified crystal of sodium formate is to be determined by the Barker method.   The presence of a center of symmetry and an axis of twofold symmetry, perpendicular to a plane of symmetry, is ascertained on inspection and will be checked by the measurements.   Two zones are measured on the goniometer and the crystal form combination is plotted in stereographic projection (Fig. 15) on the plane of symmetry $b(010)$. The monoclinic symmetry is confirmed. The observed faces are designated by arbitrary numbers, 1 to 8. The three measured interfacial angles chosen as the most reliable are:

$$3 : 8' = 76° 0', \quad 2 : 3 = 65° 26', \quad 2' : 6 = 70° 0'$$

They are shown on the projection (Fig. 15), on which various zone intersections have been numbered, from 9 to 18, for future reference.

The case is one of underdevelopment with three terminal forms; there is no ambiguity in the choice of the setting. The zone circles drawn on figure 16 make the normal pattern. The axial planes are 1, 2, and 9, the latter being an un-

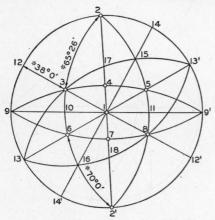

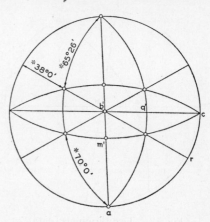

Fig. 15.—Sodium formate, measurements.   Fig. 16.—Sodium formate, three terminal forms, unique setting and orientation.

observed plane located by zone intersection. Of these three planes, plane 1 must be the b plane, by reason of symmetry. The setting is completely oriented by taking 9' as $c(001)$ and 2' as $a(100)$, so that angle cr is smaller than ra and ca is smaller than 90°. The face 1 becomes $b'(0\bar{1}0)$, since the system of coordinates must be right-handed. Faces $r(101)$ and $q'(0\bar{1}1)$ are unobserved; face $m'(1\bar{1}0)$ is the observed face originally numbered 7.

The Barker angles, calculated by spherical trigonometry from the three measured angles chosen above, are (Fig. 16):

$$cr = 28° 13', \quad ra = 58° 9', \quad \mathbf{am = 58° 46'}, \quad bq = 47° 27'$$

Crystals of sodium formate have also been observed on which faces 4 and 7 are missing. Assuming such a crystal is to be measured, the case becomes one of underdevelopment with two terminal forms.

The zones, 8-1-3, 5-1-6, and 6-3-2, determine the locations of three equatorial planes: 12, 13, and 2 (Fig. 15). The fourth equatorial plane is not developed; it is inserted harmonically, as plane 14, in angle 2-13', which is the largest of the three available angles in the equatorial zone.   The setting is unambiguously determined (Fig. 17) since zone 14-1-14' defines two additional terminal planes, 15 and 16, at its intersections with zones 2-5-8 and 2-3-6.   The axial planes are 1, 2, and 13.   Angle 2-13' is less than 90°, but the two angles, 2-14 and 13'-14, calculated by spherical trigonometry, are found to be equal within a few seconds of arc.   Since they differ from each other by less than one degree, two orientations of the setting must be calculated (Fig. 17).

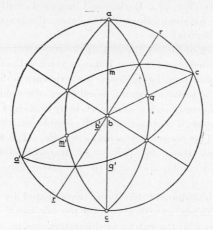

Fig. 17.—Sodium formate, two terminal forms, unique setting but two orientations.

In the first orientation, angle 13'-14 is considered smaller than 2-14.   Face 13' becomes $c(001)$ and face 2 becomes $a(100)$, with face 1 becoming $b(010)$.   Face 5 is taken as $q(011)$, and face 17 as $m(110)$.   The Barker angles are found to be:

$$cr = 31° 51', \quad ra = 31° 51', \quad \mathbf{am} = 39° 30', \quad bq = 50° 30'$$

In the second orientation, angle 2'-14' is considered smaller than 13-14'.   Face 2' becomes $c(001)$ and face 13 becomes $a(100)$.   Face 1 becomes $b'(0\overline{1}0)$.   Because of the equality of cr and ra, the Barker angles have the same values as in the first orientation.

Sodium formate will be found in the Barker index under either one of the entries: $\mathbf{am} = 58° 46'$ and $\mathbf{am} = 39° 30'$.

F.   TRICLINIC (OR ANORTHIC) SYSTEM

In this system there is no symmetry direction.   The systematic problem is thereby considerably hindered.   The treatment of the triclinic system in Barker's original essay lacks the clarity and the thoroughness which characterize that of the other crystal systems.   The rules pertaining to the latter needed only slight amendments, as was seen above.   Much work, however, remained to be done on the triclinic system.

The determinative problem, in this as in other systems, comprises two main steps: to find the setting; and to orient the setting. The second question may be considered settled. The setting, once uniquely determined, can be oriented by means of the following rules: (1) the smallest of the interfacial angles between axial planes is taken as ca; (2) cr smaller than ra, which is equivalent to cR smaller than Ra'; (3) interzonal angle abc smaller than 90°; (4) interzonal angle bac smaller than 90°. The planes with simplest indices and their systematic letters have been given above (Fig. 2). Barker had proposed another rule, the so-called hypo-monoclinic rule for determining the b plane; the present rule (1) was substituted for it by Spiller and Hey.

The preliminary task of finding the setting, however, is fraught with difficulties. Application of the Principle of Simplest Indices, which is the basic rule, taking precedence over all others, usually discloses the existence of many settings giving simplest indices to the same maximum number of observed planes. Before the ambiguity can be removed, and a setting chosen, by means of auxiliary rules designed to guide the choice, it is obvious that all possible equally simple settings must first be found out. This constitutes a major hurdle. The ambiguity may result from overdevelopment (too many planes), or from underdevelopment (too few planes), or even from a combination of both (too many planes and yet too few—of the right kind).

The case of overdevelopment has been investigated by the Barker workers (Terpstra, Donnay, Mélon, van Weerden, on the one hand, and Spiller and Hey, on the other),[10] at least to the extent of discussing sets of auxiliary rules for the removal of ambiguity. A systematic investigation of all possible cases of overdevelopment appears impossible, since such a problem has no theoretical limits. The same problem, however, when dealing with underdevelopment is amenable to mathematical treatment. It has been raised and solved by Terpstra and van Weerden.[11, 12] To what an extraordinary extent ambiguity persists after the application of the Principle of Simplest Indices is shown by van Weerden, who considers this "a serious menace to the utility of Barker's system for triclinic crystals". Some of his results will illustrate this point.

A few additional definitions must be introduced at this place. The zones of the *normal pattern* (defined above) fall into three types: *cubo-dodecahedral* (abbreviated c.d.), *cubo-octahedral* (abbreviated c.o.), and *dodecahedral-dodecahedral* (abbreviated d.d.). A d.d. zone only contains dodecahedral planes, as, for example, zone (110)–(101). This concept was not used by Barker, who recognized the other two types of zones. A *configuration* can be visualized as a normal pattern occupied by n planes ($1 \leq n \leq 13$). By erasing the zone circles of a configuration, a *complex* results. A complex is, therefore, a number of planes which can belong to a configuration. Several configurations may give the same complex. Two complexes that can be transformed into each other by an homogeneous transformation are termed equal. Usually, more than one configuration (or construction) can be ob-

---

[11] P. Terpstra and W. J. van Weerden, *Z. Krist.*, **A95**, 368 (1936).

[12] W. J. van Weerden, *Algemeene beschouwingen over Barker's "Principle of Simplest Indices."* Wolters, Groningen, 1938 (Dutch text, English summary).

tained by drawing zone circles through the planes of a complex, but these configurations are not necessarily different. Two configurations that can be transformed into each other by a collinear transformation are equal. A complex from which more than one configuration can be constructed is called ambiguous.

Terpstra and van Weerden have shown that there are 552 different configurations and 203 different complexes, including the trivial case of 1 plane only. Configurations and complexes are given appropriate symbols, and are tabulated. The configurations are divided by van Weerden into the following groups, patterned after Barker's original classification:

I. At least one four-plane zone.
    A. At least one four-plane zone is c.d.
    B. All four-plane zones are c.o.
II. No four-plane zone, but at least one three-plane zone.
    A. At least one three-plane zone is c.d.
    B. No three-plane zone is c.d.; at least one is c.o.
    C. All three-plane zones are d.d.
III. Only two-plane zones.
    A. At least one two-plane zone is c.d.
    B. No two-plane zone is c.d.; at least one is c.o.
    C. No two-plane zone is c.d.; none is c.o.; at least one is d.d.
    D. No two-plane zone is c.d.; none is c.o.; none is d.d.
IV. No zones.

In the table of complexes, each complex is indicated as unambiguous or ambiguous. All the possible constructions for each ambiguous complex are also tabulated. By means of the tables, it is easy to find the symbol of the complex (and all its constructions, if it is ambiguous) of any combination of planes observed on a crystal, provided such combination does represent a complex. Of all the triclinic combinations found in Groth's five volumes, 996, that is to say about 85%, represent complexes. The possibility of overlooking a setting is thereby eliminated, and auxiliary rules for choosing the final setting can be confidently applied.

In his dissertation, van Weerden makes inquiries into the kind of auxiliary rules that would be most powerful for removing the ambiguity of the setting. He examines several rules, some of them previously proposed by Barker or by his followers, from the double viewpoint of their "theoretical" and their "practical" usefulness in coping with ambiguity. The theoretical usefulness refers to all the mathematically possible complexes, and the practical one, to what may be considered a representative sampling of the actual triclinic crystals, namely the 996 complexes in Groth's compendium. He finds that triclinic crystals show a marked preference for a small number of complexes (19 complexes account for 90% of the cases, 6 complexes for 58%) and, unfortunately enough, precisely for those that admit of a large number of constructions. A selection of the setting by rules based on metrical considerations, such as rules of pseudosymmetry, for instance, would entail a prohibitive amount of labor, as the choice in the 996 cases examined had to be made from an average of 69 constructions.

Barker's "c.d. rule," namely, that if at least one harmonic four-plane zone be developed it shall be regarded as c.d. unless it violates the Principle of Simplest Indices, is suitable in practice, but fails adequately to remove the ambiguity. A new rule is then investigated based on symmetry considerations. The *symmetry of a configuration* being defined as the symmetry which it acquires when transformed, by homogeneous transformation, into a cubic normal pattern (Fig. 1), the rule is to select as highly symmetrical a configuration as possible. Applied in conjunction with the c.d. rule, and after the latter, this new rule appears to be very powerful, reducing the number of necessary constructions of a complex from 69 to 3 on the average. Finally, van Weerden examines the feasibility of using the complex itself, rather than one of its constructions, with determinative angles chosen from those available on the complex, for determinative purposes. He concludes that this scheme could be made practical. He refrains, however, from making definite suggestions as to which course should be followed, leaving the responsibility of the decision to the group of Barker workers.

5. Conclusions

Neither the Barker method nor, for that matter, any goniometric method of crystallochemical analysis can be used to determine isometric crystals. The Barker method is remarkably straightforward and easy in all other systems except the triclinic.

The distribution of crystalline substances among the various crystal systems can be estimated fairly well. Taking the 7183 substances listed in Groth as a representative sample, Haan[13] and Rogers[14] give figures that lead to the following percentages: triclinic, 12%; monoclinic, 47%; orthorhombic, 29%; tetragonal, 4%; hexagonal, 2%; rhombohedral, 4%; and isometric, 2%. The values obtained by Nowacki[3] from a survey of the 3063 substances investigated by x-ray analysis, for which the unit-cell dimensions and the space group are known, differ appreciably. They are as follows: triclinic, 2%; monoclinic, 20%; orthorhombic, 18%; tetragonal, 12%; hexagonal, 8%; rhombohedral, 11%; and isometric, 29%. These figures show a large increase in the high-symmetry systems, the ones most easily amenable to x-ray analysis. It is gratifying to note that x-ray diffraction data are already available for practically all the isometric substances (about 900 known in 1944), which cannot be determined by goniometric methods. The number of substances known to crystallize in the dimetric systems has increased considerably over those in Groth's compilation. Boldyrev and coworkers[15] have gathered the following

---

[13] J. H. Haan, *Kristallometrische determineeringsmethoden.* Wolters, Groningen, 1932 (Dutch text, German summary).

[14] A. F. Rogers, *Am. Mineral.*, **15**, 120 (1930); also, *personal communication.*

[15] A. K. Boldyrev and W. W. Doliwo-Dobrowolsky, *Bestimmungstabellen für Kristalle.* Band I, Erste Hälfte, *Einleitung, Tetragyrische Syngonie.* Zentrales Wissenschaftliches Institut der Geologie und Schürfung, Leningrad-Moscow, 1937 (Russian text, German translation of introduction).

totals: tetragonal, 670 (against 286 in Groth); hexagonal, 517 (against 248 in Groth); and rhombohedral, 638 (against 298 in Groth).   The representatives of the trimetric systems must also be more numerous, since most of the new substances prepared have complicated chemical formulas, and hence are more likely to crystallize in the low-symmetry systems. The only figures at hand, however, are still those of Haan, based on Groth. They must be considered minimal values: triclinic, 894; monoclinic, 3359; and orthorhombic, 2063.   Now, if one bases the percentages on the highest figures available for each system, the following results are obtained: triclinic, 10%; monoclinic, 37%; orthorhombic, 23%; tetragonal, 7%; hexagonal, 6%; rhombohedral, 7%; and isometric, 10%. As time goes on, it is probable that these percentages will tend to revert slowly to the figures obtained from the Groth survey.

The above statistical data serve to bring home one point, namely, that 80 to 85% of the crystal kingdom can be successfully and easily determined by the Barker method.   This estimate excludes the irreducible isometric crystals and the, so-far, refractory triclinic system.   When the latter has been tamed, the Barker system will be in a position to cope with 90 to 95% of the measurable crystals.   If only organic compounds are taken into account, less than one in a thousand belongs to the isometric system (only three are found in Groth), while 11 to 12% are triclinic.

As far as organic chemistry alone is concerned, 88 to 89% of the measurable crystals are now identifiable by the Barker method, and 99.9% will be when the unruly triclinic system is harnessed.   Even if the difficulties encountered in the latter did prove to be insuperable, the Barker method would still be valuable in its present state of completion.

IV.   OTHER METHODS

We have seen that the first prerequisite of a determinative method is the choice of a unit cell in a unique orientation.   Barker's determinative angles are based on a conventional, arbitrary unit cell.   The ideal, of course, would be the use of the true unit cell for determinative purposes. Goniometric data alone, however, cannot discriminate between isogonal lattices, and are thus inadequate for determining the true lattice.   Numerous attempts have been made to solve this problem by morphological considerations, such as the relative frequency and size of the various crystal forms observed.   The only method of attack that led to any measure of success is that based on the Law of Bravais.[16]

The Law of Bravais relates the importance of the forms to the lattice. By *importance* is meant essentially the frequency with which the form

---

[16] G. Friedel, *Compt. rend.*, **139**, 221 (1904).

occurs on the various crystals of different crystallization batches.   It is a refinement of the Law of Haüy, which states that the faces observed on crystals have simple indices—in other words, that the Miller indices are small integers.   The Law of Bravais adds that, among the many isogonal lattices satisfying the goniometric data, one can be found in which nets of high reticular densities, *i. e.*, nets with many nodes per unit surface, are parallel to the observed crystal faces; and that, for the main forms at least, the higher the reticular density the more important is the corresponding form.   The higher the reticular density of a net, the smaller of course is the area of its unit mesh.   Since the product of the mesh by the interplanar distance is constant, being equal to the volume of the unit cell, it follows that the Law of Bravais can also be expressed as follows: the larger the interplanar distance, the more important the form.   This statement of the law is preferred, in view of the importance of interplanar distances in x-ray diffraction work.

1. The Fedorov Method

Compliance with the Law of Bravais can thus be made the first prerequisite for the choice of the lattice.   Once the lattice is determined, it is then an easy matter to select a conventional unit cell to express it.   In the past ten years, this lattice has been called the "Haüy-Bravais lattice" or the "morphological lattice," in order to emphasize the fact that it does not coincide with the true (structural) lattice in all cases.   It was the morphological lattice that Fedorov,[1] who called it the "correct" lattice, decided to use in his system of determination.   His method for arriving at the "correct" lattice was difficult and tedious.   It involved, among other things, calculating the reticular densities[17] of many nets, listing the nets of the lattice in the order of decreasing reticular density, and comparing this list with that of the observed forms.   If, for instance, ten forms were observed on a crystal, and they corresponded to the ten densest nets of a lattice, that lattice would have been the "correct" one.   The *value of the setting*, W, was introduced to appraise the relative merits of various possible lattices. W is the ratio $R:I$, where R is the sum of the squares of the reticular densities of the n observed forms and I is the corresponding sum for the n forms, observed or not, with the highest reticular densities, *i. e.*, those that would be present if the Law of Bravais were rigorously satisfied.   By reticular density of a crystal form, we mean the density of the net which is parallel to a face of the form.   Fedorov also gave rules for the selection of a unit cell in his "correct" lattice and for its orientation.

The Fedorov system of crystallochemical analysis is the only one to date which has been carried all the way to completion.   The determination of a crystalline substance is actually possible, by means of Fedorov's monumental index, *Das Krystallreich*, provided the crystallography of the substance was known at the time of the compilation.   In 1917, for instance, Barker,[18] using Fedorov's tables,

---

[17] P. Terpstra and W. J. van Weerden, *Am. Mineral.*, **19**, 531 (1934).
[18] T. V. Barker, *The Lancet*, May 26, 1917.

successfully determined as salol a crystal "of intestinal origin" which weighed no more than 0.229 gram.   The Fedorov system, however, never gained popularity.

2.   The Boldyrev Method

Recognizing that complicated rules[19] for the choice of the unit cell were the chief drawback of Fedorov's method, Boldyrev[20] decided to eliminate the necessity for a unique conventional unit cell by using all the measured angles for determinative purposes.   Therein lies the originality of the new scheme.[21]

The first volume[15] of the *Determinative Tables for Crystals*, to which 19 workers collaborated, covers all the crystals of the tetragonal system, minerals as well as nonminerals, and consists essentially of two parts: the crystallographic description of all the substances, listed according to a crystallochemical system of classification; and the determinative "key" or index in which the angles measured on the "unknown" crystal are to be looked up.   Minerals and nonminerals are listed separately, both in the descriptive part and in the determinative key.   Appended are alphabetical indices, in Russian and in German, of the chemical names (one for nonminerals and one for minerals), and an index of compounds listed according to their chemical formulas.

The determinative key is arranged in five columns.   The first column contains the determinative angle, which is the polar distance of the face considered, namely, the angle which the normal to the face makes with the normal to the base.   The angle is printed in bold face for a main face, that is, a large, habit-controlling face, in ordinary type for a face of medium size, and between parentheses for a small face.   The second column gives the Miller indices assigned to the face in the description of the substance.   The third column indicates the relative importance of the form by a Roman numeral, that is, its rank in the order of decreasing importance.   The name and chemical formula are found in the fourth column, while the fifth refers to the substance number, under which the full crystallographic description can be located in the systematic part of the book.

The various steps of the determination are as follows:

(*1*)   Measure the unknown crystal on the goniometer.

(*2*)   Plot the stereographic projection.   Ascertain the crystal system to which the substance belongs.   List (in the case of the tetragonal system, for instance) the polar distances of all forms, in the order of decreasing size of the faces.

(*3*)   Find, in the key, the substances with which the various polar distances are compatible.   Allow ±30' for the possible inaccuracy of the measurements.   Eliminate wrong substances by means of the successive angles, the relative sizes of the faces, their symbols, and, if need be, other physical properties to be found in the descriptive section.

---

[19] A. K. Boldyrev, *Kommentarii k Rabote E. S. Fedorova, Das Krystallreich.*   Izd. Akad. Nauk, Leningrad, 1926.

[20] A. K. Boldyrev, *Mém. soc. russe minéral.*, **53**, 251 (1925) (Russian text, French summary).

[21] A. K. Boldyrew and W. W. Doliwo-Dobrowolsky, *Z. Krist.*, **A93**, 321 (1936).

An interesting feature of the Boldyrev tables is that the data obtained by x-ray methods have been incorporated. Angles have been calculated from the absolute unit-cell dimensions for a few faces, even though such faces might never have been found. This will permit the determination of a crystal occurring with faces for the first time.

General References

CRYSTALLOGRAPHIC PREREQUISITES

Barker, T. V., *Graphical and Tabular Methods in Crystallography*. Murby, London, 1922.

Donnay, J. D. H., Tunell, G., and Barth, T. F. W., "Various Modes of Attack in Crystallographic Investigation," *Am. Mineral.*, **19,** 437–458 (1934).

Tutton, A. E. H., *Crystallography and Practical Crystal Measurement*. Vols. I–II, Macmillan, London, 1922.

TWO-CIRCLE GONIOMETRY

Palache, C., "The Two-Circle Goniometer," *Am. Mineral.*, **5,** 23–33 (1920). See also: *ibid.*, 67–80, 89–99, 112–120, 129–133, 143–152, 158–166, 173–182, 185–194, 198–208. These papers have been reprinted in a single pamphlet.

Terpstra, P., "Simple Instructions for Crystal Measurement with a New Model of the Two-Circle Goniometer, Especially Adapted to the Use in Chemical Laboratories," *Rec. trav. chim.*, **57,** 893–904 (1938).

CRYSTALLOCHEMICAL ANALYSIS

Boldyrew, A. K., and Doliwo-Dobrowolsky, W. W., "Über die Bestimmungstabellen für Kristalle," *Z. Krist.*, **A93,** 321–367 (1936).

BARKER METHOD

Barker, T. V., *Systematic Crystallography, an Essay on Crystal Description, Classification and Identification*. Murby, London, 1930.

Donnay, J. D. H., "Über die Bestimmungstabellen für Kristalle," *Z. Krist.*, **A94,** 410–412 (1936).

Donnay, J. D. H., and Mélon, J., "Angles paramétriques de Barker dans une série cristalline homéomorphe," *Ann. soc. géol. Belg., Bull.*, **57,** 39–52 (1933).

Donnay, J. D. H., and Mélon, J., "Crystallo-chemical Tables for the Determination of Tetragonal Substances (Laboratory Compounds and Artificial Minerals) by Means of their Barker Angle and Auxiliary Physical Properties," *Johns Hopkins Studies Geol.*, **11,** 305–388 (1934).

Donnay, J. D. H., and Mélon, J., "Sur l'orientation cristallographique de l'iodure de méthylammonium d'après la méthode de Barker," *Ann. soc. géol. Belg., Bull.*, **59,** 68–74 (1936).

Miller, H. F., and Ashley, S. E. Q., Jr., *Crystallochemical Analysis* (unpublished, available only as a "Data Folder" from the Pittsfield Laboratory of the General Electric Company, 1941).

Porter, M. W., and Spiller R. C., "Crystallo-chemical Analysis, The Barker Index at Oxford," *Nature*, **144**, 298–302 (1939).

Terpstra, P., Donnay, J. D. H., Mélon, J., and van Weerden, W. J., "Studies on Barker's Determinative Method of Systematic Crystallography," *Z. Krist.*, **A87**, 281–305 (1934).

Terpstra, P., and van Weerden, W. J., "Studies on Barker's Principle of Simplest Indices," *Z. Krist.*, **A95**, 368–382 (1936).

CHAPTER XIV

X-RAY DIFFRACTION

I. FANKUCHEN, *Brooklyn Polytechnic Institute*

I. INTRODUCTION

X-ray diffraction has long been used as a tool in chemistry. In 1916, Debye and Scherrer[1] and, in 1919, Hull[2] described the powder method of x-ray diffraction. Subsequently, this method became an important one in chemistry almost to the exclusion, unfortunately, of other x-ray diffraction techniques. It is easy to understand this trend, for the powder technique is simple and does not require elaborate apparatus, and the interpretation of the x-ray diagrams is a comparatively simple procedure. However, the powder method is limited in scope: in most cases it can only be used for identifying materials and this, for chemists, is now its chief use. In the inorganic field, one generally does not want more from x-ray diffraction; but the organic chemist, who often works with materials of unknown

---

[1] P. Debye and P. Scherrer, *Physik. Z.*, **17, 277** (1916).
[2] A. W. Hull, *J. Am. Chem. Soc.*, **41,** 1168 (1919).

structure, would like an additional tool for working out these structures. Single-crystal x-ray studies can often give useful information in such cases, information which cannot be obtained by the powder method. The interpretation of single-crystal x-ray diagrams is not, however, an easy matter. Unless one uses reciprocal-lattice ideas—and these do not appear to be well enough known, the interpretation of single-crystal diffraction films becomes an exceedingly laborious task. Because, for all types of x-ray diagrams, the use of the reciprocal lattice simplifies the interpretation, what may perhaps appear to be unnecessary emphasis will be given to its discussion. The discussions throughout this chapter will be limited strictly to those ideas and facts essential to the organic chemist wishing to work with x-ray diffraction methods.

II. X-RAYS

1. Production and Equipment

X-rays are produced when electrons moving with sufficiently high velocities are suddenly stopped by impact with a target. The essential parts of all x-ray apparatus are similar. A source of electrons—usually a hot filament, a high tension source for accelerating the electrons, and a solid obstacle, the target, must be provided. There are many purely technological details. For instance, electrons even of very high energies are easily absorbed, and so the target and electron source must be maintained in a vacuum; targets get hot from the electron bombardment, and so must be cooled; and the x-rays usually used for x-ray diffraction work are also easily absorbed, so that thin windows of low absorbing material, Lindemann glass, or beryllium, must be provided in the walls of the tube to permit the emergence of the x-ray beam.

For most work the organic chemist may wish to do, the sealed-off x-ray tubes now commercially available, General Electric, Machlett, and Philips for example, will do very well. These are available in a large variety of types and target materials. The copper target tube is the best all-round tube although special conditions may dictate the choice of some other target material. All commercial equipment uses transformers as the source of the high voltage. For many reasons, it is desirable that some rectification, either half-wave or full wave, be used.

Because the design of auxiliary equipment, cameras, monochromators, etc., is still in a fluid state, it is highly desirable that any equipment obtained should have a flat working surface which can be cleared of encumbrances so special apparatus can be used without extensive modifications.

At this time, at least three manufacturers offer complete x-ray diffraction equipment suitable for routine x-ray diffraction work: *North American*

Philips, New York; *General Electric X-Ray Corporation*, Chicago; and *Picker X-Ray Corporation*, New York. Because most industrial laboratories employ the powder method (page 599), these manufacturers emphasize this particular type of diffraction work in the design of the apparatus. In all three, a wide variety of target materials is available, and arrangements can be made for the use of single-crystal apparatus. Each commercial apparatus, at present, has its advantages and disadvantages, although the pressure of competition will undoubtedly dictate such modifications that the differences should soon not be very great. The Philips unit, for example, has four windows, while the other outfits have only two. To counteract this advantage, the Philips tube at present has Lindemann glass windows, while the others use the somewhat more transparent, beryllium windows.

2. Properties

X-rays are electromagnetic waves (like light) of very short wave length. It is convenient, in x-ray work, to use as a unit of length the angstrom unit (Å.), equivalent to 10^{-8} centimeter. X-rays cover the region from 0.01 to 1000 Å., overlapping on the short wave length side the softer gamma rays and, on the long wave length side, the extreme ultraviolet. For diffraction work, wave lengths between 0.7 and 2 Å. are generally used.

The spectral distribution of the x-rays emitted by targets under varying conditions can be studied by absorption measurements, crystal diffraction, and ruled-grating techniques. It can be shown that the spectrum is usually composed of a background of continuous (white) radiation upon which is superimposed a more or less complex line pattern called the characteristic line spectrum. The white radiation cuts off sharply at a minimum wave length which depends only on the peak voltage applied to the x-ray tube. The relation is:

$$\lambda_{min.} = 12{,}350/V \tag{1}$$

where $\lambda_{min.}$ is the minimum wave length in angstrom units and V is the peak potential in volts. The shape and intensity of the white radiation spectrum depend, however, on the target material and on the shape of the applied voltage wave.

The characteristic line spectrum is a characteristic of the target material (hence the name). The wave lengths of the lines are independent of the voltages used, but the appearance or nonappearance of the various lines does depend on the applied voltage. The characteristic lines originate in electron jumps to excited electron shells within the target atoms, and so the various sets of lines (K, L, M, etc., in order of increasing wave length, *i. e.*, decreasing energy) can be produced only when the bombarding electrons have sufficient energy to ionize the respective shells concerned

(K, L, M, etc.). For almost all diffraction work, it is the characteristic K lines that are used, specifically the Kα doublet. The Kβ component is usually removed by filtering (see page 589). For maximum contrast of K lines to background, the peak potential applied to the x-ray tube should be from 3.5 to 4 times the excitation potential of the K shell. The excitation potential is obtained by substituting the wave length of the K edge (Table I) in equation (1).

TABLE I

WAVE LENGTHS OF K LINES AND EDGES OF SOME IMPORTANT TARGET
AND FILTER MATERIALS

Target material	Atomic number	Wave length (Å.) of			
		Kα₂ line	Kα₁ line	Kβ	K absorption edge
Ti	22	2.7468	2.7432	2.5090	2.4912
V	23	2.5021	2.4983	2.2797	2.2630
Cr	24	2.2889	2.2850	2.0806	2.0659
Mn	25	2.1015	2.0975	1.9062	1.8916
Fe	26	1.9360	1.9321	1.7530	1.7394
Co	27	1.7892	1.7853	1.6174	1.6040
Ni	28	1.6583	1.6545	1.4970	1.4839
Cu	29	1.5412	1.5374	1.3893	1.3774
Zn	30	1.4360	1.4322	1.2925	1.2805
Zr	40	0.7885	0.7843	0.7003	0.6874
Mo	42	0.7128	0.7078	0.6310	0.6185

The absorption of x-rays in traversing matter is given by:

$$I = I_0 e^{-\mu t} \tag{2}$$

where I_0 is the intensity of the beam incident upon the specimen, I is the intensity after passing through a thickness t and μ is the linear absorption coefficient. This equation can be obtained by a simple integration, the basic assumption being that, for very thin specimens, the absorption is proportional to the thickness. The linear absorption coefficient is, however, dependent on the state of the absorber; it is therefore often convenient to use instead μ_m, the mass absorption coefficient. This coefficient, $\mu_m = \mu/\rho$ where ρ is the density, is independent of the physical or chemical state of the absorber and is, for any given element, a function of the wave length, λ, of the radiation being absorbed. X-rays by absorption can also produce ionization of the various electron levels of the absorbing atom. If one studies the mass absorption coefficient of an atom as a function of wave length, one then observes that, with increasing wave length, there is an increase of absorption coefficient up to the wave length corresponding to that of the K absorption edge, then a sudden drop and a gradual increase to the succeeding L and M edges which, for our diffraction purposes, are of little interest. The K edge, however, is widely used to eliminate the Kβ

line from the radiation emitted by the tube.   One chooses as a filter a material whose K edge lies between the wave lengths of the Kα and Kβ lines.
The Kα will then pass through with little absorption while the Kβ will be
highly absorbed.   Thus, for copper targets nickel filters are used.   Nickel
foil 0.0007 inch thick will absorb only 50% of the Kα radiation but will reduce the Kβ component to $1/_{85}$ of its original strength.   Inasmuch as, in

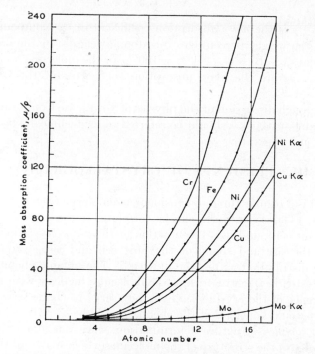

Fig. 1.—Mass absorption coefficients of the low atomic
number elements.

the original beam, the ratio of Kα to Kβ is about 6 to 1, the ratio in the
filtered beam will be 250 to 1.

Sometimes the presence of absorption edges dictates the choice of radiation.   A material rich in iron, for instance, should not be studied with copper radiation, as the Kα line of copper will excite the K level of the iron (see
Table I), producing a heavy background of fluorescent radiation.

A knowledge of the absorption coefficients is necessary for determining
the best specimen size.   Thus, in the usual powder method in which a
cylindrical specimen is used with a beam of diameter greater than the
specimen cross section, the optimum specimen diameter is $2/\mu$ centimeter,

where μ is the *linear* absorption coefficient. For a full discussion of optimum specimen size see Buerger.[3]

Figure 1 is a graph* giving the mass absorption coefficients as a function of atomic number. To find the mass absorption coefficient of a material of composition A B C . . . Z, one uses the equation:

$$\mu_{ABC...Z} = \frac{A\mu_A + B\mu_B...Z\mu_Z}{A + B + C...+Z} \tag{3}$$

where $\mu_{ABC...Z}$ is the *mass* absorption coefficient of the compound, A, B, C. . .Z are the weight percentages (or atomic weights) of the constituent atoms present, $A + B + C...+Z = 100\%$ (or the molecular weight), and μ_A, μ_B, μ_C. . .μ_Z are the mass absorption coefficients of the constituent atoms.

For a thorough discussion of the physics of x-rays, see Compton and Allison.[4] Suitable textbooks[5] should be referred to for technical data on x-ray production and apparatus.

III. ELEMENTS OF CRYSTALLOGRAPHY

A crystal is a regular three-dimensional assemblage of some fundamental repeat unit. The crystal form can be correlated to the form of the repeat unit (the unit cell), and it is the function of the x-ray crystallographer to determine the size and shape of the unit cell and also, when possible, the atomic distribution within the unit cell. The organic chemist is very much interested in the structure of the molecules he deals with but not in the appearance of the crystals save as they serve to characterize the substances. It would appear that the chemist would be satisfied with nothing less than a *complete* structure determination, since this alone gives him a full knowledge of the structure of the molecules which make up the crystal. It is, however, difficult, and in most cases at the present time impossible, to work out the complete structures of crystals of complex organic molecules. However, our inability to solve the problem completely does not prevent the x-ray approach from giving valuable information about the substances investigated.

Particularly for single-crystal studies, a knowledge of crystallographic

---

* I am indebted to F. G. Chesley for the suggestion of plotting absorption coefficient as a function of atomic number. The data for figure 1 are from W. L. Bragg, *The Crystalline State*, Macmillan, New York, 1934, Appendix III.

[3] M. J. Buerger, *X-Ray Crystallography*. Wiley, New York, 1942, p. 179.

[4] A. H. Compton and S. K. Allison, *X-Rays in Theory and Experiment*. Macmillan, New York, 1935.

[5] G. L. Clark, *Applied X-Rays*, 3rd ed., McGraw Hill, New York, 1940. C. S. Barrett, *Structure of Metals*, McGraw-Hill, New York, 1943.

nomenclature is essential.   Much of this is given by Peacock in chapter 12 (page 531).   For a more extended treatment from the point of view of the x-ray crystallographer, see Buerger.[6]   Peacock deals with the crystal lattice, or translation lattice, which is defined by a unit cell with edges a, b, c, and angles α, β, γ;   the Miller indices (hkl) used in denoting lattice planes and x-ray reflections;   the 14 lattice types, including the seven primitive types (P) and the seven centered types (I, C, F);   the grouping of the lattice types into seven or six systems;   the elements of symmetry which do not involve translations, namely the rotation axes (1), 2, 3, 4, 6, and the inversion axes, or their equivalents, $\bar{1}$ (center of symmetry), $\bar{2}$ (mirror—m), $\bar{3}$, $\bar{4}$, $\bar{6}$ $(3/m)$; and the various combinations of these symmetry elements to give the 32 crystal classes or point groups.   The elements of symmetry involving translations, and their combination in the 32 classes and the 14 lattices to give the 230 space-groups or ultimate symmetry types, are only mentioned; and therefore a short explanation of these symmetry elements and groups is given here to complete the outline of crystallographic nomenclature.

The elements of symmetry which involve translation, in addition to rotation or reflection, are the screw axes and the glide planes, respectively. An n_p screw axis is an n-fold rotation axis with a translation of p/n of the unit length in the direction of the axis;   thus a 4_1 screw is a symmetry element in which a rotation of $2\pi/4$ is combined with a translation of one-fourth of the unit length.   Similarly the translations accompanying a glide plane are always parallel to the plane and are a simple fraction of some cell dimension.   Thus, an a-glide plane translates $a/2$, b translates $b/2$, and c translates $c/2$;   an n-glide plane translates one-half the diagonal of the face to which it is parallel;   and a d-glide plane has a translation of one-fourth of the face diagonal.

Various combinations of these symmetry elements are possible in the different crystal systems.   Thus, the only symmetry element possible in the triclinic system is a center of symmetry, and 3-fold axes are not found in the monoclinic, orthorhombic, and tetragonal systems.   A possible arrangement of symmetry elements placed at the lattice points of a space-lattice is called a space-group.   A space-group is *not* a crystal structure nor an array of atoms or molecules.   It has been shown that there are 230 possible space-groups; all have been listed and described in detail.[6-9]

[6] M. J. Buerger, *X-Ray Crystallography*.   Wiley, New York, 1942.

[7] *International Tables for the Determination of Crystal Structures*.   Bell, London, 1935. J. W. Edwards, Ann Arbor, 1944.

[8] K. Lonsdale, *Structure Factor Tables*.   Bell, London, 1936.

[9] R. W. G. Wyckoff, *The Analytical Expression of the Results of the Theory of Space Groups*.   Carnegie Institution of Washington, Washington, D. C., 1930.

The modern nomenclature for the space-groups (Hermann-Mauguin) is one from which the space-group can be constructed from the symbol. The first part of the symbol is a letter which refers to the space-lattice: P is a primitive cell, A, B, C are face centered on the a, b, c faces, respectively, F is all face centered, I is body centered, H is hexagonal, and R is rhombohedral. The next symbol, if a number, refers to the principal axis, 2, 3, 4, or 6. The symbol for a reflection plane is m (mirror), and $2/m$, $3/m$, etc., stand for rotation axes with perpendicular mirror planes. If the axes are screw axes or the planes are glide planes the corresponding symbols are used (see above). Symbols for additional axes or planes then follow. For a full discussion, see Bragg[10] or Buerger.[11]

If a model of a space-lattice is slowly turned, it can be seen that the lattice points may be considered as lying in various sets of parallel planes. Peacock (page 531) discusses in detail the indexing of these planes. Any such set can be identified by the three Miller indices (hkl). Consider any such set of parallel planes. They cut the a, b, and c axes into different numbers of parts. If "a" is divided into "h" parts, "b" into "k," and "c" into "l" parts, then hkl are the Miller indices of that set of planes. If a plane (set of planes) is parallel to an axis, then the corresponding index is zero. It will be observed that h, k, and l as defined have no common factor. In discussing x-ray reflection by crystals, we shall have occasion to use sets of indices which have a common factor. This common factor is the order of the reflection. It is merely more convenient to speak of the (3, 12, 15) reflection than to say "third order of the (1, 4, 5) set of planes."

IV. REFLECTION OF X-RAYS BY CRYSTALS

1. Characteristics of Patterns

X-rays are used to study crystals because the pattern of scattered x-rays somehow reflects the order and regularity of the atomic arrangement within the specimen. All x-ray diffraction apparatus have certain characteristics in common: a system of slits or pinholes which defines the x-ray beam, a means for holding and moving the specimen in the x-ray beam, and a radiation-sensitive device—usually a photographic film—to record the scattered radiation. Photographs will vary widely in their appearance depending on the specimen character. Four representative types can be seen in figure 2. When the specimen has no crystalline order whatsoever (a piece of glass or carbon black), one nevertheless obtains a diagram (Fig. 2A) with certain distinctive characteristics, namely, there are one or more

---

[10] W. L. Bragg, *The Crystalline State*. Macmillan, New York, 1934.
[11] M. J. Buerger, *op. cit.*, Chapter IV and Table 7.

halos.   These arise because atoms have finite sizes and indicate that two
atoms cannot approach closer than the sum of their radii.   From a study of
such diagrams something may be determined about the sizes of the atoms
and their environments;   for instance, x-ray diagrams of silica glass indicate that silicon–oxygen tetrahedra of a definite size are present.

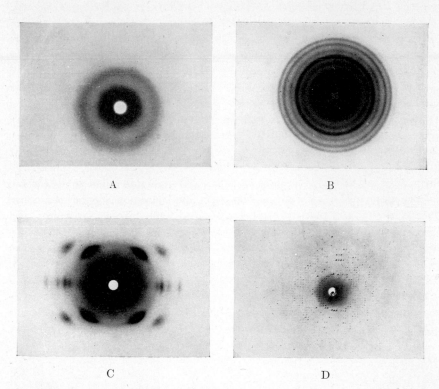

Fig. 2, A–D.—Typical x-ray diagrams.

A—Amorphous diagram
B—Crystalline powder diagram (puffed starch)
C—Fiber diagram (saran)
D—Single crystal oscillation diagram (γ-chymotrypsin)

When the specimen consists of powdered crystals, one again obtains a
series of rings (Fig. 2B); they are now sharp, not diffuse.   From the locations of the rings, it is sometimes (not always—this is one of the weaknesses
of the powder method) possible to deduce the size and shape of the unit
cell.   Because the material is crystalline, the lines are sharp in contrast to
the diffuse halos of the first example.   However, both specimens have no

specific orientation, as is shown by the continuous even rings obtained, diffuse for the amorphous and sharp for the crystalline case.

In figure 2C, the specimen is a typical fiber with not too perfect crystallinity or orientation. Here, instead of rings, there are spots—broad because the crystalline arrangement is not very good, and somewhat elongated into arcs because of imperfect orientation. The spots fall on "layer" lines which are perpendicular to the fiber axis. From the layer-line separation, the fiber period can be computed unequivocally. Finally, a good single crystal (when oscillated) gives the pattern of figure 2D, a pattern of sharp spots arranged on layer lines and row lines. In this particular case, the specimen, γ-chymotrypsin, is tetragonal, and the square character of the spot pattern shows that the specimen was oriented with one of the equal axes vertical and that during oscillation the x-ray beam was directed approximately along the tetragonal axis.

2. Bragg's Law

The reflection of x-rays by crystals is really an interference phenomenon. Considered fundamentally, every atom of the crystal bathed in the beam of x-rays is a secondary radiating source in which the wave length and phase are maintained unchanged. Laue has shown that, for a three-dimensional regular array, these secondary waves interfere with one another in such a way that, except for certain calculable directions, destructive interference occurs. In the special directions, however, there is constructive interference and strong x-ray beams can be observed. But this treatment is too complicated; and Bragg's great contribution is a much simpler treatment of the scattering phenomenon. First, he shows that scattering centers arranged in a plane act like a mirror to x-rays incident on them, i. e., constructive interference occurs for the direction of specular reflection. Through the points of a space-lattice, an infinite number of sets of parallel planes can be passed. Consider one such set of Miller indices (hkl). Each plane of this set reflects part of the incident beam specularly. Let the x-rays be monochromatic of wave length λ. For an arbitrary glancing angle, θ, the reflections from successive planes are out of phase with one another and destructive interference occurs. However, by varying θ, a set of values for θ can be found so that the path difference between x-rays reflected by successive planes will be an integral number of wave lengths, n, and then constructive interference occurs. In figure 3, the horizontal lines are the traces of two successive planes of the set. The spacing of these planes, d, is the perpendicular distance between them. The value of d can always be computed from the dimensions of the unit cell and the value of (hkl).[12]

---

[12] M. J. Buerger, op. cit., p. 103.

The path difference is $BC + CD$ and for constructive interference this must equal $n\lambda$. But $BC + CD$ is equal to $2d_{hkl} \sin \theta$. Putting these facts together we obtain Bragg's law:

$$n\lambda = 2d_{hkl} \sin \theta$$

It can be seen that, unlike the case of diffraction of light by a ruled grating, this phenomenon is critical; constructive interference (reflection) occurs only at certain critical values, θ_n, the Bragg angles. When reflection does occur it is stated that the (hkl) planes are reflecting in the nth order or, more simply, it is called the $(nh\ nk\ nl)$ reflection.

Consider a crystal with a given unit cell containing p atoms per unit cell. Taking each of the p atoms in succession as origin of a space-lattice, we can imagine the crystal as composed of p identical (as far as size and shape are concerned) but interpenetrating lattices, their displacements relative to one another being decided merely by the distribution of the p atoms within the unit cell. All these lattices will have identical Bragg angles, but the reflections from the p-independent lattices will interfere with one another. This interference will determine the intensity

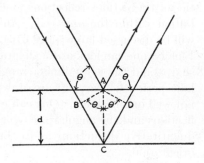

Fig. 3.—Bragg's law.

of the reflection h, k, l; but the Bragg angle will be independent of the atomic distribution *within* the cell, depending only on the external cell geometry.

When a nonprimitive unit cell is chosen, systematic absences of reflections will be observed. In a body-centered cell, only those reflections will occur for which $h + k + l$ is even; in an A face-centered lattice, $k + l$ must be even (in a B-lattice $h + l$, in a C, $h + k$); while in an F-type lattice, h, k, and l must be all odd or all even.

Screw axes and glide planes also result in the absence of certain types of reflections; thus, a b (or c) glide plane perpendicular to the "a" axis causes $(0kl)$ reflections to vanish for k (or l) odd, an a (or c) glide plane perpendicular to the b axis results in the extinction of $(h0l)$ reflections for h (or l) odd, etc. Similarly, a screw axis parallel to the a or b or c axis affects the $(h00)$ or $(0k0)$ or $(00l)$ reflections, respectively. A 2_1 screw axis permits only even orders to occur, a 3_1 screw axis only those divisible by 3, etc. For a full treatment, see Bragg[13] and Buerger.[14] It is by a study of external sym-

---

[13] W. L. Bragg, *op. cit.*, Chapter VI.
[14] M. J. Buerger, *op. cit.*, p. 505.

metry, optics (polarizing microscope studies), and systematic extinctions that the space-lattice type and finally the space-group are determined.

3. Analysis of Patterns

One can now see that the analysis of x-ray diagrams falls into three parts, a geometrical analysis, an intensity analysis, and lastly what may be called a study of the quality of the pattern.

The complete geometrical analysis is straightforward for single-crystal x-ray diagrams, but is not always possible for powder diagrams. One measures the *locations* of x-ray reflections and computes from these measurements the size and shape of a unit cell. From a study, then, of the intensities of the various reflections, one *attempts* to determine the atomic distribution within the unit cell. An ambiguity enters here, however, which will be discussed later (page 616), hence the use of the word "attempts." Finally, one can look at the diagram and say the lines are broad (or perhaps sharp) and the crystalline arrangement is therefore not too good (or perhaps perfect); the spots are drawn out, the fiber (if it is a fiber) is therefore not well oriented, etc. One can even measure the breadth of the x-ray reflections and the angular arc over which the spots are elongated and make quantitative deductions as to the perfection of the crystalline order and orientation.

V. RECIPROCAL LATTICE THEORY

For every possible set of Bragg planes of indices (*hkl*)—using (*hkl*) hereafter in the broader sense, *i. e.*, (*hkl*) may have a common factor—there is a reflection which may be characterized by the same triad (*hkl*), *i. e.*, there is a 1:1 correspondence between sets of Bragg planes and spots on a photographic film. The reciprocal lattice bears a similar relation to the set of possible reflecting planes; each *point* of the reciprocal lattice corresponds to a set of reflecting planes in the real lattice (and vice versa). Therefore, there is a 1:1 correspondence between points of the reciprocal lattice and reflections on the photographic film. Ewald, and then Bernal,[15] made use of this concept to obtain a very elegant geometrical interpretation of Bragg's law, an interpretation in which reflection from a plane in real space is replaced by the drawing of a straight line to a reciprocal lattice point. It will now be shown that this mathematical inversion makes possible the indexing of diffraction films in an easy, and indeed natural, way.

To construct the lattice reciprocal to a given space-lattice, an arbitrary origin is first chosen. From this origin, normals are drawn to the different

---

[15] J. D. Bernal, *Proc. Roy. Soc. London*, **A113**, 117 (1927).

sets of Bragg planes of indices (hkl). Point hkl in reciprocal space corresponding to planes (hkl) lies on the normal to planes (hkl) at distance d^* from the origin equal to K^2/d_{hkl} where K is an arbitrary constant and d_{hkl} is the spacing of the set of planes. It is most convenient to take $K^2 = \lambda$, the x-ray wave length (following Bernal[15]), so:

$$d^*_{hkl} = \lambda/d_{hkl} \tag{4}$$

The unit cell of a space-lattice is defined by $a, b, c, \alpha, \beta, \gamma$, or, what is equivalent, by the three pairs of planes which form the sides of the unit cell. Their Miller indices are (100), (010), (001). Now consider the arbitrarily chosen origin of the reciprocal lattice and the three points reciprocal to these three planes. They will be labeled (have the coordinates) 100, 010, 001, respectively. These four points define a lattice of reciprocal points: thus it can be shown that the point of coordinates 1, 2, 3 in reciprocal space will be reciprocal to the set of planes of Miller indices (123) and more generally the point hkl in the reciprocal lattice will be reciprocal to the (hkl) set of planes in the real lattice.[16]

To demonstrate the usefulness of the reciprocal lattice, we use it now to compute the formula for d_{hkl} for a cubic crystal. The reciprocal lattice will also be cubic of edge $a^* = \lambda/a$. Point hkl in the reciprocal lattice will be at a distance $d^{*2} = h^2 a^{*2} + k^2 a^{*2} + l^2 a^{*2}$ from the origin. By definition:

$$d_{hkl} = \frac{\lambda}{d^*_{hkl}} = \frac{\lambda}{a^* \sqrt{h^2 + k^2 + l^2}} = \frac{a}{\sqrt{h^2 + k^2 + l^2}} \tag{5}$$

This computation is, of course, very simple for the cubic case even without using the reciprocal lattice. For noncubic cases, however, the analogous computation is much simpler by reciprocal-lattice methods.

With the introduction of the sphere of reflection, some of the potentialities of the reciprocal lattice become apparent. In figure 4, let AB be the direction of a beam of x-rays of wave length, λ, incident upon a crystal at C. With C as a center, construct a sphere of unit radius to any convenient scale, say five centimeters equals unity. Line AB emerges from this sphere at O. With O as an origin, construct the reciprocal lattice for the crystal at C using the same scale as for the sphere. If the crystal at C is rotated about an axis through C, then the reciprocal lattice will rotate in the same way about a corresponding axis through O and in general any rotations about C by the crystal will be followed by corresponding rotations of the reciprocal lattice about O. In general, for an arbitrary orientation of the crystal, no point of the reciprocal lattice will lie on the surface of the unit

---

[16] M. J. Buerger, *X-Ray Crystallography*. Wiley, New York, 1942, Chapter VI.

sphere. The crystal is rotated so that a point, P^*_{hkl}, of the reciprocal lattice lies *on* the surface of the sphere. We now assert that the set of Bragg planes of indices (*hkl*) are in a reflecting position, *i. e.*, obey Bragg's law, and that moreover the direction of the reflected ray is from crystal *C* to point P^*_{hkl}. The proof is obvious. Since P^*_{hkl} is the reciprocal point corresponding to planes (*hkl*), line *OP* is normal to planes (*hkl*). The plane, normal to the paper, of which *CD* is the trace is drawn parallel to planes (*hkl*), *i. e.*, perpendicular to *OP*. It bisects angle *PCO* and line *OP*. Since *OC* is unity, *OP* is 2 sin α. But *OP* is also λ/d_{hkl} (Eq. 4). Equating, we obtain $\lambda = 2d_{hkl}$ sin α, *i. e.*, α is the Bragg angle, θ. Also, one sees from the diagram that *CP* is the direction of the reflected ray, making angle of incidence equal to angle of reflection.

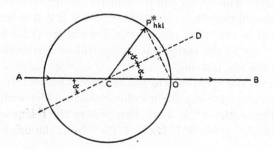

Fig. 4.—The sphere of reflection.

This proof for one point, *hkl*, of the reciprocal lattice holds, of course, for all points of the reciprocal lattice. One can now see clearly the critical character of Bragg's law. Because the reciprocal lattice is a discrete array of points, there will, for an arbitrary orientation of the crystal relative to a monochromatic x-ray beam, be no reflected rays. As the crystal is rotated, the points of the reciprocal lattice pass through the surface of the sphere. At the moment of transit, the corresponding planes will reflect and the direction of the reflected rays will be from point *C* to the reciprocal points at transit. One also sees clearly that points close together in reciprocal space will correspond to reflections close together on the film. In fact, for most techniques, the pattern one obtains is a distorted but recognizable projection of the reciprocal lattice. For points close to the origin, the distortion is slight. Thus, in figure 2D, the square character of the pattern is not very distorted and reflects the tetragonal reciprocal lattice. In fact, knowing that the crystal was tetragonal one could say merely by looking at the diagram that the oscillation was about the "*a*" axis and that the x-ray beam at one end of the oscillation was almost parallel to the tetragonal axis.

One can assign to the points of the reciprocal lattice weights which will be proportional to the intensities of the x-ray reflections. This weighted reciprocal lattice will then contain all the information one can obtain by x-ray methods; and the intensity analysis is really the transformation of the weighted reciprocal lattice into an atomic distribution in real space. The transformation is not unique in this direction (the reverse transformation from real to reciprocal space is) and generally cannot be carried out unless sufficient additional non-x-ray information is available.

VI. METHODS AND APPARATUS FOR DIFFRACTION MEASUREMENTS

For the organic chemist, only those methods using monochromatic x-rays are of much interest.   These methods use a polycrystalline specimen (the powder method), a fiber, or a single crystal (rotation, oscillation, and moving-film methods).

1.   Powder Method

The powder method is very simple technically but gives the least amount of information.   Its principal uses are for identification, precision determination of lattice constants, and particle size determination.

The specimen is usually prepared in the form of a cylinder.   Depending on the material studied, it may be sealed in thin-walled glass capillaries, extruded in the form of a crylindrical rod, or caused to adhere to the outside of a glass fiber by using an appropriate adhesive (thin shellac, for example).   Either a cylindrical camera with the rodlike specimen at the center or a flat film perpendicular to the x-ray beam is used.   Means must be provided for accurately centering the specimen and for rotating it about its axis during the exposure.   It is important that the specimen diameter should be close to the optimum value, $2/\mu$ centimeter.   Appreciable departure from this optimum value results in longer exposures and unduly heavy backgrounds, and may even give misleading relative intensities. Fortunately for organic materials and the common radiations, this optimum value ranges conveniently from 0.5 to 1.0 millimeter, and therefore dilution with light material or other artifices is usually not necessary.

It is important that the specimen holder be so designed that the specimen can be properly adjusted in a convenient manner.   Most commercial powder cameras have no provision for mechanically orienting the cylindrical specimen parallel to the axis of rotation.   Such adjustment should be first made by mounting the specimen in Plasticine and then moulding the Plasticine until the parallelism is achieved.   The specimen holder should have a slide mechanism for centering the specimen;   this adjustment can be easily made once parallelism has been obtained.   When a specimen is properly adjusted, no transverse movement of the specimen should be noticed as it is rotated.

Several alternative methods of preparing cylindrical specimens have been mentioned. If thin-walled glass capillaries are used, they should be drawn from low-absorption (for x-rays) glass tubing, Pyrex, or Lindemann glass. Soda glass should definitely be avoided. The internal diameter of such capillaries should be between 0.3 and 0.8 millimeter and the wall thickness (for Pyrex) should be less than 0.05 millimeter. Filling such capillaries is sometimes a problem, as they should be so fine that any appreciable finger pressure will crush them. An easy method is sealing one end by means of a microflame. The open end is pushed into a small heap of the material to be examined and then held vertically upwards while the capillary is caused to vibrate by stroking it gently with a fine file. The vibrations will cause the powder to fall to the closed end. The process is repeated until enough specimen has accumulated at the bottom. It can be then compacted into place by a fine glass ramrod of appropriate diameter. If the powder consists of coarse crystals, it should be ground and screened through a fine wire mesh before insertion in the capillary. If this is not done, the resulting x-ray diagrams will consist of lines of a spotty —rather than uniform—character.

The glass of the capillaries of course gives some halos in the x-ray diagram and absorbs a large fraction of the useful $K\alpha$ radiation. It is, moreover, not too easy to draw out suitable capillaries. For these reasons, extruded specimens are being more widely used. The material to be studied is wet with a suitable binder such as thin collodion or shellac or even water, and then is packed into a short length of thick-walled glass capillary of the desired bore. A piston of piano wire can be used to compact the mass and finally to extrude it. The specimen will adhere to the piston end, which can then be used as the specimen support if a short enough piston has been used. Some precautions are necessary with this technique. The glass capillaries should be cut off squarely at the extrusion end or the specimen cylinder may curve as it emerges from the capillary. With different materials, varying amounts of binder will have to be used, and some experimentation will be necessary to determine the optimum conditions.

The powder method works despite the critical nature of Bragg's law because of the random orientation of the myriad of crystallites which make up the specimen. These will make every conceivable angle with the x-ray beam, and therefore will cause every possible reflection to occur. It is easier to see what happens if one thinks in terms of the reciprocal lattice. In figure 4, there is a single crystal at C and a discrete reciprocal lattice at O. Now if the crystal at C is replaced by a powder of randomly oriented crystallites, there will be centered at O a myriad of identical reciprocal lattices, all oriented at random.   Each point hkl at distance d^*_{hkl} from O is then replaced by a sphere of radius d^*_{hkl} with center at O. This set of concentric spheres intersects the unit sphere (the sphere of reflection) in a series of circles; and, following the previous derivation, there will be reflected rays from C to these circles.   Thus the reflected rays will form a series of coaxial cones. If a film perpendicular to the x-ray beam is used to record the reflections, the result will be a series of concentric circles; a cylindrical film will intersect the cones in a set of more complicated curves.

Obviously, the dimensions of the rings (or curves) are related to the spacings of the planes responsible for the reflections. The half-angle of the cones (*i. e.*, the angle of deviation) is 2θ where $\lambda = 2d_{hkl} \sin \theta$.

For flat films, the diameter of the ring, d, is given by $d/s = 2 \tan 2\theta$ where s is the specimen-to-film distance. For cylindrical films, the corresponding distance, d, is given by $d/r = 4\theta$ in radians, where r is the camera radius.

One can measure d very accurately with a centimeter scale or comparator and use these relations to compute the spacing. This is hardly worth while, as exact comparator determinations of the reflection locations do not mean that one obtains correspondingly exact spacing determinations.   Errors enter due to film shrinkage, specimen centering, absorption, etc., so that actually accuracies much better than $\pm 0.5\%$ are difficult to attain—unless one uses the high precision techniques of back reflection. Fortunately for our purposes we are not often interested in high accuracy; errors of 0.5% are usually not troublesome. Should some specialized studies, for example of solid solutions, require high precision, it can be attained by the use of special techniques.[17]

Much time in determining the spacings of powder lines can be saved by the use of special scales. Scales can thus be made up which read spacings directly, and with these adequate precision can be obtained. However, a new scale is then necessary for every camera diameter and for every wave length. In figure 4, d^* is shown to be $2 \sin \theta$. One can plot a scale of d^* and read the values from the film. By dividing into the wave length, the spacings are obtained. Figures 5 and 6 are charts for making such scales for cylindrical and flat films, respectively. A strip of paper is placed at the appropriate specimen-to-film distance and the intervals are marked off on the strip. This is done on both sides of the center. The scale is then centered on the film and values of d^* read off. A slide-rule division into λ then gives the spacings. Scales for odd specimen-to-film distances can be made in about five minutes each. Another advantage of this reciprocal-lattice method is that the scales are independent of wave length.

---

[17] M. J. Buerger, *op. cit.*, Chapter XX.

Determination of the relative intensities of the reflections is a more difficult task. To obtain even reasonably accurate intensities (assuming all experimental conditions have been fulfilled), a photometer must be used in combination with calibrating scales. One can, of course, abandon the use of film and use instead an ionization chamber or Geiger-Müller counter. Properly designed electrical circuits in combination with the ionization chamber or counter give readings which are proportional to the x-ray intensities. If such devices were combined with angular scales and self-recording apparatus, a more than acceptable substitute for films *for powder work* would be available.

A very simple way[18] of obtaining intensities photographically is by the use of two films, one behind the other. The absorption by one film of the characteristic radiation being used is determined by experiments with strictly monochromatic radiation (crystal monochromatized—not merely filtered); thus, for Kodak no-screen film and copper $K\alpha$ radiation, one thickness of film absorbs about 75% of the incident beam. The second film will then correspond to an exposure of one-fourth of the first film, and by using the two films an intensity scale can be determined.

APPLICATIONS

Identification.—Every crystalline substance gives an unique diffraction diagram characterized by the spacings of the lines and their relative intensities. These quantitative data can, of course, be used as a means of identification. All that is needed is a catalog of patterns of known substances properly indexed. Such tables are available.[19-21] In the card index system,[21] the spacings for the three strongest lines for each substance are listed on separate cards and all cards are arranged in order of interplanar spacing. The procedure is usually to identify the component responsible for the strongest line, then eliminate all lines due to this component, then identify the strongest remaining line, etc. When the diagrams are complex and the lines overlap, elimination of lines must be done cautiously, making use not only of spacings but also of the relative intensities which are included on the cards.

The present card index system unfortunately is still in an experimental stage of development. (A recent valuable paper by Frevel[22] points out

---

[18] J. J. de Lange, J. M. Robertson, and I. Woodward, *Proc. Roy. Soc. London*, **A171**, 404 (1939).

[19] J. D. Hanawalt, H. W. Rinn, and L. K. Frevel, *Ind. Eng. Chem., Anal. Ed.*, **10**, 457 (1938).

[20] L. K. Frevel, *Ind. Eng. Chem., Anal. Ed.*, **14**, 1687 (1942).

[21] *X-Ray Diffraction Data Cards*, Am. Soc. Testing Materials, Philadelphia, Pa.

[22] L. K. Frevel, *Ind. Eng. Chem., Anal. Ed.*, **16**, 208 (1944).

some of the difficulties of the present system, and makes constructive suggestions for improving it.) While reasonable precautions were obviously taken in its preparation, nevertheless some of the data given are incorrect. One should be particularly careful in the use of the intensities, since one cannot always be certain what radiation was used in recording the diagrams or whether a slit or pinhole system was employed. However, the relative intensities of reflections not too far apart in spacing are reasonably independent of such considerations, and comparisons should thus be made only of neighboring reflections.

Precision Determination of Spacings.—There are some problems (the study of solid solutions, for example) in which slight changes in lattice constants must be followed. In such cases, one must study the back reflections occurring at Bragg angles close to 90°. It is easy to see why this is so from an inspection of Bragg's law. Near 90°, the sine curve flattens out and small changes in spacing, and therefore small changes in sine θ, correspond to large changes in θ; in other words, the locations of the back reflections are very sensitive to changes in spacing.

It has also been shown[17] that, by suitable extrapolations to $\theta = 90°$, almost all errors can be eliminated. Absolute values of lattice constants to one part in 25,000 are possible, and relative changes as small as one in 50,000 can be detected.

Many organic crystals give poor lines in the back reflection range. Should high precision be desired in such cases, one can only use great care in determining the specimen-to-film distance, in eliminating centering errors, and in correcting for absorption and film shrinkage; but even with the greatest care it is extremely difficult to determine spacings with a smaller probable error than one part in 500 when the forward reflections only are used. It is almost impossible to determine by direct physical measurement the specimen-to-film distances. This should be determined by using a known material, sodium chloride, for example, as a calibrating material and computing the effective camera radius from the resulting diffraction pattern.

Particle Size Determination.—Just as for the optical case, the resolving power of the crystal as a diffraction grating is a function (among other things) of the size of the individual crystal grains. Particles larger than about 500 Å. give a resolving power not appreciably different from infinitely large crystals. With decreasing crystal size, the resolving power decreases and the diffraction lines become broader. This subject was first treated by Scherrer[23] and extensively developed by many other workers.

---

[23] P. Scherrer, *Göttingen Nachrichten* (1918).

For recent reviews, see Patterson[24, 25] and Clark.[26] It is possible from quantitative studies of the shapes of lines to determine particle size and shape. Such studies have been made, for example, of carbon blacks and of the size of the crystalline domains in fibers. In recent years, attention has been focused on studies of small angle scattering as a method of particle size study. Both discrete line diagrams[27] and continuous small angle scattering[28-30] have given useful information about particle size and size of crystalline domains.

2. Single-Crystal Methods

It has already been shown that a single crystal arbitrarily oriented relative to an incident beam of monochromatic x-rays will generally give no reflected rays. If the crystal is rotated, then Bragg planes will move through the critical angles and reflections will flash out. In terms of the reciprocal lattice, points of the reciprocal lattice will pass through the sphere of reflection, and at the time of transit reflections will occur.

In all the common single-crystal techniques, the crystal is so adjusted that the axis of rotation (or oscillation) is parallel to a crystallographic axis, *i. e.*, parallel to a line of lattice points, because then all the reflection directions are elements of a discrete series of coaxial right circular cones the common axis of which is the axis of rotation. Moreover, there is then a very simple relation between the cone angles and the period (*not* an interplanar spacing—unless the axis happens to be an orthogonal axis) along the crystallographic direction.

A possible plane of lattice points is defined by any three noncolinear lattice points. Consider any crystallographic axis, that is, any line of lattice points. Pass a plane through it and rotate the plane with the line as axis. In one rotation the plane will pass through an infinite number of positions (if we consider the space lattice as infinite in all directions) in which it passes through other lattice points not on the axis. In each of these positions there is a set of crystallographic planes. The ensemble of all the sets of planes passing through the axis is called a zone and the axis is the zone-axis. Now consider the points of the reciprocal lattice which are reciprocal to the various planes of the zone. They will lie, by definition, on normals to the planes, and these normals will all be perpendicular to the

[24] A. L. Patterson, *Phys. Rev.*, **56**, 972 (1939).
[25] A. L. Patterson, *Phys. Rev.*, **56**, 578 (1939).
[26] G. L. Clark, *Applied X-Rays*. 3rd ed., McGraw-Hill, New York, 1940, p. 490.
[27] J. D. Bernal and I. Fankuchen, *J. Gen. Physiol.*, **25**, 111 (1941).
[28] A. Guinier, *Compt. rend.*, **204**, 1115 (1937).
[29] O. Kratky, *Naturwissenschaften*, **31**, 46 (1943).
[30] I. Fankuchen and H. Mark, *J. Applied Phys.*, **15**, 364 (1944).

zone-axis, that is, they are all coplanar.   It has thus been shown that, normal to any crystallographic axis, there is in the reciprocal-lattice one (and since it is a lattice, a set of parallel) plane(s) of reciprocal-lattice points.   Moreover, since the actual lattice is also reciprocal to the reciprocal lattice, the spacing of the planes in the reciprocal lattice is reciprocal to the separation of the points in the real space-lattice.   Following Bernal,[15] to locate points in reciprocal space, we introduce cylindrical coordinates ξ, ζ, and ϕ.   A point P_{hkl} (Fig. 7) in reciprocal space is ζ reciprocal units from a reference plane, and its projection in the plane is ξ units from the reciprocal lattice origin.   Obviously:

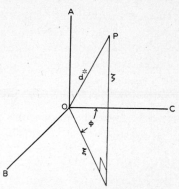

$$d^*_{hkl} = \sqrt{\xi^2 + \zeta^2}$$

Fig. 7.—Bernal's cylindrical reciprocal-lattice coordinates.

If, now, OA is a crystallographic axis (say the "a" axis) along which the lattice points are spaced "a" units apart, then the points of the reciprocal lattice reciprocal to the planes of which OA is the zone-axis—in this case the $(0kl)$ planes—will all lie in plane

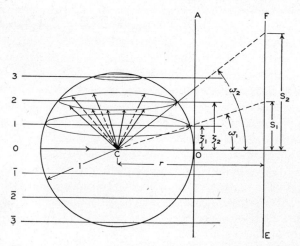

Fig. 8.—Reciprocal-lattice interpretation of layer-line formation.

BOC.   This plane is but one of a set of parallel planes, the plane above it will contain the $(1kl)$ reciprocal points, next the $(2kl)$, etc.   Moreover, the separation of these *reciprocal* planes will be λ/a.

In figure 8, OA is the direction of the axis of rotation (and, of course, also the crystallographic axis, of periodicity a), C is the crystal and center of the sphere of reflection, and O is the origin of the reciprocal lattice. The layer of reciprocal lattice points corresponding to zone OA is perpendicular to OA and to the paper. Its trace is indicated by 0, and it contains reciprocal-lattice point of type $0kl$. Parallel to this equatorial plane at heights above (and below) it, ζ_1, ζ_2, ζ_3, etc., where $\zeta_n = n\lambda/a$, are further planes of reciprocal-lattice points, the nth layer of which contains points of index type nkl. Their traces are indicated by 1, 2, 3, etc. As the crystal rotates or oscillates about an axis through C, the reciprocal lattice will rotate or oscillate about a parallel axis, OA. The layers, 0, 1, 2, etc., of reciprocal points will intersect the sphere of reflection in circles as indicated, and the points in these layers will pass through the sphere of reflection at locations of which the circles will be loci. The directions of the reflected beams will be from C to the points in the circles, $i. e.$, the reflected rays will be elements of a series of right circular cones. If a cylindrical film coaxial with the rotation axis is used to record the reflections, then the intersections of the cones with the cylinder will be a series of parallel circles. When the film is straightened, the reflections will lie on

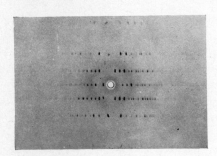

Fig. 9.—Oscillation diagram of menthol. Crystal monochromatized radiation.

a series of parallel straight layer lines (Fig. 9). If a flat film is used, the layer lines will be a series of hyperbolae. Consider the sequence of distances the various layers are from the equator (for the hyperbolae on a flat film, the measurements are made from the apices). Let EF be the intersection of the film (flat or cylindrical) with the plane of the paper. If s_n is the distance of the nth layer from the equator and r is the camera radius, then $\tan \omega_n = s_n/r$, where ω_n is the angle the elements of the nth cone make with the equator.

From figure 8, $\sin \omega_n = \zeta_n$ and $\zeta_n = n\lambda/a$. When these equations are combined:

$$a = \frac{n\lambda}{\sin \tan^{-1} s_n/r} \tag{6}$$

The value of s_n can be measured to an accuracy of about 1% if a cylindrical camera is used and the crystal axis properly adjusted to parallelism to the rotation axis. Thus the lengths of the three edges of any unit cell can be determined by rotating (or oscillating) the crystal about the three axes in turn.   It is important to notice that no interplanar *spacings* are necessarily determined by this method of measuring layer-line separations;   what is determined is a periodicity along a crystallographic axis.   This is true because the measurement is not of the location of one reflection but of the locus of many, namely, of a layer-line separation.

A.   ROTATION AND OSCILLATION METHOD

When a crystal is rotated about an axis, the layer lines are well defined (if the crystal has been properly oriented) but densely populated with reflections.   It is easy to determine the layer-line separation and consequently the periodicity, but difficult to identify (index) the individual reflections. That is because, in using a complete rotation, one reciprocal-lattice coordinate, the polar angle ϕ, has been lost.   Consider, for example, the zero layer, *i. e.*, the $0kl$ reflections when the rotation is about the "a" axis.   All $0kl$ points whose ξ value is less than two (the diameter of the sphere of reflection) will pass through the sphere during a complete rotation.   Not only is this a large number, but for a given ξ value (*i. e.*, location on the film) there may be many different reflections.   The disposition of reciprocal-lattice points in any layer will be at the corners of a parallelogram network.   In indexing a single-crystal film, such a net is drawn for the layer in question to a convenient scale (10 cm. = unity is convenient) and the ξ values of the points of the net compared with the ξ values of the points on the film (see Bernal chart discussion below).   If many points in the net are approximately at the same distance from the origin of the reciprocal lattice, then obviously unambiguous indexing becomes impossible.[31]

One solution of this difficulty is oscillation of the crystal about the axis over a small angular range, the magnitude of which will be an inverse function of the density of points in the reciprocal layers; $15°$ is a common value.   Fewer points then pass through the sphere of reflection and the layer lines in the photographs are less densely populated.   It then becomes possible to index the films unambiguously.

Bernal[15] introduced the use of reciprocal charts for the interpretation of rotation and oscillation films (Figs. 10 and 11).   The horizontal coordinate is ξ and the vertical ζ.   To determine ξ and ζ for the spots on a film, the film is placed on the appropriate chart (the charts can be reduced or enlarged to take care of different camera sizes) and the coordinates read off directly.   By means of these charts, layer-line separations and consequently axial periodicities can be determined very quickly;   the period is given by $n\lambda/\zeta_n$ where ζ_n is the coordinate of the nth layer.

In indexing an oscillation film, it is simpler to consider the sphere of re-

---

[31] M. J. Buerger, *X-Ray Crystallography*.   Wiley, New York, 1942, Chapter VIII.

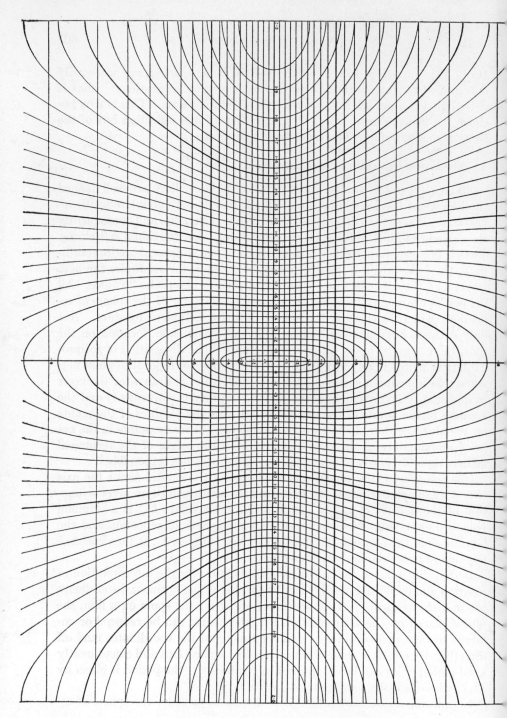

Fig. 10.—Bernal reciprocal chart for interpreting rotation and oscillation films from
cylindrical cameras.   Camera diameter 57.3 mm.

flection as oscillating (about OA as an axis, Fig. 8) and the reciprocal lattice as stationary.   The film is indexed one layer at a time.   For each layer

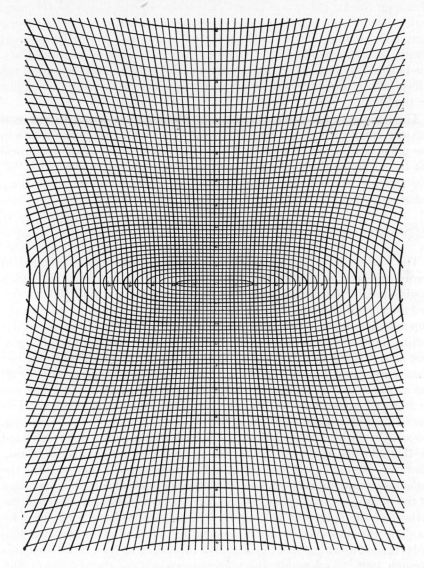

Fig. 11.—Bernal reciprocal chart for interpreting rotation and oscillation films from flat films.   Specimen to film distance 5.00 cm.

the intersection of the layer with the extreme locations of the sphere of reflection will be a pair of lunes and those points of the reciprocal layer which lie in the lunes will reflect during the oscillation. Lunes of appropriate size—depending on the ζ value of the layer line being indexed—are drawn on tracing paper and placed on a reciprocal net drawn to the same scale. For the zero layer, since it is always the same size ($\zeta = 0$), a permanent pair of lunes should be constructed on a nonshrinking transparent plastic base.[32] By matching ξ value on film to ξ value on reciprocal net, the indices may be read off directly from each location in the reciprocal net which falls in the lunes and for whose ξ value there is a corresponding one on the film.

The same net can be used for all layers about a given axis. However, if the axis is not orthogonal, then the point about which the lunes rotate in the upper layers will be displaced from the origin of the plane reciprocal net by an amount which depends on the angle that a^* makes with "a" (for the case of oscillation about the "a" axis, for example) and on the ζ value of the layer.

B. WEISSENBERG TECHNIQUE

The Weissenberg and all other moving-film methods are designed to record one layer of the reciprocal lattice at a time. The principle is easy to visualize. Consider the oscillation method using the cylindrical camera. Let the crystal oscillate through 180°. The layer lines will be too densely populated to index if the usual stationary film is used. However, by inserting a cylindrical sleeve into the camera between the film and the rotation axis, it is possible to shield off most of the reflections so that only one chosen layer hits the cylindrical film. The sleeve has a slot cut almost all the way around; by making the insert slidable, the position of the slot can be adjusted so that only one chosen cone of reflections, i. e., one layer, hits the film. The remainder of the reflections are blocked off by the opaque (to x-rays) shield. It is true that the layer line chosen will not be affected by this selective blocking off; it will be as densely populated as before. However, the individual reflections in the chosen layer do not occur at the same time; instead they flash out at different times during the revolution as the reciprocal-lattice points which correspond to them pass through the surface of the sphere of reflection. The apparatus is now modified by coupling the film cylinder to the oscillating mechanism so that the film slides up and down parallel to the axis of revolution as the crystal oscillates through 180°. As a result, the reflections, which for the stationary film were crowded into a line, are now spread out into a plane in such a way that *no* two reflections can fall in the same place. This permits unequivocal

---

[32] M. J. Buerger, *op. cit.*, Fig. 105.

indexing;   actually, with a little experience, one can index a Weissenberg film merely by looking at it and counting!

Crowfoot[33] and Buerger,[34] using the reciprocal lattice, have treated the indexing of Weissenberg films.   They have derived charts which are really the equivalent, for the Weissenberg method, of the Bernal charts for the fixed-film techniques.   The film is again placed upon the appropriate chart (here one must use a chart of the correct camera size and coupling constant), and reciprocal lattice coordinates in the plane net are read off directly.

The moving-film techniques are the most elegant techniques in x-ray diffraction for obtaining data for structure analysis.   By their use, the essential x-ray data can be collected in a minimum of time, and certainly the indexing of the films requires little labor and is less likely to permit of erroneous identification of the reflections.

A fiber diagram is similar in character to a rotation diagram;   and what has been said of the rotation method applies to the interpretation of fiber diagrams.   The fiber period can be determined unequivocally;   but most attempts to carry the interpretation further have only led to controversy.

As in so many other scientific techniques, the difference between success and failure in the study of single organic crystals with x-rays often lies in apparently small and trivial things.   Thus, the organic chemist, accustomed as he is to crystallization processes, may be unable to produce crystals suitable for x-ray and optic studies.   The reason is obvious—the chemist uses crystallization procedures not to produce good crystals but rather to produce pure materials, and the conditions for producing pure crystals are not necessarily those which result in good crystals.

Usually, slow crystallization is desirable from the viewpoint both of the x-ray worker and of the optical microscopist, since this results in larger and more perfect crystals.   It is not necessary to use large amounts of solute.   Suitable crystals of most organic materials can be obtained by slow cooling of a warm saturated solution.   A convenient way to obtain such crystals is to place about one milliliter of a warm saturated solution in a small test tube which is inserted through a hole in a large flat cork and then floated in a beaker of hot water.   As the water cools, crystals appear and grow.   When the crystals are of suitable size, the process can be stopped by removing the surplus solution.

Special techniques for recrystallizing small quantities of materials and for handling very tiny crystals have been developed in Bernal's laboratories in Cambridge and London, particularly in connection with the studies on

[33] D. Crowfoot, *Z. Krist.*, **A90,** 215 (1935).

[34] M. J. Buerger, *op. cit.*, Chapters XI–XV.

sterols,[35] proteins,[36] and viruses.[27] Perutz[37] has described one convenient manner of recrystallizing small amounts of material in such a way as to obtain clean, dry crystals. Another simple technique consists of spacing two microscope slides about one millimeter apart by means of four small lumps of Plasticine placed at the corners. A drop of warm saturated solution is inserted into the space between the slides. The subsequent crystallization as the solution cools and evaporates can be conveniently followed under the microscope. It can, furthermore, be stopped at any stage by inserting a fine capillary into the drop and sucking out the surplus solution.

A good way to mount crystals for both x-ray and goniometric studies is to attach them to fine Pyrex glass fibers of appropriate diameter. If the crystal is of the right size for x-ray work, it is too small to mount with the naked eye and should be mounted under the microscope. The fiber is embedded in a small lump of Plasticine which in turn is fastened to a rod which serves as a handle. The fiber should protrude about one-fourth of an inch from the Plasticine. The end of the fiber is wet with dilute shellac (this dries slowly enough to permit of reasonable ease in mounting) and brought at the desired angle in contact with the crystal. If the correct size of fiber has been chosen, then the shellac will be dry enough in a minute or so to permit the crystal to be mounted by means of the Plasticine on the goniometer head of the x-ray camera or optical goniometer. In adjusting the crystal on the goniometer head, it should first be set approximately at the center of the adjusting arcs and then centered roughly on the axis of rotation. The arcs are then adjusted until the desired crystal direction is parallel to the axis of rotation. When this has been attained, the crystal should be recentered without disturbing the angular adjustment.

Of course this assumes recognizable, good crystal faces. When good enough faces are not found, then only an approximate orientation can be achieved. The resulting x-ray diagrams will be distorted, i. e., the layer lines will not be straight. The necessary corrections can then be made[38] from a study of the observed distortions.

C. APPLICATIONS

Determination of Molecular Weights.—Because all the early x-ray work was done on materials of known constitution, the possibility of using x-ray diffraction measurements to determine molecular weights has been

[35] J. D. Bernal, D. Crowfoot, and I. Fankuchen, *Trans. Roy. Soc. London,* **A239,** 135 (1940). D. Crowfoot in *Vitamins and Hormones,* Vol. II, Academic Press, New York, 1944, p. 409.

[36] I. Fankuchen, *Ann. N. Y. Acad. Sci.,* **41,** 157 (1941).

[37] M. Perutz, *Z. Krist.,* **A96,** 328 (1937).

[38] O. P. Hendershot, *Rev. Sci. Instruments,* **8,** 436 (1937).

largely overlooked.   In many branches of organic chemistry, for example in the study of biological materials, the molecular weight of the material may be either unknown or known with low accuracy.   It is then possible by means of x-rays (providing, of course, that the substance is crystalline) to determine the molecular weight (or, at the worst, a small integral multiple of it).   Moreover, only a very small amount of material is necessary;   a single crystal weighing 10^{-6} grams can be used for such a determination.

The unit cell of a crystal must contain a whole number of molecules. The number is usually small and is further limited by the symmetry of the crystal.   Thus the number of molecules in an orthorhombic crystal will *almost* always be a power of two, in the tetragonal a multiple of four, etc.

From single crystal x-ray diagrams, one can determine unequivocally the size and shape of the unit cell.   The volume can then be computed; by one of the well-known methods, the density is determined;   and the product of volume and density gives the mass of the unit cell.   The mass of the hydrogen atom of atomic weight 1.008 is 1.66×10^{-24} grams.   Therefore, the weight of the cell contents referred to oxygen as 16 can be obtained by dividing by 1.65×10^{-24}.   Since 1 Å. $= 10^{-8}$ cm., 1 Å.$^3 = 10^{-24}$ ml.   The 10^{-24} is eliminated if the computation is carried out in angstrom units, and the equation for the molecular weight, *M.W.*, of the material becomes:

$$\frac{Vd}{n \times 1.65} = M.W. \tag{7}$$

where n is the number of molecules in the unit cell.

Often n turns out to be the number of general positions in the space group.   Its value can be obtained directly if one has a very approximate idea of the molecular weight.   The approximate value is put into equation (7) and the equation is solved for n.   The value for n will be close to one of the possible integral values if the approximate molecular weight used was not too far off.   The integral value for n is then used to compute the x-ray molecular weight.   This assumes that no solvent of crystallization is present.   If the crystal contains solvent of crystallization, then if *M.W.* is known, equation (7) can be used to compute the quantity of solvent present.

Determination of Other Molecular Characteristics.   Complete Structure Determination.—If a complete structure determination can be made, then the entire stereochemistry of the molecule becomes known.   It is not, however, always necessary to attempt a structure determination to obtain useful information.   Non-x-ray data can be applied to the problem. Optical measurements with the polarizing microscope are very helpful. The optical characteristics of crystals reflect the anisotropy of the molecules which make up the crystal.   Thus, flat molecules are usually optically negative and elongated molecules positive.[39] From rough ideas of the molecular size and the optics, one can guess pretty well the molecular arrangement within the unit cell and often decide between alternative stereochemical configurations. Often the absolute values of the cell constants place limitations on molecular dimensions. Sometimes the symmetry of a molecule can be determined without a complete structure analysis.

To make a complete structure determination, the intensities of the x-ray reflections must be used, for these are functions of the atomic distribution within the unit cell. It should be noted that hydrogen atoms are not located directly although their locations can usually be inferred from those of the other atoms.

The intensity of a reflection (hkl) is proportional to the square of the amplitude, F_{hkl}, of the reflected wave. The scattering of x-rays by an atom is really a scattering by the electrons within the atom. When the direction of scattering is forward, all the electrons in an atom scatter in phase and an atom of atomic number Z will scatter as though its Z electrons were all concentrated at a point. When the scattering is in any other direction, the electrons (which in all atoms are distributed over a radius roughly of the same order of magnitude as the wave length of the x-rays) do not scatter in phase and the amplitude of the resultant wave is less than that of Z electrons at a point.

It can be shown that the effective scattering of a given atom is a function of $\sin \theta/\lambda$ and this function has been evaluated both theoretically and experimentally for most atoms.[4] The shapes for all atoms are similar. At $\sin \theta/\lambda = 0$, the curves (f curves) start at Z (or $Z \mp n$ if the scattering unit is an ion of charge of $\mp ne$), then fall steadily, and finally flatten out for large $\sin \theta/\lambda$. It is to be noted that the curves for atoms of low atomic number fall off more rapidly than those for atoms of high atomic numbers. This means that, at large Bragg angles, most of the scattering can be attributed to whatever heavy atoms are present. The f values of the constituent atoms and their distribution in the unit cell determine the amplitudes, F_{hkl}, of the different reflections. A proposed structure can be tested by computing the scattering in various Bragg directions and then comparing the computed with the observed intensities.

For each set of reflecting planes, (hkl), there is a structure factor, F_{hkl}, which is a measure of the efficiency of that set of planes in reflecting x-rays. This factor arises because the scattering by the different atoms (or, more fundamentally, by the electrons) is not necessarily in phase and each reflection is therefore weaker than it would have been if all the atoms had been located in the reflecting planes and thus scattered in phase. F_{hkl} is

---

[39] R. C. Evans, *Crystal Chemistry*. Cambridge Univ. Press, London, 1939, p. 273.

the amplitude of the x-ray wave reflected by a given set of planes in terms of the scattering of the same lattice with just one electron at each lattice point as unity.

Consider a unit cell of dimensions a,b,c with n atoms per unit cell. Let the coordinates of the pth atom be $x_p y_p z_p$ when referred to the sides of the unit cell as the coordinate system (not necessarily an orthogonal system). Thus, x can vary in magnitude from 0 to a, y from 0 to b, and z from 0 to c. Then it can be shown that:

$$F_{hkl} = \sum_p f_{p, hkl} e^{2\pi i (hx_p/a + ky_p/b + lz_p/c)} \tag{8}$$

Each term in the above summation is merely the contribution of the corresponding atom to the amplitude of the scattered wave. For practically all organic crystals, the intensity of a reflection will be proportional to the square of F. A geometrical factor which is a function of θ also enters into the expression for the intensity. This factor depends on the experimental setup for its form (see Bragg[40]).

The above expression makes possible computation of the amplitudes and therefore the relative intensities of the reflections to be expected from any assumed structure. Actually, the most common way of working out structures is to assume structures, note which gives the best agreement between observed and computed intensities, modify the assumed structure slightly, recheck the intensities, etc.

There is an elegant way of utilizing the x-ray data in working out structures, namely, the method of Fourier series. The density, ρ, of electrons in a crystal is a regular periodic function in space. It can, therefore, be represented by a three-dimensional Fourier series. It can be shown that the coefficients of this series are the F_{hkl} values. The expression is:

$$\rho(xyz) = constant \cdot \sum_{-\infty}^{+\infty} \sum F_{hkl} e^{-2\pi i (hx/a + ky/b + lz/c)} \tag{9}$$

When the crystal has a center of symmetry and the origin of the coordinate system is placed at a center of symmetry, a great simplification results. The F's become real numbers, $F_{hkl} = \mp F_{\bar{h}, \bar{k}, \bar{l}}$ and:

$$\rho(xyz) = constant \cdot \sum_{-\infty}^{+\infty} \sum F_{hkl} \cdot \cos 2\pi (hx/a + ky/b + lz/c) \tag{10}$$

Even this form is too involved for frequent use. If the F's for one principal zone are used, the $hk0$ reflections for example, then the series simplifies to a two-dimensional series. This series represents the density of the projection of the cell contents onto the xy plane.

---

[40] W. L. Bragg, *The Crystalline State*.   Macmillan, New York, 1934, Chapter IX and Appendix V.

$$\rho(xy) = constant \cdot \sum_{-\infty}^{+\infty} \Sigma F_{hk0} \cos 2\pi(hx/a + ky/b) \tag{11}$$

Similar expressions can be written for $\rho(xz)$ and $\rho(yz)$. By projecting onto a chosen line instead of onto a plane, corresponding one-dimensional series can be obtained, that is, expressions for $\rho(x)$, $\rho(y)$, and $\rho(z)$.

Now $\rho(xy)$ is the projection of the electron density, *along* the c-axis onto the c-face. When a two-dimensional summation (or a plane section of a three-dimensional summation) is evaluated, it is usually plotted by using contour lines. A Fourier plot will resemble the conventional topographic contour map, the peaks representing regions of high electron density, hence atoms. The complete data for such a summation are contained on one Weissenberg film, the equatorial layer of a "c"-axis Weissenberg film for the case in question.

Methods have been worked out[41, 42] for rapidly computing such two-dimensional series. Using such methods, an average two-dimensional series can be evaluated in a day and a one-dimensional projection in about five minutes.

There is, of course, a catch in the above discussion; otherwise, any crystal for which the x-ray diagrams could be obtained could have its structure determined directly. The trouble arises because experimentally the x-ray intensity is observed, that is, a quantity proportional to $|F|^2$. From this, we can determine $|F|$, the absolute magnitude of F. However, F is in the general case a complex number (Eq. 8), and at best a real number whose sign is either plus or minus. Lacking the phase angle of the complex number (or the sign of the real number) we *do not* know the coefficients of the Fourier series; we only know their magnitudes. Generally, an approximate knowledge of the structure (or a good guess) is first required. This can be used to compute phase angles or determine signs which then can be used to compute the Fourier series. The method is really one of successive approximations.

Failing such advance knowledge of the phase angles (which may be obtained from comparison with similar substances of known structure, application of the principles of crystal chemistry, or perhaps an inspired guess), the Fourier expressions *for electron density* cannot be used and recourse must be made to other methods of analysis.

Patterson[43, 44] investigated the question of how much information could be obtained from a knowledge only of F^2 values. He was able to give a most useful physical interpretation to the summation of a three-dimen-

[41] H. Lipson and C. A. Beevers, *Proc. Phys. Soc. London*, **48**, 772 (1936).

[42] J. M. Robertson, *Phil. Mag.*, **21**, 176 (1936).

[43] A. L. Patterson, *Z. Krist.*, **A90**, 517 (1935).

[44] A. L. Patterson, *Z. Krist.*, **A90**, 543 (1935).

·sional Fourier series identical with equation (9) save for the replacement of F_{hkl} by $|F_{hkl}|^2$.   The sum of such a series is denoted by $P(xyz)$.   (There are also the corresponding two- and one-dimensional series.)   Consider an atomic distribution of N atoms in a unit cell and let it be represented by $\rho(xyz)$ of equation (9).   By starting from each atom in the unit cell, vectors may be drawn to every atom in the cell (including the identity vector, *i. e.*, to itself).   There will be N^2 such vectors.   The arrow end of each vector is weighted by a weight proportional to the product of the atomic numbers (*i. e.*, the product of the x-ray scattering efficiencies) of the atoms it connects.   An origin is selected and all the weighted vectors transferred to it.   This distribution of products of atomic numbers is then represented by $P(xyz)$ just as $\rho(xyz)$ represents the original distribution of atoms.

It is apparent that the interpretation of this Patterson summation will generally be a difficult task: Whereas the F summation contains N comparatively well-defined peaks, the F^2 summation will contain in the same volume N^2 peaks which must superimpose to a great degree.   Harker[45] has provided a modification of the F^2 summations which makes the interpretation somewhat easier in many cases.

If the crystal contains a few heavy atoms, the sorting-out process is much simplified.   Since each vector in the Patterson diagram is weighted proportionately to the product of the atomic numbers of the atoms it connects, the vectors connecting the few heavy atoms with each other produce heavy peaks.   Their identification usually permits the determination of the coordinates (parameters) of the heavy atoms.   This often constitutes enough knowledge of the approximate structure to enable the computation of phase angles of the F's and the evaluation of the F series.   A review paper by Robertson[46] provides a most comprehensive and clear discussion of the application of Fourier series to the determination of molecular structures.

VII.   Examples of Uses in Organic Chemistry

Some examples of the use of x-ray diffraction as a tool in organic chemistry are given.   Bernal *et al.*[35] made an x-ray and optic study of steroid structures.   It was early in this work that Bernal[47] showed that the generally accepted stereochemical configuration of Windaus could not be right and that the (now accepted) structure of Rosenheim and King and of Wieland and Dane was probably correct.   This result was obtained merely from a cell determination using single-crystal techniques combined with

[45] D. Harker, *J. Chem. Phys.*, **4**, 381 (1936).

[46] J. M. Robertson, in *Reports on Progress in Physics.*   Vol. IV, The Physical Society, London, 1938, p. 332.

[47] J. D. Bernal, *Nature*, **129**, 277 (1932);   *J. Soc. Chem. Ind.*, **51**, 466 (1932).

polarizing microscope studies. The Windaus molecule could not fit into the observed unit cells—hence, it could not be right. As the work on sterols continued, it was evident that it would be premature to attempt a structure determination on any single sterol. A systematic study was then undertaken of every steroid which could be obtained—about 100 in all. As a result, it was found possible to classify the steroids on the basis of the x-ray and optic studies in such a way that rapid identification of any one of them could be made. Several of the "sterols" were thus found to be mixtures of individual sterols. As a result of x-ray molecular weight computations, a few of the sterols were found to have incorrect stoichiometric formulas. These are but a few of the chemical findings of this work.

Robertson[46] has carried out the best and most extensive studies of molecular compounds using Fourier methods. The finest example to date of his work is that on the phthalocyanines.[48] Here, *by x-ray alone*, he was able to work out completely the structure of a substance about as complex as chlorophyll. This was done actually in two different ways. Phthalocyanine crystallizes in isomorphous structure either with hydrogen atoms (which do not scatter appreciably) or with a nickel atom at its center. The geometry of the x-ray diagrams for both materials is identical, but the relative intensities of the reflections are very different. Now the only difference in the scattering of the two unit cells is the scattering of the nickel atom. Its location (and therefore contribution to the amplitude of the scattered waves) was known to be, on x-ray grounds, at a center of symmetry. This made it possible to determine the signs of the structure factors (they were real because of the presence of a center of symmetry); and the resulting Fourier summation revealed the entire stereochemistry of the molecule.

In the case of platinum phthalocyanine, the structure could be worked out in detail for another reason. The platinum atoms are located at centers of symmetry and their contribution to the structure factors, F_{hkl}, could be computed. Because of the massiveness of the platinum, its contribution was sufficient to determine the sign of all but a few of the weakest reflections.

The phthalocyanines illustrate two general methods of working out structures—the use of isomorphous substitutions and of heavy atoms. These can often be used in studying organic structures.

Hargreaves and Taylor,[49] in an interesting paper, give several illustrations of the utility of the x-ray approach. In one of the examples, calycanine, $C_{16}H_{10}N_2$, is studied. By means of x-rays it was possible to decide which of 13 alternative stereochemical configurations was the most likely.

    [48] J. M. Robertson, *J. Chem. Soc.*, **1935**, 615; **1936**, 1195. J. M. Robertson and I. Woodward, *ibid.*, **1937**, 219; **1940**, 36.
    [49] A. Hargreaves and W. H. Taylor, *J. Sci. Instruments.* 18, 138 (1941).

In a brief study of biotin,[50] the use of x-rays confirmed the molecular-weight determination and suggested a flat molecule.

X-ray work has been useful in the study of proteins. Here, molecular weights must be determined (except for rare cases like hemoglobin) not by chemical analysis but by rather involved and complicated processes, the ultracentrifuge, diffusion measurements, etc. X-ray methods have resulted in reliable molecular weights[36] when good crystals and hence good diagrams (Fig. 2D) could be obtained.

Virus proteins have also been studied.[27] It was possible to obtain exact measurements of the diameter of the virus molecules. Low-angle scattering studies threw much light on the character of interparticle forces in colloidal preparations. It was also demonstrated that the virus molecules themselves had a regular internal structure, that is, they were tiny crystals themselves.

Many more examples could be cited of the utility of x-rays as a tool in chemistry. The illustrations given above have not included its use for identification by the powder method because that is a common and generally accepted technique. But enough have been given, it is hoped, to demonstrate that the x-ray diffraction method is a powerful tool in chemistry and one which should be more widely used.

---

[50] I. Fankuchen, *J. Am. Chem. Soc.*, **64**, 1742 (1942).

General References

Bragg, W. L., *The Crystalline State*. Macmillan, New York, 1934.

Buerger, M. J., *X-Ray Crystallography*. Wiley, New York, 1942.

Clark, G. L., *Applied X-Rays*. McGraw-Hill, New York, 1940.

Compton, A. H., and Allison, S. K., *X-Rays in Theory and Experiment*. Van Nostrand, New York, and Macmillan, London, 1935.

Evans, R. C., *Crystal Chemistry*. Cambridge Univ. Press, London, 1939.

Handbook of Chemistry and Physics, Tables of X-Ray Crystallographic Data. Chemical Rubber Pub. Co., Cleveland.

International Tables for the Determination of Crystal Structures. Bell, London, 1935. J. W. Edwards, Ann Arbor, 1944.

Meyer, K. H., *High Polymeric Systems*. Interscience, New York, 1942.

Wyckoff, R. W. G., *The Structure of Crystals*. 2nd ed. and supplement, Reinhold, New York, 1935.

Review Papers

"Papers on Crystallography," Annual Reports of the Chemical Society of England.

Fankuchen, I., "Crystalline Protein Molecules. B. Results," *Ann. N. Y. Acad. Sci.*, **41**, 157–168 (1941).

Huggins, M. L., "X-Ray Studies of the Structure of Compounds of Biochemical Interest," *Ann. Rev. Biochem.*, **11**, 27–50 (1942).

Loofbourow, J. R., "Borderland Problems in Biology and Physics," *Rev. Modern Phys.*, **12**, 287–303 (1940).

Robertson, J. M., "X-Ray Analysis and Application of Fourier Series Methods to Molecular Structure," in *Reports on Progress in Physics.* Vol. IV, The Physical Society, London, 1938, pp. 332–367.

Warren, B. E., "Crystalline Protein Molecules. A. Methods," *Ann. N. Y. Acad. Sci.*, **41**, 151–156 (1941).

CHAPTER XV

ELECTRON DIFFRACTION

L. O. BROCKWAY, *University of Michigan*

I. INTRODUCTION

Electron diffraction as a technique in organic chemistry is concerned chiefly with the determination of the geometric structures of molecules. The information directly afforded is the locations of the individual atoms from which may be calculated the distances between chemically bonded atoms, the angles between bonds, the characteristic configurations of typical valence bond structures, the closest approach between nonbonded atoms, and any other structural parameters of interest such as those distinguishing geometric isomers. Such studies with electron diffraction are ordinarily applied only to the vapor state because of the low penetrating power of electron beams in solids. Molecules in the crystalline state are usually studied by x-ray diffraction methods although both methods may be applied to fine crystalline powders. Electron diffraction by massive solids is used when the surface properties are to be investigated and often leads to a chemical identification of adsorbed materials or surface layers differing from the substrate[1]; this field will not be discussed here. The technique described in the following pages is intended to yield the maximum information about molecular parameters. Simplifications are introduced at certain stages in the treatment which would not be allowed in a thorough test of diffraction theory but which do not seriously affect the locating of the atomic scattering centers and are required for convenient application of the method to structural problems.

The experimental procedure involves the operation of high-vacuum, high-potential and vacuum-tube control equipment but only in more or less standard forms already applied to other experiments. Thus, the power supply for an x-ray tube can be used for the high-potential source. Although no commercial electron diffraction camera for gases has been offered for sale in this country, nearly all of the camera accessories can be assembled from commercial items, while the camera can be constructed in any good machine shop. The essential features of the design are given below. The operator will benefit considerably from some acquaintance with established principles in high-vacuum and high-potential technique.

The interpretation of the diffraction patterns and the limitations on the applicability of the method are discussed in the last two sections (pages 631 and 647). It should be noted at the outset that, as a completely independent method of structure determination, electron diffraction is very severely limited. Usually only three molecular parameters can be determined independently, and quite simple molecules would present insuperable difficulties in the absence of supplementary data. For example, the CCl_3 group in chloroform is fixed by six parameters, three carbon-chlorine and three chlorine-chlorine distances; however, with the assumption of an axis of trigonal symmetry supported by spectroscopic data on groups of this type, only two distinct distances occur. Again, in benzene, the six carbon atoms are fixed by twelve parameters, but on the basis of the chemical evidence for the equivalence of the six atoms its structure may be confidently discussed in terms of a six-membered ring fixed by only two parameters. Supplementary data bearing on the symmetry of the molecule is especially useful in the application of the electron diffraction method, but the nature of the supplementary assumptions should be clearly indicated in stating diffraction results. Another kind of assumption also extends the value of electron diffraction results. The smallness of the variations observed in bond lengths and angles for given bond types among simple organic molecules makes it probable that the characteristic values for these bonds also occur in larger molecules too complicated for direct diffraction studies.

---

[1] G. Finch, *Trans. Faraday Soc.*, **31**, 1051 (1935); *Ergeb. exakt. Naturwiss.*, **16**, 353 (1937).

II. PREPARATION OF DIFFRACTION PHOTOGRAPHS

The diffraction effect is observed by causing a beam of electrons to traverse the vapor under investigation and recording the scattered electrons on a photographic plate. The production of usable patterns requires all of the electrons to have nearly the same velocity, the unscattered beam to strike the recording plate in a very small area, and the scattering gas to meet the beam through a very short section of its path. Because of the relatively high electron-scattering power of air, the whole electron path is enclosed in a vacuum chamber. The diffraction camera consists of an electron tube for producing the beam, a magnetic lens or other means of collimating the beam, a specimen section where the gas stream crosses the electron beam, a photographic plate holder, and the auxiliary equipment including the vacuum pumps and gages and the electrical power supply. Many of the constructional details may be varied according to convenience and available shop facilities. The camera used by the author and illustrated in figure 3 (page 625) embodies a sectional style arranged for easy access to the various parts; but other cameras of different design have been used successfully. In the following paragraphs are discussed the features essential to obtaining good diffraction photographs.

1. Electron Beam

The path of the electron beam is shown in figure 1. The electrons liberated from the heated filament on the left are accelerated to the anode by a

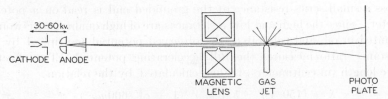

Fig. 1.—Path of electron beam.

direct-current potential of 30 to 60 kilovolts. The beam, limited in size by a small hole in the anode, passes on through a magnetic lens and through the jet of vapor to the photographic plate. The requirement mentioned above of uniform velocity for the electrons is met by providing an accelerating voltage which has a maximum variation of about 0.5%. The power supply for the accelerating potential may be assembled quite simply from a high-voltage transformer, one rectifier tube, and one filter condenser. Since the high-voltage current required is only about one milliampere, including the drain through a high resistance for measuring the potential, a filter condenser of one-half microfarad has enough capacity to pass only a small ripple voltage (less than 0.1% at 40,000 volts) even with the half-wave rectifier indicated in figure 2. A more serious difficulty often arises from voltage fluctuations in the alternating-current line supplying the high-potential transformer. If these fluctuations are as large as 1%, a low-voltage stabilizer must be used in the supply line or a high-voltage stabilizer may be inserted at the position shown in figure 2. Several stabilizer circuits suitable for 50 kilovolts have been devised but not published. The best type uses a control tube in series in the high-potential output with the plate potential varied to absorb voltage fluctuations. The actual value of the accelerating potential determines the electron wave length and should be observed at the time the diffraction exposure is

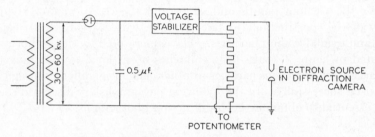

Fig. 2.—Simplified diagram of power supply.

made. A high resistance (fifty megohms or more) is connected across the high potential next to the electron diffraction tube, and the potential drop across a small series resistance at the grounded end is read on a potentiometer. Since the high and low resistances are of high quality, wire-wound, mounted in oil, and calibrated, the observed potential multiplied by the resistance ratio measures the full accelerating potential. The effective wave length (in centimeters) is then calculated by the relation:

$$\lambda = (150/V)^{1/2} \cdot h/(em_0)^{1/2}(1 + eV/600m_0c^2)^{-1/2}$$

in which V is the accelerating potential in volts, and h, e, m_0, and c are Planck's constant, the electronic charge, mass of the electron, and the velocity of light, respectively. When the current values of the physical constants[2] are used, the relation (expressed in angstrom units) becomes:

$$\lambda = (150/V)^{1/2} \cdot 1.002 \cdot (1 + 9.777 \cdot 10^{-7}V)^{-1/2}$$

If the available potential divider and potentiometers are not good enough for determining absolute potential differences, it would be almost as satisfactory to use the potentiometric measurement only to check on the con-

[2] R. T. Birge, *Phys. Rev.*, **52**, 241 (1937); **60**, 785 (1941); **61**, 204 (1942).

stancy of the potential and to calibrate the electron wave length by taking diffraction photographs of a known crystalline substance, such as gold foil. In the case of gold or any other metal whose crystal structure is based on the face-centered cubic lattice, the wave length is calculated from the Bragg relation, $\lambda = (2a_0 \sin \theta/2)/(h^2 + k^2 + l^2)^{1/2}$, in which a_0 is the length of the edge of the unit cell (4.070 Å. for gold[3]), θ is the observed angle between the incident ray and the scattered ray producing one of the diffraction rings, and h, k, and l are the integers which distinguish the reflecting crystallographic planes and which, for face-centered structures, may have any combination of values for which the three integers are all even or all odd.

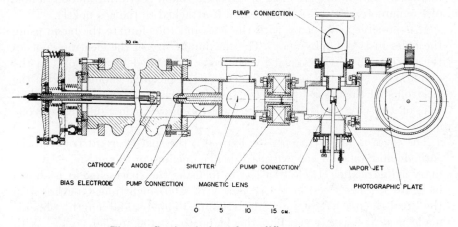

Fig. 3.—Sectional view of gas diffraction camera.

The second requirement for good diffraction patterns is that the diameter of the undeflected electron beam be small when it reaches the photographic plate since the pattern becomes more diffuse when the size of the beam is increased. The use of a magnetic lens is illustrated in figure 1, and the location of the lens in relation to the other parts of the diffraction camera is shown in figure 3. The electrons coming through the small hole in the anode (about 0.5 mm. in diameter) travel on divergent paths until they enter the field of the lens where they are caused to converge. The lens consists of about 2000 turns of wire enclosed in an iron sheath having a gap on the inside. Although the shape and size of the gap affect the focal length, it is very readily adjusted by varying the current through the winding until the electron spot observed on a fluorescent screen at the position of the photographic plate has its minimum size. When the beam is focused in this way, the minimum size of the electron spot is determined by the diame-

---

[3] M. C. Neuberger, *Z. Krist.*, **93**, 1 (1936).

ter of the hole in the anode and the ratio of the lens–plate distance to the lens–anode distance. Both these factors should have the smallest practical size. The diameter of the anode hole should not be less than a few tenths of a millimeter in order that the electron current in the beam be not too small. The ratio of the image and object distances of the lens is approximately one in the camera illustrated, and the electron spot on the plate and the anode hole have the same size. Auxiliary diaphragms are necessary to shield the plate from stray electrons, which arise from scattering at the edges of the anode hole and improper focusing of electrons passing near the edge of the lens. Figure 1 shows a diaphragm following the anode; this diaphragm is effective in eliminating most of the background scattering and has a hole of 1.5 diameter; a second diaphragm is attached to the gas nozzle.

It is possible to dispense with the lens and to collimate the beam using the holes in two diaphragms. The maximum size of the electron spot on the plate is then determined by the cone subtended by the holes in the diaphragms; and the angle of the cone must be small enough to give the electron spot the desired small size. The disadvantage arises in the reduction of the electron-beam current which follows reduction in the cone angle.

The electron-beam current is enhanced if the space current between the cathode and anode is concentrated on the opening in the anode. An auxiliary cylindrical electrode to assist in focusing the space current is shown in figure 1. The electron source is a V of 0.007-inch tungsten wire with the tip in the opening of a cylinder (10 mm. diameter and length) which is made negative with respect to the filament by 100 to 200 volts. With 40,000 volts applied between the filament and anode and a space current of 30 microamperes, the beam current may be as large as ten microamperes. The exposure of the gas stream to the electron beam is controlled from the outside by a rod acting through a flexible metal bellows to retract a movable diaphragm. This mechanical shutter is simple and convenient; and because precise timing of the exposure is usually not important it has no disadvantage in comparison with the use of magnetic or electric fields for deflecting the beam.

2. Specimen

Gases as diffraction specimens are brought into the electron beam through a small hole in the end of a nozzle just under the beam. Since the beam should meet the specimen only in a very small region, special precautions are necessary to keep the gas from spreading through the camera and meeting the beam all along its path. An earlier method provided for condensing much of the gas on a metal surface mounted close to the electron beam on the side opposite the gas jet and cooled with liquid air from the outside of the camera.   In the present arrangement, shown in figure 3, the gas jet is connected with a tube leading into a high-vacuum pump so that the gas path through the camera is entirely enclosed except for the two openings required for letting the electron beam pass through the gas stream. The sample of gas would be confined most effectively if windows could be used which would scatter electrons less effectively than the gas does; but because of the high density of the window material relative to the gas such windows would have to be extremely thin if the amount of material in the path of the beam through the windows were less than that in the beam path through the gas.

Since the exposure time for the gas diffraction photograph is never more than a few seconds, the gas is introduced in a spurt timed to the opening of the shutter controlling the beam.   The pressure of gas where the diffraction occurs cannot be measured; but, if the nozzle is connected to a reservoir of gas on the outside from which the flow is controlled by the momentary opening of a stopcock, the pressure in the reservoir required for good diffraction photographs ranges from 50 to 200 millimeters.   If the substance under study has a vapor pressure at room temperature which is higher than this range, the temperature of the reservoir is adjusted in a cooling bath.   This method is convenient for materials of boiling points down to about $-100°$ C.; in such cases, the reservoir may be a 50-milliliter glass bulb connected through a stopcock and a standard taper to the metal tube on the camera.   Into the bulb is condensed about 0.5 milliliter of liquid, an amount more than sufficient for 25 or 30 photographs.   For gases of extremely low boiling point, the sample may be handled as a gas in a 500-milliliter bulb with an initial pressure of 300 to 400 millimeters.

For substances having low vapor pressures at room temperature, diffraction photographs can sometimes be obtained without temperature baths by taking exposures of as much as 20 seconds, especially if the molecule contains several atoms of higher atomic number than carbon.   The lowest vapor pressure used in this way was five millimeters.   As a rule, clearer patterns result from short exposures with the higher pressures mentioned above.   If the temperature required lies between room temperature and 150° C., the tube supporting the gas nozzle is wound with a heating wire extending from the nozzle down to the vacuum wall.   On the outside, the stopcock and specimen holder are enclosed in a cylindrical oven having an opening through which the stopcock is operated.   One thermocouple is mounted on the gas nozzle and another in the oven.   An ordinary Pyrex stopcock may be used in this temperature range if it is lubricated with a special grease having a low temperature coefficient of viscosity, such as the one made from aluminum stearate and heavy motor oil.[4]   If the substance

4 I. E. Puddington, *J. Am. Chem. Soc.*, **65,** 990 (1943).

has enough vapor pressure only at temperatures above 150° C., it is vaporized from a small heated container placed inside the camera (Fig. 4). This nozzle has no stopcock or valve to control the flow of gas, which accordingly is continuous when the oven is heated. The pressure at room temperature is low enough not to interfere with maintaining the high vacuum in the camera, and the gas entering the camera from the oven is very readily condensed. In any of the nozzle arrangements described, it is important that the electron beam pass directly over the hole through which

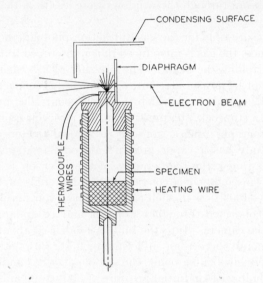

Fig. 4.—Oven for compounds to be vaporized above 150° C.

the gas comes. In each case, the nozzle is supported from a plate which is so mounted on a flexible metal bellows that the nozzle position is adjustable by means of screws on the outside of the camera. A diaphragm with a small hole is mounted on the nozzle so that, when the electron beam passes through the hole, it is correctly aligned with respect to the gas jet.

3. Vacuum System

The principal requirement of the vacuum system is that it be able to maintain the pressure in the camera at 10^{-4} millimeter or less even when the gaseous specimen is introduced. It is necessary, moreover, that there be no direct connection between the electron tube and the diffraction section in order to prevent pressure rises in the electron tube during an exposure; otherwise, destructive arcing may occur in the electron tube.

Multistage high-speed diffusion pumps operating on a low-vapor-pressure oil are connected to the electron tube and to the diffraction section. A very satisfactory pump (available from the *Distillation Products, Inc.*, Rochester, N. Y.) has a four-inch glass barrel with the vapor column and three jets made of aluminum. The oil heats rapidly from a coil immersed directly in the oil, and the low heat capacity of the pump allows the operating temperature to be reached in a few minutes. The heat of vaporization is low enough that no water cooling is required on the condensing surface, but a set of water-cooled baffle plates is required above the high-vacuum stage to prevent back-diffusion of the oil into the camera. If a diffusion pump is also connected to the gas nozzle as indicated in figure 3, a cold spot (re-entrant glass tube cooled with liquid air) in the pump line will help to

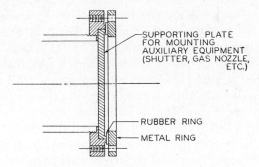

Fig. 5.—Demountable vacuum joint.

condense the vapors introduced and to reduce the contamination of the pump oil. The connecting tubes between the pumps and the apparatus must be as short as possible and not less than about two inches in diameter in order to take advantage of the high speed of the pumps. On the low-vacuum side, the diffusion pumps may be connected to a single mechanical pump which should have a speed comparable to that of the Cenco Megavac Pump.

The joints between the various sections of the camera and at the various ports where the specimen holder, auxiliary diaphragm supports, and shutter are mounted must be vacuum-tight as well as easily demounted and easily returned to the original positions. Such a joint is shown in figure 5 for a side tube closed by a plate which may be used for mounting any auxiliary device. The plate is recessed into a flange on the tube with as close a mechanical fit as may be desired. The plate and the flange each have a flat-topped bead at the joint between them; on this bead is laid a ring of $1/16$-inch gasket rubber which is compressed by a metal ring screwed to the flange. The position of the plate is not affected by variable compression on the gasket, while the joint is easily opened by removing the screws through the metal ring.

Two gages are very useful in operating the vacuum system. One operating in the range from 10^{-1} to 10^{-3} millimeter is indispensable in locating leaks in the system. The most simple and rugged gage for this range is the thermocouple type, in which a pair of wires of dissimilar metals is spot-welded together in the form of an X. A small constant voltage is applied to one pair of dissimilar leads; a microammeter attached to the other pair shows a reading which depends on the temperature of the junction and hence on the gas pressure. When the pressure falls so low that heat loss by gas conduction is much less than the radiation loss, the gage is no longer sensitive. The second gage operates in the range from about 10^{-3} to 10^{-5} millimeter and is connected to the diffraction section where it shows the pressure fluctuations attending the introduction of the sample of vapor. The best type for this use is the modified Knudsen gage described in Strong's book on experimental techniques.[5] In this gage, a vane is suspended between a pair of heated wires in such a way that gas molecules reaching the vane from the hot wires rotate the vane from its equilibrium position, through an angle which is proportional to the gas pressure. It has the advantage of being continuously indicating, registers both condensible and noncondensible gases, and is not damaged by accidental exposure to high pressure. In a series of successive exposures, the Knudsen gage indicates when the gas has been sufficiently cleared from the camera before each exposure.

4. Record

The electrons scattered by the gas molecules are recorded on a photographic plate. Because the intensity of the scattered electrons decreases extremely rapidly with increasing scattering angle, the range of intensities to be recorded over the diffraction pattern is usually greater than the photographic emulsion is capable of registering. This difficulty may be partly overcome by taking light and heavy exposures in each series of photographs so that the inner and outer parts of the pattern may be studied on different plates. While it should be possible to obtain more precise values of the number of scattered electrons using an electrical method of recording, the full angle range would have to be covered by a long series of measurements throughout which the amount of scattering matter in the gas stream is held constant. The convenience of registering the whole diffraction pattern on a photographic plate in a single exposure of about one second makes the

[5] J. Strong, *Procedures in Experimental Physics*. Prentice-Hall, New York, 1939, p. 148.

photographic method much more adaptable for extensive use; and, while only approximate values of relative intensities are afforded by the photographic emulsion, they are usually adequate for the determination of internuclear distances.

Photographic plates are preferable to films because they avoid the shrinkage which occurs in the processing of film. In the vacuum of the diffraction camera the supporting layer in the film loses water, and the film shrinks by 2% or more. On subsequent treatment in the photographic solutions the film expands, and shrinks again on drying. Its final size is smaller than originally but larger than in the vacuum-dehydrated state. Since the measured diameters of the interference maxima appearing in the photographic negative are used for determining the size of the scattering molecules, it is important to minimize size changes in the emulsion. If films are used, it is necessary to mark them *inside the vacuum camera* with a known interval of length. With plates, the shrinkage difficulty does not arise, and at the same time the glass backing holds the emulsion flat without any special provision in the plate holder design. The dehydration in the vacuum sometimes causes the emulsion to separate from the backing along the edge of the plate. The emulsion chosen should have considerable latitude because of the great range of intensities to be recorded and will not have high contrast. Eastman Commercial or Portrait Plates have been found satisfactory while Process or Lantern Slide Plates are not.

The plate holder must be designed to allow a careful determination of the distance from the photographic plate to the center of the gas nozzle since this camera distance is used with the measurements on the plate in computing scattering angles. The camera in figure 3 provides openings at the specimen section and the plate holder through which a traveling microscope may be focused for measuring the camera distance.

III. INTERPRETATION OF DIFFRACTION PHOTOGRAPHS

1. Theoretical Relation between Intensity of Scattered Electrons, Scattering Angle, and Molecular Structure

The pattern obtained on the photographic plate consists of a series of concentric light and dark rings (Fig. 6). The relative intensities and positions of these rings must now be interpreted in terms of the structure of the molecules giving rise to the pattern. The theoretical expression desired must apply to the scattering of electrons of uniform energy by a set of molecules having all possible orientations since, in the gas stream, the molecules are randomly related. The motion of the molecules is completely negligible during the time that any one electron is traversing the field of any one molecule. A more complete outline of the derivation described in the following paragraph is given in a review article.[6]

The interaction of the electrons in the beam with a scattering molecule is described by the Schroedinger amplitude equation:

$$\frac{\partial^2\psi}{\partial x^2} + \frac{\partial^2\psi}{\partial y^2} + \frac{\partial^2\psi}{\partial z^2} + \frac{8\pi^2 m}{h^2}(W - V(x, y, z))\psi = 0 \tag{1}$$

The solution, ψ, is a function of the coordinates, x, y, z, of the electron, and

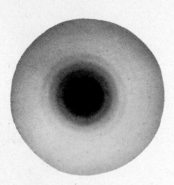

$|\psi|^2$ represents the distribution of electrons in both the incident and scattered beams. W is the energy of the electrons and is a constant determined by the accelerating potential, if the electrons do not lose energy on collision with a molecule. V is the potential energy of an electron in the field of the charges in the molecule (nuclei and electrons). The solution for a stationary molecule is obtained with the aid of the assumptions that the molecule is composed of discrete atoms having spherical distributions of extranuclear charge, that only single scattering of the electrons occurs, and that high-velocity electrons (energies greater than about 20,000 electron volts) will be used.

Fig. 6.—Electron diffraction photograph of carbon tetrachloride.

The resulting expression is averaged over all possible orientations of the stationary molecule, and the formula for the scattered electrons is:

$$I = I_0(8\pi^2 me^2/h^2)^2(1/r)^2\sum_i\sum_j f_i f_j (\sin sr_{ij})/sr_{ij} \tag{2}$$

where I_0 = the intensity of incident electron beam, r = the distance from the scattering center to a point on the photographic plate; $f_i = (Z - F)_i/s^2$, the atomic scattering factor for electrons; Z_i = the atomic number; $F_i = 4\pi\int_0^\infty p(r)[(\sin sr)/sr]r^2dr$, the atomic scattering factor for x-rays[7]; $s = 4\pi(\sin \theta/2)/\lambda$; θ = the angle of scattering; λ = the electron wave length; and r_{ij} = the distance between the ith and jth atoms. The double summation extends over all the atoms in the molecule so that the distances between all atom pairs in the molecule appear in the expanded summation. The intensity is then a function of the structure of the molecule and of the scattering angle, θ. With the aid of the above expression, scattering curves (I as a function of θ or of s) can be calculated for any molecular model, and

---

[6] L. O. Brockway, *Rev. Modern Phys.*, **8**, 231 (1936).

[7] R. W. James and G. W. Brindley, *Z. Krist.*, **78**, 370 (1931). L. Pauling and J. Sherman, *ibid.*, **81**, 28 (1932).

the plausibility of the model tested by comparison of the calculated curve with the photographs.

The formula given above assumes constant interatomic distances, but these distances vary with the thermal motions of the atoms. Since the vapor to be photographed may be at any temperature in the range from 200° to 500° or even 600° K., in many cases the molecules will have vibrational energy, and the vibrational amplitude of the atoms is not always very small in comparison with the interatomic distances. The period of the vibration is much longer than the time an electron spends in the field of the molecule so that, in effect, the electron beam meets a collection of molecules in which the distance between each atom pair varies between a minimum and a maximum value set by the vibrational amplitude. The effect on the scattered electrons may be approximately represented by the factor e^{-as^2} applied to each term in the double summation; a is proportional to the mean square of the vibrational amplitude and is accordingly a function of the temperature. For the terms in which $i = j$ (i. e., scattering by the separate atoms), a is equal to zero; for the others it may reach values up to about 0.010. If the a values for all of the terms were about the same, the effect would be a simple diminution with increasing s. Since, however, the a values are often appreciably larger for some terms than for others, the terms with larger amplitudes are reduced in relative importance. This is illustrated below. The temperature effect in molecules having internal oscillations or restricted rotations requires special treatment.[8]

The total intensity of scattered electrons includes a contribution from those which are scattered with a loss of energy. Because of the energy loss, the wave lengths of these electrons are greater than that of the incident electrons by varying degrees, and there are no coherent relations between the electron waves scattered with loss of energy by different atoms in the same molecule. For this reason, the incoherent scattering is not dependent on the structure of the molecule and is of interest only in connection with quantitative measurements on the scattered electron intensity. The contribution of the incoherent scattering is given by S_i/s^4 for each atom in the molecule, where S_i is a tabulated function[9] of $0.176sZ_i^{-2/3}$; it is very large for small scattering angles but rapidly tends toward zero in a range of s where the coherent scattering is still appreciable.

2. Methods of Comparing the Photographs with the Theoretical Relation

The theoretical relation for the coherent electrons may be written in the form (neglecting the temperature factors):

[8] P. Debye, *J. Chem. Phys.*, **9**, 55 (1941).

[9] L. Bewilogua, *Physik. Z.*, **32**, 740 (1931).

$$I = A\sum_i\sum_j \frac{(Z - F)_i(Z - F)_j}{s^4}\frac{\sin sr_{ij}}{sr_{ij}} \tag{3}$$

For a simple molecule such as carbon tetrachloride with four equal C—Cl terms and six equal Cl—Cl terms, the expression becomes:

$$I = \frac{A}{s^4}\Big[(Z - F)_C^2 + 4(Z - F)_{Cl}^2 + 8(Z - F)_C(Z - F)_{Cl}\frac{\sin sr_{C-Cl}}{sr_{C-Cl}} +$$

$$12(Z - F)_{Cl}^2\frac{\sin sr_{Cl-Cl}}{sr_{Cl-Cl}}\Big] \tag{4}$$

The terms are of two kinds: the "atomic," due to the separate atoms (summed in Curve A in Fig. 7); and the "molecular," depend on the inter-

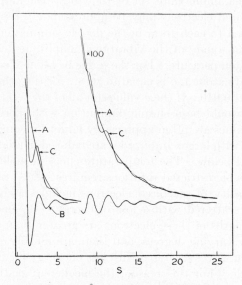

Fig. 7.—Calculated intensity curves for (A) atomic, (B) molecular, and (C) total scattering for carbon tetrachloride.

atomic distances (Curve B, Fig. 7). In the "atomic" terms, the F functions range smoothly from a value of Z at $s = 0$ down toward zero at large s values, so that the terms start from a high finite value at $s = 0$ and decrease rapidly without maxima or minima with increasing s. In the "molecular" terms, the damped sine functions produce maxima and minima whose positions and relative amplitudes depend on the interatomic distances and on the chemical elements involved. The amplitudes in the sum of the molecular terms (Curves B) decrease with increasing angle because of the factor, s^{-4}. In the total Curve C (sum of atomic and molecular scattering), the decrease in intensity with increasing angle is so rapid that maxima appear only at 2.5 and 11.0; otherwise there are only inflections about a rapidly falling background. In the application of electron diffraction to the determination of molecular structure, the problem is that of measuring the "molecular" effects in the observed scattering pattern and determining from them the interatomic distances.

The usefulness of microphotometer records of the diffraction pattern in the determination of structure is very limited. The two records of carbon tetrachloride photographs (Fig. 8) corroborate the general form of the scattering curve, *i. e.*, fluctuations about a rapidly falling background. The flat central portion of the record on the right is due to saturation of the photographic emulsion where the intensity of the electrons is too great to be registered; in the lighter exposure on the left, the photographic density drops below the sensitivity limit of the microphotometer beyond the third

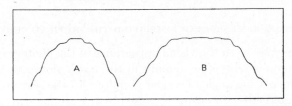

Fig. 8.—Tracings from microphotometer records of carbon tetrachloride photographs, (A) showing the first three apparent maxima and (B) at high sensitivity showing the first five apparent maxima.

"maximum." The ratio of the calculated scattered intensity at the position of the first maximum to that at the fifth (visible in the record on the right) is 100 to 1. One of the serious limitations on the use of the microphotometer record is that it registers the total intensity, of which the molecular contributions make a small part, and small changes in the relative values of the r_{ij} can therefore scarcely be detected in their effect on the photometric record. By fitting the scale of the calculated curve to that of the observed record, the size of the scattering molecule could be determined if its shape were known; but its shape cannot be determined from a record where the experimental uncertainties may be as large as the effects of the changes in shape which are to be tested. A second disadvantage of the photometric record is its failure to register the outer part of the diffraction pattern which is observed visually in the photographic negative.

The visual appearance of the diffraction photographs (Fig. 6) shows a set of concentric light and dark rings or bands. In negatives of carbon tetrachloride, the dark rings corresponding to the maxima in the molecular curve (B, Fig. 7) have been observed out to the fourteenth. It is evident that the eye does not observe the total intensity (Curve C, Fig. 7) but that it is far more sensitive to fluctuations in intensity, and magnifies the effect of the molecular contributions. The visual effect is not represented directly by Curve B because the apparent intensity of the outermost rings is about 5% of that of the first or second rings while the amplitude of the twelfth maximum in Curve B is only about 0.1% of that of the second. In spite of the fact, however, that the visual appearance cannot be directly correlated with the complete theoretical expression for coherently scattered electrons, the ability of the eye to detect the diffraction pattern far beyond the range of the microphotometer makes the subjective measurements of special value in choosing among scattering curves calculated for different molecular models. A method must then be devised for calculating simplified theoretical curves which may be used in conjunction with visual measurements on the photographic negatives. A rough justification for this correlation based on reactions of the eye has been given.[10]

A. VISUAL MEASUREMENTS AND SIMPLIFIED THEORETICAL CURVES

The difference between the visual appearance of the photographs and the complete theoretical curve lies mainly in the much slower decrease in intensity with increasing angle observed visually. In the scattering function (Eq. 4), the rapid fall in intensity is caused by the atomic scattering factor, f, whose denominator contributes a factor of $1/s^4$ in the calculated intensity. Various simplifications of the intensity function have been suggested which will cause the scattering curve to reproduce the appearance of the photographs. The most commonly used simplified curve is obtained by substituting Z, the atomic number, for f. The scattering function for carbon tetrachloride then becomes:

$$I = 8 \times 6 \times 17 \frac{\sin sr_{C-Cl}}{sr_{C-Cl}} + 12 \times 17 \times 17 \frac{\sin sr_{Cl-Cl}}{sr_{Cl-Cl}} \tag{5}$$

The atomic terms have become constant and are of no importance. The curve (I, Fig. 9) does reproduce the visual appearance of the photographs in making the fifth, seventh, and tenth maxima, respectively, stronger than the preceding ones.

The agreement between the qualitative features of the negative and the curve calculated for a particular molecular model is a test of the plausibility of the model. If distinct reversals of the apparent relative intensities of the rings occur in a given curve, the model for this curve is deemed unsatisfactory. This comparison of the qualitative features is used in determining the values of the parameters fixing the shape of a molecule. For example,

---

[10] L. Pauling and L. O. Brockway, *J. Chem. Phys.*, **2**, 867 (1934).

n figure 10 are several intensity curves for fluoroform calculated for models of trigonal symmetry (*i. e.*, having equal FCF angles and equal C—F bond

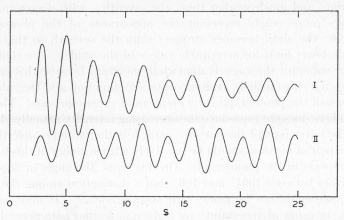

Fig. 9.—Simplified intensity curves for carbon tetrachloride.
(I) $Z_i Z_j (\sin sr_{ij})/sr_{ij}$; (II) $(Z_i Z_j/r_{ij}) \sin sr_{ij}$.

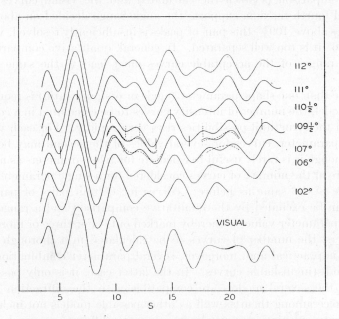

Fig. 10.—Simplified intensity curves of fluoroform showing the effect of variation of FCF angle.

lengths) with FCF angles ranging from 112° down to 102°. The "visual" curve is a representation of the appearance of the photograph. A notable feature is the rough equality of the sixth and seventh peaks with a poorly resolved minimum between. The 112° curve shows the sixth clearly resolved from, and much weaker than, the seventh; with decreasing angle the curves more nearly represent the appearance of the photographs. Below 106° the sixth becomes stronger than the seventh so that this is taken as a lower limit for acceptable values of the angle. The choice of a particular value for the angle is somewhat uncertain because this comparison between a substantially arbitrary intensity function and the subjective appearance of the photograph is by no means a precise process. The function used here does not reproduce the decreasing intensity actually observed toward the outer part of the pattern; and it is therefore possible that the outer of a pair of maxima should be relatively a little higher in this function than it appears in the photograph. On this basis, the angle in fluoroform probably lies between $109\frac{1}{2}°$ and 106°, but a distinction among the values in this range could not be made with any confidence. It may be noted here that the range of uncertainty for a given molecular parameter depends very much on how sensitive the curves are to changes in the model. A similar comparison between the calculated and the visual curves at the third and fourth maxima supports the angle range decided on above. In the curves above $109\frac{1}{2}°$ this pair of peaks is insufficiently resolved, whereas below 106° it is too well separated. In general, qualitative comparisons in different ranges of the acceptable curves must lead to the same conclusions.

If more than one shape parameter (angle or distance ratio) is required to fix the model, the number of intensity curves to be calculated in a complete survey of the structural possibilities rises very rapidly. For each value of the first parameter, curves for several values of the second may be necessary, although it is rarely useful to calculate for two parameters as many as the square of the number of curves considered for a single parameter. The procedure is the same as before; curves for certain pairs of parameter values can be excluded by the qualitative comparison and a range of acceptable parameter values is thereby marked out. For three or more shape parameters, the number of curves to be calculated in a thorough survey becomes impractical and, moreover, several parameter combinations may lead to indistinguishable curves. In the latter case, it is only possible to say that the several models are compatible with the diffraction results, and a choice among them as well as other possible models not included in the intensity calculations must be based on nondiffraction considerations. For independent determination, two shape parameters is usually the practical upper limit, and the complexity of molecules which can be studied by electron diffraction without recourse to other information is very limited.

It is often useful to limit the variations considered by assumptions based on other experimental results such as dipole moment measurements, spectroscopic measurements, symmetry properties based on chemical reactions, etc., or even on structural theories, provided in any case that the nature of the assumptions is clearly stated.   In the fluoroform molecule discussed above, the asumption of trigonal symmetry based on theory and on the spectroscopically observed symmetry in other molecules of the CXY_3 type reduces the number of shape parameters from five to one (when the weakly scattering H atom is neglected or fixed by an assumed C—H distance).

The possible effect on the curves of the exponential temperature factor referred to above must also be considered.   In the function, $\exp(-as^2)$, the a value is larger for the terms in the scattering function having the larger amplitudes of vibration, and generally the distances between nonbonded atoms will vary more than those between bonded atoms.   The terms for the nonbonded distances will become less important as the scattering angle increases.   The damping effect on the nonbonded terms is illustrated for two curves in figure 10.   The dotted line on the 107° curve has the F—F term multiplied by the factor, $\exp(-0.002s^2)$;   the two segments above correspond to a $108\frac{1}{2}$° model with the dotted lines having the F—F term multiplied by $\exp(-0.001s^2)$.   In the dotted curves the weaker peaks are made still weaker, the effect being larger in the 107° curve where the a value is larger.   In this curve the effect is too great because it makes the sixth and seventh peaks coalesce, whereas they are observed as partially resolved.   The effect in the $108\frac{1}{2}$° curve is probably also too large since the sixth peak is reduced to a shelf.   Since the magnitude of the coefficients in the temperature factors is usually not known, their effects on the curve cannot be included with any certainty;   and some allowance for this uncertainty must be considered in choosing among the models for the best qualitative agreement with the photographs.

The foregoing discussion refers to the apparent relative intensities of the peaks and only in a rough fashion to their positions.   Quantitative measurements on the positions not only may afford support for the angles or distance ratios chosen as described but also will fix the scale of the curves and thereby the size of the molecule.   In the visual method, a series of points are measured on the photograph and correlated with corresponding points on a calculated curve showing the correct qualitative features. The measurements are made on the diameters of the light and dark rings on the negative corresponding to minima and maxima in the curves. The negative is mounted on the illuminated translucent screen of a comparator having two carriages fitted with pointers.   The points are set at the darkest (or lightest) positions on the ends of a ring diameter;   and from the reading of the comparator, the measured distance from gas nozzle to photographic plate and the electron wave length, an experimental value for s [$= 4\pi \sin$

$(\theta/2)/\lambda$] is obtained for the ring measured. With the assumption that each maximum (or minimum) must occur in the photograph and in the calculated curve for the correct model at the same value of sr, the following relation is applied to each of the measurements:

$$(sr)_{\text{exp.}} = (sr)_{\text{theor.}} \quad \text{or} \quad r_{\text{exp.}} = \frac{s}{s_0} r_{\text{theor.}}$$

s_0 is computed from the measured ring diameter, s is read from the curve, $r_{\text{theor.}}$ is the value assumed for any interatomic distance in calculating the theoretical curve, and $r_{\text{exp.}}$ is the experimental result for the distance. A set of $r_{\text{exp.}}$ values for C—Cl in CCl_4 is shown in table I, where the s values in the curve (Eq. 5) were fixed by $r_{\text{theor.}}$ of 1.76 Å. for C—Cl.

TABLE I

EXPERIMENTAL VALUES FOR INTERATOMIC DISTANCES

(CCl_4–CAMERA DISTANCE = 12.19 CM., λ = 0.0604 Å.)

Max.	Min.	I_k	s_0	s	C—Cl, Å.
1		20	2.87	2.73	(1.675)
	2	−20	3.78	3.65	(1.697)
2		30	4.91	4.82	(1.727)
	3	−20	6.06	6.04	1.752
3		15	7.14	7.16	1.764
	4	−15	8.22	8.22	1.759
4		10	9.26	9.22	1.751
	5	−10	10.33	10.27	1.752
5		12	11.44	11.48	1.765
	6	−18	12.58	12.64	1.767
6		5	13.65	13.69	1.765
	7	− 5	14.71	14.71	1.760
7		5	15.81	15.76	1.756
	8	− 2	16.89	16.92	1.764
8		2	18.02	18.10	1.768
	9	− 1	19.07	19.18	1.771
9		1	20.14	20.18	1.763
	10	− 1	21.22	21.17	1.756
10		1	22.34	22.37	1.762
				AVERAGE:	1.761
				AVERAGE DEVIATION:	0.005

The average deviation of the individual values from the mean value of 1.761 Å. is 0.005 Å., while the maximum deviation is 0.010 Å. and the probable error of the mean is 0.001 Å. The absence of any large deviations means that the relative positions of the peaks in the photograph are well reproduced by the calculated curve based on the regular tetrahedral model for carbon tetrachloride and supports the probable correctness of this model. (Irregular models are eliminated by the observed zero value for the dipole moment, while the curves for planar models show relative intensities not observed in the photographs.) The first three values for C—Cl in table I are lower than all the others and were not included in the average.   This failure of the curve for s values below about 5.0 is always observed.   The poor correlation between visual measurements and the curve of equation (5) near the center of the diffraction pattern is related to the very steep fall in the background intensity in this region.   While the addition of a falling background would shift the peaks outward in the calculated curve and raise the C—Cl values obtained, the region affected is too small a part of the total pattern to warrant any such attempt.

The excellent agreement among the distance values from all of the peaks beyond the second in carbon tetrachloride is not observed when the pattern has irregular or poorly resolved peaks.   Visual measurements on the diameters of a partially resolved pair of rings of equal intensity are too small for the inner and too large for the outer in comparison with the results from the well-resolved, regularly shaped rings in the same pattern.   If one of the pair is a weaker subsidiary to the other, the weaker one is shifted in its apparent position away from the stronger one, which may be very little affected.   While the occurrence of such irregularities in the pattern is an invaluable aid in choosing among various molecular models, the measurements on the irregular features are not reliable in fixing the scale of the curve, and some allowance must be made in averaging the experimental distance values from the various rings.   The usual procedure is to exclude from the average those values based on irregular rings.   In figure 10, the positions of the visually measured maxima and minima are indicated in the "visual" curve and marked with vertical lines on the $109\frac{1}{2}°$ curve.   Here, the fourth peak and the preceding minimum and the sixth and seventh peaks are marked with broken lines to indicate the expected unreliability of the measurements on their diameters.   The seventh peak is included because it was observed to be equal to, and almost unresolved from, the sixth. Considerable deviations are sometimes observed for distinctly resolved peaks because of poor photographs or of difficulty in choosing the model which gives the optimum qualitative agreement with the photographs. These deviations increase the uncertainty of the structural parameters finally reported.

The curves used in the foregoing discussion are based on the function:

$$I = \sum\sum' Z_i Z_j \frac{\sin sr_{ij}}{sr_{ij}} \tag{6}$$

a sum of terms involving $(\sin x)/x$.   A table of this function has been published,[11] but the calculation is more convenient with the aid of a set of

---

[11] J. Sherman, Z. Krist., **85**, 404 (1933).

strips tabulating $(\sin sr)/sr$ where each strip runs through a range of s values at intervals of 0.2 and successive strips cover a range of r values at intervals of 0.01. The calculation based on equation (6) consists in choosing the appropriate strips and summing at each s value the tabulated values each multiplied by its proper coefficient.

The availability of calculating aids for summing simple harmonic terms without the damping factor has led to a consideration of the function obtained by multiplying equation (6) through by s:

$$I' = \sum\sum' Z_i Z_j \frac{1}{r_{ij}} \sin sr_{ij} \tag{7}$$

This equation applied to carbon tetrachloride is plotted in figure 9 (Curve II). There is no general decrease of amplitude at larger scattering angles; but the positions of the peaks differ from those in Curve I by less than the plotting error except at low s values, where the comparison with the photographs is unreliable anyway. The interatomic distances obtained matching s values from the curves with observed s_0 values are the same for both curves. Since Curve II also shows the correct qualitative order of intensity at the fifth, seventh, and tenth peaks, such qualitative comparisons can no doubt be used in choosing among molecular models as described for the $(\sin x)/x$ type of function. The structural results for either type of function depend for their validity on comparison with the results of other experimental methods applied to the same compound.

B.   RADIAL DISTRIBUTION FUNCTION

The procedure described above for interpreting diffraction photographs involves the assumption of possible models for the molecule and the testing of them by intensity calculations. The radial distribution function, on the other hand, provides information about the molecule without any preliminary assumption. The function is calculated on the basis of the observed relation between the intensity and the angle of electron scattering. Several forms of the function have been used, but only one of them will be described here.

The radial distribution function in its simplest form is written as follows:

$$D(r) = \sum C_k (\sin s_k r)/s_k r \tag{8}$$

$D(r)$ represents the product of the scattering powers located in volume elements separated by the vector r. C_k depends on the observed intensity at the point s_k. The function in this form can be obtained by applying the

Fourier conversion to the theoretical intensity expression in which the distribution of charge responsible for scattering the electrons is treated as a continuous function and not divided into discrete atoms. In this case, the factor C_k is equal to $s^6 I(s)$, and the summation is an integral from zero to infinity over the variable s. The practical use of the distribution function under these conditions is impossible, however, because of the difficulty in obtaining absolute values for the intensity of scattering over a wide range of s values. Since the intensities are observed visually and, therefore, do not represent the actual intensity of scattered electrons correctly for the reasons described in the preceding section, their use in equation (8) introduces an empirical factor which requires that the distribution function depend for its validity on tests with materials of known structure. The simplest procedure is to make visual estimates of the relative intensities for

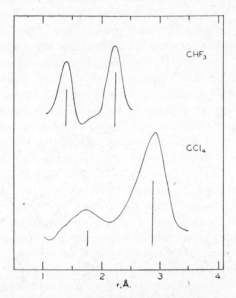

Fig. 11.—Radial distribution curves for fluoroform and carbon tetrachloride. The expected relative intensities and positions of the peaks are shown by the vertical lines.

each of the maxima appearing in the diffraction photographs and, with the s values locating these maxima, to use the summation of a finite number of terms represented in equation (8) in place of the integral.

An illustration of this method for carbon tetrachloride is shown in figure 11, in which the coefficients, C_k, are set equal to the estimated relative intensities, I_k given in table I. It will be noted that terms are included for the visually observed minima with negative coefficients; the resulting curve shows two peaks in the range from 1.0 to 3.5 Å., corresponding to the C—Cl and Cl—Cl distances. It is generally true that $D(r)$ is large when vector r is equal in length to the distance between a pair of atomic nuclei, because these distances are associated with the greatest scattering power. In the case of carbon tetrachloride, the agreement between the position of the peak in the radial distribution function and the values for the interatomic distances given by the use of theoretical intensity curves (as shown by the vertical lines at 1.76 and 2.87 Å.) is very good. When the number of terms used is small, however, spurious peaks often appear at positions not corresponding to actual interatomic distances, and the position of the true peaks may also be somewhat shifted. When the number of maxima in the photographs is small, it is accordingly useful to sketch a "visual" curve representing the appearance of the photograph with the positions of the maxima and minima determined by their observed s values and the relative heights representing their estimated intensities as shown for fluoroform in figure 10. The ordinates of this curve are read at intervals of 0.4 or less, and in this way the number of terms in the summation of equation (8) for a given range of s values is increased, and the summation more nearly approximates to an integral. The prominence of spurious peaks in the distribution function is reduced and the resolution of close-lying distances is improved, although at the expense of increased labor since the summation may now include from 50 to 100 terms. The distribution function for fluoroform in figure 11 was obtained in this way. The two vertical lines here represent by their lengths the relative scattering powers associated with the CF term at 1.35 Å. and the FF term at 2.20 Å. A useful modification of the coefficient, C_k, has been proposed in which the visually estimated intensity, I_k, is multiplied by $s^2 \exp(-as^2)$, with the effect of increasing the relative importance of the middle part of the observed pattern where the measurements of the s_0 values are more precise. Coefficient a in the exponential is adjusted to make the total coefficient of the last term equal to one-tenth that of the first term.

The usefulness of the radial distribution function lies in the information which it affords about the structure of the molecule without requiring any supplementary knowledge. It is limited by its failure to distinguish between interatomic separations having nearly the same value, and also by the difficulty of allowing suitably for the lesser reliability of poorly defined maxima in the photographs; nevertheless, it helps to exclude whole ranges of structural parameter values in considering molecular models for theoretical intensity calculations. This is especially useful for molecules having too many parameters to be determined only by the use of intensity curves; and without the distribution function the reliability of the final results reported would, in many cases, be much less.

An interesting development by Debye[12] and Hassel[13] provides an experimental method of compensating for the rapid decrease of intensity of scattered electrons with increasing angle. A brass sector is mounted just in front of the photographic plate and rotated at a speed of 600 r. p. m. or more about a center lying on the electron beam. The sector is cut so that the opening at any radius is proportional to any desired function of s. In the work of Hassel and his collaborators, the sector opening is made proportional to s^2, which has the effect of multiplying the scattering expression of equation (2) by a factor, s^2. The new function shows real maxima and minima which can be recorded and measured on a microphotometer; and Hassel has used these data in the calculation of radial distribution functions for a number of substances.

The use of rotating sectors offers the possibility of making quantitative objective measurements on the intensity of scattering of electrons by gases because the scattering at larger angles can be increased in a known way which will bring the intensity at all angles within the range of the photographic emulsion. For the determination of internuclear distances in simple molecules composed of one kind of atom, the sector opening could be made proportional to $1/f^2$, and the recorded electron intensities then would actually be equal to a summation of $(\sin sr)/sr$ terms with constant coefficients. For molecules containing different elements, some kind of average atomic scattering factor could be used for f so that the coefficients of the damped sine terms would not change very rapidly with increasing s. These possibilities have not yet been sufficiently explored and tested, but rotating sectors may in the future come into general usage in the diffraction study of the molecular structures of gases.

3. Recommended Procedure in Structure Determination

After the photographs have been taken, the ring diameters are measured and the relative intensities estimated. The first step in interpreting the pattern is the calculation of the radial distribution function. While the number of reliable values for interatomic distances afforded by this curve is usually not great enough to fix the structure, it will often fix two or three of the distances associated with the strongest terms in the intensity function and thereby limit the range of parameter values to be included in the molecular models for intensity curves. It is never really satisfactory to

[12] P. Debye, *Physik. Z.*, **40**, 66, 404 (1939).
[13] O. Hassel and T. Taarland, *Tids. Kjemi Bergvesen*, **20**, 167 (1940).   C. Finbak, O. Hassel, and B. Ottar, *Arch. Math. Naturvidenskab*, **44**, No. 13, 1 (1941).   C. Finbak and O. Hassel, *ibid.*, **45**, No. 3, 1 (1941).

base the structure determination even of simple molecules on the radial distribution function alone.

The next step is the choice of models on which to base the intensity calculations. Ordinarily, the general structure of the compound (*i. e.*, the order of attachment of the atoms) may be assumed from the structural formula based on the chemical properties. In a saturated compound of known composition, for example, the possible number of structural arrangements which provide each kind of atom with the correct number of closest neighbors is never large, at least in compounds which are not too complex for treatment by diffraction methods. It is necessary, of course, that the specimen photographed consist of a single isomer if detailed structural information is to be obtained. The principal problem in the choice of models is

TABLE II

ATOMIC RADII FOR ELEMENTS IN ORGANIC COMPOUNDS[a]

Element	Atomic radius, Å.	Element	Atomic radius, Å.
Hydrogen	0.32	Silicon	1.17
Carbon	0.77 (single)	Phosphorus	1.10
	0.67 (double)	Sulfur	1.04
	0.60 (triple)	Chlorine	0.99
Nitrogen	0.70 (single)	Germanium	1.22
	0.61 (double)	Arsenic	1.21
	0.55 (triple)	Selenium	1.17
Oxygen	0.66 (single)	Bromine	1.14
	0.56 (double)	Antimony	1.41
	0.51 (triple)	Tellurium	1.37
Fluorine	0.64	Iodine	1.33

[a] L. Pauling, *Nature of Chemical Bond.* Cornell Univ. Press, Ithaca, 1940, p. 164.

deciding on the range of interatomic distances to use. In the case of bonded atom pairs, the problem is simplified by the results of previous investigations. In compounds involving single bonds between carbon atoms, the distances observed for these bonds have never been greater than 1.55 Å. nor smaller than 1.45 Å., even in conjugated systems. The first trial models will accordingly use carbon-carbon single-bond distances in this range, while later models may involve other values in a test of the changes required to cause disagreement between the curves and photographs. In the same way, the distances first tested for carbon-carbon double bonds will lie near 1.34 Å., for carbon-carbon triple bonds near 1.20 Å., and for bonds in aromatic rings near 1.40 Å. This information for carbon and other nonmetallic elements is summarized in table II. The sum of these radii for the pair of elements in question is a value for the bond distance lying near all previously observed values, and is therefore a value to be tested in intensity calculations. Small deviations from the radius sums are often observed, but deviations as large as 30% would certainly throw the observations under suspicion.

A corresponding guide for plausible nonbonded distances can be given only in terms of the angles between the bonded distances. On a symmetrically substituted atom (in Table II) four bonds will form angles at 109° 28', and on unsymmetrically substituted atoms the angle values will usually not differ from 110° by more than a few degrees. The smallest angle observed is larger than 100° (except for 60° in cyclopropane and about 90° in cyclobutane derivatives). On an unsaturated atom three bonds are coplanar with angles ranging from 110° to 130°; in aromatic rings the angles are near 120° with the bonds external to the ring also occurring at angles near 120°. Two bonds (two double or a single and a triple) on an atom lie at 180°. For the distance between a pair of atoms separated by two or more atoms, the possibility of rotation or wide oscillations about the intervening bonds must always be considered. This statement of characteristic previous results ought not to limit the range of values tested, except that, in the case of complicated molecules involving too many structural parameters for independent determination, some may be assumed from previous results on similar compounds. In any event, the values indicated should be included among those tested.

After the calculation of several intensity curves, a choice is made by the qualitative comparison between curves and photographs as outlined in the preceding section (pages 636–642). The calculation of additional curves will then be made as required. It should be noted that two models differing only by a constant ratio between all of their corresponding atomic separations will give curves showing identical qualitative features and differing in their scales by the same constant ratio; one curve affords a complete test of all models having the same relative distances. On the curves which are good qualitatively, the positions of the maxima and minima are read (in s units) and tabulated for comparison with the s_0 values computed from the diameters measured on the photographs. The s/s_0 ratios are then averaged (with due allowance for their relative reliability), and the average ratio applied to the distances assumed in the model gives experimental values for the distances.

IV. ACCURACY OF RESULTS AND LIMITATIONS OF THE METHOD

The accuracy of the results of the visual method is affected first by the precision of the s_0 values for the observed rings. The s_0 function depends on the electron wave length, the camera distance from scatterer to plate, and the ring diameters. The wave length is fixed by the accelerating potential;

and this can be readily controlled so the uncertainty in the wave length due to fluctuating voltage is as little as 0.2%. The actual value of the wave length as determined by calibration with gold-foil pictures is reliable to about 0.3% or the limiting precision of the line-spacing measurements in the photographs of gold. The camera distance of 10 to 30 centimeters can be measured to about 0.2% with the proper camera design. The ring diameters measured visually with pointers on a comparator mounting are reproducible with about 0.5% maximum deviation for a single observer on sharp, well-defined rings. For different observers the average value of diameter measurements on the same ring may differ by 0.5%. The probable error of the s_0 values in favorable cases is less than 1%; for rings which are not clearly marked in the pattern the variations in the diameter values may amount to several per cent, and such values would not be included in averaging the s/s_0 ratios.

The s values taken from the maxima and minima in a calculated curve may be determined with very high precision by the use of small intervals in the calculation; for a molecule of one parameter (such as a diatomic molecule or the CX_4 regular tetrahedron), the uncertainty in s values can conveniently be kept to a fraction of 1%. The most questionable step in the visual method is the correlation of the calculated curves with the visual appearance of the photograph. By the nature of the procedure it is impossible to make a direct objective test of the reliability of the correlation no matter how satisfying the qualitative agreement between the two patterns may be. A test of the method is afforded, however, by comparing the results of the electron diffraction treatment and of other experimental investigations on the same compounds. For the diatomic molecules, Cl_2, Br_2, I_2, and ICl, the deviations of the electron diffraction values from the more reliable spectroscopic results are $+1.1$, $+0.4$, -0.4, and -0.6%, respectively. The electron diffraction value for C—Cl in CCl_4 is 1.76 Å.; the x-ray value[14] is 1.75 Å.—a difference equal to about one-half the experimental error of either method.

The over-all uncertainty in the experimental result is about 1% in the best cases. This figure is an estimated probable error. The formula for probable error as a function of the deviations from the mean in a series of repeated measurements is not applicable here as a measure of the reliability of the experimental results. It is true that several individual values for the interatomic distance are provided by the various rings on a single photograph; and, while the coherence of these values is one of the criteria for acceptability of a particular model, the probable error of the mean value does not show the effect of systematic subjective errors in measuring the

---

[14] C. Degard, J. Pierard, and W. van der Grinten, *Nature*, **136**, 142 (1935).

plates. The mean s/s_0 ratios determined by different observers often deviate by more than the probable error of the mean of the values from a single observer; and unless a large number of observers always measure each set of plates the experimental uncertainty is larger than the probable error of the mean s/s_0 ratio.

With two or more parameters to be determined, their uncertainties are not uniform but may be very large for some of the parameters and quite small for others. The intensity expression is a sum of terms with various coefficients; and, for a term whose coefficient is small compared with the other coefficients, the corresponding interatomic distance may be changed over a considerable range without producing a detectable effect in the calculated curve. An extreme example is the case of chloroform: the H—Cl and H—C coefficients are small enough compared with those for the Cl—Cl and C—Cl terms that the hydrogen atom cannot be located at all from the diffraction data. The calculated curves are also insensitive to changes in bond angles in the model when the bond angles are near 180° because the distance between the nonbonded atoms changes with the cosine of the bond angle. Since the angles or distance ratios fixing the geometry of the model are determined by comparing the qualitative features of several calculated curves with the photographs, a definite qualitative disagreement must appear in a curve if its parameter values are not to be included in the range reported. In particular, the observed agreement between the photographs and one curve does not fix the parameter in question unless other possible values have been definitely excluded. The exclusion of a curve is questionable unless there is a considerable discrepancy in the relative heights of the peaks in the curve and in the photographs, since it is impossible to make a quantitative intensity correlation between the simplified scattering function and the visually observed peaks.

These factors mean that many molecular structures can be only partially determined by electron diffraction. These include molecules combining atoms of high atomic number with those of low atomic number or containing a number of identical interatomic distances. An illustration of the latter difficulty is found in the paraffin hydrocarbons. In hexane, for example, the five distances equal to the C_1—C_2 separation and the four equal to the C_1—C_3 separation predominate in the scattering function; and the longer distances in the three weaker terms can be only roughly determined. The longer distances are the only ones which change with rotation around the bonds, and therefore it is difficult, if not impossible, to distinguish among various configurations of the hexane molecule. The distinction between hexane and heptane or between the normal and the branched isomers is also difficult because the differences occur in the weak terms in the scattering function. In molecules containing substituted phenyl groups, it may happen that the orientation of the benzene rings is indeterminate because of the large number of fixed distances which do not depend on the orientation of the rings.   In all such cases as those mentioned here, some of the longer distances will remain more or less indeterminate while the shorter distances may be reported with the usual accuracy.

In molecules too complicated for complete determination by electron diffraction, it is often useful to assume the size and shape of certain groups (such as the size and coplanarity of aromatic rings or the bond angles and distances in a CCl_3 group) and to determine by diffraction the remaining parameters.   In such a case, it should be borne in mind that the validity of the conclusions depends not only on the diffraction data but also on the original assumptions.   A small change in the assumed parameters may have a considerable effect on the diffraction results.

The occurrence of impurities in the diffraction specimen is another possible source of uncertainty in the results.   No serious error is caused as long as the relative scattering power of the impurity is only a few per cent of that of the principal material in the gas mixture which reaches the electron beam.   Considerable amounts of an impurity of low relative volatility or of low scattering power can be tolerated;   but if the impurity contains heavier atoms than the desired material its concentration ought not to exceed a fraction of one per cent.   The effect of a suspected impurity can always be tested by combining its electron scattering curve with that of the substance under test in the proportion of their molecular concentrations.

Electron diffraction studies have been made of more than 300 organic molecules, and the results are available on about 275.   The number of compounds classified according to the number of carbon atoms per molecule is as follows: one carbon—42;   two carbons—94;   three carbons—24; four carbons—41;   five carbons—17;   six carbons, aliphatic—22;   six carbons, aromatic—31;   twelve carbons—4.   The majority of these compounds are hydrocarbons and halogen derivatives.   The structural results obtained through June, 1943, have been tabulated.[6, 15, 16]   The diffraction and spectroscopic results for the simpler hydrocarbons have been discussed in *Annual Reports of the Chemical Society*.[17]

One of the interesting structural problems studied by electron diffraction is presented by the organic fluorides.   Early measurements showed that the CF bond length in monofluorides is 0.05 or 0.06 Å. longer than in polyfluorides (having two or more fluorine atoms on the same carbon atom). This difference is paralleled by a very great increase in the stability of the

[15] L. R. Maxwell, *J. Optical Soc. Am.*, **30**, 374 (1940).

[16] G. W. Wheland, *The Theory of Resonance*.   Wiley, New York, 1944, Appendix. p. 286.

[17] L. O. Brockway, *Ann. Repts. Chem. Soc. (London)*, **34**, 196 (1937).

polyfluorides toward hydrolysis in comparison with the monofluorides.[18] Subsequent work has indicated that the fluorine atoms influence not only each other but other atoms attached to the carbon. For example, the chlorine atom in CF_3Cl is held closer to the carbon and is removed with much more difficulty than the chlorine atom in CH_3Cl. Also, in polyfluoroethanes, the bond between the carbon atoms is shorter and much more resistant to rupture in oxidizing reactions than in the unsubstituted ethane. In trifluoroacetic acid, the carbon bond is only 1.48 Å., whereas it is 1.54 Å. in acetic acid itself. The possibility of making a quantitative correlation between bond distance and chemical reactivity in standard reactions afforded by the results of diffraction experiments is one of the most important applications of the method.

A recent study[19] of the monomeric and dimeric forms of formic and acetic acid shows that, in the carboxyl group, the carbon atom holds the two oxygen atoms with unequal bonds in both the unassociated and associated forms. The longer C—O bond is shortened by about 0.06 Å. on the formation of the dimer, but a difference of about 0.10 Å. between the two C—O bonds persists. The observed nonequivalence of the two C—O bonds in the dimer is evidence for the nonequivalence of the two OH linkages. Other recent investigations have supported the previously observed constancy of the single C—C bond length at or near 1.54 Å., of the double C—C bond at 1.34 Å., of the triple C—C bond at 1.20 Å.; the observed small interaction of two adjacent single bonds, of adjacent single and double bonds; and the large interaction of adjacent single and triple bonds.

---

[18] A. L. Henne, in H. Gilman, *Organic Chemistry*. Wiley, New York, 1943, p. 956.
[19] J. Karle and L. O. Brockway, *J. Am. Chem. Soc.*, **66,** 574 (1944).

General References

Review Articles on Gases

Beach, J. Y., *Pub. Am. Assoc. Adv. Sci.*, No. 7 (1939).
Brockway, L. O., *Rev. Modern Phys.*, **8,** 231–266 (1936).
Brockway, L. O., *Ann. Repts. Chem. Soc.* (*London*), **34,** 196–214 (1937).
Maxwell, L. R., *J. Optical Soc. Am.*, **30,** 374–395 (1940).

*Books Including Theoretical and Experimental Treatment
of Both Gases and Solids*

Mark, H., and Wierl, R., *Die experimentellen und theoretischen Grundlagen der Elektronenbeugung*. Vol. XXI, No. 1, Ser. B, of *Fortschritte der Chemie, Physik und physikalischen Chemie*. Borntraeger, Berlin, 1931, pp. 10–25 and 70–80.

Hengstenberg, J., and Wolf, K., *Elektronenstrahlen und ihre Wechselwirkung mit der Materie.* Vol. VI, Part 1A, of *Hand- und Jahrbuch der chemischen Physik,* Akadem. Verlagsgesellschaft, Leipzig, 1935, pp. 80–87 and 122–129.

Thomson, G. P., and Cochrane, W., *Theory and Practice of Electron Diffraction.* Macmillan, London, 1939, pp. 246–262.

CHAPTER XVI

REFRACTOMETRY

N. BAUER, *University of New Hampshire*, AND K. FAJANS,*

University of Michigan

* Section I, 7.

I. GENERAL

1. Refractive Index

When light passes from one medium, m, into another medium, M, it undergoes a change in velocity ($v_m \rightarrow v_M$), and unless the beam is perpendicular to the boundary between m and M, also in direction. The change in direction is measured in terms of the angle of incidence, i_m, and the angle of refraction, r_M, with the normal (N–N') to the boundary, as shown in figure 1. Snell's Law of Refraction states that the ratio:

$$n' = \sin i_m / \sin r_M \qquad (1)$$

is a constant, where n' is the refractive index of M relative to medium m. According to the wave theory of light, n' is identical with the ratio v_m/v_M. It has become the practice to refer the index of refraction to air, *i. e.*, we define the refractive index n of a single isotropic medium by the ratios:

$$n = \frac{v_{\text{air}}}{v_M} = \frac{\sin i_{\text{air}}}{\sin r_M} \qquad (2)$$

Thus n is a dimensionless constant whose value for light of a given wave length is determined by the character and state of substance M and of the

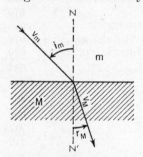

reference medium, air. If measurements of n are to be strictly comparable, it is evidently necessary to specify the state of the reference medium, as well as to control other variables which affect the velocity of light in the sample itself. The values of n ordinarily given in the literature refer to air at the temperature and pressure of the measurement or (p. 701) to air at 20° C. The correction to air at S. T. P. (0° C., 760 mm., dry) is usually of the order of magnitude of 1×10^{-5} and is for most purposes negligible. An error in n of 4×10^{-5} could arise in the comparison of two values

Fig. 1.—Refraction of a light ray.

measured under extreme natural conditions. For a discussion of the reduction to S. T. P., see Tilton.[1]

The refraction of gases is usually referred to vacuum as the reference medium. This *absolute index of refraction*, $\mathbf{n}_{\text{vac.}}$, is therefore characteristic of a single substance. According to Maxwell's theory, $(\mathbf{n}_{\text{vac.}\,\infty})^2 = \epsilon\mu$, where ϵ is the dielectric constant, μ is the magnetic permeability of the substance, and ∞ refers to light of infinitely long wave length; μ differs from 1 by less than 10^{-5} for diamagnetic substances, which applies to practically all organic compounds, except free radicals. Actually, the

---

[1] L. W. Tilton, *J. Research Natl. Bur. Standards*, **14**, 393 (1935).

difference between $n_{vac.}$ and n is very small (about 0.03%). It follows from equation (2) and the definition of $n_{vac.}$ that:

$$n_{vac.} = (n_{vac.} \text{ of air})n \tag{3}$$

For ordinary laboratory conditions, using yellow light:

$$n_{vac.} = 1.00027n \tag{4}$$

The n values of all crystals except those in the cubic system depend on the direction of transmission and vibration of the light relative to the crystal axes. In general, a single incident light ray will emerge from the crystal as two polarized rays, each corresponding to a different velocity (index) in the crystal, unless the incident ray happens to coincide in direction with one of the optic axes of the crystals. In the latter case, a single ray emerges. The indices along the optic axes and perpendicular to these axes are characteristic of the crystal.[2, 3] The tetragonal, hexagonal, and rhombohedral crystal systems are uniaxial, $i.\ e.$, have a single optic axis and two characteristic indices, n_ω and n_ϵ. The rhombic, monoclinic, and triclinic crystals are biaxial, and have the characteristic indices n_α, n_β, n_γ.[2, 3] See chapters XI, page 435, and XII, page 531. Therefore in making measurements on solids, it is usually necessary to control the orientation of the specimen. For precautions in preparing and selecting crystals which are homogeneous, see chapter III (page 97). Measurements on specimens which contain occlusions of air or of mother liquor are obviously of little use.

The values of n for organic liquids range from about 1.30 to 1.80, those for organic solids from about 1.3 to 2.5.

The refractive index is of value for the organic chemist in three respects. First, it serves as a means of identification of a substance, as a criterion of its purity, and as a means for the quantitative analysis of its solutions. The usefulness of the refractive index for these purposes is due to the high accuracy and ease with which it is determined. The precision Abbé refractometer can give n with six significant numbers, while, by interferometric methods, the difference in n between two liquids can be determined with an error only in the eighth decimal place. Second, knowledge of the refractive index is necessary for the evaluation of dipole moments of substances if the dielectric constant is measured at one temperature only (see Vol. II, Chapter XX). Third, certain functions of n, $viz.$, the molar refraction, R, are characteristic of a given molecule and indicative of its structure (see page 672).

[2] E. M. Chamot and C. W. Mason, *Handbook of Chemical Microscopy.* 2nd ed., Vol. I, Wiley, New York, 1938, p. 290.

[3] T. R. P. Gibb, *Optical Methods of Chemical Analysis.* McGraw-Hill, New York, 1942.

2. Dependence of Refractive Index on Temperature and Pressure

For a wide variety of organic liquids,[4] an increase in temperature of 1° C. causes a decrease in n of 3.5×10^{-4} to 5.5×10^{-4}. But some liquids, especially at temperatures near the boiling point, have negative temperature coefficients up to 7×10^{-4}. Thus, the commonly used average value of $dn/dt = -4.5 \times 10^{-4}$ may not always be sufficiently accurate. The effect of temperature on n is usually a few per cent greater at the violet end of the spectrum than at the red end. For solids, the values of dn/dt are much less uniform from substance to substance, but as a rule are considerably smaller than for liquids and may be positive or negative. A positive value of dn/dt (relative) may be due either to a positive $d\mathbf{n}/dt$ (absolute) or to the effect of the (negative) temperature coefficient $(d\mathbf{n}_a/dt)$ of the reference medium (air), since, by differentiating equation (3) and putting $\mathbf{n}_a \approx 1$, we have $dn/dt \approx d\mathbf{n}/dt - \mathbf{n}\, d\mathbf{n}_a/dt$. For many glasses, an increase in temperature causes a small but not negligible increase in n; e. g., $dn/dt = +1.8 \times 10^{-6}$ per degree for one of the Pulfrich refractometer prisms at room temperature. Usually dn/dt increases slightly with increasing t (roughly, 0.1% per degree C. for solids, 1% per degree C. for liquids).

Thus it is necessary to specify the temperature, $t;$ this is done by writing $t°$ C. as a superscript, e. g., n^{25}. Most data on organic compounds are given for 15°, 18°, or 20° C. Ward and Kurtz[5] recommend the use of 20° C. as the standard temperature for hydrocarbons. However, in conformity with other physicochemical data, measurements at 25° are becoming increasingly desirable. Even for the roughest measurements for identification purposes, where the accuracy is about ± 0.002 unit of n, the temperature of liquids should be controlled to within about 3°. For an accuracy in n of $\pm 1 \times 10^{-4}$, which is easily attained in rapid routine measurements, the temperature of the sample should be controlled to about $\pm 0.2°$, and corresponding closer for higher accuracy.

For 5th decimal accuracy, or for measurements at extreme temperatures, it is necessary to specify the temperature and pressure of the reference medium (air) surrounding the refractometer (see pages 654 and 700-701).

For *temperature control* to a few tenths of a degree, one can use tap water which is first passed through an electrically heated or a flame-heated coil, then through the refractometer jacket. Regulation is achieved by changing the rate of flow at the faucet or the rate of heating. The use of thermostats and pumps allows a temperature regulation to within a few thousandths of a degree if the refractometer itself is properly insulated. For in-

[4] From the data of J. Timmermans, *J. chim. phys.*, **29**, 529 (1932); **31**, 85 (1934). For empirical rules governing hydrocarbons, see M. R. Lipkin and S. S. Kurtz, Jr., *Ind. Eng. Chem., Anal. Ed.*, **13**, 291 (1941).

[5] A. L. Ward and S. S. Kurtz, Jr., *Ind. Eng. Chem., Anal. Ed.*, **10**, 559 (1938).

formation concerning thermostats, see Daniels, Mathews, and Williams,[6] Ferguson et al.,[7] and chapter X. Various types of suitable pumps are available commercially.[8] For pumps which can be built in the laboratory, see Reilly and Rae.[9]

By an increase in pressure of one atmosphere, the refractive index of liquids, according to Tilton,[1] is increased by about 3×10^{-5}. Thus, the normal fluctuations of barometric pressure produce a negligible change in $n_{liq.}$. The effect on solids should be even smaller.

Various functions of refractive index and density, such as the molar and specific refractions (page 673) are intended to be independent of temperature and pressure; the empirical formula of Eykmann (page 679) is the most successful in this respect.

3. Dependence of Refractive Index on Wave Length

The refractive index depends strongly on the wave length of light used. For instance, n^{20} of benzene is 1.49759 when measured with red light of $\lambda = 6563$ Å., but 1.52487 with violet light of 4341 Å. Because of this optical dispersion, values of n are comparable only when they refer to the same λ. The kind of light used should be designated by a subscript, as in n_D or n_{5893}. When this is lacking, it may be assumed that the value refers to the sodium D line (5893 Å.). This, it should be recalled, actually consists of two lines, D_1 (5890 Å.) and D_2 (5896 Å.), of nearly equal intensity. The difference between n_{D_1} and n_{D_2} can be appreciable for substances of high dispersion; for example, $n_{D_1} - n_{D_2} = 2 \times 10^{-5}$ for benzene. For the effect of the doublet on the critical boundary in the Pulfrich refractometer, see Guild.[10] With colored materials or in order to determine the optical dispersion, n is measured at other wave lengths, in the past most frequently with the hydrogen lines, H_α (C), H_β (F), and H_γ (G'). The optical dispersion is expressed as $n_{\lambda_1} - n_{\lambda_2}$ or as some simple function of it. Other expressions used are the "nu value," $N = (n_D - 1)/(n_F - n_C)$, and the specific dispersion, $(n_F - n_C)/d$.[11, 12] With the intense and convenient

[6] F. Daniels, J. H. Mathews, and J. W. Williams, *Experimental Physical Chemistry*. 3rd ed., McGraw-Hill, New York, 1941, p. 418.

[7] A. L. Ferguson, K. van Vente, and R. Hitchens, *Ind. Eng. Chem., Anal. Ed.*, **4**, 218 (1932).

[8] *American Instrument Co.*, Silver Spring, Md. *Eastern Engineering Co.*, New Haven, Conn.

[9] J. Reilly and W. N. Rae, *Physico-chemical Methods*. 3rd ed., Vol. I, Van Nostrand, New York, 1939, p. 239.

[10] J. Guild, *Proc. Phys. Soc. London*, **30**, 157 (1917–1918).

[11] W. Bielenberg, *Z. angew. Chem.*, **42**, 972 (1929).

[12] A. V. Grosse and R. C. Wackher, *Ind. Eng. Chem., Anal. Ed.*, **11**, 614 (1939). A. L. Ward and W. H. Fulweiler, *ibid.*, **6**, 396 (1934). A. L. Ward and S. S. Kurtz, Jr., *ibid.*, **10**, 559 (1938).

light sources now available (page 683), the optical dispersion is readily measured and frequently used. It shows greater differences among closely related compounds than n itself, and has, for instance, been used to determine the concentration of aromatic constituents in hydrocarbon oils.[12]

DISPERSION FORMULAS

If the relation between n_λ and λ is known,[13] the data, often obtained with helium, mercury, or cadmium lines, can be compared with data at other wave lengths such as those of the sodium or hydrogen spectrum.

In a spectral region which is far from an absorption band, n decreases gradually as λ increases, $i.$ $e.$, we have "normal dispersion." However, within or near a region of absorption, n may pass through a sharp maximum, then, at longer wave lengths, through a sharp minimum. Thus, between the minimum and the maximum there is a region of "anomalous dispersion" in which n will $increase$ with increasing λ. In some cases,[14, 15] depending on the nature of the absorption band,[13] the n vs. λ curve shows only a flat minimum and maximum, or merely an inflection, in the region of absorption. When the absorption bands are relatively weak, there may be no change detectable in the slope of the n vs. λ curve, using ordinary accuracy, even within the bands.[14-16] This is the case in the near ultraviolet with many colorless organic liquids for which the principal electronic absorption bands are in the far ultraviolet. Intensely colored substances can be expected to show anomalous dispersion in the visible region. Erythrosin[17] shows $n_{min.} = 1.330$ at $\lambda = 4900$ Å. and $n_{max.} = 1.380$ at $\lambda = 5500$ Å.; the absorption maximum comes at $\lambda = 5150$ Å.

In the region of normal dispersion, the $Cauchy$ $formula$, although without theoretical basis, is good enough for rough interpolation:

$$n = A + B/\lambda^2 + C/\lambda^4 \tag{5}$$

where A, B, and C are empirical constants. It is often used in the simplified form:

$$n = A + B/\lambda^2 \tag{6}$$

The constants, A and B, are evaluated from data (n_1, n_2) at two wave lengths, λ_1 and λ_2:

[13] F. Eisenlohr, $Spektrochemie$ der $organischen$ $Verbindungen$, Enke, Stuttgart, 1912. See also S. S. Kurtz, Jr., and A. L. Ward, $J.$ $Franklin$ $Inst.$, **224**, 583, 697 (1937), and K. F. Herzfeld and K. L. Wolf in $Handbuch$ der $Physik$, Vol. XX, Springer, Berlin, 1928, p. 480.

[14] T. M. Lowry and C. B. Allsopp, $Proc.$ $Roy.$ $Soc.$ $London$, **A163** 359 (1937).

[15] K. Feussner, $Z.$ $Physik$, **45**, 689 (1927).

[16] H. Voellmy, $Z.$ $physik.$ $Chem.$, **127**, 305 (1927).

[17] B. J. v. d. Plaats, $Ann.$ $Physik$, **47**, 429 (1915).

$$A = (n_1\lambda_1^2 - n_2\lambda_2^2)/(\lambda_1^2 - \lambda_2^2) \tag{7}$$

$$B = (n_1 - A)\lambda_1^2 \tag{8}$$

According to equation (6), the plot of n against $1/\lambda^2$ is a straight line, convenient for graphical interpolation.

The *Hartman interpolation formula:*

$$n - A = B/(\lambda - C)^D \tag{9}$$

also empirical, has similar limitations. The constants, A, B, C, and D, are evaluated from experimental data. In connection with the Hartman formula, tables have been published[18] which facilitate the computation of indices for the C, D, F, and G' lines from observations made on three or more lines of the mercury arc.

In order to obtain an approximate value of the difference, $n_{\lambda_1} - n_{\lambda_2}$, for any pair of λ's (in Å.) from measurements of the difference, $n_F - n_C$, one can use expressions (10) and (11), based on the Cauchy formula:

$$(n_{\lambda_1} - n_{\lambda_2})/(n_F - n_C) \approx (1/\lambda_1^2 - 1/\lambda_2^2)/(1/\lambda_F^2 - 1/\lambda_C^2) \tag{10}$$

$$(n_{\lambda_1} - n_{\lambda_2}) \approx \left(\frac{1}{\lambda_1^2} - \frac{1}{\lambda_2^2}\right)\left(\frac{n_F - n_C}{1.9095}\right) \times 10^8 \tag{11}$$

For obtaining approximate absolute values of n_F and n_C from the difference, $n_F - n_C$ and n_D, the empirical rule of Waldmann[19] is useful:

$$(n_D - n_C)/(n_F - n_C) = K = 0.29 \tag{12}$$

This relation holds for a wide variety of organic compounds within about 10%; but with compounds of high dispersion, K is likely to show still greater deviations from the average (0.29).

Equations (6) and (9) are not reliable for extrapolation, *e. g.*, a value of n_C (red) calculated with equation (6) from data on the mercury spectrum (which extends only to the yellow) is likely to be too low. It is preferable to interpolate n_C from data on the helium spectrum, which contains an intense red line at a wave length greater than that of the hydrogen C line.

A more satisfactory expression for the normal dispersion not too close to absorption bands, originating in the classical electromagnetic theory (Drude) and confirmed by quantum theory, has the form:[13]

$$\phi = \frac{n_\lambda^2 - 1}{n_\lambda^2 + 2} = \sum \frac{C_i}{(v_0)_i^2 - v^2} \tag{13}$$

---

[18] F. Weidert, in W. Ewald, *Die optische Werkstatt.* Borntraeger, Berlin, 1930, pp. 215–273.

[19] H. Waldmann, *Helv. Chim. Acta,* **21**, 1053 (1938).

where C_i is a constant, $(\nu_0)_i$ is a "characteristic frequency" related to, but not identical with, the frequency of the maximum light absorption, and ν is the frequency ($\nu = c/\lambda$, where c = velocity of light) of the light used. Concerning an alternative form to the left-hand side of equation (13), see the discussion by Kurtz and Ward.[20] According to equation (13), there will be a term, $C_i/[(\nu_0)_i^2 - \nu^2]$, for each absorption band in the visible and invisible spectrum; but it is often found for colorless substances that only a single term is necessary to represent the change of n with ν in the visible region of the spectrum, even though the substance has more than one absorption band. This means that all but one of all the nearby absorption bands are weak—all nearby C_i values but one are small, or that only one band is near enough to the visible to contribute appreciably to the dispersion in this region—only one $(\nu_0)_i$ is close enough to ν. Even when several bands contribute to the dispersion, the application of equation (13) to interpolation in the visible and even to extrapolation to long wave lengths, is a fairly simple matter. For small values of ν^2, far from $(\nu_0)_i$, a plot of $1/\phi$ against ν^2 gives a curve approaching a straight line, no matter how many absorption maxima influence the dispersion.[21] Such a linear relation is obvious for the simplest case with only one term:

$$\frac{1}{\phi} = \frac{\nu_0^2}{C} - \frac{1}{C}\nu^2 \tag{14}$$

Departure from equation (14) may be expected in the region of absorption (*i. e.*, for $\nu \approx \nu_0$) due to the limitations[13] of equation (13).

Experience has shown that a plot of $1/\phi$ vs. ν^2 becomes linear in the visible region of the spectrum for practically all colorless compounds, even though it is certain that these compounds have more than one absorption band in the invisible spectrum. Figure 2, showing the data for liquid benzene obtained by Lowry and Allsopp,[22] gives a typical dispersion curve, using this "reciprocal plotting method" developed by Wulff.[21] The downward curvature at high frequencies is often observed to begin in the blue-violet region of the visible spectrum for colorless compounds of relatively large dispersion; this is to be expected from equation (13), when two or more terms having values of $(\nu_0)_i$ greater than ν influence the dispersion. An upward curvature occasionally observed at the red end of the spectrum indicates that absorption bands in the infrared region are sufficiently near and strong to contribute to the value of $1/\phi$ in the visible region. Interpolation in the

[20] S. S. Kurtz, Jr., and A. L. Ward, *J. Franklin Inst.*, **222**, 563 (1936); **224**, 583, 697 (1937).

[21] P. Wulff, *Z. physik. Chem.*, **B21**, 370 (1933).

[22] T. M. Lowry and C. B. Allsopp, *Proc. Roy. Soc. London.* **A133**, 26 (1931).

linear part of the plot is especially reliable.   Values of n_λ can be calculated from the corresponding $(1/\phi)_\lambda$ values by equation (15).

$$n_\lambda^2 = [(1/\phi)_\lambda + 2]/[(1/\phi)_\lambda - 1] \tag{15}$$

The reciprocal plotting method has been applied to the extrapolation of $(1/\phi)_\lambda$ values to infinite wave length.[21, 23]   In this way, the quantity $\mathbf{D} = R_D - R_\infty$ has been obtained from the molar refraction, R, and used as a measure of the molar dispersion.[23]   In evaluating the electronic polariz-

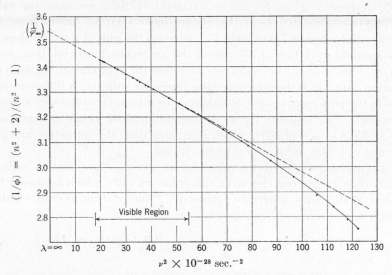

Fig. 2.—Reciprocal plotting method of interpolation and extrapolation of n_λ.
Dispersion of liquid benzene at 20° C. from data of Lowry and Allsop.[22]

ability for the calculation of dipole moments (Chapter XX, Volume II), R_∞ obtained by the above linear extrapolation from measurements in the visible does not include the influence of atomic polarization (absorption bands in the infrared).   Other methods of extrapolation, e. g., by the Cauchy formula, are likely to include appreciable contributions from atomic polarization, since the infrared absorption frequently influences the refractive index at the red end of the spectrum.

4.   Effect of Concentration on Refractive Index of Solutions

If the refractive index is to be used as a measure of concentration, or vice versa, the most reliable method is interpolation from an empirical calibration curve.   In certain cases there exists a linear relationship be-

[23] N. Bauer and K. Fajans, *J. Am. Chem. Soc.*, **64**, 3023 (1942).

tween these two quantities (see page 663), but more generally the data are represented by a curve, the shape of which is influenced by the way in which the concentration is expressed. Molarity, C, is more likely to give a nearly linear relationship than weight per cent, p. For example, the data of Koenig-Gressmann[24] on acetone (n_1) –carbon tetrachloride (n_2) solutions show only a slight departure from the straight line, $C_1 = k(\Delta n)$, where $\Delta n = n - n_2$; $k = 1000\ d_1/M_1(n_1 - n_2)$, d_1 = density, M_1 = molecular weight of pure acetone, over the whole range from $C_1 = 0$ to $C_1 = 13.54$ (100% acetone). Thus, for $\Delta n = -0.06481$ (47.46% acetone), the value of C_1 (8.68) calculated from the above linear relation differs from the experimental value (8.75) by only 1%, whereas the plot of p vs. Δn shows a corresponding deviation of 36% from the analogous linear relation, $p_1 = [100/(n_1 - n_2)](\Delta n)$. For solutions in which the components undergo association or in which the intermolecular forces are sufficiently different from those in the pure components, a maximum or minimum in the n vs. C curve may occur. For instance, for water containing 65.61 weight per cent acetone at 25° C., $n = 1.3634$, which is greater than the refractive index of pure water, 1.3326, or of pure acetone, 1.3563.

If it is necessary to predict a value of n for a given concentration without a calibration curve, one can often use equation (16), which is among the simplest of the many functions proposed[25-28] for relating refractive index, density, d, and composition of a mixture.

$$\frac{100(n - 1)}{d} = \frac{p_1(n_1 - 1)}{d_1} + \frac{(100 - p_1)(n_2 - 1)}{d_2} \tag{16}$$

The subscripts refer to the two components; p is weight per cent. Equation (16) is based on the assumption that the Gladstone–Dale specific refraction, $r = (n - 1)/d$, of a binary mixture is additively composed of the corresponding r values of the components. To solve (16) for n, an experimental value for the density, $d_{exp.}$, of the solution should be known. For the above-mentioned acetone–water solution, $d_{exp.} = 0.8809$ and, since $d_1 = 0.7862$ for acetone and $d_2 = 0.9977$ for water, one obtains from equation (16) $n_{calc.} = 1.3630$ which agrees well with $n_{exp.} = 1.3634$. It may be possible to estimate d with sufficient accuracy from equation (8) of chapter III (page 74) if the volume change due to mixing is negligible. However, the formation of the 65.61 weight per cent acetone solution is accompanied by a strong contraction, and the assumption of volume additivity would

[24] M. L. Koenig-Gressmann, *thesis*, University of Munich, 1938.

[25] C. Cheneveau, *Ann. chim. phys.*, **12**, 145, 289 (1907).

[26] K. Lichtenecker, *Physik. Z.*, **27**, 115 (1926).

[27] G. DeLattre, *J. chim. phys.*, **24**, 289 (1927).

[28] D. A. G. Bruggeman, *Physik. Z.*, **37**, 906 (1936).

give $d_{calc.}$ = 0.8479, which is considerably smaller than $d_{exp.}$; using $d_{calc.}$ one finds $n_{calc.}$ = 1.3494, which is very much lower than $n_{exp.}$. A relation based on additivity of the Lorentz–Lorenz refraction (see page 680) is often used instead of equation (16). Although the additivity of the Lorentz–Lorenz refraction for mixtures is not always as exact as that of other expressions for refraction, e. g., $n_{calc.}$ = 1.3645 for the above case of 65.61% acetone, using $d_{exp.}$ in the relation on page 680, its application has an advantage in that the deviations from additivity are often related in a simple way to the forces within and between the molecules.

5. Effect of Impurities. Precision Data. Standards

The following formula is useful in certain cases in estimating to a first approximation the degree of purification necessary for measurements of a given accuracy:

$$n - n_0 \approx 0.01 p_1 (n_1 - n_0) \qquad (17)$$

where n, n_0, and n_1 refer to the mixture, the pure substance, and the impurity, respectively. Equation (17) is based on equation (16) and on the further assumption that the densities of both components are equal to the density of the mixture; it applies best to solutions containing a small amount of solute having physical and chemical properties closely similar to those of the solvent, which is a situation frequently encountered in the final purification of liquids. Other kinds of impurities may have a much larger effect on n than is shown by equation (17). Volume per cent may be used instead of p_1 in equation (17) with about equal success.

One can, and should, estimate the accuracy with which it is justified to measure n for a substance having a probable content p_1 of impurity. For example, suppose that a benzene (n_0^{20} = 1.50100) sample is contaminated with 0.3% (p_1) thiophene (n_1^{20} = 1.52850). We calculate from equation (17) that $n - n_0 \approx 0.00008$. It is evidently not possible to obtain the n value of benzene to better than about 0.0001 from measurements on a sample which may contain up to 0.3% thiophene. The fact that refractive indices reliable to 0.0001 have been collected for a relatively small number of organic compounds is due mainly to insufficient purity.

The refractometric technique in itself should not be considered as an obstacle to obtaining exact data. For example, it does not require much more labor or skill to measure n_λ^t to ±0.00003 (precision Abbé refractometer) than it does to measure n_D with an accuracy of only ±0.002 (Fisher refractometer), once the appropriate apparatus has been set up. The relative ease of performing precision measurements is even more striking if differential methods are used. It is actually simpler to measure the difference, $n - n_0 = 0.0006$ to $\pm 5 \times 10^{-7}$ by the precise interferometric technique (page 724) than it is to measure this same difference to ± 0.0002 with the Abbé refractometer. However, improper use of the instruments

TABLE I

REFERENCE LIQUIDS

Liquid	$t°$ C.	n_D^t	$\frac{(-dn/dt)}{\times 10^5}$	Literature
Methanol	15	1.3307^a	39	(1)
Water	15	1.33339^b	07	(13)
	20	1.33299^b	09	
	25	1.33250^b	11	
	30	1.33194^b	12	
Acetone	15	1.3616		(2)
	20	1.3591	50	(3)
Acetic acid	15	1.3739	38	(1)
	25	1.3698		(4)
2,2,4-Trimethylpentane*	20	1.3915		(5)
	25	1.3890		(6), (7)
Methylcyclohexane*	15	1.4256	47	(8)
	20	1.4231		(6)
	25	1.4206		(6)
Chloroform	15	1.4486	59	(8)
Carbon tetrachloride	15	1.4631	55	(8)
	20	1.4603		(9)
	25	1.4576		(3)
Toluene*	15	1.4999	60	(8)
	25	1.4941		
Benzene	15	1.5044	63	(8)
	20	1.5012		(9)
	25	1.4981		(10), (11)
Chlorobenzene	15	1.5275	54	(8)
	20	1.5247		(9)
Dibromomethane	15	1.5446^a	55	(12)
Bromobenzene	15	1.5625	49	(8)
Bromoform	15	1.6005	57	(8)
Iodobenzene	15	1.6230^a	55	(12)
Carbon disulfide	15	1.6319	78	(2)
Diiodomethane	15	1.7443	64	(12)

* Available as reference standards from *National Bureau of Standards*, Washington, D. C.   See page 666.
  ^{a} Helium D$_3$ line. ^{b} Values relative to dry air at $t°$ C. and 760 mm. Hg pressure.

(1)   J. Timmermans and Mme. Hennaut-Roland, *J. chim. phys.*, **27**, 401 (1930).
(2)   J. Timmermans and F. Martin, *J. chim. phys.*, **25**, 411 (1928).
(3)   E. Pahlavorini, *Bull. soc. chim. Belg.*, **36**, 533 (1927).
(4)   N. A. Puschin and P. G. Matavulj, *Z. physik. Chem.*, **A161**, 341 (1932).
(5)   C. P. Smyth and W. N. Stoops, *J. Am. Chem. Soc.*, **50**, 1883 (1928).
(6)   J. P. Wibaut, H. Hoog, S. L. Langedijk, J. Overhoff, and J. Smittenberg, *Rec. trav. chim.*, **58**, 329 (1939).
(7)   D. B. Brooks, F. L. Howard, and H. C. Crafton, Jr., *J. Research Natl. Bur. Standards*, **24**, 33 (1940).
(8)   J. Timmermans and F. Martin, *J. chim. phys.*, **23**, 733 (1926).
(9)   R. M. Davies, *Phil. Mag.*, **21**, 1008 (1936).
(10)   M. Wojciechowski, *J. Research Natl. Bur. Standards*, **17**, 453, 721 (1936).
(11)   M. Wojciechowski, *J. Research Natl. Bur. Standards*, **19**, 347 (1937).
(12)   J. Timmermans and Mme. Hennaut-Roland, *J. chim. phys.*, **29**, 529 (1932).
(13)   L. W. Tilton and J. K. Taylor, *J. Research Natl. Bur. Standards*, **20**, 419 (1938).

or even defects in their construction (see page 711) lead to serious errors in refractometry. In order that the technique of measurement can be checked and that the calibration of individual instruments may be verified or corrected, it is advisable to perform tests with standard reference liquids. The importance of comparative differential measurements as a means of obtaining consistent data has been emphasized by Swietoslawski.[29] For differential measurements of refractive index, it is desirable to have a series of reference liquids, the n values of which cover the usual range at intervals of about 0.03 units. Table I gives the refractive index, n_D^t or $n_{D_3}^t$, and the temperature coefficient, $-dn^t/dt$, for a number of liquids which have been purified and measured carefully. Most of them were selected from the collection by Timmermans[30] of the best values for about 500 organic liquids. The values at 15° C. and the corresponding temperature coefficients were measured at Bureau International des Etalons in Brussels.

TABLE II

DISPERSION OF PURE WATER AT 25.00° C. ACCORDING TO TILTON AND TAYLOR[a]

(RELATIVE TO DRY AIR AT 25° C. AND 760 MM. HG PRESSURE)

Spectral line	n^{25}	Spectral line	n^{25}
He_{r_1}	1.329544_5	Hg_g	1.333977_1
He_{r_2}	1.330397_3	He_g	1.335859_9
H_α	1.330671_9	H_β	1.336627_8
$Na_{5892.6}$	1.332502_6	He_b	1.337434_7
He_{D_3}	1.332555_5	He_v	1.338924_6
Hg_{y_2}	1.332894_1	Hg_{bv}	1.339709_6
		Hg_v	1.342238_6

[a] L. W. Tilton and J. K. Taylor, *J. Research Natl. Bur. Standards*, **20**, 419 (1938).

Table II gives the refractive indices of water at 25° C. for various wave lengths corresponding to spectral lines in table V. The values are taken from the very careful work of Tilton and Taylor,[31] who provide an extensive interpolation table by which n_λ^t for water can be found to within 1×10^{-6} for any temperature between 0° and 60° (intervals of 0.5°) and for wave lengths between 4000 and 7000 Å. These data allow the use of water as reference standard in checking the dispersion curves of refractometer prisms. It is to be noted that the difference in n for ordinary water ($n_D^{20} = 1.33300$) and D_2O ($n_D^{20} = 1.32844$) is appreciable.

Samples to be used as standards must, of course, meet rigid specifications. The preparation of standard water is described in chapter III

[29] W. Swietoslawski, *J. chim. phys.*, **27**, 329 (1930); *Bull. soc. chim. Mém.*, **49**, 1582 (1931). See also chapter II, page 65.

[30] *Annual Tables of Physical Constants and Numerical Data*. National Research Council, Frick Chem. Lab., Princeton, 1941, Sec. 921C.

[31] L. W. Tilton and J. K. Taylor, *J. Research Natl. Bur. Standards*, **20**, 419 (1938).

TABLE III

Densities and Refractive Indices Certified by the National Bureau of Standards[a]

Sample:	Toluene, 211a			2,2,4-Trimethylpentane, 217			Methylcyclohexane, 218		
Temperature:	20° C.	25° C.	30° C.	20° C.	25° C.	30° C.	20° C.	25° C.	30° C.
Density, g./ml. (air-satd.):	0.86696	0.86231	0.85764	0.69193	0.68781	0.68366	0.76939	0.76506	0.76077
λ, Å. Line									
6678.1 Helium	1.49180	1.48903	1.48619	1.38916	1.38670	1.38424	1.42064	1.41812	1.41560
6562.8 Hydrogen C	1.49243	1.48966	1.48682	1.38945	1.38698	1.38452	1.42094	1.41842	1.41591
5892.6[b] Sodium D₁, D₂	1.49693	1.49413	1.49126	1.39145	1.38898	1.38650	1.42312	1.42058	1.41806
5460.7 Mercury e	1.50086	1.49803	1.49514	1.39316	1.39068	1.38820	1.42497	1.42243	1.41989
5015.7 Helium	1.50620	1.50334	1.50041	1.39544	1.39294	1.39044	1.42744	1.42488	1.42233
4861.3 Hydrogen F	1.50847	1.50559	1.50265	1.39639	1.39389	1.39138	1.42847	1.42590	1.42334
4358.3 Mercury g	1.51800	1.51506	1.51206	1.40029	1.39776	1.39523	1.43269	1.43010	1.42752

[a] Further compounds are being added to this list.   [b] Intensity-weighted mean of doublet, D_1, D_2.

(page 72). Methods of purification for the other substances in table I are given in the corresponding references. For some of these substances, there is still disagreement between the results of various investigators which may amount to 1 or 2 units in the 4th decimal. Thus, for highest accuracy, it is imperative, even when the purification is made with great care, to submit reference samples to the *National Bureau of Standards*, Washington, D. C., for certification. The Bureau of Standards, under "Test Fee Schedule 445," will measure n_λ^t at various standard temperatures and wave lengths of both liquids and solids. The testing and calibration of Pulfrich and of Abbé refractometers come under "Test Fee Schedule 444."

The U. S. National Bureau of Standards* has recently made available toluene (Standard Sample 211a), 2,2,4-trimethylpentane (Standard Sample 217), and methylcyclohexane (Standard Sample 218) with certified densities and refractive indices.

The densities were "measured in a pycnometer of special design having a volume of 108 ml. The temperature of the bath was maintained constant to ±0.01° C. It is believed that the uncertainties in the values of density, which are given in" table III, "are less than ±0.00002 g./ml. The values of density are on the basis of weights

* The NBS plans to issue on July 1, 1945, a complete list of NBS standard samples of hydrocarbons (approximately 60).

in vacuum, with the" samples "at a pressure of one atmosphere and saturated with air.   The density of air-free material is greater than that of air-saturated material by about 0.01%.   Near one atmosphere, the change of density with pressure is of the order of 0.01% per atmosphere.   For a description of the method and apparatus used, reference is made to the following publications: *Technological Paper* No. 77 (1916) and *Bulletin*, **9,** 405 (1913)."

"The indices of refraction . . . were measured with a spectrometer by the minimum-deviation method, by use of a water-jacketed hollow prism mounted in a stirred air bath on the spectrometer table.   A platinum resistance thermometer was immersed in the liquid during the measurements.   The values of refractive index are corrected to refer to air at the listed temperatures and at a pressure of 76 cm. Hg. It is believed that the uncertainties in the values of refractive index, which are given in table III, are less than ± 0.00002.   As measured on a spectrometer, in air, values of refractive index decrease by 0.000005 for each 1 cm. Hg increase in pressure of the air.   See *J. Research Natl. Bur. Standards*, **14,** 400 (1935) RP 776. When determined by the use of refractometers, such as those of the Abbé and Pulfrich types, the refractive index is, in general, largely independent of the condition of the air at the emergence face of the refractometer block.   This is especially true when a strictly comparative procedure is followed. Consequently, the refractive indices of "unknown" samples thus observed are referred to conditions essentially the same as those for the standard samples with which the instrument is adjusted.   See *J. Research Natl. Bur. Standards*, **30,** 320 (1943) RP 1535.   For a description of the apparatus and method of measurement, reference is made to the following publications: *J. Research Natl. Bur. Standards*, **20,** 419 (1938) RP 1085; *J. Optical Soc. Am.*, **32,** 371 (1942)."

6.   Evaluation of Lorentz–Lorenz Molar Refraction

The Lorentz–Lorenz molar refraction, $R = [(n^2 - 1)/(n^2 + 2)]M/d$, is a function of the refractive index, the density, d, and the molecular weight, M, which has been used as an additive and constitutive property (see pages 672–683).   It will also be shown that even small deviations from additivity of R allow one to draw important conclusions concerning inter- and intramolecular forces.   It is therefore of importance to consider the ways in which exact values of the Lorentz–Lorenz function can be obtained. An extended study of the experimental and theoretical aspects of this problem has been carried out in a series (I–LV) of "Refractometric Investigations."[32-58]   Although this study has been concerned primarily with inorganic substances, the improved apparatus used, in addition to the meth-

---

[32] N. Bauer and K. Fajans (LV), *J. Am. Chem. Soc.*, **64,** 3023 (1942).

[33] A. Braun and P. Hoelemann (LII), *Z. physik. Chem.*, **B34,** 357 (1936).

[34] K. Fajans and G. Joos (I), *Z. Physik*, **23,** 1 (1924).

[35] K. Fajans and C. A. Knorr (II), *Ber.*, **59,** 249 (1926).

[36] K. Fajans, P. Hoelemann, and Z. Shibata (XXI), *Z. physik. Chem.*, **B13,** 354 (1931).

(*Footnotes continued on page 668.*)

ods of evaluation and theoretical treatment, can be applied to organic substances as well. The papers of the series to which reference will be made throughout this chapter are given in footnotes 32–58.

Pure Liquids.—Two experimental precautions are important in obtaining reliable values of the molar refraction: (1) The measurements of density and of refractive index should both be made on the same sample in order to minimize the influence of impurities. (2) The temperature of measurement of n and of d should not differ appreciably; a direct comparison of the thermometers used is advisable. The temperature difference permissible for a given accuracy can be calculated from the temperature coefficients of n and of d (pages 656 and 73, respectively) according to (18).

By differentiating the expression for R, above, one obtains an equation for evaluating the error, ∇R, in the molar refraction caused by a given experimental error, ∇n and ∇d, in n and d, respectively:

$$\frac{\nabla R}{R} = \frac{6n}{(n^2 + 2)(n^2 - 1)} \nabla n - \frac{\nabla d}{d} \tag{18}$$

Consider, for example, the error in R^{25} of ethyl alcohol ($n^{25} = 1.3576$, $d^{25} = 0.7850$) if n is measured at 26.0° C. and d at 25.0° C. Assuming that other errors are negligible and knowing that $-dn/dt = 0.0004$ per degree for this compound, one substitutes $\nabla n = 4 \times 10^{-4}$ and $\nabla d = 0$ in equation (18), obtaining 0.1% as the error in R^{25} caused by the 1.0° C. temperature dif-

[37] K. Fajans et al. (XXX–XXXVI), Z. physik. Chem., **B24**, 103-214 (1934).

[38] W. Geffcken and H. Kohner (X), Z. physik. Chem., **B1**, 456 (1928).

[39] W. Geffcken (XI), Z. physik. Chem., **B5**, 81 (1929).

[40] W. Geffcken (XIX), Z. Elektrochem., **37**, 233 (1931).

[41] W. Geffcken, C. Beckmann, and A. Kruis (XXIII), Z. physik. Chem., **B20, 398** (1933).

[42] W. Geffcken and A. Kruis (XXIX), Z. physik. Chem., **B23**, 175 (1933).

[43] W. Geffcken and A. Kruis, Z. physik. Chem., **B45**, 411 (1939).

[44] H. Goldschmidt and P. Hoelemann (XLV), Z. physik. Chem., **B32, 341** (1936).

[45] P. Hoelemann (XLVI), Z. physik. Chem., **B32**, 353 (1936).

[46] P. Hoelemann and H. Kohner (XIX), Z. physik. Chem., **B13**, 338 (1931).

[47] O. Johnson, thesis, University of Michigan, 1942.

[48] M. L. Koenig-Gressmann, thesis, University of Munich, 1938.

[49] H. Kohner (IX), Z. physik. Chem., **B1**, 427 (1928).

[50] A. Kruis and W. Geffcken (XXVI), Z. physik. Chem., **A166**, 16 (1933).

[51] A. Kruis (XLVII, XLVIII, LI), Z. physik. Chem., **B34**, 1, 13, 82 (1936).

[52] A. Kruis and W. Geffcken (IL, L), Z. physik. Chem., **B34**, 51 and 70 (1936)

[53] G. Pesce and P. Hoelemann (XXXVIIa), Z. Elektrochem., **40**, 1 (1934).

[54] P. Wulff (XV), Z. Krist., **77**, 61 (1931).

[55] P. Wulff and A. Heigl (XVI), Z. Krist., **77**, 107 (1931).

[56] P. Wulff (XXV), Z. physik. Chem., **B21**, 368 (1933).

[57] P. Wulff and D. Schaller (XXVII), Z. Krist., **A87**, 51 (1934).

[58] J. Wüst and H. Reindel (XXXI), Z. physik. Chem., **B24**, 155 (1934).

ference in the measurement of n and d. A considerably greater error in the absolute value of the temperature, if equal for both measurements, is permissible, since the temperature coefficient of R itself is very small (see page 683). For instance, if both n and d in the above example were obtained at 26.0° C., the resulting R^{26} value would differ from R^{25} by only about $+0.01\%$, since the temperature coefficient of d is -9×10^{-4} g. per cc. per degree.

Consider also the use of equation (18) in estimating the maximum relative error, $(\nabla R/R)_{max.}$, in R for ethyl alcohol when the error in both n and d is $\pm 1 \times 10^{-4}$; such an accuracy is easily obtained in routine measurements. Substituting, one has:

$$(\nabla R/R)_{max.} = \frac{6 \times 1.36}{3.85 \times 0.85}(1 \times 10^{-4}) + \frac{1 \times 10^{-4}}{0.80} = 3.8 \times 10^{-4}$$

Since $R^{25} = 12.78$ cc., the maximum absolute error, $\nabla R_{max.}$, is 0.005 cc. This accuracy is sufficient for many purposes.

Pure Solids.—The sufficiently accurate direct determination of R for crystals is often difficult and time consuming. Three methods are available which allow an indirect determination (Method 1) or at least an estimation (Methods 2 and 3) of R of a crystalline substance: (1) Measurement of n of a liquid, the refractive index of which has been found, preferably by an interferometric method (see pages 719–731), to be equal to that of the crystal. (2) Measurements of n (and d) on the molten substance[59] (see also pages 733–734). The molar refraction is only slightly influenced by changes in state or temperature (see page 683); moreover, the small changes in R due to these causes are similar in magnitude for a wide variety of organic compounds, so that a correction can be applied to $R_{liq.}$. (3) Evaluation of $R_{app.}$, the apparent molar refraction, of the substance, by measuring the n and d of its solution of a known concentration in a suitable solvent (see page 670). The refractions of mixtures of organic substances show in general such small deviations from additivity (see page 680) that the value of $R_{app.}$ should in most cases be equal to $R_{cryst.}$ within a few hundredths of a cc.

The same experimental precautions and the equation (18) for errors apply to solids as to liquids. It is especially important to measure n and d on the same sample, since crystals often contain bubbles or other imperfections. The anisotropy of many solids makes necessary a somewhat different treatment of the data. It has been concluded[55] that the value of R which in the simplest way represents the average polarizability of a slightly anisotropic solid is obtained from the geometric mean of the

---

[59] M. Furter, *Helv. Chim. Acta*, **21**, 1666 (1938)

characteristic indices of refraction. For biaxial crystals, the mean index $\bar{n}$ is given by:

$$\bar{n} = \sqrt[3]{n_\alpha n_\beta n_\gamma} \tag{19}$$

for uniaxial crystals by:

$$\bar{n} = \sqrt[3]{n_\epsilon^2 n_\omega} \tag{20}$$

For the definition of n_α, n_ϵ, etc., see pages 454–471, 655, and reference 2.

Solutions.—The precision technique for measuring the apparent molar refraction of solutes, $R_{app.}$, has been developed in the series of "Refractometric Investigations" by Kohner,[49] Geffcken,[40–43] and Kruis[50–52] for aqueous solutions, by Koenig-Gressmann[48] for mixtures of organic liquids and applied by Johnson[47] to salt solutions in ether and acetone. Geffcken and Kruis emphasize the importance of differential measurements and of a temperature control commensurate with the improved precision. The reliability of the results depends on the following precautions: (1) Solution and solvent should be compared under identical conditions, e. g., at the same temperature and with the same instrument. (2) Measurement of the difference between refractive index of solution and solvent $(n - n_0)$ should be made on a sample identical with that used for the determination of the density difference $(d - d_0)$. (3) The solvent used in preparing the solution and the reference liquid should come from the same source. (4) Special devices should be employed for transferring and storing liquids to prevent change of concentration of solutions by evaporation. (5) If the change of $R_{app.}$ with concentration is required, the various concentrations should be made up by diluting a *single* carefully analyzed stock solution, using weight burettes.

The apparent molar refraction, $R_{app.}$, of a solute of molecular weight M_1 is defined by the condition that the total refraction, R, of a solution containing one mole of solute is the sum of $R_{app.}$ and the refraction which the amount (W_0 grams) of solvent present in this solution would have in the pure state. We use the Lorentz–Lorenz expression (page 673) for the specific and molar refraction and designate quantities referring to the solution by no index, those referring to the solvent by the index 0, and those referring to the solute by the index 1. Then it is seen that:

$$R = R_{app.} + r_0 W_0 \tag{21}$$

and:

$$R_{app.} = \frac{n^2 - 1}{n^2 + 2} \cdot \frac{M_1 + W_0}{d} - \frac{n_0^2 - 1}{n_0^2 + 2} \cdot \frac{W_0}{d_0} \tag{22}$$

While r_0 is the specific refraction of the solvent in the pure state, $R_{app.}$ is not identical with the molar refraction of the pure solute, R_1. The difference, $R_{app.} - R_1$, indicates the deviation from exact additivity in the mixture due to all possible causes; it includes any refractometric effect of a change in the state of the solute and the solvent which might arise as a result of mixing. $R_{app.} - R_1$ will be small for solutions in which the components have similar physical properties, or do not exert strong forces on each other (see pages 663 and 680).

In terms of molality, m = moles solute per 1000 grams solvent, $R_{app.}$ is expressed by:

$$R_{app.} = \left(\frac{n^2 - 1}{n^2 + 2} \cdot \frac{1}{d} \cdot \frac{1000 + mM_1}{m} \right) - \left(\frac{n_0^2 - 1}{n_0^2 + 2} \cdot \frac{1}{d_0} \cdot \frac{1000}{m} \right) \quad (23)$$

Another very convenient expression for $R_{app.}$ which separates the influence of n and d on $R_{app.}$ has been derived by Geffcken:[39]

$$R_{app.} = \phi(\Phi + \Pi) \quad (24)$$

Π is a function of n:

$$\Pi = \frac{1000}{\phi_0 C} (\phi - \phi_0) \quad (25)$$

where:

$$\phi = (n^2 - 1)/(n^2 + 2) \quad (26)$$

and:

$$\phi_0 = (n_0^2 - 1)/(n_0^2 + 2) \quad (27)$$

Φ, the apparent molar volume of the solute, is a function of d (see chapter III, page 75):

$$\Phi = \frac{M_1}{d_0} - \frac{1000}{C} \cdot \frac{\Delta d}{d_0} \quad (28)$$

where $\Delta d = d - d_0$ and C = concentration in moles per liter.

The accuracy in $R_{app.}$ depends primarily on the accuracy of the differences Δn and Δd and of the concentration, C. Kohner[49] and Johnson[47] obtained the following approximate formula for the maximum error, $\nabla R_{app.}$ in $R_{app.}$ caused by experimental errors, $\nabla(\Delta n)$ and $\nabla(\Delta d)$, in Δn and Δd:

$$\nabla R_{app.} = \frac{1000}{C} \left[\frac{6 n_0}{(n_0^2 + 2)^2} \cdot \nabla(\Delta n) + \frac{\phi_0}{d_0} \cdot \nabla(\Delta d) \right] \quad (29)$$

For the case of dilute aqueous solutions, assuming $0.10 > \Delta n > 0.01$, equation (29) becomes:

$$\nabla R_{app.} = \frac{100}{C} [6 \nabla(\Delta n) + 2 \nabla(\Delta d)] \quad (30)$$

If, for example, $\nabla(\Delta n) = 3 \times 10^{-5}$, $\nabla(\Delta d) = 2 \times 10^{-5}$, and $C = 1$, then $\nabla R_{\text{app.}} = 0.02$ cc. As C becomes smaller, the error in $R_{\text{app.}}$ becomes larger because, with a decrease in Δn and Δd, their constant absolute errors become relatively more important. To obtain a value of $R_{\text{app.}}$ accurate to ± 0.1 cc., one can measure Δn with a Pulfrich refractometer and Δd with a pycnometer (Chapter III) on solutions as dilute as $0.1\ M$. For lower concentrations or higher accuracy, the more sensitive methods directly measuring Δn (interferometer) and Δd (float method,[41] see chapter III) should be used.

The error in $R_{\text{app.}}$ caused by an error, ∇p, in the weight (p grams) of solute per 100 grams solution is given by:

$$\nabla R_{\text{app.}} = M_1(r_1 - r_0)(\nabla p/p) \tag{31}$$

where r refers to the specific refraction (refraction per gram of substance). For example, if $(\nabla p/p) = 0.001$ (i. e., per cent error in $p = 0.1\%$) for a solution of p-nitrobenzene ($M_1 = 137$, $r_1 = 0.2789$), in benzene ($r_0 = 0.3352$) we have $\nabla R_{\text{app.}} = 137 (0.2789 - 0.3352) (0.001) = -0.008$ cc.

Kohner[49] has also analyzed the influence of errors in d_0 and n_0 and of impurities.

7. Additivity of Molar Refraction and Its Limitations

A. GENERAL

The molar refraction, R, is a property characteristic of a given molecule and indicative of its structure. For a long time the term "characteristic of the molecule" was understood to mean that the value of R is independent of temperature and pressure and whether the substance is present in the gaseous, liquid, or solid state. In mixtures, R was supposed to constitute the share of the given substance, in proportion to its mole fraction, in the total molar refraction (see Eq. 43, page 680). "Indicative of the molecular structure" was understood to mean that R of a molecule is a property which can be additively composed of empirical increments, connected with atoms and atomic groups present in the molecule, but also dependent on the constitution, i. e., on the kind of binding between these components.

Thus, the molar refraction has been considered to be at the same time additive and constitutive, a point of view which has been applied to many properties since its introduction by Kopp (1842) in the comparison of boiling points and molar volumes of organic substances (page 75). In the field of molar refraction, the additive method was applied first by Berthelot (1856), using equation (32) for molar refraction, and by Gladstone and Dale (1863) and Landolt (1864), who applied equation (33). The symbols are explained on pages 662 and 667.

$$R = (n^2 - 1) M/d \tag{32}$$

$$R_\lambda = (n_\lambda - 1) M/d \tag{33}$$

In 1882, Landolt based the additive increments on the new Lorentz–Lorenz formula for the specific (Eq. 34) and molar (Eq. 35) refraction for the wave length, λ:

$$r_\lambda = \frac{n_\lambda^2 - 1}{n_\lambda^2 + 2} \cdot \frac{1}{d} \tag{34}$$

$$R_\lambda = \frac{n_\lambda^2 - 1}{n_\lambda^2 + 2} \cdot \frac{M}{d} \tag{35}$$

R and r have the dimension of volume and are expressed in cubic centimeters. Equation (35) is now almost generally used.[60] It shows that molar refraction depends on wave length λ. In fact, the molar dispersion, $R_{\lambda_1} - R_{\lambda_2}$, itself is a characteristic property of molecules. Brühl, who since 1880 developed the field considerably, included (1891) in his table of additive constants those for molar dispersion. The

TABLE IV

INCREMENTS FOR THE LORENTZ–LORENZ REFRACTION AND DISPERSION OF ATOMS AND GROUPS IN CC. PER MOLE[a]

Atom or group	Refraction		Dispersion	
	H_α	D	$H_\beta - H_\alpha$	$H_\gamma - H_\alpha$
CH₂	4.598	4.618	0.071	0.113
C	2.413	2.418	0.025	0.056
H	1.092	1.100	0.023	0.029
⊢ (C=C)	1.686	1.733	0.138	0.200
⊨ (C≡C)	2.328	2.398	0.139	0.171
O' (hydroxyl)	1.522	1.525	0.006	0.015
O < (ether)	1.639	1.643	0.012	0.019
O'' (carbonyl)	2.189	2.211	0.057	0.078
Cl	5.933	5.967	0.107	0.168
Br	8.803	8.865	0.211	0.340
I	13.757	13.900	0.482	0.775
N (primary amine)	2.309	2.322	0.059	0.086
N (secondary amine)	2.478	2.502	0.086	0.119
N (tertiary amine)	2.808	2.840	0.133	0.186

[a] According to F. Eisenlohr, Z. physik. Chem., 75, 585 (1910); 79, 129 (1912). See also Landolt-Börnstein, Physikalisch-Chemische Tabellen, Vol. II, 986, 1923; Erg. I, 527 et seq. (1927); IIb, 822 et seq. (1931); IIIb, 1694 et seq. (1935).

increments, calculated by Eisenlohr, who revised the values of Brühl, and which are listed in table IV, apply to the sodium D line and to hydrogen lines α, β, and γ. The data given in the following text apply to the D line if wave length is not mentioned.

The method of constant additive increments has been criticized by Eykman (see page 679) and others.[61, 62] In order to apply table IV with the proper discrimination, it is necessary to explain its foundation and to examine its limits. In

[60] See, however, S. S. Kurtz, Jr., and A. L. Ward, J. Franklin Inst., 224, 583, 697 (1937) and M. L. Huggins, J. Am. Chem. Soc., 63, 116 (1941).

[61] See, for example, W. Swietoslawski, J. Am. Chem. Soc., 42, 1945 (1920).

[62] J. M. Stevels, Polarizability and Cohesion Energy, thesis, Univ. of Leiden, 1937.

doing so it is well to take into account the electronic structure of the molecules, since optical properties depend on the state of the valence electrons. We shall consider, besides the increments in table IV, the bond and octet refractions (Table V),

TABLE V

INCREMENTS FOR THE LORENTZ–LORENZ REFRACTION OF BINDING ELECTRONS AND ELECTRON OCTETS FOR THE D LINE IN CC. PER MOLE[a]

Bond	Equivalent to values in table IV	R_D
C:C:H H	CH_2 or $C + 2 H$	4.63
C:H	$\frac{1}{4} CH_4$ or $\frac{1}{4} C + H$	1.7
C:C	$\frac{1}{2} C$	1.2
C::C	$\mid^- + C$	4.1_5
C:::C	$\mid^- + \frac{3}{2} C$	6.0

Octet	Equivalent to values in table IV	R_D
C:Ö:H	$O' + \frac{1}{4} C + H$	3.2
C:Ö:C	$O < + \frac{2}{4} C$	2.8_5
C::Ö	$O'' + \frac{2}{4} C$	3.4
C:Cl:	$Cl + \frac{1}{4} C$	6.6
C:Br:	$Br + \frac{1}{4} C$	9.5
C:Ï:	$I + \frac{1}{4} C$	14.5
C:N:H H	N (primary amine) $+ \frac{1}{4} C + 2 H$	5.1
C:N:C H	N (secondary amine) $+ \frac{2}{4} C + H$	4.8
C:N:C C	N (tertiary amine) $+ \frac{3}{4} C$	4.6_5

[a] According to C. P. Smyth, *Phil. Mag.*, **50**, 361, 715 (1925) and K. Fajans and C. A. Knorr, *Ber.*, **59**, 249 (1926). In the latter paper, the increments of this table were given with four significant figures, as were the refractions in table IV. In view of the discussion on pages 678 *et seq.*, the R_D values in this table are rounded off. Those in table IV are left unchanged because many calculations found in the literature are based upon them.

which are closely connected with the former. Both sets of constants are based on equation (35).

B. ATOMIC, BOND, AND OCTET CONSTANTS

The experimental foundation for the application of the principle of additivity is the approximate constancy of the difference between the molar refraction of adjacent members of homologous series, *i. e.*, of the increment R_{CH_2} for the CH_2 group.

For liquids at 20° C. and the sodium D line, this value is near 4.6 cc. (see page 679). The increment, R_{CH_2}, is expressed in the system of atomic refractions by:

$$R_{CH_2} = R_C + 2 R_H \qquad (36)$$

and in the system of bond refractions by:

$$R_{CH_2} = R_{C-C} + 2 R_{C-H} \qquad (37)$$

Correspondingly, the molar refraction of a saturated hydrocarbon C_nH_{n+2} is:

$$R = nR_C + (2n + 2)R_H = nR_{CH_2} + 2 R_H \qquad (38)$$

or:

$$R = (n - 1)R_{C-C} + (2n + 2)R_{C-H} = (n - 1)R_{CH_2} + 4 R_{C-H} \qquad (39)$$

In case of exact additivity of the molar refraction, it would be sufficient to use the experimental value, R, for any saturated hydrocarbon, and the value $R_{CH_2} = 4.6$ in order to obtain the values R_H and R_C or R_{C-C} and R_{C-H}.   The relation between the atomic and bond constants is given by equations (40) and (41):[63]

$$R_{C-H} = {}^1/_4 R_C + R_H \qquad (40)$$

$$R_{C-C} = {}^1/_2 R_C \qquad (41)$$

The fact that table IV contains only one value for C and one for H both given to three decimals would seem to imply that the molar refraction of saturated hydrocarbons is additive with corresponding accuracy.   This is not the case (see page 678).   Moreover, Brühl found that olefins and acetylenes have considerably larger molar refractions than one would expect on the basis of the atomic constants for C and H.   He accounted for this by introducing constant increments for the double, $\models$, and triple, $\models$, carbon to carbon bond.   This is not consisten with the fact that, in the atomic system, no increment is used for the single bond.   For oxygen and nitrogen, the optical effect caused by a variation in the kind of binding is expressed differently.   Landolt used only one constant for oxygen.   Brühl introduced a special atomic constant for carbonyl oxygen (O″), and Conrady (1889) distinguished between etheric (O<) and hydroxylic (O′) oxygen.   This choice of constants is arbitrary;   one might just as well use only one atomic constant for oxygen, add an increment for C=O, and use different atomic constants of hydrogen depending on whether it is bonded to carbon or oxygen.   A corresponding remark applies to the distinction between the three atomic constants of nitrogen in primary, secondary, and tertiary amines.   In the first two, some of the hydrogen atoms are bonded to carbon and some to nitrogen, and it is arbitrary to ascribe the optical differences only to the nitrogen.

The above criticism should not impair the practical use of table IV as long as the number and nature of the constants chosen are adequate and the conclusions

---

[63] See A. L. von Steiger, *Ber.*, **54**, 1381 (1921), and reference 61.

drawn do not go beyond the limitations of the system.   Valuable applications of table IV have been described often,[64-66] and need not be discussed here.

Table V was derived in an attempt to understand refractometric data in terms of Lewis' electronic interpretation of Kekulé's valence bonds.   A single bond corresponds to two electrons, a double bond to four and a triple bond to six binding electrons.   In the case of saturated and unsaturated hydrocarbons in which all electrons are assumed to be used in bonds, it is possible to arrive at values not only for C:H and C:C (see page 675), but also for C::C and C:::C.   Thus, the inconsistency of the older system is avoided.   However, the values for the double and triple bond are derived on the arbitrary assumption that the refractometric value of C:H in unsaturated hydrocarbons is the same as in saturated.   The results obtained were clarifying in several respects.   For instance, corresponding to the increased number of electrons involved, the bond refractions increase in the series C:C (1.2), C::C (4.15), and C:::C (6.0).   That the increase, from the single to the double and triple bond, is very much larger than proportional to the number of electrons seems to indicate that the latter are "looser" in the unsaturated compounds.   This is in agreement with the fact that the energies of dissociation of the double and triple bonds,[67] approximately $E_{C=C} = 2E_{C-C} - 20$ kcal. and $E_{C\equiv C} = 3E_{C-C} - 50$ kcal., respectively, are less than proportional to the number of electrons.

In molecules containing other elements besides C and H, only part of the electrons participate in the binding, according to Lewis' theory.   Thus, subtracting

$$H$$
$$\overset{..}{} \overset{..}{}$$

from the molar refraction of methyl chloride, $H:\overset{..}{C}:\overset{..}{Cl}:$, the refraction of the C:H

$$H$$

electrons, assumed to be equal to their refraction in hydrocarbons, one obtains the value of the chlorine octet, two of the electrons of which are supposed to be shared with carbon and six to be unshared.   The value obtained (6.6) gives an indication of the state of the electronic shell of the chlorine octet attached to carbon.   Comparison of this value with that of the chlorine octet in the free state (Cl^-, 9.0) and in HCl (6.67) shows that the combination with carbon influences the chlorine octet very nearly as strongly as when its electronic shell is penetrated by a proton.   In a similar way, it was possible to compare the influence of a proton with that of carbon on fluorine, bromine, or iodine octets, and, in the case of the oxygen octet, the influence of two protons, in H_2O, with that of one proton and one carbon atom, in H_3COH, and with that of two carbons, in H_3COCH_3.

C.   LACK OF EXACT ADDITIVITY

It is of theoretical as well as practical importance to gage how well the additive atomic, bond, or octet constants express the experimental data.   The impression

[64] S. Glasstone, *Text-Book of Physical Chemistry.*   Van Nostrand, New York, 1940, pp. 518–533.

[65] F. Eisenlohr, *Spektrochemie der organischen Verbindungen.*   Enke, Stuttgart, 1912.

[66] W. Hückel, *Theoretische Grundlagen der organischen Chemie.*   Vol. II, Akadem. Verlagsgesellschaft, Leipzig, 1931, pp. 91–114.

[67] K. Fajans, *Ber.*, **55**, 2826 (1922).

is easily gained that the agreement between calculated and observed values is satis-factory except for substances containing either conjugated systems or rings. For instance, for n-heptane, $R_{calc.}$ = 34.526 and $R_{obs.}$ = 34.54, and for acetic acid, $R_{calc.}$ = 12.972 and $R_{obs.}$ = 12.99.

Influence of Conjugation.—For a compound, C_6H_{10}, with two double bonds, $R_{calc.}$ is 28.974. While $R_{obs.}$, 28.99, of diallyl, $CH_2{=}CHCH_2CH_2CH{=}CH_2$, approaches this value very closely, $R_{obs.}$ of 2,4-hexadiene, $CH_3CH{=}CHCH{=}CHCH_3$, is 30.64. The positive deviation (+1.67), exaltation, has been connected with the conjugation of the double bonds in the latter isomer. However, it is not possible to use a new constant increment for the conjugation because, for example, the re-fraction, 29.75, of $CH_2{=}C(CH_3)C(CH_3){=}CH_2$, the conjugated diisopropenyl, dif-fers less from that of the unconjugated isomer diallyl (by +0.76) than from that of 2,4-hexadiene (by −0.89).

The exaltations have been extensively studied by Brühl, von Auwers and others,[68] and are considered as anomalous effects. However, exaltations are not restricted to conjugated double bonds. For instance, in deriving the atomic refraction of chlorine, Eisenlohr confirmed the observation of Brühl that a higher value is obtained from acid chlorides (6.336 as an average of five values varying from 6.231 to 6.500) than from other compounds (average 5.967). Eisenlohr assumed that this exalta-tion in the acid chlorides is due to some kind of conjugation between the carbonyl group and the chlorine atom, and excluded this "special" value of Cl from his table of "normal" atomic refractions.

Influence of Ring Structure.—The opposite effect was observed with furan and analogous substances. The calculated value for $\begin{array}{c}CH{=}CH \\ | \qquad\qquad \\ CH{=}CH\end{array}\!\!\!\!>O$, with an etheric oxygen and two double bonds, is 19.181. Since the double bonds are conjugated, a higher refraction was expected by Brühl. However, the experimental value, 18.426,[69] is even lower than the calculated. Explanation of this depression as caused by the ring structure did not lead to a general rule. In spite of the ring structure of cyclohexane, $R_{calc.}$ = 6 × 4.618 = 27.708 agrees well with $R_{obs.}$ (= 27.68) for 15°. Neither can the depression in furan, thiophene, or pyrrole[70] be attributed to their heterocyclic character. The experimental value of benzene, 26.14 (15°), also shows a depression (0.17) when compared with that calculated for six CH and three double bonds, even if the conjugation is neglected. Recently[71] resonance has been mentioned in connection with these depression effects.

Differences between Chain Isomers.—While these difficulties have been gen-erally realized for a long time, it is necessary to emphasize that the exact meas-urements of the last two decades have shown deviations from additivity in many cases which were usually regarded as normal. A good agreement between $R_{calc.}$

[68] See, for example, K. von Auwers, *Ann.*, **437**, 63 (1924).

[69] See E. C. Hughes and J. R. Johnson, *J. Am. Chem. Soc.*, **53**, 737 (1931).

[70] See R. Nasini *et al.*, *Atti accad. Lincei*, **1**, 617 (1886); *Z. physik. Chem.*, **17**, 539 (1895).

[71] See J. A. Leermakers and A. Weissberger, in H. Gilman, *Organic Chemistry*. 2nd ed., Wiley, New York, 1943, p. 1752.

and $R_{obs.}$ such as that for n-heptane is not general even for paraffins. Smyth and Stoops[72] found, for nine isomeric heptanes at 20°, values between 34.61, for 2,2-dimethylpentane, and 34.25, for 3-ethylpentane. The difference (0.36) between these extremes is three times larger than that (0.118) between (O<) and (O'). Measurements of Timmermans and his associates[73] contain many examples of chain isomers of substituted saturated hydrocarbons with similar differences in molar refraction. For instance, R for n- and sec-butyl iodide is 33.48 and 33.85, respectively. Still larger discrepancies are shown by organometallic compounds. The molar refraction of $C_{12}H_{28}Pb$ has the values 78.07, 78.60, and 79.87 for the dimethyldiisoamyl, the tetra-n-propyl and the tetraisopropyl lead, respectively. If one attempts to derive the atomic refraction of lead from the PbR_4 compounds, one finds 17.31 when R is CH_3 and 20.05 when R is iso-C_3H_7. The corresponding values of the atomic dispersion $H_\gamma - H_\alpha$ are 1.43 and 2.31, respectively.[74] It would not be justified to average such widely diverging values.

Influence of Association.—Not only isomerism but even mere association of neutral molecules can lead to large changes of molar refraction. While $R_{obs.}$ = 12.99 for liquid acetic acid agrees satisfactorily with $R_{calc.}$ (see page 677), the vapor between 190° and 300° C., the range within which acetic acid consists practically completely of the monomer, CH_3COOH, gives the value 13.216 ± 0.002 cc.[44] For the dimer, $1/2 (CH_3COOH)_2$, the value 13.416 ± 0.01 cc. was derived from measurements between 120° and 190°. Both values for the vapor apply to the Hg_g line; the corresponding value for the liquid is 13.05. It is noteworthy that, while one would be inclined to assume that the dimer is intermediate between the monomer and the liquid, $R_{obs.}$ of the dimer is higher than that of either.

D.   CRITICISM OF METHOD OF CONSTANT IMCREMENTS

A detailed analysis even of the experimental material available in 1910 shows that the values for a given atom or type of binding, listed in table IV with four significant figures, are averages of single values which deviate considerably from each other. For example, in the derivation of the increment $\Gamma = 1.733$, Eisenlohr excluded not only compounds with conjugated double bonds but also allyl derivatives giving Γ values which he considered much too low. In the remaining 26 compounds, the increments for CH_2, H, and the different kinds of oxygen, were treated as constants and Γ values were obtained which vary between 1.530 and 1.943. This variation exceeds considerably the experimental error. The average, 1.733, is more or less accidental, and it would be more appropriate to draw the conclusion that $\Gamma = 1.7 \pm 0.2$. Then it would not be surprising to find[75] that the molar refraction of $CH_3CH=CHCH_2COOH$ leads to the high value, 1.969, for Γ although the $C=C$ bond in this acid is not conjugated with the $C=O$ bond of the carbonyl group.

Table IV is almost always used in spite of all these discrepancies. When values

---

[72] C. P. Smyth and W. N. Stoops, *J. Am. Chem. Soc.*, **50**, 1883 (1928).
[73] J. Timmermans *et al.*, eight papers in *J. chim. phys.*, **23–34** (1926–1937). See references to table I, page 664.
[74] G. Grüttner and E. Krause, *Ann.*, **415**, 338 (1918).
[75] E. Schjånberg, *Z. physik. Chem.*, **A178**, 274 (1937).

calculated from it are compared with experimental molar refractions, the deviations are sometimes very large. For instance, in a series of 26 furan derivatives, the molar exaltation varies from -1.078 for 3-bromofuran to $+5.524$ for furfural pinacolone.[69] With compounds of an element like fluorine, which is not contained in table IV, one subtracts from the experimental value the sum of all the other increments in order to obtain the atomic refraction of fluorine. In this way, extended investigations[76] gave for R_F values between 0.68, in $CCl_2{=}CClF$, and 1.60, in $CCl_2{=}CCl\text{-}CCl_2F$.[77] Without elucidating the reason for these deviations, one can say only that R_F is around 1 cc.

In the opinion of the writer, Kopp's method of using a limited number of constant increments has been shown by modern measurements of *any* property of compounds to be only a first approximation. Ostwald[78] recognized the reason for this lack of strict additivity: a given substitution in two different molecules cannot be expected to have an identical effect. Eykman[79], on the basis of very broad experimental material and using for the molar refraction the expression $R = (M/d) \cdot (n^2 - 1)/(n^2 + 0.4)$, concluded (1893–1911) that the same effect is produced by CH_2 in different types of compounds only in the case of its addition to a long $(CH_2)_n$ chain. However, near the end of chains, in branched chains, and in the neighborhood of groups other than CH_2 deviations from additivity occur.

E. CASES OF SATISFACTORY ADDITIVITY OF REFRACTION

A review of modern experimental results also shows satisfactory additivity in homologous series for the Lorentz–Lorenz expression, and with the same limitations Eykman found. (See above.) The increment for the CH_2 group within a normal chain, in different series of liquid substances at 20° C., differs from an average value of 4.63 for the D line only by a few hundredths of a cc.,[80] except for the first few members of the series, for which larger systematic deviations occur (see, for instance, the case of methane and formic acid, page 681). The value 4.618 given in table IV nearly coincides with this average.

It is therefore recommended in "computing" molar refractions that the experi-

---

[76] F. Swarts, *J. chim. phys.*, **20**, 30 (1923). A. L. Henne *et al.*, *J. Am. Chem. Soc.*, **1934–1944**.

[77] G. Schiemann, *Z. physik. Chem.*, **156**, 397 (1931), obtained R_F from 20 compounds: 2.03 was the highest value of the "atomic refraction" of fluorine (in *o*-fluoronitrobenzene); 0.63 was the lowest value (in *p*-fluoroanisole); Schiemann derives an average of 0.997. See also A. V. Grosse, R. C. Wackher, and C. B. Linn, *J. Phys. Chem.*, **44**, 275 (1940).

[78] W. Ostwald, *Grundriss der allgemeinen Chemie*. 3rd ed., Engelmann, Leipzig, 1899, p. 130.

[79] J. F. Eykman, "Recherches réfractométriques," edited by A. F. Holleman, *Natuurkund. Verhandel. Hollandsche Mij. Wetenschappen Haarlem*, **1919**.

[80] See A. F. Shepard, A. L. Henne, and T. Midgley, Jr., *J. Am. Chem. Soc.*, **53**, 1948 (1931) (paraffins); P. Bruylants and R. Merckx, *Bull. classe Sci., Acad. roy. Belg.*, **19**, 1003 (1933) (nitriles); P. Ceuterick, *Bull. soc. chim. Belg.*, **45**, 545 (1936) (ketones); H. I. Waterman and W. J. C. De Kok, *Rec. trav. chim.*, **52**, 251, 298 (1933) and **53**, 725 (1934) (olefins).

mental values of the nearest homologous substances be used wherever possible and 4.63 for CH_2. It may be shown by one example that this method is more reliable than the use of the other additive constants of table IV. The molar refraction of the esters of furoic acid, C_4H_3OCOOR, would be expected to be, on the basis of table IV, 30.071 for $R = CH_3$ and 39.307 for $R = C_3H_7$. When calculated from the experimental value for furan (18.426), the expected values would be 29.310 and 38.546, respectively. The true values[69] for the methyl ester ($R_{exp.} = 30.896$) and propyl ester ($R_{exp.} = 40.255$) differ widely from both sets of the predicted ones. However, if we start with the true value for the ethyl furoate ($R_{exp.} = 35.61$) and use the increment for CH_2 (4.63), the computed value for the propyl ester ($R_{calc.} = 40.24$) differs only by 0.015 cc. from the true one. For the first member of the series, the methyl ester, $R_{calc.} = 35.61 - 4.63 = 30.98$, deviates by 0.08 from $R_{exp.} = 30.896$.

The Lorentz–Lorenz refraction also shows a satisfactory additivity for *mixtures of neutral molecules* which do not exert strong forces on each other.[81, 82] If in a binary mixture x_1 is the mole fraction of component 1, the refraction of one mole of the mixture is represented by formula (42) and the additive value is given by formula (43):

$$R_{exp.} = \frac{n^2 - 1}{n^2 + 2} \cdot \frac{x_1 M_1 + (1 - x_1) M_2}{d} \tag{42}$$

$$R_{add.} = x_1 \frac{n_1^2 - 1}{n_1^2 + 2} \cdot \frac{M_1}{d_1} + (1 - x_1) \frac{n_2^2 - 1}{n_2^2 + 2} \cdot \frac{M_2}{d_2} \tag{43}$$

In mixtures of CCl_4 with C_6H_6, of acetone with CCl_4 or C_6H_6, the deviations from additivity of the volume of one mole are small (below 0.1 cc. per mole of mixture). Correspondingly, $R_{exp.} - R_{add.}$ is small (below 0.06 cc.).

A somewhat wider departure from additivity is shown by measurements of Hubbard[83] on two mixtures containing CS_2 which is an easily polarizable molecule (see page 681).

F. DEVIATIONS FROM ADDITIVITY CAUSED BY ELECTRIC INTERACTIONS

If one dilutes a solution containing one mole of lithium perchlorate in 1.3 moles of ether[84] by a further 14.2 moles of ether, a volume contraction of 17 cc. per mole $LiClO_4$ takes place and the molar refraction decreases by 0.91 cc. In this case, strong electric forces are acting between the molecules of the perchlorate and ether.

An extensive experimental evidence concerning the molar refraction of inorganic and organic substances leads[85] to the conclusion that deviations from additivity of

---

[81] See, for example, C. P. Smyth, E. W. Engel, and E. Bright Wilson, *J. Am. Chem. Soc.*, **51**, 1736 (1929), and M. L. Koenig-Gressmann, *thesis*, University of Munich, 1938.

[82] J. Wellm, *thesis*, University of Königsberg, 1934.

[83] J. C. Hubbard, *Phys. Rev.*, I, **30**, 740 (1910); *Z. physik. Chem.*, **74**, 207 (1910).

[84] K. Fajans and O. Johnson, *Trans. Electrochem. Soc.*, **82**, 273 (1942).

[85] K. Fajans *et al.*, Refractometric Investigations, I–LV (1924–1942). See references 32–58 and the references cited in paper LV (reference 32).

the Lorentz–Lorenz equation (43) can be considered as an indication and measure of changes in the electronic systems involved.   These changes are due to intra- and intermolecular electric interactions between the parts of the system.

It is beyond the scope of this work to discuss the way in which this point of view has been applied to the deviations from additivity of the molar refraction, dispersion, and volume of molecules, crystals, and solutions derived from ions.[85]   However, a few indications may show how exact measurements of molar refractions of organic substances can again be made valuable in the clarification of structural problems.

(a)   The Lorentz–Lorenz refraction for infinitely long waves[86] is considered a measure of the electronic polarizability of the molecule, i. e., of the looseness of its electronic system.   The following regularities have been found to have general validity: (1)   An electronic system is tightened, i. e., its molar refraction is decreased, by adjacent positive charges.   (2)   An electronic system is loosened, i. e., its molar refraction is increased, by adjacent negative charges.   (3) When, within a given electronic system, the nuclear charge is split or the distribution of the positive charges becomes less symmetrical, the electronic system is loosened, i. e., the molar refraction is increased.

(b)   These rules become especially fruitful when combined with the consideration[87] of the electron configuration in molecules and ions in respect to the principal quantum numbers.   In the isoelectronic series Ne (1.00) < HF (1.9) < H_2O (3.75) < H_3N (5.67) < H_4C (6.58), the molar refraction increases from 1.0 to 6.58.   In all these particles, the eight outer electrons can be considered to form a closed unit, quantized in respect to the embedded atomic cores.   The loosening of this electronic shell is due to the gradual splitting of the 8+ core of neon leading finally to the C^{4+} + 4 H^+ cores of methane.   The increase (by 0.91) of R from H_3N to H_4C is less than could be expected from the gradation of the preceding molecules of the series because the tetrahedral distribution of the protons in H_4C is the most symmetrical.

(c)   Methane shows an abnormally low refraction also in the series of saturated hydrocarbons, the difference between ethane and methane being 4.8 cc. instead of 4.63.   This tightness of the electronic shell in methane is obviously responsible for the relatively high binding energy of this molecule,[88] and especially for the high energy of the dissociation of the first hydrogen atom from it.[89]   On the other hand, for formic acid $R_{exp.}$ = 8.56 is larger than could be expected from R of acetic acid (12.99 − 4.63 = 8.36).   The looseness of the electronic system of formic acid is reflected also in its binding energy.   While the heat of combustion for higher members of homologous series increases by 157 kcal. for each CH_2 group, the difference between acetic and formic acid is 147 kcal.   Thus, formic acid has a relatively large heat of combustion, i. e., a relatively small binding energy.

---

[86] Concerning the reciprocal plotting method of P. Wulff for the extrapolation to $\lambda = \infty$ from measurements in the visible, see reference 56 and pages 660–661.

[87] See K. Fajans, J. Chem. Phys., **10**, 759 (1942).   K. Fajans and T. Berlin, Phys. Rev., **63**, 309 (1943).

[88] F. D. Rossini, J. Research Natl. Bur. Standards, **13**, 21 (1934).

[89] H. G. Andersen, C. B. Kistiakowsky, and E. R. van Artsdalen, J. Chem. Phys., **10**, 305 (1942).

(d)   The *particles*, N_2, CO, CN^-, HCN, and H_2C_2, all have *ten valence electrons*, which are considered to be subdivided, like those in the neon atom, into a group of two electrons with the principal quantum number I and a group of eight electrons with the principal quantum number II.   The electronic structure, for example, of N_2 and H_2C_2 is represented as:

$$:N^{5+}:N^{5+}: \qquad \text{and} \qquad :H^+C^{4+}:C^{4+}H^+:$$

Indicating only the core charges of these five particles, one has the following gradation of the molar refraction:

$$N^{5+}N^{5+}(4.4) \; < \; H^+C^{4+}N^{5+}(6.5) \; < \; H^+C^{4+}C^{4+}H^+(9.0)$$
$$\wedge \qquad\qquad\qquad \wedge$$
$$C^{4+}O^{6+}(5.0) \qquad\quad C^{4+}N^{5+}(8.6)$$

The gradual increase of refraction between N_2 and H_2C_2 is thus due to the splitting of the first and then of the second N^{5+} core into C^{4+} and H^+.   On the other hand, CO has a higher refraction than N_2 because the distribution of the core charges is less symmetrical in CO;   HCN has a smaller refraction than CN^- because the positively charged proton tightens the electronic shell.

(e)   Since the *change in the distribution of positive charges within an electronic shell* of a definite quantization can cause such pronounced differences in the tightness of the shell, it is not surprising that even *chain isomers* show distinct differences in molar refraction (page 678).   They differ in respect to the symmetry of the distribution of the cores and perhaps also to the quantization of the electrons.   A rule

TABLE VI

PROPERTIES OF NORMAL AND ISOPROPYL ESTER OF PROPIONIC ACID[a]

Compound	Heat of combustion, kcal.	Heat of vaporization, kcal.	d	n_D	R_D	$R\gamma - R\alpha$
Normal	855.9	8.6	0.8808	1.3936	31.501	0.732
Iso	852.3	8.3	0.8660	1.3872	31.576	0.744
Δ	3.6	0.3	0.0148	0.0064	−0.075	−0.012

[a] E. Schjånberg, Z. *physik. Chem.*, **172**, 197 (1935).

which applies, although not without exceptions, to the comparison of many normal and iso (isopropyl at end of chain) compounds can be stated here as follows:[90]

The iso compound has a larger intramolecular binding energy (smaller heat of combustion), weaker intermolecular forces (smaller heat of vaporization), smaller density, and smaller refractive index, but a larger molar refraction and molar dispersion.   As usual, the difference in dispersion is relatively larger than that in refraction.

Table VI[91] illustrates the rule.

[90] K. Fajans, to be published in *J. Am. Chem. Soc.*
[91] E. Schjånberg, Z. *physik. Chem.*, **172**, 197 (1935).

There is a good reason[90] to believe that the nearly generally occurring increase of the Lorentz–Lorenz refraction caused by increase of temperature of a liquid (0.005–0.015% per degree[92]) or accompanying its vaporization (about 1%[45]) is a real indication of the loosening of the electronic shell due to the increase of the distance between the molecules. These facts and the above properties of normal and iso compounds and of lithium perchlorate ether solutions (page 680) are examples of the parallelism between the change of molar volume and that of molar refraction. The exceptional case of the decrease of the molar refraction and dispersion of liquid water with increasing temperature[93] and of the vapor of acetic acid when the dimer dissociates (page 678), must be due to specific tightening effects. Displacement of the protons involved in the intermolecular "hydrogen bridges" may be of influence in the case of water.

II. APPARATUS AND MEASUREMENTS

It often happens that appreciable errors are made through failure of the observer to control external conditions properly, e. g., in placing the sample, adjusting the light source, etc. Moreover, an individual instrument may fail to meet the optical and mechanical requirements of the measurement. Thus, the published n values even of very pure compounds show striking disagreement; for example, the data on eight carefully purified hydrocarbons obtained in two separate investigations with different Abbé refractometers were found[94] to differ by an average of 22×10^{-5}. Discrepancies in dispersion measurements are likely to be even more serious (the difference $n_F - n_C$ may be as much as 100% in error if the ordinary Abbé refractometer is used!). Many sources of error can be avoided by recalibration of the instruments with standard substances and by a better understanding of the instruments.

1. Light Sources

In order to obtain an intense source of radiation containing the desired spectral lines, one relies now chiefly on the use of *electric discharge tubes* of various types. A list and description of the most important lines used in the laboratory or encountered in the literature are given in table VII.

Available commercially[95] are *sodium lamps* which operate directly on 110 volts alternating current. The radiation consists almost entirely of the very intense yellow D_1 and D_2 doublet; the other sodium lines have a negligible intensity.

---

[92] See, for example, K. Fajans, P. Hoelemann, and Z. Shibata (XXI), *Z. physik. Chem.*, **B13,** 360 (1931).

[93] See A. Kruis (LI), *Z. physik. Chem.*, **B34,** 92 (1936).

[94] B. J. Mair, *J. Research Natl. Bur. Standards*, **9,** 472 (1932).

[95] Sodium Lab-Arc, *General Electric Co.*, Schenectady, N. Y. Gates Sodium Laboratory Arc, *The Emil Greiner Co.*, New York, N. Y.

The *mercury lamp*[96] which furnishes four very intense lines between yellow and violet is recommended for dispersion measurements. Unfortunately, mercury gives no lines at the red end of the spectrum.

Various *"Geissler" tubes*, filled with hydrogen or the noble gases, are also available. These must be operated at a high potential (500 to 15,000 volts).

The *hydrogen* discharge tube, widely used in the past because of the simplicity of the spectrum and the availability of the gas, suffers from

TABLE VII
SPECTRAL LINES[a] USED IN REFRACTOMETRY

Element	Symbol	Color	λ, Å. in air, 15° C, 1atm.	$\lambda^2 \times 10^{-10}$ cm.^{2}	$\nu^2 \times 10^{-28}$ sec.$^{-2}$
Helium	He_{r_1}	Red	7065.19	49.917	17.993
Lithium	Li_r	Red	6707.84$_6$	44.995	19.961
Helium	He_{r_2} or r	Red	6678.14$_9$	44.598	20.139
Hydrogen	$H\alpha$ or C	Red	6562.8	43.070	20.853
Cadmium	Cd_r	Red	6438.469$_6$	41.454	21.666
Sodium	$\left.\begin{matrix}D_1\\D_2\end{matrix}\right\}D$	Yellow Yellow	$\left.\begin{matrix}5890\\5896\end{matrix}\right\}5893$	34.73	25.86
Helium	D_3	Yellow	5875.61$_6$	34.523	26.016
Mercury	Hg_{y_1}	Yellow	5790.66	33.532	26.785
Mercury	Hg_{y_2}	Yellow	5769.60	33.288	26.982
Mercury	Hg_g or e	Green	5460.74	29.820	30.119
Thallium	Tl_g	Green	5350.48	28.628	31.373
Cadmium	Cd_g	Green	5085.82$_4$	25.866	34.724
Helium	He_g or ν	Green	5015.67$_5$	25.157	35.702
Helium	$He_{b\ g}$	Blue-green	4921.93	24.225	37.075
Hydrogen	$H\beta$ or F	Blue	4861.33	23.633	38.005
Cadmium	Cd_{b_1}	Blue	4799.91	23.039	38.984
Helium	He_b or c	Blue	4713.14$_3$	22.214	40.433
Cadmium	Cd_{b_2}	Blue	4678.15	21.885	41.040
Helium	He_v or i	Blue-violet	4471.47$_7$	19.994	44.922
Mercury	$Hg_{b.v.}$ or g	Blue-violet	4358.34$_3$	18.995	47.283
Hydrogen	$H\gamma$ or G'	Violet	4340.46	18.840	47.672
Mercury	Hg_v.	Violet	4046.56	16.375	54.850

[a] Values of λ taken from Landolt-Börnstein, *Physikalisch-Chemische Tabellen*, 5th ed., II, p. 816, and Erg. I, pp. 335–366.

several serious disadvantages. Some of the hydrogen lines fade out each time the tube is operated more than a few minutes, while none of the lines are as intense as those from the best sodium or mercury lamps. In addition, slight contamination often leads to the appearance of spurious lines. The tube has a short life, which can be extended only by rather elaborate refilling procedures; a satisfactory refillable hydrogen tube is available commercially.[97] Ward and Fulweiler[98] describe a hydrogen tube which can

[96] For example, the General Electric H-4 capillary mercury arc, General Electric Co., or the Hanovia mercury arc, *Hanovia Chemical & Manufacturing Co.*, Newark, N. J.

[97] See the pamphlet, "Reference Manual to Precision Refractometer," *Bausch & Lomb Optical Co.*, Rochester, N. Y.

[98] A. L. Ward and W. H. Fulweiler, *Ind. Eng. Chem., Anal. Ed.*, 6, 396 (1934).

be continuously refilled; it also simultaneously emits lines of the mercury spectrum. A relatively stable tube has been described by Goyan[99] which emits simultaneously the C and F hydrogen lines and the sodium D line, and which can be made in the laboratory.

The *helium tube*, one form of which is shown in figure 3, is a most convenient, stable source of intense, well-separated spectral lines distributed over the entire visible range. It is especially recommended for use with the Pulfrich refractometer, where the instrument itself serves to separate the spectral lines. This source has the great advantage that the yellow helium D_3 line has practically the same wave length (5876 Å.) as the commonly used sodium D line. For most colorless organic compounds, the value of n_{D_3} is larger than n_D by only one or two units in the fourth decimal. For maximum intensity, the tube is filled with helium at a pressure of 15 to 20

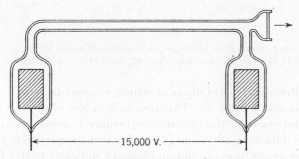

Fig. 3.—Helium discharge tube.

mm. and is caused to discharge between the hollow, cylindrical nickel electrodes by applying a potential of up to 15,000 volts from an ordinary "luminous sign" transformer (30 ma. secondary). A similar discharge tube, containing only a few millimeters pressure of helium and a small amount of cadmium metal, serves as a source of helium radiation when operated at a few thousand volts, and as a source of numerous intense cadmium lines at higher potentials.

To separate the lines of discontinuous light sources or to isolate certain regions of continuous light, *filters*[100] or *monochromators*, based on the principle of the spectroscope, are used. Sets of filters for the separation of the yellow, green, and blue-violet mercury lines are listed in table VIII. The W77A filter transmits an especially pure radiation ($\lambda = 5460.7$) which is useful in precision interferometry. For other possible combinations, see

[99] F. M. Goyan, *Ind. Eng. Chem., Anal. Ed.*, **14**, 60 (1942).

[100] See "Glass Color Filters," *Corning Glass Works*, Corning, N. Y., "Wratten Filters," *Eastman Kodak Co.*, Rochester, N. Y., and "Jena Colored Optical Filter Glasses," *Fish-Schurman Corp.*, New York, N. Y.

Strong[101] and Gibb.[102] It must be kept in mind that filters usually do not sharply separate spectral lines which are closer to each other than about 100 Å. The relative intensities of the various wave lengths transmitted by a given filter can be calculated from its absorption curve[100] (per cent absorption *vs.* λ) and from the relative intensities[103] of the spectral lines in the source.

For the sake of convenience, many refractometric techniques have been adapted to the use of ordinary white light, *e. g.*, that emitted by a tungsten

TABLE VIII

FILTERS FOR MERCURY LINES[a]

Wave length, λ...	4358	5460.7	5769 to 5790
Filter..........	C.G. (038 + 511) or W. 50	C.G. (350 + 430 + 512) or W. 62	C.G. (349.2 × std. + 401,[b] $1/_2$ × std.) or W. 70

[a] C.G. refers to Corning glass filters, W. to Eastman Wratten filters.
[b] See W. M. D. Bryant, *J. Am. Chem. Soc.*, **65**, 96 (1943); *ibid.*, 128.

lamp, the intensity distribution of which corresponds to a mean wave length ($\bar{\lambda}$) at about 5600 Å. This results in a loss of accuracy, especially where the dispersion of the measured substance is great (see, for instance, the Nichols refractometer, page 734). By using appropriate filters before the tungsten source, one can obtain colors of sufficient purity for measurements of $n_{\bar{\lambda}}$ to an accuracy of a few units in the fourth decimal. Filters which transmit an intense light comparable to the D line of sodium are the W. 64, the W. 73 and the C.G. (428 + 348).

2.   Refractometers Measuring Critical Angle

The most widely used Abbé and Pulfrich refractometers measure the angle of refraction, r, of a light ray which has a corresponding angle of incidence i on passing from a substance, m, into a more highly refracting glass prism, P (Fig. 4). In other words, we use equation (1) in the form $n = n_P$ (sin r/sin i), where n_P refers to the refractive index of the prism.

The problem of obtaining accurately r and i is greatly simplified by making the angle of incidence i equal to 90° (grazing incidence; sin $i = 1$). We then have a refracted ray at the so-called critical angle of refraction, r_c, which is particularly easy to observe since no rays are refracted into P

[101] J. Strong, *Procedures in Experimental Physics.* Prentice-Hall, New York, 1942.

[102] T. R. P. Gibb, *Optical Methods of Chemical Analysis.* McGraw-Hill, New York, 1942.

[103] G. R. Harrison, *Wavelength Tables.* Wiley, New York, 1939.

at an angle greater than r_c. As can be seen in figure 4, all beams of light entering P at a point o with angles of incidence i from $0°$ to $90°$, are refracted into an angular region of the prism bounded on one side by the normal-line N–N' (along which no change in direction of the rays occurs) and on the other side by the critical ray.   In other words, the critical angle of refraction r_c, forms a sharp dividing line (critical boundary) between a light and a dark region inside the prism.   Angle r_c is sometimes called the *critical angle of reflection*, because a ray traveling in the reverse direction of the arrow in figure 4 and striking point o at an angle slightly greater than r_c, would not pass into m but would be totally reflected at the interface m–P.

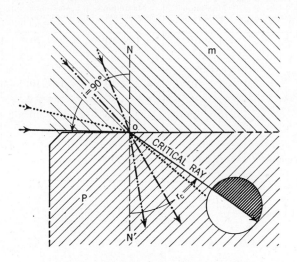

Fig. 4.—Critical boundary inside a prism.

In practice, the conditions represented by figure 4 are somewhat modified. The value of r_c is not obtained directly.   In order to observe the "critical boundary" with a telescope, the rays must pass from the prism into air, suffering, in general, an additional change in direction.   Thus, as shown in figure 5a, the observed apparent angle of refraction, r_c', is smaller than r_c:

$$\sin (90° - r_c') = \frac{\mathbf{n}_P}{\mathbf{n}_{\text{air}}} \sin (90° - r_c) = n_P \sin (90° - r_c) \qquad (44)$$

Moreover, in actual refractometers, the whole surface of the prism instead of one point is illuminated with light at or near the grazing incidence.   The telescope collects all rays traveling parallel to each other, *i. e.*, all rays with the same r, into one line in the focal plane.   Thus, the *critical boundary* shows up in the telescope as a sharp line of demarcation between a dark field and a brightly illuminated field having the color of the monochromatic light used. Slightly modified considerations apply to the cases in which white light or sources containing several wave lengths are used (see pages 689 and 709).

Table IX summarizes accuracy and range of some commercial critical-angle refractometers.

TABLE IX

MAXIMUM ACCURACY AND RANGE OF CRITICAL ANGLE REFRACTOMETERS

Refractometer	Maximum accuracy, n_D	Maximum accuracy, Δn	Maximum accuracy, $(n_F - n_C)$	Range of n
Pulfrich[a, b]	$\pm 1 \times 10^{-4}$	$\pm 1 \times 10^{-5}$	$\pm 2 \times 10^{-5}$	1.33–1.61 1.47–1.74 1.64–1.86
Abbé[a–e]	$\pm 1 \times 10^{-4}$	$\pm 2 \times 10^{-4}$	$\pm 1 \times 10^{-4}$	1.30–1.70 or 1.45–1.84
Precision Abbé[c, e]	$\pm 2 \times 10^{-5}$	$\pm 2 \times 10^{-5}$	$\pm 2 \times 10^{-5}$	1.33–1.64 or 1.36–1.50 or 1.40–1.70
Dipping (immersion)[b, c]	$\pm (7 \times 10^{-5})$	$\pm 7 \times 10^{-5}$	. . . .	1.32–1.54 (6 prisms)[c]

[a] Hilger.
[b] Zeiss.
[c] Bausch and Lomb.
[d] Spencer.
[e] Valentine.

A.   PULFRICH REFRACTOMETER[104]

This instrument is particularly useful for differential measurements, including dispersion. Although absolute values obtained with the Pulfrich refractometer are not reliable in the 5th decimal place, largely because of mechanical faults,[105] a *comparison* at two wave lengths or of two substances can be made to $\pm 1 \times 10^{-5}$. Solids and liquids of index less than 1.84 can be investigated over a wide temperature range; for $t > 100°$ C., a specially mounted prism must be used. The Pulfrich refractometer is suited to investigations in which liquid samples must be excluded from contact with air, e. g., hygroscopic liquids or volatile solutions. Although n cannot be read directly, but must be deduced from a set of observations, once the apparatus has been set up a value of n can be obtained about every five minutes.

[104] *Adam Hilger, Ltd.*, London. *Carl Zeiss, Inc.*, New York, N. Y.
[105] J. Guild, *Proc. Phys. Soc. London*, **30**, 157 (1917–1918).

Optical Principles.—The instrument measures the angle of emergence, α ($\alpha = 90° - r_c'$, Fig. 5a), of the critical ray passing from the prism, P, of index n_P into air. From equations (1) and (2) and figure 5a, $(\sin \alpha)/\sin (90° - r_c) = n_P$ and $n/n_P = \sin r_c/\sin 90° = \sin r_c/1$; and, by eliminating r_c:

$$n = \sqrt{n_P^2 - \sin^2\alpha} \qquad (45)$$

The "Pulfrich" is not restricted to the use of a monochromatic light source. With the exception of the unusual case that $dn/d\lambda = dn_P/d\lambda$, i. e., that the dispersions of sample and prism are identical,[106] there exists

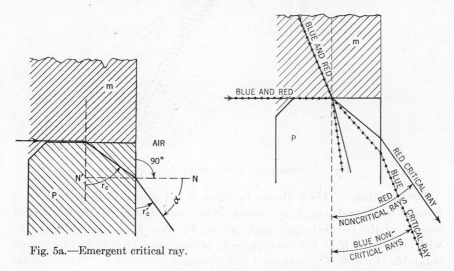

Fig. 5a.—Emergent critical ray.

Fig. 5b.—Overlapping of blue critical ray by red rays.

a different value of α for each wave length in the source, as illustrated in figure 5b. At first thought, one might expect that in using a multicolored light source the boundary between the dark and light region in the refractometer would be obscured by the superposition of the differently colored noncritical rays which always form a diffuse fringe of color on one side of the corresponding critical ray. However, by confining the incident beam to within very close limits of grazing incidence (compare Figs. 5b and 5c) and choosing sources with spectral lines at well-spaced intervals (Table VII), one obtains a separate sharp critical boundary for each λ. Thus, the Pulfrich refractometer within certain limits serves as its own monochromator.

---

[106] W. A. Roth and F. Eisenlohr, *Refractometrisches Hilfsbuch.* Veit, Leipzig, 1911.

Spectral lines as close as 50 Å. can be distinguished using the ordinary prisms. For the behavior of the sodium D doublet, see Guild.[105]

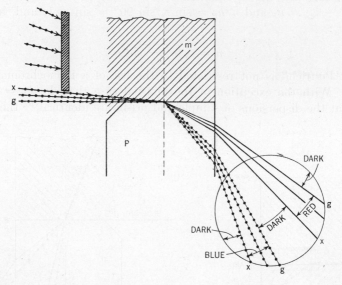

Fig. 5c.—Separation of blue and red critical rays.

Construction.—This is shown in figure 6. A pencil of light from S is focused by a condenser, c, to provide rays which just graze the horizontal surface of the beveled right-angle prism, P. An observing telescope, T, with cross hairs H at $45°$ in eyepiece E, is permanently attached to a large rotatable circle, $G. C.$, graduated in half-degrees of arc (θ_n). The telescope may be inclined at any angle between $\theta = 0°$ and $\theta = 75°$, as indicated by the vernier, when clamping screw, $C. S.$, is loosened, so as to allow location of the critical rays. (At the critical position, the telescope cross hairs are at $\theta = \alpha + \theta_z$; see eq. 49.) For convenience, the refracted rays are first collected by a reflecting prism, P', in front of the telescope objective, L_3, causing all rays to be bent at right angles into the telescope so that one can always comfortably make observations from a position facing the plane of the graduated circle. The elliptical stop, st, in front of P' can and should be rotated so as to close off and protect the glass when the instrument is not in use. Another section of the stop can be used to cut off successively light from each half of the prism when making direct comparisons of two substances placed side by side on the prism.

A slow motion of the circle over a limited range ($\approx 5°$ of arc) is provided by the micrometer tangent screw, $M. S.$, so that the cross hairs can be accurately set at the position of the critical boundary line. The slow motion is transmitted to the circle only when the clamping screw is tightened; the clamping screw should be kept loose except when the micrometer screw is in use in order to avoid accidental mechanical strain on the telescope mount-

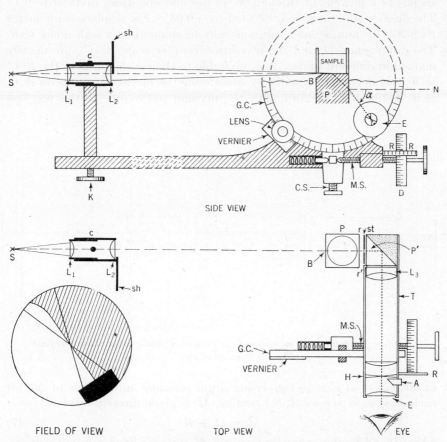

SIDE VIEW

FIELD OF VIEW   TOP VIEW   EYE

Fig. 6.—Schematic view of the Pulfrich refractometer: α, critical angle of emergence A, Abbé prism (zero point); B, prism bevel; C, condenser; $C. S.$, clamping screw; D, micrometer drum; E, eyepiece; $G. C.$, graduated circle; H, cross hairs; K, condenser screw; L_1, L_2, condenser lenses; L_3, telescope objective; $M. S.$, micrometer screw; N, normal line to prism surface; P, refracting prism (interchangeable); P', reflecting prism; r–r', refracting edge of prism; R–R, reference line carrying revolution counter scale; S, light source; sh, shutter; st, elliptical stop; T, telescope.

ing. The micrometer screw is also used for the accurate measurement of small angular displacements of the circle, $\Delta\theta$, which is defined by:

$$\Delta\theta = \theta_2 - \theta_1 \qquad (46)$$

where θ_1 and θ_2 are the two positions of the $G. C.$

The drum attached to the head of the micrometer screw is marked with 200 equal divisions, the number of divisions going past reference line R–R being a measure of $\Delta\theta$ (Fig. 7). One revolution of the drum corresponds to a movement through $20'$ of arc and one drum division to $0.1'$. The drum reading can be estimated to $\pm 0.03'$. For displacements larger than $20'$, the number of revolutions may be counted on a scale along R–R. The drum scale, D, and the revolution counter scale, $R.\ C.$, are usually marked in different units. It is advisable to change the units of the $R.\ C.$ scale from degrees to minutes by considering the successive marks on $R.\ C.$ as indicating the 0th, 20th, 40th. . . , division and so on. In this way one

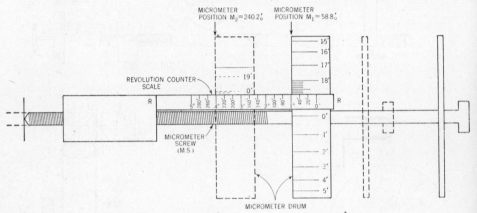

Fig. 7.—Micrometer screw scales of the Pulfrich refractometer labeled to read in minutes of arc.

avoids errors of sign in converting drum positions into values of $\Delta\theta$, for each *micrometer screw* ($M.\ S.$) *reading*, M, is given directly by:

$$M = D + R \qquad (47)$$

where D and R refer to the drum and $R.\ C.$ scale readings in minutes of arc, respectively. We then have simply:

$$\Delta\theta = M_2 - M_1 \qquad (48)$$

for any two settings (1) and (2) of the graduated circle, where $M_2 > M_1$. For rapid conversion of scale readings to values of M, it is helpful to refer to an enlarged replica of the $R.\ C.$ scale, along which have been placed the values of R corresponding to each mark on the scale, as in figure 7.

For large angular displacements, the inaccuracy in the pitch of the screw and errors in its mounting[105] may cause a discrepancy between the true value of $\Delta\theta$, as read from the $G.\ C.$, and the value read from the $M.\ S.$ scales. This discrepancy may amount to as much as $1.0'$ of arc (1×10^{-4}

in Δn), but can usually be ignored if $\Delta\theta < 0.5°$. A rough check on the accuracy of the screw is made by bringing successively two arbitrarily selected marks on the *G. C.*, *e. g.*, 50° and 54°, into coincidence with the reference mark (0 on vernier), each time recording the *M. S.* reading, M_n. To make certain that a discrepancy is not caused by an error in the graduated circle, the operation is repeated for a few other *G. C.* positions (*e. g.*, 54° to 58°, 58° to 62°, etc.). A complete calibration[39, 105] for very careful work involving a large number of similar comparisons along the whole length of the screw is essential for accurate dispersion measurements. Another, preferable, calibration method is the measurement of $\Delta\theta$ at close intervals along the screw when two standard substances are placed side by side or successively on the prism. The observed deviations of $\Delta\theta$ from the (known) correct value are plotted against the corresponding mean micrometer screw reading, $\bar{M}$. From this curve, if a sufficiently small $\Delta\theta$ is used, the total correction required for any M can be calculated and plotted.

The instrument is set up against a dark background in a space in which the temperature stays reasonably constant, or in a thermostated box. An appropriate prism, P, is mounted firmly on the triangular base by tightening the set screw in its mount.

Solid samples are placed on the horizontal prism surface according to the methods described on pages 704–706. Various kinds of "refractometer vessels" may be attached to the prism for holding liquid samples (see pages 702–703).

Illumination.—With the sample placed on the horizontal surface of P, the light source is fixed a few centimeters from condenser c (Fig. 6) and lens L_1 is shifted back and forth until a sharp (inverted) image of the source is observed on a piece of tissue paper just in front of the prism at B. To obtain maximum intensity, the whole surface of P should be illuminated with slightly converging rays. Consequently, the source image should be at least as wide as the prism, and should be approximately bisected by its horizontal surface. For colored liquids, the image should be raised somewhat higher.[106] These conditions will usually not be attained by the single focusing operation described above; to obtain the proper size of the image the relative position of source and condenser will have to be adjusted, followed by a refocusing of the image. The image is displaced up or down by moving condenser screw K. For the final adjustment of the condenser, K is turned slowly while viewing the critical boundary through the telescope until maximum sharpness is obtained.

For accurate dispersion measurements (5th decimal), an adjustment of the prism block relative to the telescope may be necessary, since the central ray of the illuminating beam should pass through the center of the telescope objective, L_3. Proper illumination of the objective is achieved when its aperture is fully or at least symmetrically filled with light.[105] To this end the prism block is adjusted on its supporting pillar while examining the "exit pupil" of the telescope with a magnifying lens. The "exit pupil" (or eyepoint) of a telescope is an area, through which pass all rays of the image. It is somewhat smaller than the eyepiece lens surface, and located near the position where the eye would normally be placed to view the image. If a piece of paper is placed at the exit pupil, a bright disk of light is seen. This has an elliptical shape at the exit pupil of the Pulfrich refractometer; it is usually smaller than the superimposed dark image of the elliptical stop (st, Fig. 6). Adjustments should be made until the bright and dark ellipses appear symmetrical with respect to each other.

Temperature Control.—For absolute measurement of n_D of liquids to ±0.0001 under conditions in which the room temperature is fairly constant, the instrument may be used without special thermal control if the temperature of the sample is measured directly to ±0.2° at the time of measurement. In this case, one should know or roughly measure the value of dn/dt (page 656) so as to allow interpolation of n at some standard temperature. However, it is usually just as convenient to provide temperature control of the sample to ±0.2° by circulating tap water around the prism.

To achieve the highest accuracy (±1 × 10⁻⁵) with which it is possible to measure Δn (e. g., $n_F - n_C$, or $n_{soln.} - n_{solv.}$), it is necessary to keep the temperature fluctuation of *liquid* samples within about 0.02°. This requirement is partly taken care of on the standard instruments by the circulation of thermostated water through the prism jacket and through a hollow silver cylinder (fitted with a 0.1° thermometer) which is lowered (rack and pinion) into the open refractometer vessel until it touches the sample. For a modified all-glass "refractometer vessel" providing for temperature control of a completely enclosed liquid, see page 703. This device eliminates cooling by evaporation and prevents contamination. It does not provide for the immersion of a thermometer directly into the sample. The temperature may be found accurately enough by taking the average of the readings of thermometers placed in the path of the circulating liquid at inlet i and outlet o of the jacket.

If the working temperature differs considerably (>5° C.) from that of the room, disturbing temperature gradients are set up in the prism because its large vertical surface is necessarily exposed. The most satisfactory way to eliminate such disturbances is to place the entire instrument in an insulated box which can be thermostated to ±1.0° C.; this also serves to define the temperature of the reference medium, air. For modifications of the instrument which improve its use at temperatures around 100° C., see Hoelemann and Kohner[46] and Pesce and Hoelemann.[53]

Conditions for a Sharp Boundary.—When the telescope is in the proper position, the field of view should have the appearance of figure 6 (upper field dark, entire lower field bright, when shutter *sh* is not interposed) if the liquid sample (see page 705 for solids) is correctly illuminated (see page 693) with monochromatic light. Contrast may be improved by adjusting the shutter. When the source is a discharge tube furnishing several spectral lines, some or all of these wave lengths should appear as bright colored bands, sharp on the upper edge. The normal order of the bands is violet, blue, green, yellow, and red, looking into the telescope field from left to right (*i. e.*, $\alpha_{\text{red}} < \alpha_{\text{violet}}$). When the dispersion of the sample is near that of the prism (rare case), the order may be inverted or rearranged (see example, page 702). The width and sharpness of these bands can be changed by shutter *sh* (Fig. 6). When the serrated edge of the shutter is moved so as to cut off more and more of the top part of the light pencil, the colored bands become narrower on the diffuse side, and the whole field of view becomes less intense, while the contrast at the critical boundary is improved. There is never any doubt as to which edge of the band is the critical boundary because its position is never changed by moving the shutter.

Any of the following may cause blurring of the critical boundary: (*1*) Improper focusing of light source (see page 693). (*2*) Poor temperature control, or instrument not at temperature equilibrium. (*3*) Dirt on refractometer vessel or prism surface, turbidity in the sample. If the incident light is scattered, the intensity of the bands is decreased, and the contrast at the critical boundary is diminished by stray light. Such obstructions may also prevent rays at grazing incidence from entering the prism. This shielding effect can cause appreciable errors in the refractive index. (*4*) Intensity of light source too low. The critical boundaries for some spectral lines are inherently of lower intensity; for instance, because of this factor, one can obtain $n_{\text{He}v}$ with only about one-third the accuracy possible for $n_{\text{He}D_3}$. (*5*) Overlapping of bands corresponding to neighboring wave lengths in the source. Adjustment of the shutter will eliminate the blurring.

Measurement of Critical Angle of Emergence, α.—The angle which is read from the graduated circle, *G. C.*, when the cross hairs of the telescope are set to coincide exactly with the critical boundary is defined as the apparent critical angle of emergence, θ. The true critical angle of emergence is:

$$\alpha = \theta - \theta_z \tag{49}$$

the *zero point correction*, θ_z, being the *G. C.* reading when the telescope axis (dotted plane, Fig. 6, top view) coincides with a line (*N*, Fig. 6, side view) perpendicular to the vertical prism surface. The deviation from zero, θ_z, of the $G.\ C.$ reading when the telescope is truly at 90° with respect to the prism may be as much as 0.5°.

The true zero position, that is, the true horizontal position of the telescope ($G.\ C.$ at θ_z), is found by locating, with the cross hairs, the light rays which leave the prism exactly perpendicular to its surface. To produce

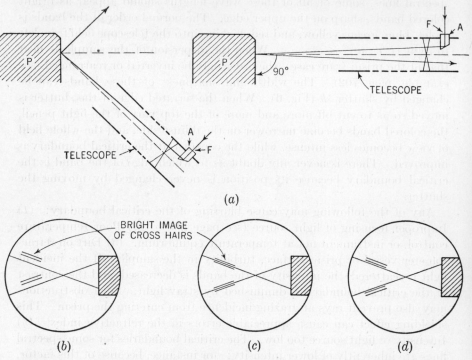

Fig. 8.   (a) Alignment of telescope in the true horizontal (90°) position for zero point. The part of the telescope axis passing through the cross-hair intersection in (a) actually makes a 90° angle with respect to the plane of the paper (see Fig. 6).   (b–d) Field of view at or near zero point (Pulfrich refractometer).

such rays, the telescope is placed approximately at the horizontal position ($\theta \approx 0°$) and the small Abbé autocollimating prism A (Fig. 6) is illuminated. Light entering the Abbé prism face, F (Fig. 8a), is directed to the vertical surface of prism P, where part of it is reflected back into the telescope, provided its axis is nearly horizontal. In this case, on looking through the eyepiece, a bright image of part of the cross hairs will be observed which is slightly displaced from the cross hairs themselves (Fig. 8b). To obtain optimum brightness and uniform appearance of the cross-hair image, one adjusts the direction and intensity of illumination of face

F (Fig. 8a). This is most conveniently done by converging on F with an ordinary lens or telescope the light from a small flashlight bulb. The true horizontal position is now obtained by moving the telescope with the micrometer screw until the cross hairs and its image exactly coincide (Fig. 8c). For many instruments, the optical alignment is such that this coincidence can never be obtained. In this case, the correct position of the telescope is one in which the image appears symmetrical with respect to the cross hairs (as, for example, in Fig. 8d). Consecutive settings on this true zero position can be made to agree within $\pm0.05'$. The value of θ_z is read directly from the vernier to within $0.5'$ or to within $0.25'$ using the relation:

$$\theta_z = M_z{'} - M_0 \tag{50}$$

(compare with Eqs. 47 and 48), where M_z and M_0 are the micrometer readings when $G. C.$ is set at the true zero position and at the apparent zero position, respectively.

θ_z must be checked from time to time. However, when a number of similar measurements are being made, one can usually assume θ_z to remain constant, unless there is a specific reason for suspecting a change, particularly if one prism has been substituted for another or if samples or vessels have been attached to or detached from the prism, which sometimes is done too forcefully. In general, one should measure the zero point whenever the instrument has suffered some undue mechanical strain, or after it has been subjected to large temperature changes. The changes in θ_z are usually irregular, and during normal use amount to several minutes of arc (4th decimal of n).

To measure the apparent critical angle, θ, move the telescope along with the graduated circle until the critical boundary approximately bisects the field of view. Arrest $G. C.$ with clamping screw $C. S.$ and make the intersection of the cross hairs coincide with the sharp edge of the critical boundary (Fig. 6, lower left) by turning $M. S.$ It is best to make the cross hairs approach the boundary from the bright side of the field, so that the intersection is strongly illuminated during all but the very last part of the setting. With the intense spectral lines (e. g., He_{D_3}), the settings are reproducible to within $\pm0.05'$ on the micrometer scale, which corresponds to an accuracy of better than $\pm1 \times 10^{-5}$ in n. For a measurement of the *absolute* value of n, an accuracy of α of $\pm1.0'$ is sufficient, since inherent instrumental errors limit the absolute accuracy to $\pm1 \times 10^{-4}$. The vernier can be read to $\pm0.5'$. Several settings should be made. It is advisable to check the instrument by a trial measurement of standard water.

Measurement of Differences ($\Delta n = n_2 - n_1$).—In order to determine differences in n, it is necessary to measure the absolute value of only one (e. g., α_1) of the two critical angles (α_1 and α_2). The value of α_1 should be determined by the displacement method described below since the accuracy in α allowed by direct vernier readings ($\pm 1'$) is not always sufficient to give the fullest possible accuracy in Δn. The measurement of the other critical angle, α_2, is obtained with the highest accuracy relative to the first, α_1, if the angular displacement, $\Delta\theta = \theta_2 - \theta_1$ (see Eq. 46), is obtained directly from the micrometer screw while $G. C.$ is clamped and if the zero point remains constant. When these conditions hold, $\Delta\alpha = \Delta\theta$, where by definition, for $\alpha_2 < \alpha_1$,

$$\Delta\alpha = \alpha_2 - \alpha_1 \tag{51}$$

In case the two angles, θ_1 and θ_2, differ by more than the range of the micrometer screw ($0.5°$), each should be evaluated by the following *displacement method*. The method is based on the principle that one can bring two line segments ($-$ $-$)·into the same line ($-$ $-$) more accurately than one can interpolate on a vernier. The cross hairs are set on the critical boundary ($M.S.$ reading is M_c). Then the micrometer screw is used to bring the zero mark of the vernier in exact coincidence with some nearby whole or half degree mark θ_n on the graduated circle ($M.S.$ reading is M_n; see Eq. 47 for definition of M). The angular displacement $\Delta\theta_n$ is:

$$\Delta\theta_n = M_c - M_n \tag{52}$$

and the required angle, θ, is:

$$\theta = \theta_n + \Delta\theta_n \tag{53}$$

It is advisable always to record a rough value of θ from the vernier reading in order to avoid a mistake in the sign of $\Delta\theta_n$. This displacement method allows a reproducibility of about $\pm 0.25'$ for θ, corresponding to an error of $\sim 2 \times 10^{-5}$ in n. For the same purpose, Geffcken and Kohner[38] use, instead of the vernier, an additional rigidly mounted telescope with two parallel hairs as fiducial lines. Observing the $G.C.$ through this telescope and making the separation of the hairs about equal to the width of the marks on the circle, the angular position of $G.C.$ can be reproduced to about $\pm 0.03'$. Such a refinement is justified only when the marks on the graduated circle are narrower and more accurate than is the case for the common instruments, as was the case in the work of Geffcken and Kohner, or when the graduated circle has been completely recalibrated with a variety of standard substances.

The accuracy of the difference, Δn, is limited chiefly by that of $\Delta\theta$. Under the best conditions, Δn can be determined within $\pm 1 \times 10^{-5}$. Although the absolute values of n are accurate to only about $\pm 1 \times 10^{-4}$ due to inherent instrumental errors, these errors are practically constant and nearly cancel out in the calculation of Δn if all measurements are made in succession with the same instrument so that the alignments of prism and telescope remain the same.

Measurements of Dispersion ($\Delta n = n_{\lambda_1} - n_{\lambda_2}$).—Using an appropriate light source (*e. g.*, a helium tube) and with the telescope free to move, the colored band system is located. If the critical boundaries for all spectral lines can be viewed simultaneously (dispersion of sample is relatively close to that of prism), $G. C.$ is clamped so that, when the cross hairs are set near the middle of the spectrum, the micrometer drum is about at the midpoint of the R–R scale.

The values of n_λ for any two sufficiently intense lines can now be directly compared within $\pm 2 \times 10^{-5}$ by setting the cross hairs on the critical boundaries and finding the corresponding readings, M_{λ_1} and M_{λ_2} (Eq. 47).   For a complete dispersion curve, the values of M are recorded for all lines present.   In addition, a measurement is made of the absolute value of α for one spectral line (e. g., He_{D_3}). For weak lines, where the accuracy of the setting is diminished, it may be advantageous to seek a greater contrast at the critical boundary by cutting off some of the incident light with the shutter (sh, Fig. 6a, page 691).   For those cases in which the spectral lines are spread so far apart that one cannot view the extreme ends of the spectrum without resetting the graduated circle, it is necessary to measure the position of all wave lengths relative to some intense spectral line in the green or yellow region (e. g., He_{D_3}).   In this way, the red and violet lines may be indirectly but accurately compared.

Although the *accuracy* of $n_{\lambda_1} - n_{\lambda_2}$ is limited by any uncertainty in the relative values of $n_{\lambda(P)}$ (Eq. 45) and in the calibration of the micrometer screw (p. 692), the *reproducibility* is determined chiefly by $\Delta\theta$ and may be as good as 1×10^{-5}.

Comparison of Two Substances.—When Δn is sufficiently small, it is possible to have the critical lines (monochromatic light) for both substances present at the same time in the field of view by placing the (solid or liquid) samples side by side on the prism surface (see pages 690, 703).   When the bands overlap ($\Delta\theta$ very small, or light source has many wave lengths), the critical line for each sample can be observed separately by closing half of the aperture in front of the telescope objective.

To obtain the *accuracy* of 1×10^{-5} when the Δn value is large enough (~ 0.005) to require a considerable range of the micrometer screw, a calibration of the screw (see page 692) is essential.   The best *reproducibility* is obtained when the same range of the screw is always used.

If the samples are placed successively on the same prism surface, great care must be exercised to avoid strain on telescope and prism.   When Δn is large ($\Delta n > 0.025$), the micrometer screw cannot be used to measure $\Delta\theta$ directly.   However, by using the displacement method (p. 698), it is possible to obtain values of Δn as large as 0.05 with an accuracy of about $\pm 3 \times 10^{-5}$, provided the same reference mark, θ_n, is selected for both θ_1 and θ_2.   The accuracy of still larger values of Δn will depend considerably on the accuracy of the graduated circle.   The angular distance between marks on the circle may be checked by comparing measured values of Δn with the known values for various pairs of standard substances.

Conversion of Data to Values of n_λ^t.—Values of n_λ^{20} at certain standard wave lengths, λ, can simply be interpolated from the tables of α *vs.* n_λ^{20} supplied with each instrument.   Such tables apply only to the particular kind of prism glass (indicated on the prism mount) and only at a given temperature, usually 20° C.   Usually the tables supply values for the C, D, D_3, e, F, and g spectral lines.   Note that the "correction value" given for the C line is always negative, *i. e.*, it must be subtracted from the n value given for the D line.   The other correction values are positive.

For wave lengths, λ', not included in the tables, $n_{\lambda'}^{20}$ is obtained from $\alpha_{\lambda'}$

by means of equation (45); this requires a knowledge of the refractive index of the prism at λ' and $20°$ C., $n^{20}_{\lambda'(P)}$. The direct measurement of $n^{20}_{\lambda'(P)}$ by means of a precision spectrometer is beyond the means of the ordinary laboratory. The reciprocal plotting method (page 660) can be used to interpolate values of $n^{20}_{\lambda'(P)}$ from values of $n^{20}_{\lambda(P)}$ published by the manufacturers.[107] More reliable is the method of measuring the difference $\Delta\alpha$ (see page 698) between the emergent critical angles, α_λ and $\alpha_{\lambda'}$, for some standard substance (e. g., water) having accurately known values of n at the two wave lengths. The required value for the prism is calculated by using $\alpha_{\lambda'}$ and $n^{20}_{\lambda'(H_2O)}$ in equation (45). One finds $\alpha_{\lambda'}$ from the relation $\alpha_{\lambda'} = \alpha_\lambda + \Delta\alpha$, where α_λ is obtained by substituting the known values of $n^{20}_{\lambda(P)}$ and $n^{20}_{\lambda(H_2O)}$ in equation (45). In this way $n^{20}_{\lambda'(P)}$ can be conveniently determined with an accuracy of $\pm 2 \times 10^{-5}$ relative to $n^{20}_{\lambda(P)}$.

Prism Temperature Correction.—In order to obtain an accuracy of $\pm 1 \times 10^{-4}$ in n when the temperature of the determination is considerably above or below the standard temperature (usually $20°$ C.), it is necessary to take into account the effect of the change of the prism index with temperature, dn_P/dt. EXAMPLE: Suppose that, for p-nitrotoluene at $55°$ C., using a prism for which $n^{20}_{D_3} = 1.62$ one finds the value, $n'_{D_3} = 1.5383_3$ obtained directly from the tables, which are based on n^{20}_P. The value 1.5383_3 is too low because $n^{55}_{D_3(P)}$ is greater than $n^{20}_{D_3(P)}$ (see Eq. 45), that is, $n^{55}_{D_3} = n'_{D_3} + k$, where k is the correction to be applied. The correction is given by:[107a]

$$k = \frac{n_P}{n'} \cdot \frac{dn_P}{dt} \, (t - 20°) \tag{54}$$

where t is in degrees C. Knowing that $dn_P/dt = 0.28 \times 10^{-5}$ for this prism for the D_3 line, and substituting in equation (54), we have $k = +(1.62/1.54) \, (0.28) \times 10^{-5} \, (55 - 20) = +1.0 \times 10^{-4}$. So $n^{55}_{D_3} = 1.5383_3 + 0.00010 = 1.5384_3$, relative to air at $55°$ C.

If one must use equation (45) to obtain values of $n^t_{\lambda'}$ (i. e., for certain wave lengths, λ'), the effect of prism temperature is accounted for by calculating the corrected prism index at the temperature of measurement, n^t_P, from the value at $20°$ C., n^{20}_P, given with the tables. It is apparent that:

$$n^t_{\lambda'(P)} = n^{20}_{\lambda'(P)} + \frac{dn_{\lambda'(P)}}{dt} \, (t - 20) \tag{55}$$

The manufacturer usually supplies values of the coefficient $dn_{\lambda(P)}/dt$. The corrected values of n^t_λ obtained by equation (54) or (55) refer to air at $t°$ C. and the prevailing pressure, if the coefficient dn_P/dt corresponds to the *relative* index $(n^t_P)_{a^t} = \mathbf{n}^t_P/\mathbf{n}^t_a$ ($\mathbf{n}^t_a$ is the absolute index of air at $t°$ C. and prevailing pressure),

---

[107] See reference 57 for values which have been interpolated for certain Zeiss prisms.
[107a] See ref. 115, pages 319–320.

i. e., if $dn_P/dt \approx (d\mathbf{n}_P/dt) - \mathbf{n}_P(d\mathbf{n}_a/dt)$ is used. However, if the coefficient of the *absolute* index, $d\mathbf{n}_P/dt$, is used in equation (54) or (55), the resulting $(n_\lambda^t)_{a^{20}}$ values refer to air at room temperature and the prevailing pressure. The latter frequently encountered mode of expression is correct only in case the effective air temperature is 20° C., as it is when the telescope is surrounded by air at 20° C. and when the temperature gradient of air near the prism–air interface is uniform. Otherwise it is advisable to maintain the air bath at $t°$ C. and express n_λ^t relative to air at $t°$ C. (In either case it may be necessary ultimately to refer the values to dry air at S.T.P.; see page 654.) The value of $(n_D^t)_{a^{20}}$ is approximately 1×10^{-5} less than $(n_D^t)_{a^t}$ for every 7° of excess of t over 20° C. The manufacturers usually supply tables of $d\mathbf{n}_P/dt$ (*absolute* values); Tilton[107a] gives such data, as well as dn_P/dt (*relative* to air) for various wave lengths, temperatures, and kinds of glass.

The temperature coefficient of the prism depends strongly on the wave length as well as on the type of glass. Thus, the temperature correction is especially important for dispersion measurements. The change in dn_P/dt with temperature is only about 0.1% per ° C. Therefore it is permissible to assume dn_P/dt is constant in equations (54) and (55), even when 5th decimal relative accuracy is required, provided $(t - 20)$ is less than about 50° C. When working at temperatures at which the correction is large, it is advisable to verify the effect of dn_P/dt by making measurements at various temperatures on a standard substance having an accurately known temperature coefficient of dispersion, for example, H_2O.

SAMPLE CALCULATION OF $n_{\lambda_2}^t$ AND $\Delta n = n_{\lambda_1} - n_{\lambda_3}$

Substance: molten *p*-nitrotoluene, $CH_3C_6H_4 \cdot NO_2$.

Temperature: 55.00° C. (The air is also at 55° C.)

Prism: $n_D^{20} = 1.62$; $dn_P/dt \times 10^5 = 0.23, 0.28, 0.46$ for $\lambda = He_{r_2}, He_{D_3}, He_v$.

Spectral lines: He_{r_2}, He_{D_3}, He_v.

The graduated circle, *G.C.*, remains clamped during the following operations and the zero point remains constant.

Zero point correction, θ_z (see page 659): When *G. C.* is set at (*1*) the true horizontal position and (*2*) the 0.00° mark, the *M. S.* reading, M (page 692), is (*1*) 185.5$_5$ and (*2*) 185.0$_3$. $\theta_z = M_1 - M_2 = 185.5_5 - 185.0_3 = 0.5_2'$.

Refractive index, $n_{D_3}^{55}$: When *G.C.* is set at (*1*) position of D_3 critical boundary line *i. e.*, at θ_{D_3}) and (*2*) 30° 30′ mark (θ_n), reading M is (*1*) 168.8$_9$ and (*2*) 155.0$_3$. By inspection, $\theta_{D_3} \approx 30.7°$.

$$\Delta\theta_n = M_1 - M_2 \text{ (Eq. 52)} = 168.8_9 - 155.0_3 = 13.8_6'$$

$$\theta_{D_3} = \theta_n + \Delta\theta_n \text{ (Eq. 53)} = 30° 30' + 13.8_6' = 30° 43.8_6'$$

$$\alpha_{D_3} = \theta_{D_3} - \theta_z \text{ (Eq. 49)} = 30° 43.8_6' - 0.5_2' = 30° 43.3_4'$$

By interpolation in the tables, one finds that α_{D_3} corresponds to $n_{D_3}' = 1.5383_3$, where n_{D_3}' refers to an assumed prism temperature of 20° C. According to the example on page 700, the corrected value is: $n_{D_3}^{55} = 1.5383_4 + 0.0001_0$; $n_{D_3}^{55} = 1.5384_3 \pm 0.0001_0$.

Dispersion.—Data for He_{r_2} line (*designated below as r*): When *G.C.* is set at (*1*) position of red line r, *i. e.*, at $\theta_r = \alpha_r + \theta_z$, and (*2*) position of D_3 line, *i. e.*, at $\theta_{D_3} = \alpha_{D_3} + \theta_z$, ($\alpha_{D_3} = 30° 43.3_4'$), reading M is (*1*) 195.0$_6$ and (*2*) 168.8$_9$. By inspection, $\alpha_r \approx 31.2°$.

$$\Delta\theta = \Delta\alpha = M_1 - M_2 \text{ (page 698 and Eq. 48)} = 195.0_6 - 168.8_9 = 26.1_7'$$

$$\alpha_r = \alpha_{D_3} + \Delta\alpha \text{ (Eq. 51)} = 30° 43.3_4' + 26.1_7' = 31° 9.5_1'$$

Most tables do not give values of n_r. Then, in order to use equation (45), we must first find $n_{r(P)}^{55}$ of the prism. If we have determined (see page 700) that $n_{r(P)}^{20} = 1.61523$, we can calculate its value at 55° C. from equation (55). We substitute the appropriate value (0.23 $\times$ 10^{-5}) of dn_P/dt and obtain $n_{r(P)}^{55} = 1.61523 + 0.23$ (55 − 20) $\times$ 10^{-5}, or $(n_{r(P)}^{55})^2 = 2.60922_9$. Equation (45) becomes

$$n_r^{55} = \sqrt{2.60922_9 - \sin^2 (31° 9.5_1')} = 1.5301_9,$$

this absolute value being correct within about $\pm 1 \times 10^{-4}$. The *difference*, $n_{D_3} - n_r = 0.00825$, is correct within about $\pm 3 \times 10^{-5}$ (page 699).

Dispersion.—Data for He_v line (*designated as v*): When *G.C.* is set at (*1*) position of violet line, *i. e.*, at $\theta_v = \alpha_v + \theta_z$ and (*2*) position of D_3 line ($\alpha_{D_3} = 30° 43.3_4'$) reading M is (*1*) 235.8$_9$ and (*2*) 168.8$_9$.

$$\Delta\theta = \Delta\alpha = 235.8_9 - 168.8_9 = 67.0_0'$$

$$\alpha_v = 30° 43.3_4' + 67.0_0' = 31° 50.3_4'$$

Using equation (55) as before, we can find $(n_{v(P)}^{55})^2 = 2.69157_4$. Accordingly:

$$n_v^{55} = \sqrt{2.69157_4 - \sin^2 (31° 50.34')} = 1.5534_7$$

The dispersion of *p*-nitrotoluene at 55° C. can then be expressed as $(n_v - n_r)^{55}$ = 0.02328 $\pm$ 0.00005. It is interesting to note that, because the dispersion of this compound (0.02328) is almost as great as the dispersion of the prism (0.02537), one observes an abnormal sequence of the colored critical boundaries violet, red, and yellow instead of violet, yellow, and red.[106]

Handling of Liquids.—A layer of liquid about 0.5 mm. thick ($\cong$ 0.2 ml.) covering the entire horizontal prism surface is sufficient for the most accurate measurements. If a smaller area of the prism were used for very small samples, there would be a proportionate decrease in the intensity of the critical boundary. Correspondingly, the symmetry of illumination of the telescope aperture would become more important.[105] Ordinarily, about 4 ml. of sample is used, half of this for preliminary rinsing of the glass surfaces until a constant value of n is obtained.

A simple, cylindrical tube, ground at the base to fit the prism (standard equipment) serves to confine the liquid and provides a vertical window for the incident light rays. When this arrangement is used, the vessel may be filled by a pipette, but the liquid should be removed with a piece of lens paper to avoid scratching of the relatively soft prism surface. Filter paper should not be used. The simple tube arrangement is not always satisfactory. An *improved vessel* by Geffcken and Kohner[38] (Fig. 9) allows rapid filling and draining while excluding the atmosphere. A wash-bottle type of flask is connected to the vessel through ground joint *J* and liquid is forced into the space above the prism by gas pressure. Rinsing is facilitated by providing an air outlet (*e. g.*, through a small channel in ground joint *G*) which allows the vessel to be filled while stopcock *S* is closed. After a measure-

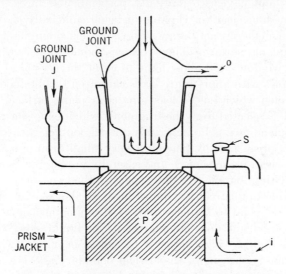

Fig. 9.—Improved vessel for liquids (Pulfrich re-fractometer). Thermostated water enters at inlet *i* and leaves at outlet *o*.

ment, pressure can be applied through *J* to remove most of the liquid, and the interior of the vessel then can be cleaned rapidly by rinsing with pure solvent and drying with a stream of pure air.—A special *double-chamber cell* is useful for the direct comparison of two liquids. The usual tube is provided with a black glass partition perpendicular to both prism faces which bisects the polished horizontal prism surface.—If a suitable cement can be found, the vessels should be sealed to the prism bevel to prevent loss by evaporation and to increase mechanical strength. It is essential that the double-chamber type be tightly cemented. In selecting a cement, the following considerations are of prime importance: (*1*) The *dry* cement should not be soluble in the liquid, or should have only a very slow rate of dissolution; and (*2*) the dry cement must be easily softened by some solvent. The vessel should never be removed by force; otherwise, (1) the zero point will change, and (2) the prism may become seriously chipped. The cement may be tested in the following way. When the cement is dry, a minimum amount of the liquid under investigation is filled into the vessel. The vessel is covered tightly, and the instrument thermostated. An excessive interaction of liquid and cement is revealed by a change in θ over a period of several hours. Occasionally, a cement is attacked by a liquid only during the first few hours of contact, and can be used thereafter.

Handling of Solids.—*Large Pieces of Sample.*—The material must be homogeneous and have two mutually perpendicular faces, one of which must be plane and clear (or capable of being sufficiently polished). The other face, which merely acts as a window for the incident light, can have an irregular nonplanar surface. The two faces should intersect in a sharp line so that the "window" will allow light to enter the crystal at grazing incidence. Samples with appropriate faces can often be obtained by crushing a large specimen which has at least one clear plane surface. The largest suitable piece is selected from the fragments which have sharp edges.

The clear plane face is brought into optical contact with the horizontal refractometer prism face by placing a very small drop of an appropriate liquid on the clean prism surface and carefully pressing the solid into place so that a very thin, bubble-free film separates the two surfaces. The liquid used to provide optical contact must have an index of refraction *greater* than that of the solid to be measured. 1-Bromonaphthalene ($n_D = 1.68$) is commonly used. It does not matter if this liquid slowly dissolves the solid. Excess liquid which happens to collect near the "window" is removed; it causes blurring of the critical boundary and is the source of a serious error if rays at grazing incidence become shielded.

If the liquid film contained between the sample and prism has the shape of a wedge (which it almost invariably does) it may cause an appreciable error[108] by altering the effective angle of the refractometer prism. An error as great as 2×10^{-4} can arise from this wedge effect. The latter is minimized when the refractive index of the contact liquid does not greatly exceed that of the solid sample. However, the only certain way to eliminate this source of error is properly to control the shape and orientation of the liquid layer.

We use the method of interference fringes to observe the slope of the liquid wedge. Monochromatic light passing through or reflected from the two broad surfaces of the wedge forms a set of interference fringes consisting of equally spaced light and dark bands parallel to the edge of the wedge.

---

[108] For a quantitative discussion of the wedge effect, see: L. W. Tilton, *J. Research Natl. Bur. Standards*, **30**, 323 (1943); *J. Optical Soc. Am.*, **32**, 376 (1942); and J. Guild, *Proc. Phys. Soc. London*, **30**, 157 (1917–1918).

These bands can be observed either by directly viewing the broad surface of the wedge from above (assuming the sample is sufficiently transparent) or by inspecting the exit pupil (see page 694) of the telescope with a simple magnifying lens. The greater the number of bands observed per unit length of wedge, the greater are the wedge angle and the error. By exerting just the right pressure on various parts of the sample, it would be possible to decrease the slope of the wedge until the interference fringes disappear, that is, the liquid layer becomes a plane-parallel window which causes no error. However, in actual practice it is not necessary to eliminate the wedge completely. It has been calculated[108] that one-third of a fringe of yellow light per centimeter length of wedge (viewed through the exit pupil) corresponds to an error of about 1×10^{-5} in the index of refraction of the sample. When viewed from above the sample, this number is one or two fringes per 1×10^{-5} error in n, depending somewhat on the index of the liquid relative to the prism. Thus, for accurate dispersion measurements it would be necessary to adjust the wedge until not more than a single fringe could be seen in the exit pupil (the prism surface allows the formation of a wedge about 2 cm. long). For measurements of n_D to 4th place accuracy, as many as six to eight fringes can be tolerated.

Practically no error will result if the wedge has its sharp edge *perpendicular* to the refracting edge of the prism. The refracting edge of the prism (rr' in Fig. 6) is perpendicular to the optic axis of the collimator. Hence, even for a fairly steep wedge, it suffices to exert pressure on the sample so that the interference fringes become perpendicular to the refracting edge, *i. e.*, perpendicular to the critical boundary, if viewed at the exit pupil. The wedge should be tested both before and after a measurement to insure against a change.

Concerning fine interference bands parallel to the critical boundary (Herschel fringes), appearing when a plane-parallel layer of liquid is enclosed between the prism and another plane surface, see Tilton.[108]

Powders.—A convenient and accurate method of measuring n (to ± 0.0002) for small amounts of isotropic powders has been suggested by Le Blanc.[109] When particles of such a solid are immersed in a liquid of identical index of refraction it is possible to observe a characteristic sharp critical boundary and thus to measure n_D; when the two media have slightly different values of n, the boundary is diffuse, or disappears.

Two liquids (L_I, L_{II}) are selected which do not appreciably (or rapidly) dissolve the solid in question, one (L_I) with a lower and the other (L_{II}) with a higher index than the solid. For many organic compounds, one can use saturated aqueous potassium mercuric iodide ($n_{II} = 1.73$) and H_2O

[109] M. Le Blanc, *Z. physik. Chem.*, **10**, 433 (1892).

($n_I = 1.33$). Kaiser and Parrish[110] discuss immersion liquids for solids. Enough of L_I is filled into the refractometer vessel so that the contents can be stirred. A few milligrams of the powder are added to form a fine deposit on the prism surface (too much sample would scatter all the light). The average cross section of the particles may vary from 1 to 0.01 mm. The stirring is commenced and L_{II} is slowly dropped in while an observation is made through the telescope, with monochromatic light. At first, the entire field is dark for all positions of the telescope. When $n_{liq.}$ comes fairly close to n_{solid}, one can observe a broad diffuse band of light, bordered on

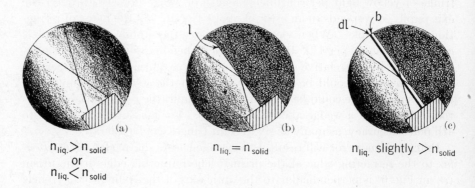

Fig. 10.—Field of view in Le Blanc's powder method for isotropic powders.

either side by a dark region (see Fig. 10a). When $n_{liq.} = n_{solid}$, the band develops one fairly sharp border line, l, toward the upper (right) part of the field of view (Fig. 10b). On a further very small addition of L_{II}, the light and dark areas become separated by an intense bright band, b, and an adjacent fine dark line, dl, as shown in figure 10c. The cross hairs can be most accurately set on line dl, which gives a value of n_{solid} only slightly greater ($\sim 1 \times 10^{-4}$) than the true value. During the final stage of gradually increasing $n_{liq.}$, it may be more convenient to depend on the evaporation of L_I if this is the more volatile component. A slow drift of several degrees in the liquid temperature is permissible during the procedure as long as the critical boundary remains sharp at the actual time of measurement, since dn/dt for most solids is small.

---

[110] E. P. Kaiser and W. Parrish, *Ind. Eng. Chem., Anal. Ed.*, **11**, 560 (1939). See also E. M. Chamot and C. W. Mason, *Handbook of Chemical Microscopy*, 2nd ed., Vol. I, Wiley, New York, pp. 373–375, 381–382; T. R. P. Gibb, *Optical Methods of Chemical Analysis*, McGraw-Hill, New York, 1942, pp. 251–253.

B. ABBÉ REFRACTOMETER[111]

Like the Pulfrich, the Abbé refractometer measures the critical angle of refraction (or reflection). Its usual type requires a sample of only about 0.05 ml. of liquid and is designed for a maximum speed, convenience, and simplicity compatible with fairly high accuracy (n_D accurate to ±0.0001). The *scale reads directly* in n_D. The instrument is ordinarily used with white light. With such a source, the dispersion, $n_F - n_C$, can be obtained with an accuracy of from 1 to 30%, depending largely on the compensator [112] (see page 713). The range of the available models [111] ($n = 1.3$ to 1.7 and 1.45 to 1.84) is adequate for most organic liquids, but the range of a given instrument cannot be changed. The convenience of the "Abbé" is somewhat offset by certain limitations. It is not well suited to the accurate measurement of solutions with a volatile component (page 710) or of powders. On the other hand, some models are applicable to opaque solids which cannot be measured with the Pulfrich. The usual instrument is not suited to measurement of n for lines other than the sodium D (see page 712). However, a recent version, a precision Abbé refractometer (see page 713), is almost as accurate as the Pulfrich refractometer for dispersion measurements, and surpasses all other commercial instruments in the accuracy for absolute values of n (5th decimal). A new model of the Spencer Abbé is also adapted to measurements with various spectral lines. The Valentine refractometer[113] is an Abbé type of refractometer which can give 5th place accuracy for n_D.

Ordinary Instrument.—Figure 11 illustrates the path of the rays and the mechanical arrangement for locating the critical boundary. The upper, P, of two big prisms is mounted rigidly on a bearing, B, which has an arm, or alidade, A, extending at right angles to the upper face of P. The rotatable arm A carries a small plate, pl, with a reference mark, R, which can be viewed through a magnifying glass, M, mounted above the plate. The telescope is firmly mounted on the arm of a similar bearing, B', which also rotates about the axis of the prism-bearing B. Telescope arm A' carries a curved scale (sector scale S) which is closely fitted against the alidade plate so that scale S and reference mark R can be viewed simultaneously with the magnifying glass. Thus one can rotate the refracting prism (P) relative to the axis (T–T') of the telescope, while the telescope itself can be moved to any convenient inclination. Some instruments are provided with a rack and pinion mounted on S for moving the prism;

---

[111] Manufactured by: *Bausch & Lomb Optical Co.*, Rochester, N. Y.; *Spencer Lens Co.*, Buffalo, N. Y.; *Adam Hilger, Ltd.*, London; *Carl Zeiss, Inc.*, New York, N. Y.; and *Industro Scientific Co.*, Bellmore, Long Island, N. Y.

[112] L. E. Dodd, *J. Optical Soc. Am.*, **22**, 477 (1932).

[113] *Industro Scientific Co.*, Bellmore, Long Island, N. Y.

in others, it is rotated by hand except in the final stages of adjustment, when a slow-motion tangent screw is used. A rotation of the prism is accompanied by a motion of R along scale S. The reading of the sector scale re'ative to R is a measure of the angle, r, between the normal line, N–N', to the prism surface and the telescope axis, T–T'. When a properly illuminated sample is placed on the lower face S' of prism P and the telescope cross hairs are set on the critical boundary, the resulting angle, r_c,

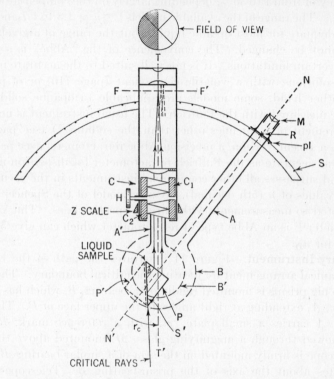

Fig. 11.—Abbé refractometer: A, alidade; A', telescope arm; B, prism bearing; B', telescope bearing; C, compensator; C_1, C_2, Amici prisms; F-F', focal plane; H, milled head; M, magnifying glass; N–N', normal line to upper surface of prism; P (upper) reflecting prism; P', auxiliary prism; pl, alidade plate; r, reference mark on pl; rc, emergent critical angle; S, sector scale; S', sample–prism interface; T–T', telescope axis.

is the emergent critical angle characteristic of the sample, of P and of the air. Analysis shows that r_c is related to n of the sample by the equation (56):

$$n = \sin r_c \cos \beta + \sin \beta \sqrt{n_P^2 - \sin^2 r_c} \qquad (56)$$

where β is the prism angle and n_P its index of refraction. Actually, the sector scale is calibrated in terms of n_D^{20} (or even in terms of concentration of aqueous sugar solution, etc.).

Although white light is used, n is obtained for the sodium D line. Ordinarily, with white light, the critical boundary is diffuse and has the appearance of a rainbow because of the divergence of critical rays having different wave lengths (dispersion effect). In this case, the value of n is not accurately defined. The width of the color band depends on the relative dispersion of sample and prism. The critical boundary can be sharpened and its color removed by means of the compensator, C (Fig. 11), as follows: If two identical Amici prisms, C_1 and C_2, are properly placed in the path of the critical rays, a dispersion of these rays results which is equal and opposite to that caused by the sample plus prism. Thus, by collecting the divergent critical rays so that all wave lengths are superimposed on one line in focal plane F–F' of the telescope, the Amici prisms compensate for the dispersion of the rays leaving the big prism, and the resultant critical boundary is practically white. The compensator prisms are constructed so that rays for the sodium D line are not deviated, while the dispersion introduced for other wave lengths is proportional to the angle, σ, through which one of the C prisms is rotated relative to the other. The correct amount of compensating dispersion is obtained by rotating the milled head, H, until the critical boundary is sharp and colorless. There are two positions of the compensator, 180° apart, which give an achromatic boundary. If the sodium D line is used for the illumination, the compensator is, of course, unnecessary. Other monochromatic sources are not suitable unless an elaborate calibration is made (see page 713).

Measurement of Liquids.—PLACING AND ILLUMINATING THE SAMPLE.—An auxiliary prism, P' (Fig. 11), below the refracting prism serves to illuminate and confine the sample. It is hinged so that its ground-glass hypotenuse is either clamped almost in contact with the refracting prism, or swung out. When a drop of liquid is placed on the ground surface and the two prisms are locked together with the clamp, a thin film (0.1 mm.) of liquid is held against upper prism P. When the ground face of P' is illuminated by tilting the mirror, some of the light scattered at its mat surface passes into the liquid at nearly grazing incidence ($i = 90°$), and produces a sharp critical boundary (for $i = 90°$, $r = r_{\max}$). The same light (day or electric) should be used for measurements and calibration.

PRECAUTIONS.—(1) Clean the delicate prism surfaces with alcohol, touching them only with soft lens paper. Leave no lint. Rinse with the liquid under investigation. The liquid itself must be clear or the boundary line becomes blurred. For somewhat opaque liquids, see page 710. (2) Make certain, by looking through the top surface of P, that the liquid is spread evenly between the prisms when clamped together. For hygroscopic liquids, or those with a volatile component, hold the two prisms barely apart during filling, and lock them as soon as possible. Lack of protection for the sample is often a serious disadvantage of the Abbé. Even after locking of the prisms, the sample may acquire moisture or evaporate. *(3)* Allow time for establishment of temperature equilibrium. *(4)* Tilt the mirror to give maximum illumination of the field of view. A change in the position of the mirror or light source does not change the position of the boundary, if it is the true critical boundary. If spurious lines are observed, make the light source more uniform in intensity. *(5)* Incline the prisms by moving the alidade until the critical boundary is in the middle of the field; focus the eyepiece if necessary; and achromatize the boundary by rotating the compensator. With a slow motion of the alidade, cause the sharp colorless critical boundary to cross exactly the intersection of the cross hairs, as in figure 11. The reproducibility of the individual readings on the sector scale is ± 0.0001. Another setting on the critical boundary should be made with the compensator in the other achromatizing position. The two index readings will almost always differ. Tilton[114] has pointed out that the mean value is free from the particular instrumental error giving rise to this effect. *(6)* After a measurement, clean the prisms at once, since the prism orientation can change by contact of the mounting cement with various liquids.[115]

Measurement of Solids.—The method of attaching a large solid sample to the lower surface of the Abbé prism is identical with that discussed on page 704. It should be recalled that an improperly oriented wedge of the liquid used in making contact between sample and prism may cause errors in the 4th decimal of n. The auxiliary prism, lowered as far as possible, reflects rays into the sample "window" at grazing incidence. Otherwise the procedure is identical with that for liquids except that temperature control need not be as exact.

OPAQUE OR COLORED SOLIDS AND LIQUIDS.—Some models of the Abbé refractometer provide a refracting prism with a window for illuminating the lower surface of P from within. By this means, light can be *reflected* from this surface, S', into the telescope when the surface is covered with an opaque or a transparent sample. A sharp critical boundary is observed when the telescope axis is at the critical angle of reflection, which is equal to the critical angle of refraction (see page 687). The intensity of the field is somewhat less than with light entering a transparent sample by refraction at grazing incidence. Otherwise the observations and measurements are the same in both cases.

[114] L. W. Tilton, *J. Optical Soc. Am.*, **32**, 373 (1942).

[115] L. W. Tilton, *J. Research Natl. Bur. Standards*, **30**, 311 (1943).

Temperature Control and Corrections.—Both prisms are mounted in a jacket through which thermostated water can be circulated. For most liquids, the temperature must be controlled to ±0.2° to realize the full accuracy of the instrument. The thermostating should commence about 20 minutes before using the instrument to insure temperature equilibrium in the prisms. The constancy of the first measurement should be checked by observations over a period of about five minutes. At first, the critical border may appear blurred, due to temperature gradients. Once equilibrium has been established, it takes only a few minutes for each new sample to reach the correct temperature. Grosse[116] has described a method for using the Abbé refractometer down to −50° C. for volatile substances.

For precise work considerably above or below room temperature, a correction should be applied to the scale readings because of a change in refractive index of the prisms. The scale values on the instrument are almost always given for a temperature of the prism of 20° C. (*i. e.*, $n_P \equiv n_P^{20}$ in Eq. 56). The prism temperature correction is negligible in the range from about 15° to 25° C. for a calibration temperature of 20°. Between 25° and 35° the true index, n^t, of the liquid is approximately 1×10^{-4} greater than the apparent value, n', obtained directly from the sector scale. Similarly, for the range between 15° and 5°, n^t is about 1×10^{-4} less than n'. The correction to n' depends somewhat on the absolute value of n, that is, it is different for different parts of the sector scale. The correction to n' depends also on the temperature and temperature gradient of the air at the prism surface[115] although the n' values are probably independent of air temperature if the telescope is maintained at 20° C.

Because the temperature of the compensating prisms must also be taken into account, it is not convenient or always reliable to calculate a prism temperature correction from the known temperature coefficient, dn_P/dt, of the prism glass. A method of calculation for the Hilger instrument is given by Tilton,[115] who also points out the limitations of such a procedure. It is preferable to calibrate directly the sector scale at the working temperature ($t°$ C.) by measurements with standard substances (see Table I) whose values of n_D at $t°$ C. (relative to air at the prevailing temperature and pressure) are known, or whose dn/dt values are known in addition to n^t; thermostating the entire instrument with an air bath is then desirable.

Testing the Instrument.—In view of the many construction elements which can lead to errors in individual instruments, and of accidental changes in calibration,[114, 115] it is advisable to check the compensator and the sector scales from time to time. A description of simple tests for various common defects of Abbé refractometers is given by Tilton.[114, 115] It is possible to

---

[116] A. V. Grosse, *J. Am. Chem. Soc.*, **59**, 2739 (1937).

have tests and recalibrations made by the National Bureau of Standards (see page 666). The sector scale readings are tested by measurements with a set of standards (page 665). Test plates of glass, furnished by the manufacturers, are convenient standards, although it is preferable to use them only when calibrating the instrument for measurements of solids. Test plates may be sent to the *National Bureau of Standards*, Washington, D. C., for calibration. The value of n_D obtained for a liquid is usually too low if the instrument is adjusted to give the correct value for a solid of the same n. The discrepancy can be as much as 3×10^{-4} for liquids of low n, due to shielding of rays at grazing incidence and/or the presence of "Herschel fringes." [114, 117]

Any discrepancy between the known n value of the standard and the value n' read from the sector scale can be corrected for in two ways: *(1)* With the standard on the prism, the alidade is set at the scale reading which represents the correct value of n. The critical boundary is then brought into exact coincidence with the cross-hair intersection by turning with a small screw driver or special key the small screw located in the telescope just above the compensator. This effects a shift in the position of the telescope objective. *(2)* The observed difference δn between n and n' is applied as a numerical correction to all readings, *i. e.*, $n = n' + \delta n$. The second method is to be preferred where the highest accuracy is required, since it will be found that many instruments, if adjusted to read correctly (to ± 0.0001) at one end of the scale, will have an error of ± 0.0003 or more at the other end. By calibrating the instrument with a set of standards, the appropriate correction, δn, can be applied to every region of the scale.

Dispersion Measurements.—The achromatization of the critical boundary furnishes a means of estimating the dispersion, $n_F - n_C$. It is evident that the greater the dispersion of the sample, the greater will be the necessary angle of rotation of the compensator. The amount of compensation is read on the so-called Z scale attached to the collar of the compensator (Fig. 11, page 708). The scale is marked arbitrarily with 60 equal divisions. The value of Z can be obtained to ± 0.05 division by "hunting" for the achromatic position,[118] *i. e.*, oscillating the compensator with decreasing amplitude until the critical border is colorless. From Z the dispersion is obtained by:

$$n_F - n_C = A + kBS \qquad (57)$$

where A and B are optical constants depending on n_D, given in tables, and k corrects for certain errors in each individual instrument. S is a function,

---

[117] B. J. Mair, *J. Research Natl. Bur. Standards*, **9**, 461 (1932).

[118] L. E. Dodd, *Rev. Sci. Instruments*, **2**, 466 (1931).

given in tables, of angle σ (page 709) through which the C prisms are turned; σ is found in tables from the reading Z.

It is essential, in using the Abbé refractometer for dispersion, to test the reliability of each instrument by making measurements on several standard substances covering a range of indices and dispersions. Many, especially the older instruments, are not supplied with reliable tables for converting Z readings to values of S and for finding A and B from n_D. Dodd[112] has shown that $n_F - n_C$ may be in error by up to 30% when the "blanket calibration charts" of A, B, and S are used without taking into account the characteristics of individual instruments. It is a laborious task to prepare[118] a corrected chart of A and B vs. n_D. For some instruments, adequate A, B, and S tables are given but a value for k is not; k becomes important if the compensator prisms happen to be mounted somewhat out of line. Tilton[114] has suggested that k can be conveniently found by using a hydrogen discharge tube as a light source for a calibration with substances of known dispersion. The dispersion, $n_F - n_C$, can be obtained to within 2% with the best instruments, provided they are used with proper light sources. The value, Z, by which the compensator is turned depends on the relative intensities of the various wave lengths in the source and, to a certain extent, on the limitations of the eye in judging color. Differences in $n_F - n_C$ as great as 100% can arise in measurements of the same sample with different light sources.[114] The instrument should therefore always be used with the light source for which it is calibrated.

Using monochromatic light, it is possible to measure n_λ to ± 0.0002. With the prism clamped in the position of the n_D reading, the critical boundaries for various spectral lines are successively brought into coincidence with the cross-hair intersection by turning the compensator, and Z is read. The calibration and calculation,[114, 118] necessary for converting Z_λ and n_D into n_λ are elaborate and time consuming, and measurements of n_λ on the Pulfrich refractometer are much simpler and more accurate.

Precision Abbé Refractometers.—A modified Abbé refractometer based in part on the suggestions of Straat and Forrest[119] has recently been placed on the market by Bausch and Lomb. This precision Abbé refractometer shown in figure 12 is capable of measuring the absolute value of n to ± 0.00002, yet retains the simplicity and convenience of its prototype. It should be kept in mind, however, that the full accuracy of the instrument may not always be realized when used for liquids, because of contact with the atmosphere or because of solvent action on the prism matrix;[115] changes in prism orientation may be detected by frequent tests with standards. Differences can be measured, under favorable conditions, with an accuracy

[119] H. W. Straat and J. W. Forrest, *J. Optical Soc. Am.*, **29**, 240 (1939).

of from 2×10^{-5} to 6×10^{-5}, depending on the range of n and Δn. An outstanding feature of this precision Abbé, in contrast to the ordinary Abbé, is that it can easily be used to measure n_λ for a variety of wave lengths. Instruments are available with ranges of n of 1.30 to 1.50, 1.40 to 1.70, and 1.33 to 1.64.

The improved accuracy is obtained by dispensing with the compensating prisms and by the use of unusually large and precise Abbé prisms mounted on a long, vertical, taper bearing. A monochromatic light source is mounted

Courtesy Bausch & Lomb Optical Co.

Fig. 12a.—Precision Abbé refractometer: *1*, alidade; *2*, reflector; *3*, scale; *4*, vernier; *5*, scale magnifier; *7*, scale switch; *8*, scale lamp connector; *12*, telescope; *14*, knurled heads; *15*, prism box; *17*, drip trough; *19*, water connections; *20*, drain connection; *21*, hand wheel; *22*, adjusting nut; *23*, sodium Lab-Arc; *24*, Lab-Arc transformer; *25*, polarity plug; *26*, lamp bracket lock screw; *31*, prism hinge.

with the instrument, and may be readily interchanged with other sources, for instance, a mercury arc. The sector is marked in equal arbitrary divisions; and a table is used to convert scale readings to values of n_λ. The technique of measurement, described in detail in the Bausch and Lomb pamphlet,[97] is somewhat simpler than with the ordinary Abbé because the achromatization is eliminated. Otherwise, the operations are about the same as discussed above. A vernier reads directly to 0.01 division, corresponding to about 2×10^{-5} in n at the upper end of the scale and to about 6×10^{-5} at the lower end. With a good critical boundary, a setting of the cross hairs may be reproduced within 0.005 division, the nearest half-hundredth mark being estimated. For such high precision, the temperature must be controlled to within ±0.02°. A useful feature of the Bausch and Lomb precision Abbé refractometer is the auxiliary lens which can be moved into the telescope barrel to furnish a view of the liquid layer on the prism. In this way, air bubbles in the sample may be detected easily, or the interference fringes observed. This instrument is adapted

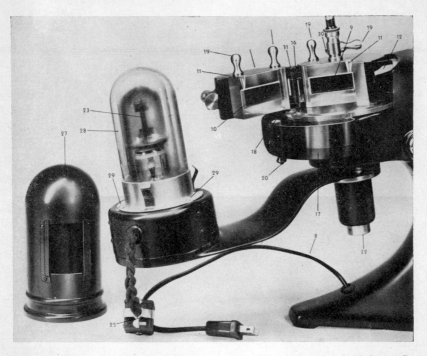

Courtesy Bausch & Lomb Optical Co.

Fig. 12b.—Precision refractometer prism system: *9*, working prism; *10*, illuminating prism; *11*, tubulation; *12*, telescope; *15*, prism box; *16*, light shield; *17*, drip trough; *18*, drain plug; *19*, water connections; *31*, prism hinge.

to opaque samples, for which the refracting surface of the prism is illuminated internally through a prism window.

In working with a precision refractometer a few degrees above or below the calibration temperature, corrections for changes in prism index and in the state of the reference medium (air) become very important (see pages 654 and 700). These corrections can be calculated,[115] but, as Tilton[115] shows, it is more reliable to recalibrate the instrument with known standards.

The Valentine improved precision refractometer[113] is an Abbé-type instrument adapted to white light; it allows a reproducibility of 2×10^{-5} and an accuracy of 5×10^{-5} in absolute values.   The optical system is designed to eliminate haziness of borderline when reading solutions which tend to diffuse light.

The Spencer Abbé refractometer without compensator prisms is used with monochromatic light, thus allowing greater than usual accuracy in dispersion measurements.

C.   DIPPING REFRACTOMETER

The dipping, or immersion, refractometer[120] is in principle very much like the ordinary Abbé.   It is designed for greater convenience and somewhat greater accuracy.   A reading can be taken simply by immersing the attached prism in the thermostated sample and observing the position of the achromatized critical boundary on a scale in the eyepiece of the telescope.   The dipping refractometer is used primarily for determining the concentrations of solutions, e. g., in the sugar industry.[121]   Calibration curves are established by measurements with known solutions.   The refractive index can be obtained from scale readings by interpolation in tables furnished by the manufacturers, if a zero point correction is made. Browne and Zerban[121] and Gibb[102] also give conversion tables.   It is frequently stated that the accuracy of a determination under favorable conditions is about $\pm 3.5 \times 10^{-5}$ in n, corresponding to ± 0.1 scale divisions. It should be emphasized that ± 0.1 scale division is the *reproducibility* of each setting, while the *accuracy* of n s about ± 2 (3.5×10^{-5}) inasmuch as the value of n depends not only on the scale reading for the sample but also upon a second measurement with some standard substance in order to define a reference (zero) point on the scale;   thus all measurements are differential.   With a special eyepiece and under certain favorable conditions which depend on the nature of the sample, the illumination and the temperature control, the reproducibility of a setting may be made as high as ± 0.02 scale division.[121]   The convenience of the ordinary dipping refractometer is somewhat offset by the difficulty of controlling the temperature, by lack of protection for the sample, and by the limited range of n. The range covered by each one of the six interchangeable prisms of the Bausch and Lomb instrument (~ 0.04 in Δn) is only slightly greater than that covered by the precision micrometer screw of the Pulfrich refractometer.   Moreover, the compensator readings are only a semiquantitative measure of the dispersion; in this respect the ordinary Abbé is superior.

[120] Manufactured by *Bausch & Lomb Optical Co.*, Rochester, N. Y., and by *Carl Zeiss, Inc.*, New York, N. Y.
[121] C. A. Browne and F. W. Zerban, *Physical and Chemical Methods of Sugar Analysis.* 3rd ed., Wiley, New York, 1941.

The construction of the instrument and the path of the rays are shown in figure 13. The detachable prism, P, is mounted rigidly at the objective end of the telescope and, when dipped into the sample, allows the formation of a critical boundary in the usual way; an image of the critical boundary is formed within the telescope in the focal plane F–F'. The position of this image is located with reference to a micrometer scale engraved in equal arbitrary divisions on the focal plane of the objective, F–F', that is, on the plane surface of the eyepiece lens, e_2. A micrometer screw, S, allows the scale (lens e_2) to be shifted by known amounts, as read from the micrometer screw drum, D. In this way, the position of the critical boundary between two marks on the scale may be interpolated with higher accuracy than by direct estimation.

Zero Point.—In order to use the tables for converting readings to refractive index, the scale must be set to read properly when some standard substance (*e. g.*, water) is measured, or else a correction must be applied to subsequent readings. The latter method is recommended unless the discrepancy between measured and tabular value is large. To adjust the scale, the micrometer drum is loosened from the screw and reset to read correctly while the critical boundary is held in coincidence with the appropriate whole-division mark of the scale.

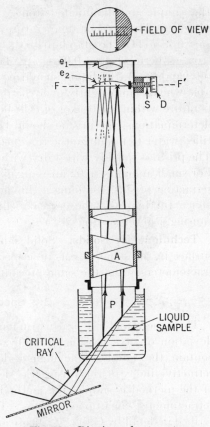

Fig. 13.—Dipping refractometer.

Directions for loosening and resetting the drum differ from model to model and are usually given by the manufacturer. Browne and Zerban[121] describe the method for some models. The zero-point correction must be determined anew each time one prism is substituted by another.

Technique for Liquids.—The instrument is mounted on a frame above a water bath so that white light from a mirror below the (transparent) floor of the bath passes at grazing incidence into the completely immersed prism, *P*, after passing through a thermostated glass beaker containing about 15 ml. of sample. When temperature equilibrium has been reached, the critical boundary is made as sharp as possible by tilting the mirror or the instrument, by achromatizing with the compensator (*A*, Fig. 13), and by focusing the eyepiece lens, e_1, on the scale, if necessary. A particularly sharp boundary can be obtained if a small mirror is placed directly below the sample and illuminated from above. A blurred or shifting boundary usually indicates poor temperature control. Some workers find it necessary to modify the standard bath by supplying it with circulating water from a thermostat (±0.05° C.). To avoid local cooling and other effects of evaporation, the liquid should be kept covered. Special cells are available which clamp tightly over the prism to protect the sample. The temperature within the beaker or cell should be measured each time. Between determinations, the prisms should be kept immersed in thermostated distilled water to minimize the time needed for reaching thermal equilibrium. The prism is quickly wiped dry with a soft cloth just before and after use. For small amounts (0.02 ml.), auxiliary prisms may be clamped below the refracting prisms, confining a thin layer of liquid as in the Abbé refractometer. In this case, the critical boundary is not at maximum sharpness, causing a lower accuracy.

Technique for Solids.—Solid samples are placed on the lower prism surface in the same way as described above for the Pulfrich and Abbé refractometers; and the same precautions apply.

3. Spectrometer

The spectrometer is an instrument for measuring directly the angular deviation of rays passing through a prism. The prism can consist of, or contain, the sample. The angle of deviation is a function of the angle and refractive index of the prism (Eq. 1, page 654). Although the principle of the method is simple, the method usually requires more care than the refractometers mentioned above. The technique required has been described in detail by Guild.[122] There are some cases in which this instrument may be indispensable. Since any magnitude of angular deviation can be measured, there is no upper or lower limit to the refractive index which can be obtained with the spectrometer. Also, observations on the less intense spectral lines can easily be made. The spectrometer is used primarily for highly accurate measurements on solids ($\pm 1 \times 10^{-6}$ in the absolute value of n_λ) or where a careful orientation of the solid specimen is important (*e. g.*, for anisotropic crystals). However, by using a hollow

---

[122] R. Glazebrook, *Dictionary of Applied Physics.* Vol. IV, Macmillan, London, 1923, pp. 760–772.

prism, formed, for instance, by two windows attached at an angle to the ends of a tube, it is also possible to obtain very accurate values ($\pm 1 \times 10^{-6}$) of n_λ for liquids. Tilton and Taylor[123] have obtained probably the best refractometric data on water in this way; they give a detailed description of the apparatus. The ordinary spectrometer is capable of an accuracy of about 2×10^{-4} in n_D.

Various instruments based on the principle of the spectrometer have been described[124-127] (see also page 733). They are usually combined with a photographic means of locating the refracted rays which, with quartz optics, is especially suited to the investigation of dispersion in the ultraviolet.

4. Instruments Based on Interference of Light

The interference of light waves has been extensively applied to very accurate measurements of differences in index of refraction. Two intersecting light beams from the same source are made to produce a set of "interference bands" in the plane of intersection, which is viewed with a lens. If a transparent substance of index n is placed in the path of one beam and another substance of equal length but different index, n_0, in the path of the other beam, there is a displacement of the interference bands. The interferometer allows one to determine the difference, $n - n_0$, by measuring the shift in position of the interference bands.

The ordinary commercial instruments have a maximum accuracy of about $\pm 5 \times 10^{-7}$ in Δn for liquids when white light is used. With monochromatic light, an accuracy of $\pm 1 \times 10^{-7}$ can be obtained and with certain modifications (see page 730) in the instrument, of $\pm 1 \times 10^{-8}$. The range which can be covered is inversely proportional to the accuracy; it can be adjusted by placing the sample in cells of various length. Thus, when an accuracy of $\pm 5 \times 10^{-7}$ is required, the maximum difference which can be measured is about $(\Delta n)_{max.} = 0.0006$. Increasing the range to $(\Delta n)_{max.} = 0.05$ by using the shortest practicable cell (1 mm.) causes the error to increase to about $\pm 4 \times 10^{-5}$. Certain modifications of technique and appropriate monochromatic sources permit measurement of the dispersion $(n_{\lambda_1} - n_{\lambda_2})$ or of n_λ, relative to a standard (page 729).

An important advantage of the interferometer is that, because it is a

[123] L. W. Tilton and J. K. Taylor, *J. Research Natl. Bur. Standards,* **20,** 419 (1938).

[124] K. Feussner, *Z. Physik,* **45,** 689 (1927).

[125] H. Voellmy, *Z. physik. chem.,* **127,** 305 (1927).

[126] H. Martens, *Ann. Physik,* **6,** 603 (1901).

[127] See the discussion of the Fèry refractometer in J. Reilly and W. N. Rae, *Physicochemical Methods.* 3rd ed., Vol. II, Van Nostrand, New York, 1939, p. 232.

differential instrument, the requirements of temperature control are not nearly as exacting as with the previously mentioned refractometers.   The interferometer is the most convenient, as well as the most accurate, instrument for measuring the apparent refraction of solutes in dilute solutions, or $\Delta n = n_{\text{soln.}} - n_{\text{solv.}}$.   However, with organic compounds, the error due to impurities will ordinarily be greater than the error of the measurement, unless the compounds are prepared with special care.   On the other hand, there are many problems in which the interferometer is invaluable as a means of analyzing solutions or of observing small changes in concentration. Thus, for example, one can continuously follow the *rate* of a reaction without removing samples.   The purity of a substance may be checked rapidly by a comparison with a standard, or by comparing successive portions obtained by distillation or recrystallization.   A rapid technique for the determination of concentration of protein in blood serum has been based on the use of the interferometer.[128]

A.   OPTICAL PRINCIPLES

The principle of the interferometer is explained by the simplified model illustrated in figure 14.   A converging lens, L, is placed in the path of two

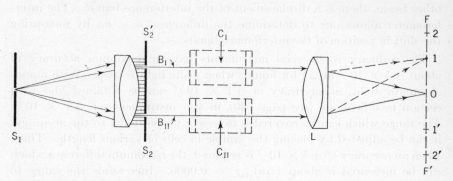

Fig. 14.—Simplified interferometer (slits S_1, S_2, and S_2' refer to the openings in the heavy lines).

narrow parallel beams, B_I and B_{II}, defined by the secondary slits, S_2 and S_2', of monochromatic light coming from the *same source*.   An image of the source, primary slit S_1, is formed in the focal plane F-F' of L, which can be viewed with an eyepiece placed in front of F-F'.   If the primary slit, originally large, is made more and more narrow, the appearance of the image changes.   It finally consists not of a single image of S_1 but of alternate dark

[128] P. Hirsch, in E. Abderhalden, *Handbuch der biologischen Arbeitsmethoden*.   Section II, Vol. II, Urban & Schwarzenberg, Berlin and Vienna, 1926, p. 761.

and light bands, equally spaced and approximately equal in width (see Fig. 15b). This interference pattern is caused by the alternating reinforcement and cancellation of the intersecting wave fronts in the focal plane.

Figure 15a shows the effect of the intersection of monochromatic wave fronts which require different lengths of time to reach the same point in the focal plane, i. e., which travel different optical path lengths between the time of their separation at the source and their reunion in the plane F–F'. At some points in this plane the wave crests of one ray are superimposed on the troughs of the other; at other points, crest is superimposed on crest.

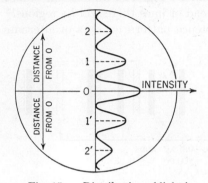 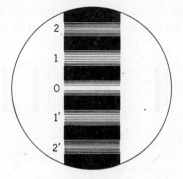

Fig. 15a.—Distribution of light in the interference pattern, with monochromatic light and finite slit width.

Fig. 15b.—Appearance of interference bands with monochromatic light and finite slit width. The ruled areas represent regions of continuously decreasing intensity on either side of the central maximum.

At still other points, the relation between crests and troughs is intermediate. When the waves are completely out of phase, i. e., the crests of one coincide with the troughs of the other, absence of light results (see points midway between *0* and *1*, *1* and *2* in figure 15a).

The condition for minimum (zero) light intensity at a point in the focal plane is:

$$P = (N + \tfrac{1}{2})\lambda \tag{58}$$

and for maximum intensity:

$$P = l_{\mathrm{II}} - l_{\mathrm{I}} = N\lambda \tag{59}$$

P is the *optical path difference* in centimeters, N is an integer called "band order," and l_{I} and l_{II} refer to the optical path length traversed by the two rays. The optical path length is defined as $l = \Sigma n_i d_i$, where n_i and d_i

refer to the refractive index and thickness, respectively, of the ith medium traversed by the light ray; l is thus equal for two paths for which the light requires the same time to traverse. λ refers to the wave length in centimeters.

For infinitely narrow secondary slits (S_2, S_2') there exists one line in focal plane F–F' for which $N = 0$, $i.\ e.$, $l_{II} = l_I$ (0 in Fig. 14). Accordingly, 0 is a position of maximum light intensity. The latter falls off rapidly on either side of 0 to reach a minimum at a distance corresponding to $P = \lambda/2$. At a still greater distance from 0, corresponding to $P = \lambda$, the intensity reaches a maximum again (1 and 1′, Fig. 14), and so on. Since slits S_2 and S_2' have a finite width, instead of lines there will be regions[129] of maximum intensity, and the interference pattern consists of alternate

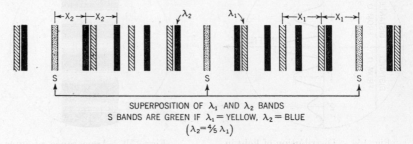

SUPERPOSITION OF λ_1 AND λ_2 BANDS
S BANDS ARE GREEN IF $\lambda_1 =$ YELLOW, $\lambda_2 =$ BLUE
$(\lambda_2 = {}^4\!/_5\,\lambda_1)$

Fig. 16.—Overlapping of colored bands (interferometer).

dark and light bands with rather sharp edges (Fig. 15b). A minimum corresponding to $P = (N + {}^1\!/_2)\lambda$ is called Nth order minimum, the bright band corresponding to $P = N\lambda$, "Nth order maximum," the central maximum $(N = 0)$ the 0 order band. The distance, x, between the maxima is approximately proportional to the wave length of the light used ($i.\ e.$, $x_1 \approx k\lambda_1$).[129]

With polychromatic light, there is a different set of bands for each λ and at certain intervals the bands of one set overlap with those of another. Consider, for example, that just two wave lengths, λ_1 and λ_2, are present in the source, with $\lambda_2 = {}^4\!/_5\,\lambda_1$. Then, assuming $x_1 = k\lambda_1$, $x_2 = k\lambda_2$, $x_2 = {}^4\!/_5\,x_1$. Hence, in the region near the 0 order band, a band from the λ_1 set will be superimposed on a λ_2 band at intervals of $5x_2$ centimeters. The result is illustrated in figure 16, where, if $\lambda_1 =$ yellow and $\lambda_2 =$ blue, every ninth band (S) will be green.

When white light is used, as in many applications of the interferometer, only the 0 order band is white because here all wave lengths are superimposed. It is bordered by a sharply defined black region. All other bands will be colored (Fig. 17) due to the unequal spacing of the maxima for the various wave lengths. Only the im-

---

[129] See, for example, W. E. Williams, *Applications of Interferometry*. Methuen, London, 1930.

mediate neighbors of the 0 order band are fairly distinct: Since $\lambda blue < \lambda red$, they are fringed with blue on the side nearest the central band, and with red on the other side. However, even a short distance from 0 the overlapping becomes so uniform that only a few distinct bands are observed.

If in each beam of figure 14 are placed identical transparent air-filled chambers, C_I and C_{II}, no change in the interference bands will occur. A reference line is now selected in the focal plane, for example, 0 in figure 14, by means of a cross hair rigidly fixed in the eyepiece so that its image is superimposed on the edge of one of the bands, the 0 order band, for instance.

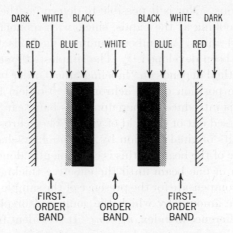

DARK WHITE BLACK   BLACK WHITE DARK

RED BLUE   WHITE   BLUE RED

FIRST-ORDER BAND   0 ORDER BAND   FIRST-ORDER BAND

Fig. 17.—Appearance of interference bands with white light.

By gradually replacing the air, n_1, in one of the chambers by some gas of index n_2 ($n_2 > n_1$), the bands will slowly move. After a while, the first-order band will reach the position defined by the cross hair, to be followed by the second-order band, and so on. Eventually the lower order bands pass out of the field of view; and by the time the one chamber has been completely refilled, an Nth order band at, or near, the cross hairs is being viewed. By counting the number of bands (ΔN) which correspond to the change (ΔP) in the optical path difference at 0, the difference in index ($n_1 - n_2$) between the unknown gas and the air or another reference substance can be calculated. Differentiation of equation (58) yields the relation between change in path difference and change in band order at any point:

$$\Delta P = \lambda(\Delta N) \tag{60}$$

If both beams pass through a thickness, d, of each gas, it follows from equation (59) and from the definition of optical path length (see page 721) that:

$$\Delta P = n_1 d - n_2 d \tag{61}$$

Substituting in Equation (60):

$$n_1 - n_2 = \frac{\lambda}{d} (\Delta N) \tag{62}$$

This method is, in principle, actually used in measuring $n_1 - n_2$ for gases. However, for liquids, the number of bands which go past the reference mark cannot be counted because the introduction of the sample is necessarily discontinuous. Nor is it possible to determine the order of interference by merely looking at the bands, since, with monochromatic light, all bands look almost alike. A number of indirect methods of determining the band order have been developed.[130] The simplest, though not always the most reliable, method depends on "labeling" the 0 order fringe by the use of white light. The position of the achromatic (0 order) band is observed; then the sample is introduced, whereupon this band can no longer be seen because it has passed out of the field of view. The achromatic band can be brought back to its original position by continuously changing the optical path length in one of the beams; this is conveniently done by tilting a glass plate in the path of one beam until the effective thickness of the plate is great enough to compensate for the presence of the sample in the path of the other beam. The amount by which the compensator plate is turned is a measure of the difference in index, $n_1 - n_2$. It is evident from equation (62) that smaller values of $n_1 - n_2$ can be measured by increasing the cell length.

B. RAYLEIGH–HABER–LÖWE INTERFEROMETER FOR LIQUIDS

The models of this instrument manufactured by Hilger and Zeiss differ only in small details. The essential parts are shown in figure 18. The optics are nearly the same as those discussed for the simplified case of figure 14. However, instead of cross hairs, an auxiliary set of interference bands is used as the frame of reference. This is accomplished by equally dividing each of the two beams, B_I and B_{II} (Fig. 14), so that four beams, b_I, b_{II}, B_I, and B_{II}, result. The lower beams, b_I and b_{II}, traverse only air and the optical parts including the lifting prism, Pr, and form the auxiliary reference set of vertical bands in the lower half of the field of view. Each upper beam, B_I and B_{II}, passes through a cell, c_1, c_2, and a plane-parallel glass plate, compensator plate P_1, P_2. This pair forms a set of bands above the reference pattern, as in figure 19. Prism Pr serves to raise beams b_I and b_{II} toward B_I and B_{II} so that only a fine dark line separates the two sets of

130 See, for example, W. Geffcken, Z. Elektrochem., 37, 233 (1931).

bands in the field of view.   By changing the orientation of P_1 relative to fixed plate P_2, the optical path length of beam B_I can be increased or de-

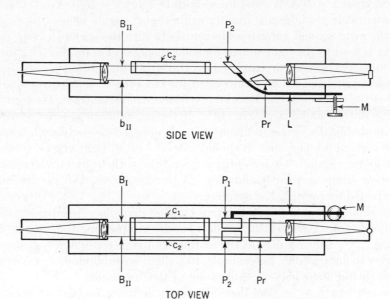

Fig. 18.—Rayleigh–Haber–Löwe interferometer.

creased. Thus, the upper set of bands can be moved relative to the fixed auxiliary set by turning micrometer screw M which, through lever L, transmits a slow tilting motion to P_1. The amount of tilting is measured on the micrometer screw scale. The effective thickness of P_1 becomes very great when the plate is nearly parallel to the light beam, and changes considerably for a very small tilting. However, when the plate is perpendicular to the beam, the effective thickness is very insensitive to a given displacement of the micrometer screw.

To measure Δn on this type of instrument, one ordinarily uses the compensation method described on

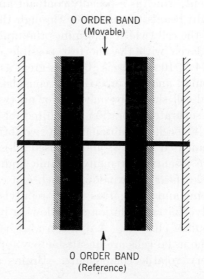

Fig. 19.—Center of field of view at coincidence, Rayleigh-Haber-Löwe interferometer.

page 724. When white light is used, the value of Δn corresponds very closely to that which would be obtained by using sodium D light (for white light, *average* $\lambda = 5600$ Å., and for sodium D light, $\lambda = 5893$ Å.). The micrometer scale readings are usually calibrated in terms of concentration.

A three- to six-volt tungsten filament bulb with rheostat to vary the intensity is used as the light source for some models. For others, a "Pointolite" tungsten source* is employed. Too great an intensity illuminates the background and reduces contrast at the band edge. The corresponding parts of the two sets of bands should be of the same brightness, the separating line narrow and sharp (Fig. 19). If these conditions are not satisfied most probably the tungsten filament is not oriented properly with respect to the vertical primary slit; it should cross the slit at right angles so that a point source results. Under optimum conditions, the central white bands will show sharp vertical boundaries. A deviation from the vertical may be corrected by rotating the eyepiece.

One should be able to set the two band systems in coincidence within about $\pm^1/_{20}$ of a band width, $^1/_{20}$ of a band corresponding to about 0.05% of $(\Delta n)_{max.}$. The accuracy of the settings can vary considerably from one observer to another due, for example, to a slight color blindness; thus each person should make his own calibration of the instrument.

The cell length to be used depends on the accuracy and range required, as well as on the amount of sample available. In the "portable" instrument, which is especially compact and rugged, a mirror system causes the light beams to pass twice through the sample. Thus, the effective length of the cell (which determines the range and accuracy) is doubled.

Even with the shortest possible cell (1 mm.), the accuracy of about $\pm 4 \times 10^{-5}$ in Δn is about as great as for the Pulfrich or the dipping refractomer, and the procedure is considerably more convenient. Each individual cell should be marked, for no two cells have exactly the same length. A separate calibration is required for each pair of cells.

The cells are obtainable in two forms, as gold-plated metal troughs with cemented windows and as fused all-glass cells without cement. The latter are essential for many organic liquids. Occasionally, they have minute holes near the windows which can cause serious errors without otherwise being apparent. It is therefore advisable to test each cell by filling it with silver nitrate solution and allowing it to stand a few hours in a solution of sodium chloride. A dye can also be used as a detector of imperfections. The usual cells are unsatisfactory for hygroscopic liquids or solutions with very volatile components. Bruins and Cohen[131] suggest a tight-fitting

---

* See Vol. II, Chapter XIX.

[131] E. Bruins and H. K. Cohen, **Z.** *physik. Chem.*, **103**, 337 (1923).

brass plug for the chamber opening. Bartell and Sloan[132] describe a cover with a mercury seal.

The two cells, containing sample and reference solution, respectively, must be at the same temperature within very close limits. To measure Δn to 2×10^{-7}, the difference must not be more than about $0.002°$ C. Temperature gradients within a cell, or excessive differences between the two cells, will cause the interference bands to have a wavy, indistinct appearance. This is a frequent source of error. On the other hand, measurements with the interferometer are not greatly influenced by changes in the absolute value of the temperature; it usually suffices to keep the bath temperature within about $0.5°$ of that of the calibration. The per cent error, E, in Δn per degree C. is given by:

$$E = \frac{d(\Delta n)}{dt} \cdot \frac{1}{n} = \frac{r_1 - r_2}{t_1 - t_2} \cdot \frac{100}{r_1} \tag{63}$$

where r_1 and r_2 are the scale readings at t_1 and t_2 degrees C. E is usually about 0.2% per degree.

The Hilger instrument should be placed in a thermostated box since it has no jacket around the cells. For the Zeiss instrument, it is usually necessary to make special provision for stirring the water bath which comes in contact with the cells.[128] With long cells it may also be necessary to stir the liquids themselves. In this way, temperature equilibrium is reached within a few minutes. Since the light passes through a considerable thickness of thermostat water, the bath should be kept free of turbidity by frequent renewal or a decrease in band intensity results. The bath liquid must have about the same refractive index as that of the sample, if the cell windows are not exactly parallel[133]; e. g., for $n > 1.42$, a n-dibutyl phthalate ($n = 1.49$) bath would be preferable to water ($n = 1.33$). Volatile liquids often cause cooling by evaporation, resulting in wavy or blurred bands. In this case, the cell should be provided with a special cover.

Comparison of Liquids. White Light.—With the reference liquid in both chambers, the adjustments for obtaining sharp straight achromatic bands are made (see page 726). The micrometer screw is turned until the upper achromatic band exactly coincides with the reference band, as in figure 19. The mean of several such readings, which will have a value of about 1 or 2, gives the zero point, r_0. The latter should be checked daily or whenever a different pair of cells is used.

Cell c_1 (Fig. 18) is emptied and refilled with the unknown sample after thorough rinsing. The micrometer screw is turned until the bands again

---

[132] F. E. Bartell and C. K. Sloan, *J. Am. Chem. Soc.*, **51**, 1637 (1929).

[133] F. Löwe, *Fortschritte der chemischen Technologie in Einzeldarstellung*. Vol. VI, Steinkopf, Dresden, 1925, p. 155.

coincide. The setting is repeated several times, and the corresponding mean scale reading, r is obtained. The difference $\Delta n = n - n_0$ or $\Delta c = c - c_0$ is obtained from $r - r_0$ by means of an appropriate calibration curve.

A typical calibration curve for concentration determinations is shown in Fig. 20. Either c or c/r may be plotted[134] for a number of known solutions against $r - r_0$. At certain intervals, the plot may show discontinuities of about 20 scale divisions (1 band). In the region of a discontinuity (Fig. 20, dotted lines), alternative values of c are obtained for a given $r - r_0$, because the curve segments overlap. The discontinuities are caused by the fact that it is not always possible to locate the 0 order band unambiguously. It becomes difficult to distinguish the latter from the first-order band when the optical dispersion of solution plus glass plate P_1 differs too much from the dispersion of reference liquid plus P_2. If this difference in

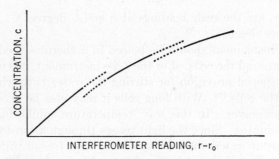

Fig. 20.—Typical calibration curve of interferometer.

dispersion were continuously increased from zero, the edges of the 0 order band would gradually become colored, while one of the adjacent first-order bands would lose its usual color fringe and become white. The other first-order band would at the same time acquire broader color fringes and appear more like the original second-order band. Thus the location of the 0 order band will be in error by one whole band width because the reference set remains, of course, unchanged. The apparent shift of the 0 order band is a consequence of using white light: If the optical dispersions of the two beams are different, not all wave lengths will be exactly superimposed in the position of the 0 order band. The latter now has colored fringes. Moreover, the blue side of one of the first-order bands is overlapped with red light from the 0 order band; similarly, its red side is overlapped with blue light from the adjacent second-order band. As a result, this first-order band becomes white. For still greater differences in dispersion, the adjacent second-order band becomes white, and so on. See page 722.

---

[134] See L. H. Adams, *J. Am. Chem. Soc.*, **37**, 1181 (1915).

The insidious error arising from this "dispersion effect" can be minimized by limiting the measurements to small concentration differences. With substances of low dispersion, it is usually safe to make comparisons as long as the scale readings are not greater than about one-third of the maximum range. Aliphatic compounds show, in general, a much smaller dispersion effect than do aromatic compounds. For example, Macy[135] reports that certain aliphatic compounds in water show no break in the calibration curve up to one gram per liter while, for the same cell and solvent, phenylurethane shows a break at about 200 milligrams per liter. Similarly, compounds with conjugated double bonds, with halogen substituents, or with other easily polarizable groups, can be expected to give the "dispersion effect." The shift in the achromatic band hardly ever occurs for $r - r_0 < \frac{1}{15}$ of its maximum value.[134] It is therefore nearly always possible to obtain reliable results by comparing the unknown solution directly with a known solution of slightly lower or higher index. In a limited range, it is permissible to make a linear interpolation for c (that is, assume $r - r_0 = kc$). If, during a measurement, there is any doubt as to the identity of the 0 order band, the comparison should be repeated with a reference solution closer to the unknown. In this way, very concentrated solutions may be compared; but it is usually tedious to prepare known standard solutions which are sufficiently close to the unknown to exclude the dispersion effect.[136] When the full range of the instrument is required or when many routine measurements are to be performed, the calibration method of Karagunis, Hawkinson, and Damköhler[136] is recommended. These authors label the 0 order band so that it can be identified even though colored.

Monochromatic Light. Dispersion.—The use of monochromatic light becomes necessary whenever an accuracy of better than about 0.1% in Δn is required. A discussion of the technique for careful measurements of Δn with monochromatic light is given by Brodsky and Scherschever,[137] by Prang,[138] and by Geffcken and Kruis.[42, 51, 52]

In its present form, the interferometer is not very convenient for measuring relative dispersion, especially since monochromatic light sources of very high purity are required to prevent "overlapping." The line spectra of the alkali metals, and the λ 5460.7 line of the mercury arc in conjunction with filters are most suitable. (For a further discussion of light sources, see Kruis.[51]) The usual, rather laborious, method consists in finding the order of interference for each wave length in the following steps: (1)

---

[135] R. Macy, *J. Am. Chem. Soc.*, **49**, 3070 (1927).

[136] G. Karagunis, A. Hawkinson, and G. Damköhler, *Z. physik. Chem.*, **A151**, 433 (1930).

[137] A. E. Brodsky and J. Scherschever, *Z. physik. Chem.*, **A155**, 417 (1931).

[138] W. Prang, *Ann. Physik*, **31**, 681 (1938).

With pure solvent in the cells, the zero point reading, r_0, is determined with white light in the usual way. (2) With solvent replaced by solution in one cell, using white light, the compensator plate is turned until the achromatic bands coincide. This approximately locates the 0 order band. Monochromatic light is substituted, keeping the compensator fixed. The monochromatic 0 order bands will now be the ones at or nearly at coincidence; the 0 order band of the movable set is then located more exactly by carefully adjusting to closer coincidence and noting the corresponding scale reading, r. (3) The micrometer is slowly turned toward r_0, the number of bands passing being counted until, at scale reading r', coincidence is obtained between bands nearest to r_0. The position of the nearest band (r') can be determined unambiguously by setting the compensator at r_0, then turning the screw by the minimum amount required to bring about a coincidence; the scale reads r'. The number of bands, N_i, counted between r and r' is the value of (ΔN), to the nearest whole number, i. e., $(\Delta N)_\lambda = N_i \pm f$, where f is a fraction less than 0.5. (4) The fractional part of a band, f, can be determined from the difference, $r_0 - r'$, by measuring for each wave length the conversion factor k_λ, the number of scale divisions which are equivalent to the separation between corresponding parts of adjacent bands. Each k_λ must be determined in the neighborhood of reading r_0 since ΔN is not an exactly linear function of r. Then $f = (r_0 - r')k$. The fraction, f, is added to or subtracted from N_i, depending on whether r' is larger or smaller than r_0. Equation (62) in the form:

$$(n_\lambda - n_{0\lambda}) = \frac{\lambda}{d} (\Delta N) \tag{62a}$$

is then applied to each wave length, which allows the calculation of n_λ if $n_{0\lambda}$ of the reference liquid is known, or allows the calculation of $n_{\lambda 1} - n_{\lambda 2}$ if $n_{0\lambda 1} - n_{0\lambda 2}$ is known. This method is, of course, also subject to the errors caused by the "dispersion effect." For recent improvements in the use of the interferometer for accurate dispersion measurements, see below.

C. MODIFICATIONS OF RAYLEIGH–HABER–LÖWE INTERFEROMETER

Kruis and Geffcken[42, 51, 52] have described precautions and refinements in the usual instrument necessary to obtain an accuracy of 1×10^{-8} in Δn, using monochromatic light. Methods of temperature control are given special consideration.[139] An ingenious modification of the Rayleigh interferometer by Geffcken[40, 50] eliminates the dispersion effect by using monochromatic light in conjunction with a "rotating chamber." The band order is determined by counting the number of bands which pass

---

[139] See also N. F. Hall and T. O. Jones, *J. Am. Chem. Soc.*, **58**, 1917 (1936).

while the cells are slowly turned through a given angle with respect to the axis of the interferometer. It is unfortunate that this chamber device is not yet available commercially, for with it one would be able to make rapid precision measurements of even very large differences in n for monochromatic light and also to measure the relative dispersion more conveniently. Measurements of the absolute value of refractive index of a liquid substance may also be made with the rotating chamber, but the experimental details have not been published.[50–52]

Application to Crystals.—The Rayleigh interferometer has been adapted to the measurement of the refractive index of crystals (n to $\pm 3 \times 10^{-5}$).[54] For isotropic solids, the technique is very simple. The ordinary interferometer cells are replaced by a single vessel having parallel windows which are large enough to allow both beams to pass. The vessel is filled with an appropriate liquid whose index of refraction can be varied continuously. A single crystal fragment as small as 0.5 millimeter in cross section is immersed in the liquid and placed in the path of one of the beams. If $n_{\text{liq.}}$ differs slightly from n_{solid}, the ordinary interference bands appear distorted, having a V-shaped notch. However, when $n_{\text{liq.}} = n_{\text{solid}}$, the bands have sharp straight edges, as if no crystal were in the beam at all. A measurement of n of the liquid gives n of the solid. The method, with modifications, is also applicable to anisotropic solids; for these substances, the specimens must be tested at various orientations with polarized light, as described by Wulff.[54]

The Rayleigh–Williams interference refractometer,[140] with quartz optics, promises to be very useful in refractometric work because it allows accurate and rapid measurement in the whole range from 8000 to 2000 Å. Using a spectrograph in conjunction with the Rayleigh–Williams interferometer, one can at once make a photographic record of the dispersion for all spectral lines, using an appropriate single light source. The combination of an interferometer with a spectrograph is known as a *spectral interferometer*. The quartz optics makes possible the investigation in the ultraviolet, *e. g.*, of compounds which are strongly colored in the visible region of the spectrum. A spectral interferometer of especially high accuracy by Geffcken and Kruis[43] resembles in some respects the Rayleigh–Williams instrument.

D. OTHER INTERFEROMETERS

Rau and Roseveare[141] have described an easily constructed interferometer for liquids which can detect differences in n as small as 5×10^{-7},

---

[140] W. E. Williams, *Proc. Phys. Soc. London*, **44**, 45 (1932). Manufacturer, *Adam Hilger, Ltd.*, London.

[141] D. Rau and W. E. Roseveare, *Ind. Eng. Chem., Anal. Ed.*, **8**, 72 (1936).

using white light, and which has a range (0.002) exceeding that of the commercial instruments with the same sensitivity.

Lowry and Allsopp[142] have described an interferometer which photographically records the dispersion data for spectral lines in the range of 8000 to 2000 Å. An accuracy of 1×10^{-4} in n_λ is obtained. This instrument has been used for an extensive series of dispersion measurements of organic liquids within or near absorption bands, especially in the ultraviolet.

5.   Measurement of Gases and Vapors

The refractive indices of a gas are almost invariably determined with an interferometer. The principle of the method is the same as that discussed on pages 720–724. The instruments described on pages 724–732 can be used if they are provided with chambers of about 50–100 cm. length. Watson and Ramaswamy[143] describe the technique of handling gases and easily condensable vapors with the Rayleigh–Haber–Löwe interferometer. Cuthbertson and Cuthbertson[144] and Lowery[145] describe the use of the Jamin interferometer. Wüst and Reindel[58] and others[37] adapted a modified Zehnder interferometer to the measurements of gases at high temperatures.

In order to obtain the molar refraction of a gas it is necessary to correct the experimental values of n obtained at arbitrary temperatures and pressures to $\mathbf{n}^*$ (see, e. g., ref. 58), of an ideal gas, usually at 0° C. and 760 mm. Since $\mathbf{n}^*$ differs little from 1, the Lorentz–Lorenz expression assumes the simplified form $R = {}^2/_3(\mathbf{n}^* - 1)\,22415$, which is sufficiently accurate for most purposes. The methods of making the correction from n to $\mathbf{n}^*$ are given in references 58 and 143–145. The considerable deviation between reported $\mathbf{n}^*$ values for even such gases as methane ($R_D = 6.58$[146] and 6.50[147]), ethane (11.47[146] and 11.38[148]), and propane (16.40[146] and 16.09[143]) may be due partly to improper correction to the ideal gas state and partly to impurities. Watson and Ramaswamy[143] and Weiss[149] point out that measurements of easily condensable vapors must be carried out at

[142] T. M. Lowry and C. B. Allsopp, *Proc. Roy. Soc. London*, **A133**, 26 (1931).

[143] H. E. Watson and K. L. Ramaswamy, *Proc. Indian Acad. Sci.*, **A4**, 675 (1936); *Proc. Roy. Soc. London*, **A156**, 144 (1938).

[144] C. Cuthbertson and M. Cuthbertson, *Proc. Roy. Soc. London*, **A135**, 40 (1932); *ibid.*, **A97**, 152 (1920); *ibid.*, **A84**, 13 (1910).

[145] H. Lowery, *Proc. Phys. Soc. London*, **40**, 23 (1927); *Proc. Roy. Soc. London*, **A133**, 188 (1931). H. Huxley and H. Lowery, *ibid.*, **A182**, 207–216 (1943).

[146] S. Friberg, *Z. Physik*, **41**, 378 (1927).

[147] T. Larsen, *Z. Physik*, **111**, 394 (1938).

[148] H. Lowery, *Proc. Phys. Soc. London*, **39**, 421 (1927).

[149] M. Weiss, *Ann. Physik*, **20**, 557 (1934).

low pressures to avoid large errors due to adsorption on the chamber windows.

6.   Techniques for Small Amounts

Alber and Bryant[150] have reviewed the micromethods applicable to organic liquids.   The accuracy attained by the various techniques on amounts of sample ranging from 0.02 to 1 × 10^{-4} ml. varies between ±0.003 to ±0.0005 in n.   The most widely used microtechniques for solids are considerably more complicated than those for liquids.   For methods using the microscope, see chapter XI, page 489.

A.   ADAPTATION OF STANDARD INSTRUMENTS

Liquids.—Using an Abbé refractometer, one can reduce the amount of sample to about 0.01 ml. by distributing the liquid on lens paper, which is then clamped between the two prisms.[150]   By properly confining the liquid (a vertical "window" must be provided for the incident light), as little as 0.02 ml. could be measured with the Pulfrich refractometer, since a layer of sample only 0.15 mm. thick is required on the horizontal prism surface.

Solids.—The accurate method of Le Blanc (see page 705) with the Pulfrich refractometer requires only a few milligrams of the powdered isotropic substance.   The interferometric method of Wulff (see page 731) can be employed with crystal fragments as small as 0.5 mm. in cross section (*i. e.*, ≅ 0.2 mg.).   The microscopic method (Chapter XI) is often used.

B.   IMAGE-DISPLACEMENT METHODS FOR LIQUIDS

Jelley,[151] Edwards and Otto,[152] Nichols,[153] and Alber and Bryant[150] have described simple refractometers which allow the rapid measurement of small samples.   Two of these are available commercially.[154, 155]   In all these instruments, the liquid sample is made into a minute 45° prism by placing a drop of it between an appropriate set of glass surfaces.   If an object (*e. g.*, an illuminated line or slit) is viewed through such a liquid prism, its apparent position is shifted from the true position by an amount which can be observed on a scale mounted behind the prism.   The scale readings can be converted into the corresponding values of n by use of equation (1) or, better, by a calibration with standard liquids.

The Jelley–Fisher refractometer[154] has a scale which gives values of n

---

[150] H. K. Alber and J. T. Bryant, *Ind. Eng. Chem., Anal. Ed.*, **12**, 305 (1940).

[151] E. E. Jelley, *Kodak Research Labs. Abstract. Bull.*, **17**, 18 (1935).

[152] A. E. Edwards and C. E. Otto, *Ind. Eng. Chem., Anal. Ed.*, **10**, 225 (1938).

[153] L. Nichols, *Natl. Paint Bull.*, **1**, 12 (1937).

[154] Jelley–Fisher Refractometer, *Fisher Scientific Co.*, Pittsburgh, Pa.

[155] Nichols Refractometer, *Arthur H. Thomas Co.*, Philadelphia, Pa.

directly to ±0.002 in the range of 1.30 to 1.90. Samples as small as 1 ×
10^{-4} ml. have been measured to ±0.001 with a modification of this instrument.[151] Liquids of high dispersion cause the slit image to be fringed with
color, due to the white light source. Frediani[156] has proposed that the
width of this colored band be used as a semiquantitative measure of the
dispersion. Following a suggestion given in Jelley's original paper,[151]
Frediani[156] has described a method for applying the instrument to high
temperature measurements (up to 200° C.). A controllable electric heating
device is attached to the cell which shapes the liquid prism. In this way, a
variety of substances which are ordinarily solid may be measured in the
molten state. The melting point (to ±3°) can be conveniently obtained at
the same time.

The Nichols refractometer[155] consists of two cells mounted on a microscope slide, one of which is used in the ranges of n = 1.30 to 1.40 and 1.65
to 2.0, the other between 1.40 and 1.65. The cells require about 0.005 ml. of
sample, 60% of which can be recovered. A microscope having an eyepiece
scale is used to measure the separation of two displaced images of an illuminated reference line scratched on the slide. A calibration curve is obtained from measurements on a set of standard liquids. The calibration is
simplified by the fact that the distance of separation of the images is a
linear function of the refractive index. The usual accuracy of ±0.001 can
be increased to ±0.0005 by using monochromatic light, and by controlling
the temperature to about ±0.5°. A cylindrical water jacket surrounding
each cell may be cemented to the slide, or a hot stage may be used for temperature control.

7. Guide for Selection of Methods

Table X is designed to facilitate the selection of instruments available
commercially for various types of problems. Some of the instruments in
table X can be modified, as described in the text, to allow a greater accuracy
than indicated in the table; *e. g.*, a commercial interferometer can be
adapted to an accuracy of 1 × 10^{-8}, compared with the usual 5 × 10^{-7}.

---

[156] H. A. Frediani, *Ind Eng. Chem., Anal. Ed.*, **14**, 439 (1942).

TABLE X

RECOMMENDED INSTRUMENTS FOR VARIOUS PROBLEMS

Required conditions	Recommended instrument	Usual accuracy, n_D or (Δn)	Page
A. PURE LIQUIDS			
High accuracy in n_λ	Precision Abbé	3×10^{-5}	713
Rapidity, convenience	Abbé	2×10^{-4}	707
B. SOLUTIONS OR PURE LIQUIDS			
Highest accuracy in n_λ, any value of n_λ	Spectrometer	1×10^{-6}	718
Volatile component and/or hygroscopic	Pulfrich	1×10^{-4}	688
Accuracy in dispersion $\Delta n = n_{\lambda_1} - n_{\lambda_2}$	Pulfrich	2×10^{-5}	698
Detection of small concentration changes, $\Delta n = n - n_0$	Interferometer	5×10^{-7}	728
Routine analysis of solutions	Dipping	7×10^{-5}	716
Precision comparison, $\Delta n < 0.05$	Pulfrich	3×10^{-5}	699
Rapidity, convenience, no temperature control	Jelley–Fisher	2×10^{-3}	734
	{ Abbé	2×10^{-4}	733
Small amounts (10^{-2} to 10^{-4} cc.)	{ Image displacement	5×10^{-4}	733
Low temperatures	Pulfrich	1×10^{-4}	694
Temperatures up to 100° C.	Pulfrich	1×10^{-4}	694
Temperatures up to 200° C.	Jelley–Fisher	2×10^{-3}	734
C. SOLIDS			
Large, homogenous specimen, high accuracy in n_λ	Precision Abbé	3×10^{-5}	713
Accuracy in dispersion, $\Delta n = n_{\lambda_1} - n_{\lambda_2}$, large homogenous specimen	Pulfrich	2×10^{-5}	704
Opaque solids	Abbé	2×10^{-4}	710
Semisolids	Abbé	2×10^{-4}	710
Isotropic powders, $n < 1.9$	Pulfrich, Le Blanc	2×10^{-4}	705
Small anisotropic crystals ($n < 1.9$)	{ Immersion, microscope	1×10^{-3}	489
	{ Immersion, interferometer	3×10^{-5}	731
Shaped, polished specimen, highest accuracy in n_λ, any value of n	Spectrometer	1×10^{-6}	718

General References

Adams, L. H., *J. Am. Chem. Soc.*, **37,** 1181 (1915).

Alber, H. K., and Bryant, J. T., *Ind. Eng. Chem., Anal. Ed.*, **12,** 305 (1940).

Brode, W. R., and Leermakers, J. A., in H. Gilman, *Organic Chemistry*. Wiley, New York, 1938, p. 1741.

Browne, C. A., and Zerban, F. W., *Physical and Chemical Methods of Sugar Analysis*. 3rd ed., Wiley, New York, 1941.

Eisenlohr, F., *Spektrochemie der organischen Verbindungen.*   Enke, Stuttgart, 1912.

Eykman, J. F., "Recherches réfractométriques," edited by A. F. Holleman, *Natuurkund. Verhandel. Hollandsche Mij. Wetenschappen Haarlem,* **1919.**

Fajans, K., *Radioelements and Isotopes; Chemical Forces* and *Optical Properties of Substances.*   McGraw-Hill, New York, 1931, pp. 68–82.

Fajans, K. *et al., Refractometric Investigations,* I to LV (1924–1942).   See the references in paper LV, K. Fajans and N. Bauer, *J. Am. Chem. Soc.,* **64,** 3023 (1942), and refs. 32–58, this chapter.

Furter, M., *Helv. Chim. Acta,* **21,** 1666 (1938).

Gibb, T. R. P., *Optical Methods of Chemical Analysis.*   McGraw-Hill, New York, 1942.

Glasstone, S., *Text-Book of Physical Chemistry.*   Van Nostrand, New York, 1940. pp. 518–533.

Glazebrook, R., *Dictionary of Applied Physics.*   Vol. IV, Macmillan, London, 1923.

Guild, J., *Proc. Phys. Soc., London,* **30,** 157 (1917–1918).

Hirsch, P., in E. Abderhalden, *Handbuch der biologischen Arbeitsmethoden.*   Section II, Vol. II, Urban & Schwarzenberg, Berlin and Vienna, 1926.

Hückel, W., *Theoretische Grundlagen der organischen Chemie.*   Vol. II, Akadem. Verlagsgesellschaft, Leipzig, 1931, pp. 91–114.

Kessler, H., in E. Abderhalden, *Handbuch der Biologischen Arbeitsmethoden.*   Section 2, Vol. II, Urban & Schwarzenberg, Berlin and Vienna, 1926.

Reilly, J., and Rae, W. N., *Physico-chemical Methods.*   3rd ed., Vol. II, Van Nostrand, New York, 1939.

Roth, W. A., and Eisenlohr, F., *Refraktometrisches Hilfsbuch.*   Verlag Veit, Leipzig, 1911.

Sidgwick, N. V., *Some Physical Properties of the Covalent Link in Chemistry.*   Cornell Univ. Press, Ithaca, 1933, pp. 31 *et seq.*

Smyth, C. P., *Dielectric Constant and Molecular Structure.*   Chem. Catalog Co., New York, 1931, pp. 142–168.

Tilton, L. W., *J. Optical Soc. Am.,* **32,** 373 (1942); *J. Research Natl. Bur. Standards,* **30,** 311 (1943).

Ward, A. L., Kurtz, S. S., and Fulweiler, W. H., in A. E. Dunstan *et al., Science of Petroleum.*   Vol. II, Oxford Univ. Press, New York, 1938.

Williams, W. E., *Applications of Interferometry.*   Methuen, London, 1930.